MW01028625

ИЗДАТЕЛЬСТВО · МИР

Н. С. ПИСКУНОВ

ДИФФЕРЕНЦИАЛЬНОЕ И ИНТЕГРАЛЬНОЕ ИСЧИСЛЕНИЯ

ТОМ I

ИЗДАТЕЛЬСТВО «НАУКА» МОСКВА

N. PISKUNOV

DIFFERENTIAL

AND

INTEGRAL

CALCULUS

VOL. I

Translated from the Russian
by
George Yankovsky

MIR PUBLISHERS MOSCOW

CBS PUBLISHERS & DISTRIBUTORS PVT. LTD.
New Delhi • Bengaluru • Chennai • Kochi • Kolkata • Mumbai • Pune

First published 1964
Second printing 1966
Third printing 1969
Second edition 1974
Fourth printing 1981

На английском языке

© English translation, Mir Publishers, 1974

ISBN: 81-239-0492-4

First Indian Reprint: 1996

Copyright © English Translation, Mir Publishers, Moscow, 1974

This edition has been published in India by arrangement with
Mir Publishers, Moscow

Published by:
Satish Kumar Jain for CBS Publishers & Distributors Pvt. Ltd.,
4819/XI Prahlad Street, 24 Ansari Road, Daryaganj, New Delhi - 110002
delhi@cbspd.com, cbspubs@airtelmail.in • www.cbspd.com
Ph.: 23289259, 23266861, 23266867 • Fax: 011-23243014

Corporate Office: 204 FIE, Industrial Area, Patparganj, Delhi - 110 092
Ph: 49344934 • Fax: 011-49344935
E-mail: publishing@cbspd.com • publicity@cbspd.com

Branches:
• *Bengaluru:* 2975, 17th Cross, K.R. Road, Bansankari 2nd Stage,
  Bengaluru - 70 • Ph: +91-80-26771678/79 • Fax: +91-80-26771680
  E-mail: cbsbng@gmail.com, bangalore@cbspd.com
• *Chennai:* No. 7, Subbaraya Street, Shenoy Nagar, Chennai - 600030
  Ph: +91-44-26681266, 26680620 • Fax: +91-44-42032115
  E-mail: chennai@cbspd.com
• *Kochi:* Ashana House, 39/1904, A.M. Thomas Road, Valanjambalam,
  Ernakulum, Kochi • Ph: +91-484-4059061-65
  Fax: +91-484-4059065 • E-mail: cochin@cbspd.com
• *Kolkata:* 6-B, Ground Floor, Rameshwar Shaw Road, Kolkata - 700014
  Ph: +91-33-22891126/7/8 • E-mail: kolkata@cbspd.com
• *Mumbai:* 83-C, Dr. E. Moses Road, Worli, Mumbai - 400018
  Ph: +91-9833017933, 022-24902340/41 • E-mail: mumbai@cbspd.com
• *Pune:* Bhuruk Prestige, Sr. No. 52/12/2+1+3/2,
  Narhe, Haveli (Near Katraj-Dehu Road Bypass), Pune - 411041
  Ph: +91-20-64704058/59, 32342277 • E-mail: pune@cbspd.com

Printed at: J.S. Offset Printers, Delhi

CONTENTS

CHAPTER 6. THE CURVATURE OF A CURVE

CHAPTER 7. COMPLEX NUMBERS. POLYNOMIALS

CHAPTER 8. FUNCTIONS OF SEVERAL VARIABLES

CHAPTER 9. APPLICATIONS OF DIFFERENTIAL CALCULUS TO SOLID GEOMETRY

CHAPTER 10. THE INDEFINITE INTEGRAL

CHAPTER 11. THE DEFINITE INTEGRAL

Contents

CHAPTER 12. GEOMETRIC AND MECHANICAL APPLICATIONS
OF THE DEFINITE INTEGRAL

CHAPTER I

NUMBER. VARIABLE. FUNCTION

1.1 REAL NUMBERS. REAL NUMBERS AS POINTS ON A NUMBER SCALE

Number is one of the basic concepts of mathematics. It originated in ancient times and has undergone expansion and generalization over the centuries.

Whole numbers and fractions, both positive and negative, together with the number zero are called *rational numbers*. Every rational number may be represented in the form of a ratio, $\frac{p}{q}$, of two integers p and q; for example,

$$\frac{5}{7}, \quad 1.25 = \frac{5}{4}$$

In particular, the integer p may be regarded as a ratio of two integers $\frac{p}{1}$; for example,

$$6 = \frac{6}{1}, \quad 0 = \frac{0}{1}$$

Rational numbers may be represented in the form of periodic terminating or nonterminating fractions. Numbers represented by nonterminating, but nonperiodic, decimal fractions are called *irrational numbers*; such are the numbers $\sqrt{2}$, $\sqrt{3}$, $5 - \sqrt{2}$, etc.

The collection of all rational and irrational numbers makes up the set of *real numbers*. The real numbers are *ordered in magnitude*; that is to say, for each pair of real numbers x and y there is one, and only one, of the following relations:

$$x < y, \quad x = y, \quad x > y$$

Real numbers may be depicted as points on a number scale. A *number scale* is an infinite straight line on which are chosen: (1) a certain point O called the origin, (2) a positive direction indicated by an arrow, and (3) a suitable unit of length. We shall usually make the number scale horizontal and take the positive direction to be from left to right.

If the number x_1 is positive, it is depicted as a point M_1 at a distance $OM_1 = x_1$ to the right of the origin O; if the number x_2

is negative, it is represented by a point M_2 to the left of O at a distance $OM_2 = -x_2$ (Fig. 1). The point O represents the number zero. It is obvious that every real number is represented by a definite point on the number scale. Two different real numbers are represented by different points on the number scale.

The following assertion is also true: each point on the number scale represents only one real number (rational or irrational).

To summarize, all real numbers and all points on the number scale are in one-to-one correspondence: to each number there corresponds only one point, and conversely, to each point there corresponds only one number. This frequently enables us to regard "the number x" and "the point x" as, in a certain sense, equivalent expressions. We shall make wide use of this circumstance in our course.

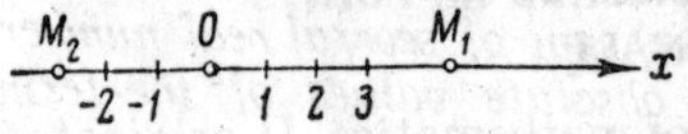

Fig. 1

We state without proof the following important property of the set of real numbers: *both rational and irrational numbers may be found between any two arbitrary real numbers.* In geometrical terms, this proposition reads thus: *both rational and irrational points may be found between any two arbitrary points on the number scale.*

In conclusion we give the following theorem, which, in a certain sense, represents a bridge between theory and practice.

Theorem. *Every irrational number α may be expressed, to any degree of accuracy, with the aid of rational numbers.*

Indeed, let the irrational number $\alpha > 0$ and let it be required to evaluate α with an accuracy of $\frac{1}{n} \Big($ for example, $\frac{1}{10}$, $\frac{1}{100}$, and so forth $\Big)$.

No matter what α is, it lies between two integral numbers N and $N + 1$. We divide the interval between N and $N + 1$ into n parts; then α will lie somewhere between the rational numbers $N + \frac{m}{n}$ and $N + \frac{m+1}{n}$. Since their difference is equal to $\frac{1}{n}$, each of them expresses α to the given degree of accuracy, the former being too small and the latter, too large.

Example. The irrational number $\sqrt{2}$ is expressed by the rational numbers:
1.4 and 1.5 to one decimal place,
1.41 and 1.42 to two decimal places,
1.414 and 1.415 to three decimal places, etc.

1.2 THE ABSOLUTE VALUE OF A REAL NUMBER

Let us introduce a concept which we shall need later on: the absolute value of a real number.

Definition. *The absolute value* (or *modulus*) *of a real number* x (written $|x|$) *is a nonnegative real number that satisfies the conditions*

$$|x| = x \quad \text{if } x \geqslant 0$$
$$|x| = -x \quad \text{if } x < 0$$

Examples. $|2| = 2$, $\ |-5| = 5$, $\ |0| = 0$.

From the definition it follows that the relationship $x \leqslant |x|$ holds for any x.

Let us examine some of the properties of absolute values.

1. *The absolute value of an algebraic sum of several real numbers is no greater than the sum of the absolute values of the terms*

$$|x + y| \leqslant |x| + |y|$$

Proof. Let $x + y \geqslant 0$, then

$$|x + y| = x + y \leqslant |x| + |y| \text{ (since } x \leqslant |x| \text{ and } y \leqslant |y|)$$

Let $x + y < 0$, then

$$|x + y| = -(x + y) = (-x) + (-y) \leqslant |x| + |y|$$

This completes the proof.

The foregoing proof is readily extended to any number of terms.

Examples.

$$|-2 + 3| < |-2| + |3| = 2 + 3 = 5 \text{ or } 1 < 5,$$
$$|-3 - 5| = |-3| + |-5| = 3 + 5 = 8 \text{ or } 8 = 8.$$

2. *The absolute value of a difference is no less than the difference of the absolute values of the minuend and subtrahend:*

$$|x - y| \geqslant |x| - |y|, \quad |x| > |y|$$

Proof. Let $x - y = z$, then $x = y + z$ and from what has been proved

$$|x| = |y + z| \leqslant |y| + |z| = |y| + |x - y|$$

whence

$$|x| - |y| \leqslant |x - y|$$

thus completing the proof.

3. *The absolute value of a product is equal to the product of the absolute values of the factors:*

$$|xyz| = |x| \, |y| \, |z|$$

4. *The absolute value of a quotient is equal to the quotient of the absolute values of the dividend and the divisor:*

$$\left| \frac{x}{y} \right| = \frac{|x|}{|y|}$$

The latter two properties follow directly from the definition of absolute value.

1.3 VARIABLES AND CONSTANTS

The numerical values of such physical quantities as time, length, area, volume, mass, velocity, pressure, temperature, etc. are determined by measurement. Mathematics deals with quantities divested of any specific content. From now on, when speaking of quantities, we shall have in view their numerical values. In various phenomena, the numerical values of certain quantities vary, while the numerical values of others remain fixed. For instance, in the uniform motion of a point, time and distance change, while the velocity remains constant.

A *variable* is a quantity that takes on various numerical values. A *constant* is a quantity whose numerical values remain fixed. We shall use the letters x, y, z, u, ..., etc. to designate variables, and the letters a, b, c, ..., etc. to designate constants.

Note. In mathematics, a constant is frequently regarded as a special case of variable whose numerical values are the same.

It should be noted that when considering specific physical phenomena it may happen that one and the same quantity in one phenomenon is a constant while in another it is a variable. For example, the velocity of uniform motion is a constant, while the velocity of uniformly accelerated motion is a variable. Quantities that have the same value under all circumstances are called *absolute constants*. For example, the ratio of the circumference of a circle to its diameter is an absolute constant: $\pi = 3.14159....$

As we shall see throughout this course, the concept of a variable quantity is the basic concept of differential and integral calculus. In "Dialectics of Nature", Friedrich Engels wrote: "The turning point in mathematics was Descartes' variable magnitude. With that came *motion* and hence *dialectics* in mathematics, and *at once*, too, *of necessity* the differential and integral calculus."

1.4 THE RANGE OF A VARIABLE

A variable takes on a series of numerical values. The collection of these values may differ depending on the character of the problem. For example, the temperature of water heated under ordinary conditions will vary from room temperature (15-18 °C) to the boiling point, 100 °C. The variable quantity $x = \cos\alpha$ can take on all values from -1 to $+1$.

The values of a variable are geometrically depicted as points on a number scale. For instance, the values of the variable $x = \cos\alpha$ for all possible values of α are depicted as the set of points of the interval from -1 to 1, including the points -1 and 1 (Fig. 2).

Definition. The set of all numerical values of a variable quantity is called the *range* of the variable.

We shall now define the following ranges of a variable that will be frequently used later on.

An *interval* is the set of all numbers x lying between the given points a and b *(the end points)* and is called closed or open accordingly as it does or does not include its end points.

An *open interval* is the collection of all numbers x lying between and *excluding* the given numbers a and b ($a < b$); it is denoted (a, b) or by means of the inequalities $a < x < b$.

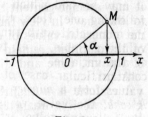

Fig. 2

A *closed interval* is the set of all numbers x lying between and *including* the two given numbers a and b; it is denoted $[a, b]$ or, by means of inequalities, $a \leqslant x \leqslant b$.

If one of the numbers a or b (say, a) belongs to the interval, while the other does not, we have a *partly closed (half-closed) interval*, which may be given by the inequalities $a \leqslant x < b$ and is denoted $[a, b)$. If the number b belongs to the set and a does not, we have the half-closed interval $(a, b]$, which may be given by the inequalities $a < x \leqslant b$.

If the variable x assumes all possible values greater than a, such an interval is denoted $(a, +\infty)$ and is represented by the conditional inequalities $a < x < +\infty$. In the same way we regard the infinite intervals and half-closed infinite intervals represented by the conditional inequalities

$$a \leqslant x < +\infty, \quad -\infty < x < c, \quad -\infty < x \leqslant c, \quad -\infty < x < +\infty$$

Example. The range of the variable $x = \cos \alpha$ for all possible values of α is the interval $[-1, 1]$ and is defined by the inequalities $-1 \leqslant x \leqslant 1$.

The foregoing definitions may be formulated for a "point" in place of a "number".

The *neighbourhood* of a given point x_0 is an arbitrary interval $(a\ b)$ containing this point within it; that is, the interval (a, b) whose end points satisfy the condition $a < x_0 < b$. One often considers the neighbourhood (a, b) of the point x_0 for which x_0 is the midpoint. Then x_0 is called the *centre of the neighbourhood* and the

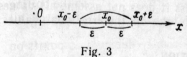

Fig. 3

quantity $\dfrac{b-a}{2}$, the *radius of the neighbourhood*. Fig. 3 shows the neighbourhood $(x_0 - \varepsilon, x_0 + \varepsilon)$ of the point x_0 with radius ε.

1.5 ORDERED VARIABLES.
INCREASING AND DECREASING VARIABLES. BOUNDED VARIABLES

We shall say that the variable x is an *ordered variable quantity* if its range is known and if about each of any two of its values it may be said which value is the preceding one and which is the following one. Here, the notions "preceding" and "following" are not connected with time but serve as a way to "order" the values of the variable, i. e., to establish the order of the respective values of the variable.

A particular case of an ordered variable is a variable whose values form a *number sequence* x_1, x_2, x_3, ..., x_n, ... Here, for $k' < k$, the value $x_{k'}$ is the preceding value, and the value x_k is the following value, irrespective of which one is the greater.

Definition 1. A variable is called *increasing* if each subsequent value of it is greater than the preceding value. A variable is called *decreasing* if each subsequent value is less than the preceding value.

Increasing variable quantities and decreasing variable quantities are called *monotonically varying* variables or simply *monotonic quantities*.

Example. When the number of sides of a regular polygon inscribed in a circle is doubled, the area s of the polygon is an increasing variable. The area of a regular polygon circumscribed about a circle, when the number of sides is doubled, is a decreasing variable. It may be noted that not every variable quantity is necessarily increasing or decreasing. Thus, if α is an increasing variable over the interval $[0, 2\pi]$, the variable $x = \sin \alpha$ is not a monotonic quantity. It first increases from 0 to 1, then decreases from 1 to -1, and then increases from -1 to 0.

Definition 2. The variable x is called *bounded* if there exists a constant $M > 0$ such that all subsequent values of the variable, after a certain one, satisfy the condition

$$-M \leqslant x \leqslant M \quad \text{or} \quad |x| \leqslant M$$

In other words, a variable is called bounded if it is possible to indicate an interval $[-M, M]$ such that all subsequent values of the variable, after a certain one, will belong to this interval. However, one should not think that the variable will necessarily assume all values on the interval $[-M, M]$. For example, the variable that assumes all possible rational values on the interval $[-2, 2]$ is bounded, and nevertheless it does not assume all values on $[-2, 2]$, namely, it does not take on the irrational values.

1.6 FUNCTION

In the study of natural phenomena and the solution of technical and mathematical problems, one finds it necessary to consider the variation of one quantity as dependent on the variation of another.

For instance, in studies of motion, the path traversed is regarded as a variable which varies with time. Here, the path traversed is a **function** of the time.

Let us consider another example. We know that the area of a circle, in terms of the radius, is $Q = \pi R^2$. If the radius R takes on a variety of numerical values, the area Q will also assume various numerical values. Thus, the variation of one variable brings about a variation in the other. Here, the area of a circle Q is a function of the radius R. Let us formulate a definition of the concept "function".

Definition 1. If to each value of a variable x (within a certain range) there corresponds one definite value of another variable y, then y is a *function* of x or, in functional notation, $y = f(x)$, $y = \varphi(x)$, and so forth.

The variable x is called the *independent variable* or *argument*. The relation between the variables x and y is called a *functional relation*. The letter f in the functional notation $y = f(x)$ indicates that some kind of operations must be performed on the value of x in order to obtain the value of y. In place of the notation $y = f(x)$, $u = \varphi(x)$, etc. one occasionally finds $y = y(x)$, $u = u(x)$, etc. the letters y, u designating both the dependent variable and the symbol of the operations to be performed on x.

The notation $y = C$, where C is a constant, denotes a function whose value for any value of x is the same and is equal to C.

Definition 2. The set of values of x for which the values of the function y are determined by the rule $f(x)$ is called the *domain of definition of the function*.

Example 1. The function $y = \sin x$ is defined for all values of x. Therefore, its domain of definition is the infinite interval $-\infty < x < +\infty$.

Note 1. If we have a function relation of two variable quantities x and $y = f(x)$ and if x and $y = f(x)$ are regarded as ordered variables, then of the two values of the function $y^* = f(x^*)$ and $y^{**} = f(x^{**})$ corresponding to two values of the argument x^* and x^{**}, the subsequent value of the function will be that one which corresponds to the subsequent value of the argument. The following definition is therefore natural.

Definition 3. If the function $y = f(x)$ is such that to a greater value of the argument x there corresponds a greater value of the function, then the function $y = f(x)$ is called *increasing*. A *decreasing* function is similarly defined.

Example 2. The function $Q = \pi R^2$ for $0 < R < \infty$ is an increasing function because to a greater value of R there corresponds a greater value of Q.

Note 2. The definition of a function is sometimes broadened so that to each value of x, within a certain range, there corresponds

not one but several values of y or even an infinitude of values
of y. In this case we have a *multiple-valued* function in contrast
to the one defined above, which is called a *single-valued* function.
Henceforward, when speaking of a function, we shall have in view
only **single-valued** functions. If it becomes necessary to deal with
multiple-valued functions we shall specify this fact.

1.7 WAYS OF REPRESENTING FUNCTIONS

I. Tabular representation of a function

Here, the values of the argument x_1, x_2, ..., x_n and the corresponding values of the function y_1, y_2, ..., y_n are written out
in a definite order.

x	x_1	x_2	....	x_n
y	y_1	y_2	....	y_n

Examples are tables of trigonometric functions, tables of
logarithms, and so on.

An experimental study of phenomena can result in tables that
express a functional relation between the measured quantities. For
example, temperature measurements of the air at a meteorological
station on a definite day yield a table like the following.

The temperature T (in degrees) is dependent on the time t
(in hours).

t	1	2	3	4	5	6	7	8	9
T	0	−1	−2	−2	−0.5	1	3	3.5	4

This table defines T as a function of t.

II. Graphical representation of a function

If in a rectangular coordinate system on a plane we have a set
of points $M(x, y)$ and no two points lie on a straight line parallel
to the y-axis, this set of points defines a certain single-valued
function $y = f(x)$; the abscissas of the points are the values of

the argument, the corresponding ordina-.
tes are the values of the function (Fig. 4).

The collection of points in the *xy*-plane whose abscissas are the values of the independent variable and whose ordinates are the corresponding values of the function is called a *graph* of the given function.

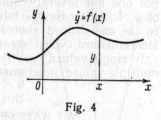

Fig. 4

III. Analytical representation of a function

Let us first explain what "analytical expression" means. By *analytical expression* we will understand a series of symbols denoting certain mathematical operations that are performed in a definite sequence on numbers and letters which designate constant or variable quantities.

By totality of known mathematical operations we mean not only the mathematical operations familiar from the course of secondary school (addition, subtraction, extraction of roots, etc.) but also those which will be defined as we proceed in this course.

The following are examples of analytical expressions:

$$x^4 - 2, \quad \frac{\log x - \sin x}{5x^2 + 1}, \quad 2^x - \sqrt{5 + 3x}$$

If the functional relation $y = f(x)$ is such that f denotes an analytical expression, we say that the function y of x is *represented* or *defined analytically*.

Examples of functions defined analytically are: (1) $y = x^4 - 2$, (2) $y = \frac{x+1}{x-1}$, (3) $y = \sqrt{1 - x^2}$, (4) $y = \sin x$, (5) $Q = \pi R^2$, and so forth.

Here, the functions are defined analytically by means of a single formula (a formula is understood to be an equality of two analytical expressions). In such cases one may speak of the *natural* domain of definition of the function.

The set of values of x for which the analytical expression on the right-hand side has a definite value is the *natural domain of definition of a function* represented analytically. Thus, the natural domain of definition of the function $y = x^4 - 2$ is the infinite interval $-\infty < x < +\infty$, because the function is defined for all values of x. The function $y = \frac{x+1}{x-1}$ is defined for all values of x, with the exception of $x = 1$, because for this value of x the denominator vanishes. For the function $y = \sqrt{1 - x^2}$, the natural domain of definition is the closed interval $-1 \leqslant x \leqslant 1$, and so on.

Note. It is sometimes necessary to consider only a part of the natural domain of a function, and not the whole domain. For

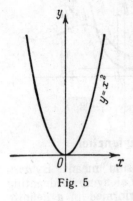

Fig. 5

instance, the dependence of the area Q of a circle upon the radius R is defined by the function $Q = \pi R^2$. The domain of this function, when considering the given geometrical problem, is the infinite interval $0 < R < +\infty$. But the natural domain of this function is the infinite interval $-\infty < R < +\infty$.

If the function $y = f(x)$ is represented analytically, it may be shown graphically on a coordinate xy-plane. Thus, the graph of the function $y = x^2$ is a parabola as shown in Fig. 5.

1.8 BASIC ELEMENTARY FUNCTIONS. ELEMENTARY FUNCTIONS

The basic elementary functions are the following analytically represented functions.

I. *Power function:* $y = x^\alpha$, where α is a real number.*

II. *General exponential function:* $y = a^x$, where a is a positive number not equal to unity.

III. *Logarithmic function:* $y = \log_a x$, where the logarithmic base a is a positive number not equal to unity.**

IV. *Trigonometric functions:* $y = \sin x$, $\quad y = \cos x$, $\quad y = \tan x$, $y = \cot x$, $y = \sec x$, $y = \csc x$.

V. *Inverse trigonometric functions:*

$$y = \arcsin x, \quad y = \arccos x, \quad y = \arctan x,$$
$$y = \operatorname{arccot} x, \quad y = \operatorname{arcsec} x, \quad y = \operatorname{arccsc} x.$$

Let us consider the domains of definition and the graphs of the basic elementary functions.

Power function $y = x^\alpha$.

1. α is a positive integer. The function is defined in the infinite interval $-\infty < x < +\infty$. In this case, the graphs of the function for certain values of α have the form shown in Figs. 6 and 7.

2. α is a negative integer. In this case, the function is defined for all values of x with the exception of $x = 0$. The graphs of the functions for certain values of α have the form shown in Figs. 8 and 9.

Figs. 10, 11, and 12 show graphs of a power function with fractional rational values of α.

---

*If α is irrational, this function is evaluated by taking logarithms and antilogarithms: $\log y = \alpha \log x$. It is assumed here that $x > 0$.

**Throughout this book, the symbol log stands for the logarithm to the base 10.

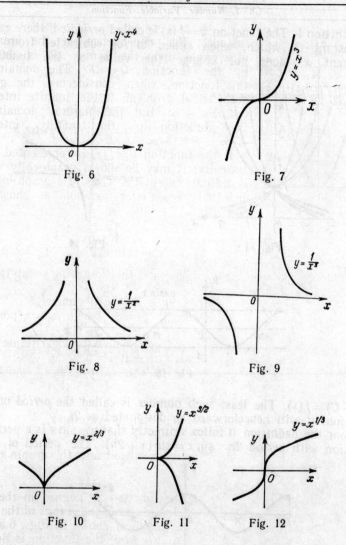

Fig. 6

Fig. 7

Fig. 8

Fig. 9

Fig. 10

Fig. 11

Fig. 12

General exponential function, $y = a^x$, $a > 0$ and $a \neq 1$. This function is defined for all values of x. Its graph is shown in Fig. 13.

Logarithmic function, $y = \log_a x$, $a > 0$ and $a \neq 1$. This function is defined for $x > 0$. Its graph is shown in Fig. 14.

Trigonometric functions. In the formulas $y = \sin x$, etc. the independent variable x is expressed in radians. All the enumerated trigonometric functions are periodic. We give a general definition of a periodic function.

Definition 1. The function $y = f(x)$ is called *periodic* if there exists a constant C, which, when added to (or subtracted from) the argument x, does not change the value of the function:

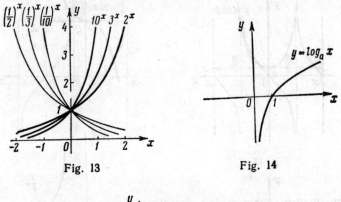

Fig. 13   Fig. 14

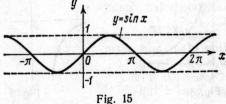

Fig. 15

$f(x + C) = f(x)$. The least such number is called the *period* of the function; it will henceforward be designated as $2l$.

From the definition it follows directly that $y = \sin x$ is a periodic function with period 2π: $\sin x = \sin(x + 2\pi)$. The period of $\cos x$

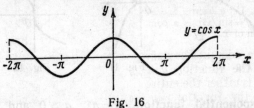

Fig. 16

is likewise 2π. The functions $y = \tan x$ and $y = \cot x$ have a period equal to π.

The functions $y = \sin x$, $y = \cos x$ are defined for all values of x; the functions $y = \tan x$ and $y = \sec x$ are defined everywhere except at the points $x = (2k + 1) \frac{\pi}{2}$ $(k = 0, \pm 1, \pm 2, \ldots)$; the functions

$y = \cot x$ and $y = \csc x$ are defined for all values of x except at the points $x = k\pi$ $(k = 0, \pm 1, \pm 2, \ldots)$. Graphs of trigonometric functions are shown in Figs. 15 to 19.

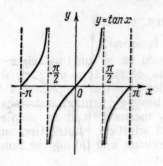

Fig. 17

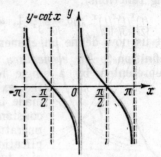

Fig. 18

The inverse trigonometric functions will be discussed in more detail later on.

Let us now introduce the concept of a function of a function. If y is a function of u, and u (in turn) is dependent on the variable x, then y is also dependent on x. Let $y = F(u)$ and $u = \varphi(x)$. We get y as a function of x:

$$y = F[\varphi(x)]$$

This function is called a *function of a function* or a *composite function*.

Example 1. Let $y = \sin u, u = x^2$. The function $y = \sin(x^2)$ is a composite function of x.

Note. The domain of definition of the function $y = F[\varphi(x)]$ is either the entire domain of the function, $u = \varphi(x)$, or that part of it in which those values of u are defined that do not lie outside the domain of the function $F(u)$.

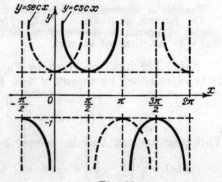

Fig. 19

Example 2. The domain of definition of the function $y = \sqrt{1 - x^2}$ $(y = \sqrt{u}, u = 1 - x^2)$ is the closed interval $[-1, 1]$, because when $|x| > 1$ $u < 0$ and, consequently, the function $\sqrt{u}$ is not defined (although the function $u = 1 - x^2$ is defined for all values of x). The graph of this function is the upper half of a circle with centre at the origin of the coordinate system and with radius unity.

The operation "function of a function" may be performed any number of times. For instance, the function $y = \ln [\sin (x^2 + 1)]$ is obtained as a result of the following operations (defining the following functions);

$$v = x^2 + 1, \quad u = \sin v, \quad y = \ln u$$

Let us now define an elementary function.

Definition 2. An *elementary function* is a function which may be represented by a single formula of the type $y = f(x)$, where the expression on the right-hand side is made up of basic elementary functions and constants by means of a finite number of operations of addition, subtraction, multiplication, division and taking the function of a function.

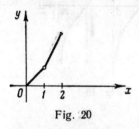

Fig. 20

From this definition it follows that elementary functions are functions represented analytically.

Examples of elementary functions:

$$y = |x| = \sqrt{x^2}, \quad y = \sqrt{1 + 4\sin^2 x}, \quad y = \frac{\log x + 4\sqrt[3]{x} + 2\tan x}{10^x - x + 10}$$

Example of nonelementary function:
The function $y = 1 \cdot 2 \cdot 3 \cdot \ldots \cdot n \ [y = f(n)]$ is not elementary because the number of operations that must be performed to obtain y increases with n, that is to say, it is not bounded.

Note. The function given in Fig. 20 is elementary even though it is represented by means of two formulas:

$$f(x) = x \qquad \text{if} \quad 0 \leqslant x \leqslant 1$$
$$f(x) = 2x - 1 \quad \text{if} \quad 1 \leqslant x \leqslant 2$$

This function can also be defined by a single formula:

$$f(x) = \frac{3}{2}\left(x - \frac{1}{3}\right) + \frac{1}{2}|x - 1| = \frac{3}{2}\left(x - \frac{1}{3}\right) + \frac{1}{2}\sqrt{(x - 1)^2}$$

for $0 \leqslant x \leqslant 2$. (See also Examples 139-144 in the exercises of Chapter 5.)

1.9. ALGEBRAIC FUNCTIONS

Algebraic functions include elementary functions of the following kind:

I. The rational integral function, or polynomial

$$y = a_0 x^n + a_1 x^{n-1} + \ldots + a_n$$

where a_0, a_1, ..., a_n are constants called *coefficients* and n is a nonnegative integer called the *degree of the polynomial*. It is obvious that this function is defined for all values of x, that is, it is defined in an infinite interval.

Examples. 1. $y = ax + b$ is a *linear function*. When $b = 0$, the linear function $y = ax$ expresses y as being directly proportional to x. For $a = 0$, $y = b$, the function is a constant.

2. $y = ax^2 + bx + c$ is a *quadratic function*. The graph of a quadratic function is a parabola (Fig. 21). These functions are considered in detail in analytic geometry.

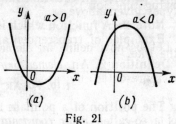

Fig. 21

II. Fractional rational function. This function is defined as the ratio of two polynomials:

$$y = \frac{a_0 x^n + a_1 x^{n-1} + \ldots + a_n}{b_0 x^m + b_1 x^{m-1} + \ldots + b_m}$$

For example, the following is a fractional rational function:

$$y = \frac{a}{x}$$

It expresses inverse variation. Its graph is shown in Fig. 22. It is obvious that a fractional rational function is defined for all values

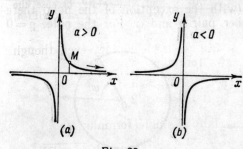

Fig. 22

of x with the exception of those for which the denominator becomes zero.

III. Irrational function. If in the formula $y = f(x)$, operations of addition, subtraction, multiplication, division and raising to a power with rational nonintegral exponents are performed on the right-hand side, the function $y = f(x)$ is *irrational*. Examples of ir-

rational functions are: $y = \dfrac{2x^2 + \sqrt{x}}{\sqrt{1 + 5x^2}}$, $y = \sqrt{x}$, etc.

Note 1. The three types of algebraic functions mentioned above do not exhaust all algebraic functions. An *algebraic function* is any function $y = f(x)$ which satisfies an equation of the form

$$P_0(x) y^n + P_1(x) y^{n-1} + \ldots + P_n(x) = 0 \tag{1}$$

where $P_0(x)$, $P_1(x)$, ..., $P_n(x)$ are certain polynomials in x.

It may be proved that each of these three types of function satisfies a certain equation of type (1), but not every function that satisfies an equation like (1) is a function of one of the three types given above.

Note 2. A function which is not algebraic is called *transcendental*. Examples of transcendental functions are $y = \cos x$, $y = 10^x$ and the like.

1.10. POLAR COORDINATE SYSTEM

The position of a point in a plane may be determined by means of a so-called *polar coordinate system*.

We choose a point O in a plane and call it the *pole;* the half-line issuing from this point is called the *polar axis*. The position

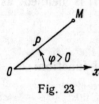

Fig. 23

of the point M in the plane may be specified by two numbers: the number ρ, which expresses the distance of M from the pole, and the number φ, which is the angle formed by the line segment OM and the polar axis. The positive direction of the angle φ is reckoned counterclockwise. The numbers ρ and φ are called the *polar coordinates* of the point M (Fig. 23).

We will always take the radius vector ρ to be nonnegative. If the polar angle φ is taken within the limits $0 \leqslant \varphi < 2\pi$, then to each point of the plane (with the exception of the pole) there corresponds a definite number pair ρ and φ. For the pole, $\rho = 0$ and φ is arbitrary.

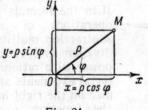

Fig. 24

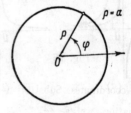

Fig. 25

Let us now see how the polar and rectangular Cartesian coordinates are related. Let the origin of the rectangular coordinate system coincide with the pole, and the positive direction of the x-axis, with the polar axis. From Fig. 24 it follows directly that

$$x = \rho \cos \varphi, \quad y = \rho \sin \varphi$$

and, conversely, that

$$\rho = \sqrt{x^2 + y^2}, \quad \tan \varphi = \frac{y}{x}$$

Note. To find φ, it is necessary to take into account the quadrant in which the point is located and then take the corresponding value of φ. The equation $\rho = F(\varphi)$ in polar coordinates defines a certain line.

Example 1. The equation $\rho = a$, where $a = \text{const}$, defines in polar coordinates a circle with centre in the pole and with radius a. The equation of this circle (Fig. 25) in a rectangular coordinate system situated as shown in Fig. 24 is

$$\sqrt{x^2 + y^2} = a \text{ or } x^2 + y^2 = a^2$$

Example 2. $\rho = a\varphi$, where $a = \text{const}$.
Let us tabulate the values of ρ for certain values of φ

φ	0	$\dfrac{\pi}{4}$	$\dfrac{\pi}{2}$	$\dfrac{3}{4}\pi$	π	$\dfrac{3}{2}\pi$	2π	3π	4π
ρ	0	$\approx 0.78a$	$\approx 1.57a$	$\approx 2.36a$	$\approx 3.14a$	$\approx 4.71a$	$\approx 6.28a$	$\approx 9.42a$	$\approx 12.56a$

The corresponding curve is shown in Fig. 26. It is called the *spiral of Archimedes*.

Example 3. $\rho = 2a \cos \varphi$.
This is the equation of a circle of radius a, the centre of which is at the point $\rho_0 = a$, $\varphi = 0$ (Fig. 27). Let us write the equation of this circle in rect-

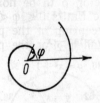

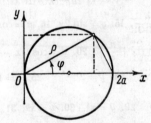

Fig. 26   Fig. 27

angular coordinates. Substituting $\rho = \sqrt{x^2 + y^2}$, $\cos \varphi = \dfrac{x}{\sqrt{x^2 + y^2}}$ into the given equation, we get

$$\sqrt{x^2 + y^2} = 2a \, \frac{x}{\sqrt{x^2 + y^2}}$$

or

$$x^2 + y^2 - 2ax = 0$$

Exercises on Chapter 1

1. Given the function $f(x) = x^2 + 6x - 4$. Verify that $f(1) = 3$, $f(3) = 23$.
2. $f(x) = x^2 + 1$. Evaluate: (a) $f(4)$. *Ans.* 17. (b) $f(\sqrt{2})$. *Ans.* 3. (c) $f(a+1)$. *Ans.* $a^2 + 2a + 2$. (d) $f(a) + 1$. *Ans.* $a^2 + 2$. (e) $f(a^2)$. *Ans.* $a^4 + 1$. (f) $[f(a)]^2$. *Ans.* $a^4 + 2a^2 + 1$. (g) $f(2a)$. *Ans.* $4a^2 + 1$.

3. $\varphi(x) = \dfrac{x-1}{3x+5}$. Write the expressions $\varphi\left(\dfrac{1}{x}\right)$ and $\dfrac{1}{\varphi(x)}$. *Ans.* $\varphi\left(\dfrac{1}{x}\right) =$

$= \dfrac{1-x}{3+5x}$, $\dfrac{1}{\varphi(x)} = \dfrac{3x+5}{x-1}$.

4. $\psi(x) = \sqrt{x^2+4}$. Write the expressions $\psi(2x)$ and $\psi(0)$. *Ans.* $\psi(2x) =$
$= 2\sqrt{x^2+1}$, $\psi(0) = 2$.

5. $f(\theta) = \tan\theta$. Verify the equation $f(20) = \dfrac{2f(\theta)}{1-[f(\theta)]^2}$.

6. $\varphi(x) = \log\dfrac{1-x}{1+x}$. Verify the equation $\varphi(a) + \varphi(b) = \varphi\left(\dfrac{a+b}{1+ab}\right)$.

7. $f(x) = \log x$; $\varphi(x) = x^3$. Write the expressions:
(a) $f[\varphi(2)]$. *Ans.* $3\log 2$. (b) $f[\varphi(a)]$. *Ans.* $3\log a$.
(c) $\varphi[f(a)]$. *Ans.* $[\log a]^3$.

8. Find the natural domain of definition of the function $y = 2x^2+1$.
Ans. $-\infty < x < +\infty$.

9. Find the natural domains of definition of the functions: (a) $\sqrt{1-x^2}$.
Ans. $-1 \leqslant x \leqslant +1$. (b) $\sqrt{3+x} + \sqrt[4]{7-x}$. *Ans.* $-3 \leqslant x \leqslant 7$. (c) $\sqrt[3]{x+a} -$
$- \sqrt[5]{x-b}$. *Ans.* $-\infty < x < +\infty$. (d) $\dfrac{a+x}{a-x}$. *Ans.* $x \neq a$. (e) $\arcsin^2 x$. *Ans.*
$-1 \leqslant x \leqslant 1$. (f) $y = \log x$. *Ans.* $x > 0$. (g) $y = a^x$ $(a > 0)$. *Ans.* $-\infty < x < +\infty$.

Construct the graphs of the functions:

10. $y = -3x+5$. **11.** $y = \dfrac{1}{2}x^2+1$. **12.** $y = 3-2x^2$. **13.** $y = x^2+2x-1$.

14. $y = \dfrac{1}{x-1}$. **15.** $y = \sin 2x$. **16.** $y = \cos 3x$. **17.** $y = x^2-4x+6$. **18.** $y = \dfrac{1}{1-x^2}$.

19. $y = \sin\left(x+\dfrac{\pi}{4}\right)$. **20.** $y = \cos\left(x-\dfrac{\pi}{3}\right)$. **21.** $y = \tan\dfrac{1}{2}x$. **22.** $y = \cot\dfrac{1}{4}x$.

23. $y = 3^x$. **24.** $y = 2^{-x^2}$. **25.** $y = \log_2\dfrac{1}{x}$. **26.** $y = x^3+1$. **27.** $y = 4-x^3$.

28. $y = \dfrac{1}{x^2}$. **29.** $y = x^4$. **30.** $y = x^5$. **31.** $y = x^{\frac{1}{2}}$. **32.** $y = x^{-\frac{1}{2}}$. **33.** $y = x^{\frac{1}{3}}$.

34. $y = |x|$. **35.** $y = \log_2|x|$. **36.** $y = \log_2(1-x)$. **37.** $y = 3\sin\left(2x+\dfrac{\pi}{3}\right)$.

38. $y = 4\cos\left(x+\dfrac{\pi}{2}\right)$. **39.** The function $f(x)$ is defined on the interval $[-1, 1]$
as follows:

$$f(x) = 1+x \quad \text{for} \quad -1 \leqslant x \leqslant 0,$$
$$f(x) = 1-2x \quad \text{for} \quad 0 \leqslant x < 1$$

40. The function $f(x)$ is defined on the interval $[0, 2]$ as follows:

$$f(x) = x^3 \quad \text{for} \quad 0 \leqslant x \leqslant 1,$$
$$f(x) = x \quad \text{for} \quad 1 \leqslant x \leqslant 2.$$

Construct curves given by the polar equations:

41. $\rho = \dfrac{a}{\varphi}$ (*hyperbolic spiral*). **42.** $\rho = a^\varphi$ (*logarithmic spiral*). **43.** $\rho = a\sqrt{\cos 2\varphi}$
(*lemniscate*). **44.** $\rho = a(1-\cos\varphi)$ (*cardioid*). **45.** $\rho = a\sin 3\varphi$.

CHAPTER 2

LIMIT. CONTINUITY OF A FUNCTION

2.1 THE LIMIT OF A VARIABLE.
AN INFINITELY LARGE VARIABLE

In this section we shall consider ordered variables that vary in a special way defined as follows: "the variable approaches a limit". Throughout the remainder of the course, the concept of the limit of a variable will play a fundamental role, for it is intimately bound up with the basic concepts of mathematical analysis, such as derivative, integral, etc.

Definition 1. A constant number a is said to be the *limit* of a variable x, if for every preassigned arbitrarily small positive number ε it is possible to indicate a value of the variable x such that all subsequent values of the variable will satisfy the inequality

$$|x-a| < \varepsilon$$

If the number a is the limit of the variable x, one says that x approaches the limit a; in symbols we have

$$x \to a \text{ or } \lim x = a$$

In geometric terms, limit may be defined as follows.

The constant number a is the *limit* of the variable x if for any preassigned arbitrarily small neighbourhood with centre in the point a and with radius ε there is a value of x such that all points corresponding to subsequent values of the variable will be within this neighbourhood (Fig. 28).

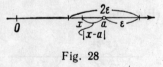
Fig. 28

Let us consider several cases of variables approaching limits.

Example 1. The variable x takes on the successive values

$$x_1 = 1 + 1, \ x_2 = 1 + \frac{1}{2}, \ x_3 = 1 + \frac{1}{3}, \ \ldots, \ x_n = 1 + \frac{1}{n}, \ \ldots$$

We shall prove that this variable has unity as its limit. We have

$$|x_n - 1| = \left|\left(1 + \frac{1}{n}\right) - 1\right| = \frac{1}{n}$$

For any ε, all subsequent values of the variable beginning with n, where $\frac{1}{n} < \varepsilon$, or $n > \frac{1}{\varepsilon}$, will satisfy the inequality $|x_n - 1| < \varepsilon$, and the proof is complete. It will be noted here that the variable quantity decreases as it approaches the limit.

Example 2. The variable x takes on the successive values

$$x_1 = 1 - \frac{1}{2}, \; x^2 = 1 + \frac{1}{2^2}, \; x_3 = 1 - \frac{1}{2^3}, \; x_4 = 1 + \frac{1}{2^4}, \; \ldots, \; x_n = 1 + (-1)^n \frac{1}{2^n}, \; \ldots$$

This variable has a limit of unity. Indeed,

$$|x_n - 1| = \left| \left(1 + (-1)^n \frac{1}{2^n} \right) - 1 \right| = \frac{1}{2^n}$$

For any ε, beginning with n, which satisfies the relation $\frac{1}{2^n} < \varepsilon$, from which it follows that

$$2^n > \frac{1}{\varepsilon}, \quad n \log 2 > \log \frac{1}{\varepsilon} \text{ or } n > \frac{\log \dfrac{1}{\varepsilon}}{\log 2},$$

all subsequent values of x will satisfy the relation $|x_n - 1| < \varepsilon$. It will be noted here that the values of the variable are greater than or less than the limit, and the variable approaches its limit by "oscillating about it".

Note 1. As was pointed out in Sec. 1.3, a constant quantity c is frequently regarded as a variable whose values are all the same: $x = c$.

Obviously, the limit of a constant is equal to the constant itself, since we always have the inequality $|x - c| = |c - c| = 0 < \varepsilon$ for any ε.

Note 2. From the definition of a limit it follows that a variable cannot have two limits. Indeed, if $\lim x = a$ and $\lim x = b$ $(a < b)$, then x must satisfy, at one and the same time, two inequalities:

$$|x - a| < \varepsilon \text{ and } |x - b| < \varepsilon$$

for an arbitrarily small ε; but this is impossible if $\varepsilon < \frac{b - a}{2}$ (Fig. 29).

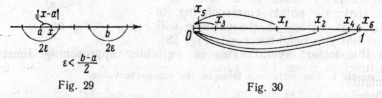

Fig. 29   Fig. 30

Note 3. One should not think that every variable has a limit. Let the variable x take on the following successive values (Fig. 30):

$$x_1 = \frac{1}{2}, \quad x_2 = 1 - \frac{1}{4}, \quad x_3 = \frac{1}{8}, \quad \ldots, \quad x_{2k} = 1 - \frac{1}{2^{2k}}, \quad x_{2k+1} = \frac{1}{2^{2k+1}}$$

For k sufficiently large, the value x_{2k} and all subsequent values with even labels will differ from unity by as small a number as we please, while the next value x_{2k+1} and all subsequent values of x with odd labels will differ from zero by as small a number as we please. Consequently, the variable x does not approach a limit.

In the definition of a limit it is stated that if the variable approaches the limit a, then a is a constant. But the word "approaches" is used also to describe another type of variation of a variable, as will be seen from the following definition.

Definition 2. A variable x *approaches infinity* if for every preassigned positive number M it is possible to indicate a value of x such that, beginning with this value, all subsequent values of the variable satisfy the inequality $|x| > M$.

If the variable x approaches infinity, it is called an *infinitely large* variable and we write $x \to \infty$.

Example 3. The variable x takes on the values

$$x_1 = -1, \ x_2 = 2, \ x_3 = -3, \ \ldots, \ x_n = (-1)^n n, \ \ldots$$

This is an infinitely large variable quantity, since for an arbitrary $M > 0$ all values of the variable, beginning with a certain one, are greater than M in absolute value.

The variable x "approaches plus infinity", $x \to +\infty$, if for an arbitrary $M > 0$ all subsequent values of the variable, beginning with a certain one, satisfy the inequality $M < x$.

An example of a variable quantity approaching plus infinity is the variable x that takes on the values $x_1 = 1$, $x_2 = 2$, $\ldots$, $x_n = n$, $\ldots$.

A variable approaches minus infinity, $x \to -\infty$, if for an arbitrary $M > 0$ all subsequent values of the variable, beginning with a certain one, satisfy the inequality $x < -M$.

For example, a variable x that assumes the values $x_1 = -1$, $x_2 = -2$, $\ldots$, $x_n = -n$, $\ldots$, approaches minus infinity.

2.2 THE LIMIT OF A FUNCTION

In this section we shall consider certain cases of the variation of a function when the argument x approaches a certain limit a or infinity.

Definition 1. Let the function $y = f(x)$ be defined in a certain neighbourhood of a point a or at certain points of this neighbourhood. *The function $y = f(x)$ approaches the limit b $(y \to b)$ as x approaches a $(x \to a)$, if for every positive number ε, no matter how small, it is possible to indicate a positive number δ such* that for all x, different from a and satisfying the inequality*

$$|x-a| < \delta$$

we have the inequality

$$|f(x)-b| < \varepsilon$$

If b is the *limit of the function* $f(x)$ as $x \to a$, we write

$$\lim_{x \to a} f(x) = b$$

or $f(x) \to b$ as $x \to a$.

If $f(x) \to b$ as $x \to a$, this is illustrated on the graph of the
function $y = f(x)$ as follows (Fig. 31). Since from the inequality

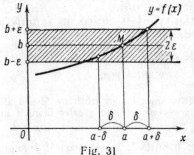

Fig. 31

$|x-a| < \delta$ there follows the ine-
quality $|f(x)-b| < \varepsilon$, this means
that for all points x that are not
more distant from the point a than
δ, the points M of the graph of
the function $y = f(x)$ lie within a
band of width 2ε bounded by the
lines $y = b - \varepsilon$ and $y = b + \varepsilon$.

Note 1. We may also define the
limit of the function $f(x)$ as $x \to a$
as follows.

Let a variable x assume values
such (that is, ordered in such fashion) that if

$$|x^*-a| > |x^{**}-a|$$

then x^{**} is the subsequent value and x^* is the preceding value;
but if

$$|\bar{x}^*-a| = |\bar{x}^{**}-a| \text{ and } \bar{x}^* < \bar{x}^{**}$$

then $\bar{x}^{**}$ is the subsequent value and $\bar{x}^*$ is the preceding value.

In other words, of two points on a number scale, the subsequent
one is that which is closer to the point a; at equal distances, the
subsequent one is that which is to the right of the point a.

Let a variable quantity x ordered in this fashion approach the
limit a $[x \to a$ or $\lim x = a]$.

Let us further consider the variable $y = f(x)$. We shall here and
henceforward consider that of the two values of a function, the

*Here we mean the values of x that satisfy the inequality $|x-a| < \delta$
and belong to the domain of definition of the function. We will encounter
similar circumstances in the future. For instance, when considering the behaviour of a function as $x \to \infty$, it may happen that the function is defined
only for positive integral values of x. And so in this case $x \to \infty$, assuming
only positive integral values. We shall not specify this when it comes up
later on.

subsequent one is that which corresponds to the subsequent value of the argument.

If, as $x \rightarrow a$, a variable y thus defined approaches a certain limit b, we shall write

$$\lim_{x \to a} f(x) = b$$

and we shall say that the function $y = f(x)$ approaches the limit b as $x \rightarrow a$.

It is easy to prove that both definitions of the limit of a function are equivalent.

Note 2. If $f(x)$ approaches the limit b_1 as x approaches a certain number a so that x takes on only values less than a we write $\lim\limits_{x \to a - 0} f(x) = b_1$ and call b_1 the *limit on the left at the point a of the function.* If x takes on only values greater than a, we write $\lim\limits_{x \to a + 0} f(x) = b_2$ and call b_2 the *limit on the right at the point a of the function* (Fig. 32).

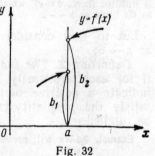

Fig. 32

It can be proved that if the limit on the right and the limit on the left exist and are equal, that is, $b_1 = b_2 = b$, then b will be the limit in the sense of the foregoing definition of a limit at the point a. And conversely, if there exists a limit b of a function at the point a, then there exist limits of the function at the point a both on the right and on the left and they are equal.

Example 1. Let us prove that $\lim\limits_{x \to 2} (3x+1) = 7$. Indeed, let an arbitrary $\varepsilon > 0$ be given; for the inequality $|(3x+1)-7| < \varepsilon$ to be fulfilled it is necessary to have the following inequalities fulfilled:

$$|3x-6| < \varepsilon, \quad |x-2| < \frac{\varepsilon}{3}, \quad -\frac{\varepsilon}{3} < x-2 < \frac{\varepsilon}{3}$$

Thus, given any ε, for all values of x satisfying the inequality $|x-2| < \frac{\varepsilon}{3} = \delta$, the value of the function $3x+1$ will differ from 7 by less than ε. And this means that 7 is the limit of the function as $x \rightarrow 2$.

Note 3. For a function to have a limit as $x \rightarrow a$, it is not necessary that the function be defined at the point $x = a$. When finding the limit we consider the values of the function in the neighbourhood of the point a that are different from a; this is clearly illustrated in the following case.

Example 2. We shall prove that $\lim\limits_{x \to 2} \dfrac{x^2 - 4}{x-2} = 4$. Here, the function $\dfrac{x^2 - 4}{x-2}$ is not defined for $x = 2$.

It is necessary to prove that for an arbitrary ε there will be a δ such that the following inequality will be fulfilled:

$$\left|\frac{x^2-4}{x-2}-4\right|<\varepsilon \qquad (1)$$

if $|x-2|<\delta$. But when $x\neq2$ .inequality (1) is equivalent to the inequality

$$\left|\frac{(x-2)(x+2)}{x-2}-4\right|=|(x+2)-4|<\varepsilon$$

or

$$|x-2|<\varepsilon \qquad (2)$$

Thus, for an arbitrary ε, inequality (1) will be fulfilled if inequality (2) is fulfilled (here, $\delta=\varepsilon$), which means that the given function has the number 4 as its limit as $x\rightarrow2$.

Let us now consider certain cases of variation of a function as $x\rightarrow\infty$.

Definition 2. *The function $f(x)$ approaches the limit b as $x\rightarrow\infty$ if for each arbitrarily small positive number ε it is possible to indicate a positive number N such that for all values of x that satisfy the inequality $|x|>N$ the inequality $|f(x)-b|<\varepsilon$ will be fulfilled.*

Example 3. We will prove that

$$\lim_{x\to\infty}\left(\frac{x+1}{x}\right)=1$$

or

$$\lim_{x\to\infty}\left(1+\frac{1}{x}\right)=1$$

It is necessary to prove that, for an arbitrary ε, the following inequality is fulfilled

$$\left|\left(1+\frac{1}{x}\right)-1\right|<\varepsilon \qquad (3)$$

provided $|x|>N$, where N is determined by the choice of ε. Inequality (3) is equivalent to the following inequality: $\left|\frac{1}{x}\right|<\varepsilon$, which will be fulfilled if

$$|x|>\frac{1}{\varepsilon}=N$$

which means that $\lim_{x\to\infty}\left(1+\frac{1}{x}\right)=\lim_{x\to\infty}\frac{x+1}{x}=1$ (Fig. 33).

If we know the meanings of the symbols $x\rightarrow+\infty$ and $x\rightarrow-\infty$, the meanings of the following expressions are obvious:

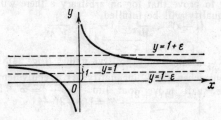

Fig. 33

"$f(x)$ approaches b as $x \longrightarrow +\infty$" and
"$f(x)$ approaches b as $x \longrightarrow -\infty$" or, in symbols,

$$\lim_{x \to +\infty} f(x) = b,$$

$$\lim_{x \to -\infty} f(x) = b$$

2.3. A FUNCTION THAT APPROACHES INFINITY. BOUNDED FUNCTIONS

We have considered cases when a function $f(x)$ approaches a certain limit b as $x \longrightarrow a$ or as $x \longrightarrow \infty$.

Let us now take the case where the function $y = f(x)$ approaches infinity when the argument varies in some way.

Definition 1. The function $f(x)$ approaches infinity as $x \longrightarrow a$, i.e., it is an *infinitely large* quantity as $x \longrightarrow a$ if for each positive number M, no matter how large, it is possible to find a $\delta > 0$ such that for all values of x different from a and satisfying the condition $|x - a| < \delta$, we have the inequality $|f(x)| > M$.

If $f(x)$ approaches infinity as $x \longrightarrow a$, we write

$$\lim_{x \to a} f(x) = \infty$$

or $f(x) \to \infty$ as $x \longrightarrow a$.

If $f(x)$ approaches infinity as $x \longrightarrow a$ and, in the process, assumes only positive or only negative values, the appropriate notation is $\lim\limits_{x \to a} f(x) = +\infty$ or $\lim\limits_{x \to a} f(x) = -\infty$.

Example 1. We shall prove that $\lim\limits_{x \to 1} \dfrac{1}{(1-x)^2} = +\infty$. Indeed, for any $M > 0$

we have

$$\frac{1}{(1-x)^2} > M$$

provided

$$(1-x)^2 < \frac{1}{M}, \quad |1-x| < \frac{1}{\sqrt{M}} = \delta$$

The function $\frac{1}{(1-x)^2}$ assumes only positive values (Fig. 34).

Example 2. We shall prove that $\lim\limits_{x \to 0}\left(-\frac{1}{x}\right) = \infty$. Indeed, for any

$M > 0$ we have

$$\left|-\frac{1}{x}\right| > M$$

provided

$$|x| = |x-0| < \frac{1}{M} = \delta$$

Here $\left(-\frac{1}{x}\right) > 0$ for $x < 0$ and $\left(-\frac{1}{x}\right) < 0$ for $x > 0$ (Fig. 35).

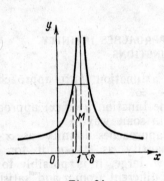
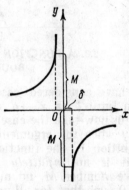

Fig. 34   Fig. 35

If the function $f(x)$ approaches infinity as $x \to \infty$, we write

$$\lim_{x \to \infty} f(x) = \infty$$

and we may have the particular cases

$$\lim_{x \to +\infty} f(x) = \infty, \quad \lim_{x \to -\infty} f(x) = \infty, \quad \lim_{x \to +\infty} f(x) = -\infty$$

For example,

$$\lim_{x \to \infty} x^2 = +\infty, \quad \lim_{x \to -\infty} x^3 = -\infty \text{ and the like.}$$

Note 1. The function $y = f(x)$ may not approach a finite limit or infinity as $x \to a$ or as $x \to \infty$.

Example 3. The function $y = \sin x$ defined on the infinite interval $-\infty <$ $< x < +\infty$, does not approach either a finite limit or infinity as $x \to \div \infty$ (Fig. 36).

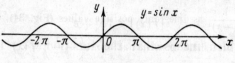

Fig. 36

Example 4. The function $y = \sin \dfrac{1}{x}$ defined for all values of x, except $x = 0$, does not approach either a finite limit or infinity as $x \to 0$. The graph of this function is shown in Fig. 37.

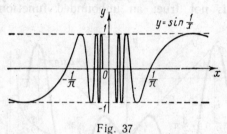

Fig. 37

Definition 2. A function $y = f(x)$ is called *bounded* in a given range of the argument x if there exists a positive number M such that for all values of x in the range under consideration the inequality $|f(x)| \leqslant M$ is fulfilled. If there is no such number M, the function $f(x)$ is called *unbounded* in the given range.

Example 5. The function $y = \sin x$, defined in the infinite interval $-\infty <$ $< x < +\infty$, is bounded, since for all values of x

$$|\sin x| \leqslant 1 = M$$

Definition 3. The function $f(x)$ is called *bounded as* $x \to a$ if there exists a neighbourhood, with centre at the point a, in which the given function is bounded.

Definition 4. The function $y = f(x)$ is called *bounded as* $x \to \infty$ if there exists a number $N > 0$ such that for all values of x satisfying the inequality $|x| > N$, the function $f(x)$ is bounded.

The boundedness of a function approaching a limit is decided by the following theorem.

Theorem 1. *If* $\lim\limits_{x \to a} f(x) = b$, *where* b *is a finite number, the function* $f(x)$ *is bounded as* $x \to a$.

Proof. From the equation $\lim\limits_{x \to a} f(x) = b$ it follows that for any $\varepsilon > 0$ there will be a δ such that in the neighbourhood $a - \delta <$

$< x < a + \delta$ the inequality

$$|f(x) - b| < \varepsilon$$

or

$$|f(x)| < |b| + \varepsilon$$

is fulfilled, which means that the function $f(x)$ is bounded as $x \longrightarrow a$.

Note 2. From the definition of a bounded function $f(x)$ it follows that if

$$\lim_{x \to a} f(x) = \infty \quad \text{or} \quad \lim_{x \to \infty} f(x) = \infty$$

that is, if $f(x)$ is an infinitely large function, it is unbounded. The converse is not true: an unbounded function may not be infinitely large.

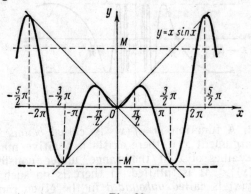

Fig. 38

For example, the function $y = x \sin x$ as $x \longrightarrow \infty$ is unbounded because, for any $M > 0$, values of x can be found such that $|x \sin x| > M$. But the function $y = x \sin x$ is not infinitely large because it becomes zero when $x = 0$, π, 2π, ... The graph of the function $y = x \sin x$ is shown in Fig. 38.

Theorem 2. *If* $\lim\limits_{x \to a} f(x) = b \neq 0$, *then the function* $y = \dfrac{1}{f(x)}$ *is a bounded function as* $x \longrightarrow a$.

Proof. From the statement of the theorem it follows that for an arbitrary $\varepsilon > 0$ in a certain neighbourhood of the point $x = a$ we will have $|f(x) - b| < \varepsilon$, or $||f(x)| - |b|| < \varepsilon$, or $-\varepsilon < |f(x)| - |b| < \varepsilon$, or $|b| - \varepsilon < |f(x)| < |b| + \varepsilon$.

From the latter inequality it follows that

$$\frac{1}{|b| - \varepsilon} > \frac{1}{|f(x)|} > \frac{1}{|b| + \varepsilon}$$

For example, taking $\varepsilon = \frac{1}{10}|b|$, we get

$$\frac{10}{9|b|} > \frac{1}{|f(x)|} > \frac{10}{11|b|}$$

which means that the function $\frac{1}{f(x)}$ is bounded.

2.4 INFINITESIMALS AND THEIR BASIC PROPERTIES

In this section we shall consider functions approaching zero as the argument varies in a certain manner.

Definition. The function $\alpha = \alpha(x)$ is called *infinitesimal* as $x \to a$ or as $x \to \infty$ if $\lim\limits_{x \to a} \alpha(x) = 0$ or $\lim\limits_{x \to \infty} \alpha(x) = 0$.

From the definition of a limit it follows that if, for example, $\lim\limits_{x \to a} \alpha(x) = 0$, this means that for any preassigned arbitrarily small positive ε there will be a $\delta > 0$ such that for all x satisfying the condition $|x - a| < \delta$, the condition $|\alpha(x)| < \varepsilon$ will be satisfied.

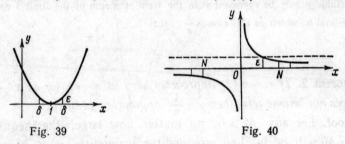

Fig. 39   Fig. 40

Example 1. The function $\alpha = (x-1)^2$ is an infinitesimal as $x \to 1$ because $\lim\limits_{x \to 1} \alpha = \lim\limits_{x \to 1} (x-1)^2 = 0$ (Fig. 39).

Example 2. The function $\alpha = \frac{1}{x}$ is an infinitesimal as $x \to \infty$ (Fig. 40) (see Example 3, Sec. 2.2).

Let us establish a relationship that will be important later on.

Theorem 1. *If the function* $y = f(x)$ *is in the form of a sum of a constant b and an infinitesimal α:*

$$y = b + \alpha \qquad (1)$$

then

$$\lim y = b \quad (as \ x \to a \ or \ x \to \infty)$$

Conversely, *if* $\lim y = b$, *we may write* $y = b + \alpha$, *where α is an infinitesimal.*

Proof. From (1) it follows that $|y - b| = |\alpha|$. But for an arbitrary ε, all values of α, from a certain value onwards, satisfy the relationship $|\alpha| < \varepsilon$; consequently, the inequality $|y-b| < \varepsilon$ will be fulfilled for all values of y from a certain value onwards. And this means that $\lim y = b$.

Conversely: if $\lim y = b$, then, given an arbitrary ε, for all values of y from a certain value onwards, we will have $|y-b| < \varepsilon$. But if we denote $y-b = \alpha$, then it follows that for all values of α, from a certain one onwards, we will have $|\alpha| < \varepsilon$; and this means that α is an infinitesimal.

Example 3. We have the function (Fig. 41)

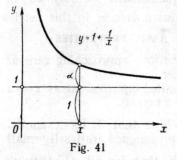

Fig. 41

$$y = 1 + \frac{1}{x}$$

Then

$$\lim_{x \to \infty} y = 1$$

and, conversely, since

$$\lim_{x \to \infty} y = 1$$

the variable y may be represented in the form of a sum of the limit 1 and an infinitesimal α, which in this case is $\frac{1}{x}$; that is,

$$y = 1 + \alpha$$

Theorem 2. *If $\alpha = \alpha(x)$ approaches zero as $x \to a$ (or as $x \to \infty$) and does not become zero, then $y = \dfrac{1}{\alpha}$ approaches infinity.*

Proof. For any $M > 0$, no matter how large, the inequality $\dfrac{1}{|\alpha|} > M$ will be fulfilled provided the inequality $|\alpha| < \dfrac{1}{M}$ is fulfilled. The latter inequality will be fulfilled for all values of α, from a certain one onwards, since $\alpha(x) \to 0$.

Theorem 3. *The algebraic sum of two, three or, in general, a definite number of infinitesimals is an infinitesimal function.*

Proof. We shall prove the theorem for two terms, since the proof is similar for any number of terms.

Let $u(x) = \alpha(x) + \beta(x)$, where $\lim\limits_{x \to a} \alpha(x) = 0$, $\lim\limits_{x \to a} \beta(x) = 0$. We shall prove that for any $\varepsilon > 0$, no matter how small, there will be a $\delta > 0$ such that when the inequality $|x-a| < \delta$ is satisfied, the inequality $|u| < \varepsilon$ will be fulfilled. Since $\alpha(x)$ is an infinitesimal, a δ_1 will be found such that in a neighbourhood with centre at the point a and radius δ_1 we will have

$$|\alpha(x)| < \frac{\varepsilon}{2}$$

Since $\beta(x)$ is an infinitesimal, there will be a δ_2 such that in a neighbourhood with centre at the point a and radius δ_2 we will have $|\beta(x)| < \dfrac{\varepsilon}{2}$.

Let us take δ equal to the smaller of the two quantities δ_1 and δ_2; then the inequalities $|\alpha| < \dfrac{\varepsilon}{2}$ and $|\beta| < \dfrac{\varepsilon}{2}$ will be fulfilled in a neighbourhood of the point a of radius δ. Hence, in this neighbourhood we will have

$$|u| = |\alpha(x) + \beta(x)| \leqslant |\alpha(x)| + |\beta(x)| < \frac{\varepsilon}{2} + \frac{\varepsilon}{2} = \varepsilon$$

and so $|u| < \varepsilon$, as required.

The proof is similar for the case when

$$\lim_{x \to \infty} \alpha(x) = 0, \quad \lim_{x \to \infty} \beta(x) = 0$$

Note. Later on we will have to consider sums of infinitesimals such that the number of terms increases with a decrease in each term. In this case, the theorem may not hold. To take an example, consider $u = \underbrace{\dfrac{1}{x} + \dfrac{1}{x} + \ldots + \dfrac{1}{x}}_{x \text{ terms}}$ where x takes on only positive integral values $(x = 1, 2, 3, \ldots, n, \ldots)$. It is obvious that as $x \to \infty$ each term is an infinitesimal, but the sum $u = 1$ is not an infinitesimal.

Theorem 4. *The product of the function of an infinitesimal $\alpha = \alpha(x)$ by a bounded function $z = z(x)$, as $x \to a$ (or $x \to \infty$) is an infinitesimal quantity (function).*

Proof. Let us prove the theorem for the case $x \to a$. For a certain $M > 0$ there will be a neighbourhood of the point $x = a$ in which the inequality $|z| < M$ will be satisfied. For any $\varepsilon > 0$ there will be a neighbourhood in which the inequality $|\alpha| < \dfrac{\varepsilon}{M}$ will be fulfilled. The following inequality will be fulfilled in the least of these two neighbourhoods:

$$|\alpha z| < \frac{\varepsilon}{M} M = \varepsilon$$

which means that αz is an infinitesimal. The proof is similar for the case $x \to \infty$. Two corollaries follow from this theorem.

Corollary 1. *If $\lim \alpha = 0$, $\lim \beta = 0$, then $\lim \alpha\beta = 0$* because $\beta(x)$ is a bounded quantity. This holds for any finite number of factors.

Corollary 2. *If $\lim \alpha = 0$ and $c = $ const, then $\lim c\alpha = 0$.*

Theorem 5. *The quotient $\dfrac{\alpha(x)}{z(x)}$ obtained by dividing the infinitesimal $\alpha(x)$ by a function whose limit differs from zero is an infinitesimal.*

Proof. Let $\lim \alpha(x) = 0$, $\lim z(x) = b \neq 0$. By Theorem 2, Sec. 2.3, it follows that $\frac{1}{z(\alpha)}$ is a bounded quantity. For this reason, the fraction $\frac{\alpha(x)}{z(x)} = \alpha(x) \cdot \frac{1}{z(x)}$ is a product of an infinitesimal by a bounded quantity, that is, an infinitesimal.

2.5 BASIC THEOREMS ON LIMITS

In this section, as in the preceding one, we shall consider sets of functions that depend on the same argument x, where $x \to a$ or $x \to \infty$.

We shall carry out the proof for one of these cases, since the other is proved analogously. Sometimes we will not even write $x \to a$ or $x \to \infty$, but will take one or the other of them for granted.

Theorem 1. *The limit of an algebraic sum of two, three or, in general, any definite number of variables is equal to the algebraic sum of the limits of these variables:*

$$\lim(u_1 + u_2 + \ldots + u_k) = \lim u_1 + \lim u_2 + \ldots + \lim u_k$$

Proof. We shall carry out the proof for two terms since it is the same for any number of terms. Let $\lim u_1 = a_1$, $\lim u_2 = a_2$. Then on the basis of Theorem 1, Sec. 2.4, we can write

$$u_1 = a_1 + \alpha_1, \quad u_2 = a_2 + \alpha_2,$$

where α_1 and α_2 are infinitesimals. Consequently,

$$u_1 + u_2 = (a_1 + a_2) + (\alpha_1 + \alpha_2)$$

Since $(a_1 + a_2)$ is a constant and $(\alpha_1 + \alpha_2)$ is an infinitesimal, again by Theorem 1, Sec. 2.4, we conclude that

$$\lim(u_1 + u_2) = a_1 + a_2 = \lim u_1 + \lim u_2$$

Example 1.

$$\lim_{x \to \infty} \frac{x^2 + 2x}{x^2} = \lim_{x \to \infty}\left(1 + \frac{2}{x}\right) = \lim_{x \to \infty} 1 + \lim_{x \to \infty} \frac{2}{x} = 1 + \lim_{x \to \infty} \frac{2}{x} = 1 + 0 = 1$$

Theorem 2. *The limit of a product of two, three or, in general, any definite number of variables is equal to the product of the limits of these variables:*

$$\lim u_1 \cdot u_2 \cdot \ldots \cdot u_k = \lim u_1 \cdot \lim u_2 \cdot \ldots \cdot \lim u_k$$

Proof. To save space we carry out the proof for two factors. Let $\lim u_1 = a_1$, $\lim u_2 = a_2$. Therefore,

$$u_1 = a_1 + \alpha_1, \quad u_2 = a_2 + \alpha_2,$$
$$u_1 u_2 = (a_1 + \alpha_1)(a_2 + \alpha_2) = a_1 a_2 + a_1 \alpha_2 + a_2 \alpha_1 + \alpha_1 \alpha_2$$

The product $a_1 a_2$ is a constant. By the theorems of Sec. 2.4, the quantity $a_1 \alpha_2 + a_2 \alpha_1 + \alpha_1 \alpha_2$ is an infinitesimal. Hence, $\lim u_1 u_2 = = a_1 a_2 = \lim u_1 \cdot \lim u_2$.

Corollary. *A constant factor may be taken outside the limit sign.*

Indeed, if $\lim u_1 = a_1$, c is a constant and, consequently, $\lim c = c$, then $\lim (cu_1) = \lim c \cdot \lim u_1 = c \cdot \lim u_1$, as required.

Example 2.

$$\lim_{x \to 2} 5x^3 = 5 \lim_{x \to 2} x^3 = 5 \cdot 8 = 40$$

Theorem 3. *The limit of a quotient of two variables is equal to the quotient of the limits of these variables if the limit of the denominator is not zero:*

$$\lim \frac{u}{v} = \frac{\lim u}{\lim v} \quad if \lim v \neq 0$$

Proof. Let $\lim u = a$, $\lim v = b \neq 0$. Then $u = a + \alpha$, $v = b + \beta$, where α and β are infinitesimals.

We write the identities

$$\frac{u}{v} = \frac{a+\alpha}{b+\beta} = \frac{a}{b} + \left(\frac{a+\alpha}{b+\beta} - \frac{a}{b} \right) = \frac{a}{b} + \frac{\alpha b - \beta a}{b(b+\beta)}$$

or

$$\frac{u}{v} = \frac{a}{b} + \frac{\alpha b - \beta a}{b(b+\beta)}$$

The fraction $\frac{a}{b}$ is a constant number, while the fraction $\frac{\alpha b - \beta a}{b(b+\beta)}$ is an infinitesimal variable by virtue of Theorems 4 and 5 (Sec. 2.4), since $\alpha b - \beta a$ is an infinitesimal, while the denominator $b(b+\beta)$ has the limit $b^2 \neq 0$. Thus, $\lim \frac{u}{v} = \frac{a}{b} = \frac{\lim u}{\lim v}$.

Example 3.

$$\lim_{x \to 1} \frac{3x+5}{4x-2} = \frac{\lim_{x \to 1}(3x+5)}{\lim_{x \to 1}(4x-2)} = \frac{3 \lim_{x \to 1} x + 5}{4 \lim_{x \to 1} x - 2} = \frac{3 \cdot 1 + 5}{4 \cdot 1 - 2} = \frac{8}{2} = 4$$

Here, we made use of the already proved theorem for the limit of a fraction because the limit of the denominator differs from zero as $x \to 1$. If the limit of the denominator is zero, the theorem for the limit of a fraction is not applicable, and special considerations have to be invoked.

Example 4. Find $\lim\limits_{x \to 2} \dfrac{x^2-4}{x-2}$.

Here the denominator and numerator approach zero as $x \to 2$, and, consequently, Theorem 3 is inapplicable. Perform the following identical transformation:

$$\frac{x^2-4}{x-2} = \frac{(x-2)(x+2)}{x-2} = x+2$$

The transformation holds for all values of x different from 2. And so, having in view the definition of a limit, we can write

$$\lim_{x \to 2} \frac{x^2-4}{x-2} = \lim_{x \to 2} \frac{(x-2)\,(x+2)}{x-2} = \lim_{x \to 2} (x+2) = 4$$

Example 5. Find $\lim_{x \to 1} \dfrac{x}{x-1}$. As $x \to 1$ the denominator approaches zero but the numerator does not (it approaches unity). Thus, the limit of the reciprocal is zero:

$$\lim_{x \to 1} \frac{x-1}{x} = \frac{\lim\limits_{x \to 1} (x-1)}{\lim\limits_{x \to 1} x} = \frac{0}{1} = 0$$

Whence, by Theorem 2 of the preceding section, we have

$$\lim_{x \to 1} \frac{x}{x-1} = \infty$$

Theorem 4. *If the inequalities $u \leqslant z \leqslant v$ are fulfilled between the corresponding values of three functions $u = u(x)$, $z = z(x)$ and $v = v(x)$, where $u(x)$ and $v(x)$ approach one and the same limit b as $x \to a$ (or as $x \to \infty$), then $z = z(x)$ approaches the same limit as $x \to a$ (or as $x \to \infty$).*

Proof. For definiteness we shall consider variations of the funcctions as $x \to a$. From the inequalities $u \leqslant z \leqslant v$ follow the inequalities

$$u - b \leqslant z - b \leqslant v - b$$

it is given that

$$\lim_{x \to a} u = b, \qquad \lim_{x \to a} v = b$$

Consequently, for $\varepsilon > 0$ there will be a certain neighbourhood, with centre at the point a, in which the inequality $|u-b| < \varepsilon$ will be fulfilled; likewise, there will be a certain neighbourhood with centre at the point a in which the inequality $|v-b| < \varepsilon$ will be fulfilled. The following inequalities will be fulfilled in the smaller of these neighbourhoods:

$$-\varepsilon < u - b < \varepsilon \quad \text{and} \quad -\varepsilon < v - b < \varepsilon$$

and thus the inequalities

$$-\varepsilon < z - b < \varepsilon$$

will be fulfilled; that is,

$$\lim_{x \to a} = b$$

Theorem 5. *If, as $x \to a$ (or as $x \to \infty$) the function y takes on nonnegative values $y \geqslant 0$ and, at the same time, approaches the limit b, then b is a nonnegative number $b \geqslant 0$.*

Proof. Assume that $b < 0$, then $|y-b| \geqslant |b|$; that is, the difference modulus $|y-b|$ is greater than the positive number $|b|$ and, hence, does not approach zero as $x \rightarrow a$. But then y does not approach b as $x \rightarrow a$; this contradicts the statement of the theorem. Thus, the assumption that $b < 0$ leads to a contradiction. Consequently, $b \geqslant 0$.

In similar fashion we can prove that if $y \leqslant 0$ then $\lim y \leqslant 0$.

Theorem 6. *If the inequality $v \geqslant u$ holds between corresponding values of two functions $u = u(x)$ and $v = v(x)$ which approach limits as $x \rightarrow a$ (or as $x \rightarrow \infty$), then $\lim v \geqslant \lim u$.*

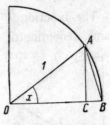

Fig. 42

Proof. It is given that $v - u \geqslant 0$. Hence, by Theorem 5, $\lim (v - u) \geqslant 0$ or $\lim v - \lim u \geqslant 0$, and so $\lim v \geqslant \lim u$.

Example 6. Prove that $\lim\limits_{x \to 0} \sin x = 0$.

From Fig. 42 it follows that if $OA = 1$, $x > 0$, then $AC = \sin x$, $\widehat{AB} = x$, $\sin x < x$. Obviously, when $x < 0$ we will have $|\sin x| < |x|$. By Theorems 5 and 6, it follows, from these inequalities, that $\lim\limits_{x \to 0} \sin x = 0$.

Example 7. Prove that $\lim\limits_{x \to 0} \sin \dfrac{x}{2} = 0$.

Indeed, $\left| \sin \dfrac{x}{2} \right| < |\sin x|$. Consequently, $\lim\limits_{x \to 0} \sin \dfrac{x}{2} = 0$.

Example 8. Prove that $\lim\limits_{x \to 0} \cos x = 1$; note that

$$\cos x = 1 - 2 \sin^2 \frac{x}{2}$$

therefore,

$$\lim_{x \to 0} \cos x = \lim_{x \to 0} \left(1 - 2 \sin^2 \frac{x}{2} \right) = 1 - 2 \lim_{x \to 0} \sin^2 \frac{x}{2} = 1 - 0 = 1.$$

In some investigations concerning the limits of variables, one has to solve two independent problems:

(1) to prove that the limit of the variable exists and to establish the boundaries within which the limit under consideration exists;

(2) to calculate the limit to the necessary degree of accuracy.

The first problem is sometimes solved by means of the following theorem which will be important later on.

Theorem 7. *If a variable v is an increasing variable, that is, each subsequent value is greater than the preceding one, and if it is bounded, that is, $v < M$, then this variable has the limit $\lim v = a$, where $a \leqslant M$.*

A similar assertion may be made with respect to a decreasing bounded variable quantity.

We do not give the proof of this theorem here since it is based on the theory of real numbers, which we do not consider in this text. *

In the following two sections we shall derive the limits of two functions that find wide application in mathematics.

2.6 THE LIMIT OF THE FUNCTION $\frac{\sin x}{x}$ AS $x \to 0$

The function $\frac{\sin x}{x}$ is not defined for $x=0$ since the numerator and denominator of the fraction become zero. Let us find the limit of this function as $x \to 0$. We consider a circle of radius 1 (Fig. 43); denote the central angle MOB by $x \left(0 < x < \frac{\pi}{2} \right)$. From Fig. 43 it follows that

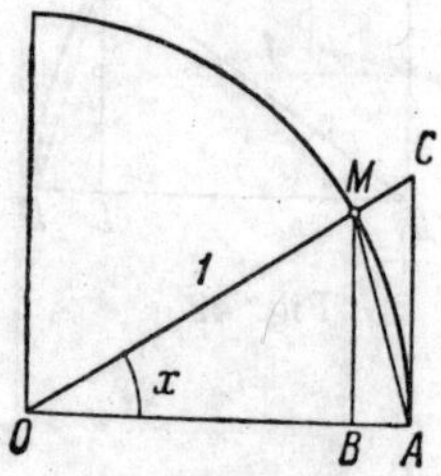

$$\text{area of } \triangle MOA < \text{area of sector}$$
$$MOA < \text{area of } \triangle COA. \qquad (1)$$

Fig. 43

The area of $\triangle MOA = \frac{1}{2} OA \cdot MB = \frac{1}{2} \cdot 1 \cdot \sin x = \frac{1}{2} \sin x.$

The area of sector $MOA = \frac{1}{2} OA \cdot \widehat{AM} = \frac{1}{2} \cdot 1 \cdot x = \frac{1}{2} x.$

The area of $\triangle COA = \frac{1}{2} OA \cdot AC = \frac{1}{2} \cdot 1 \cdot \tan x = \frac{1}{2} \tan x.$

After cancelling $\frac{1}{2}$, inequalities (1) can be rewritten as

$$\sin x < x < \tan x$$

Divide all terms by $\sin x$:

$$1 < \frac{x}{\sin x} < \frac{1}{\cos x}$$

or

$$1 > \frac{\sin x}{x} > \cos x$$

We derived this inequality on the assumption that $x > 0$; noting that $\frac{\sin(-x)}{(-x)} = \frac{\sin x}{x}$ and $\cos(-x) = \cos x$, we conclude that it holds for $x < 0$ as well. But $\lim_{x \to 0} \cos x = 1$, $\lim_{x \to 0} 1 = 1.$

* The proof of this theorem is given in G. M. Fikhtengolts' *Principles of Mathematical Analysis*, Vol. I, Fizmatgiz, 1960 (in Russian).

Hence, the variable $\dfrac{\sin x}{x}$ lies between two quantities that have the same limit (unity). Thus by Theorem 4 of the preceding section,

$$\lim_{x \to 0} \frac{\sin x}{x} = 1$$

The graph of the function $y = \dfrac{\sin x}{x}$ is shown in Fig. 44.

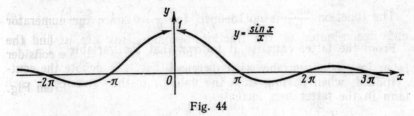

Fig. 44

Examples.

1. $\lim\limits_{x \to 0} \dfrac{\tan x}{x} = \lim\limits_{x \to 0} \dfrac{\sin x}{x} \cdot \dfrac{1}{\cos x} = \lim\limits_{x \to 0} \dfrac{\sin x}{x} \cdot \lim\limits_{x \to 0} \dfrac{1}{\cos x} = 1 \cdot \dfrac{1}{1} = 1.$

2. $\lim\limits_{x \to 0} \dfrac{\sin kx}{x} = \lim\limits_{x \to 0} k\, \dfrac{\sin kx}{kx} = k \lim\limits_{\substack{x \to 0 \\ (kx \to 0)}} \dfrac{\sin (kx)}{(kx)} = k \cdot 1 = k \quad (k = \text{const}).$

3. $\lim\limits_{x \to 0} \dfrac{1-\cos x}{x} = \lim\limits_{x \to 0} \dfrac{2\sin^2 \dfrac{x}{2}}{x} = \lim\limits_{x \to 0} \dfrac{\sin \dfrac{x}{2}}{\dfrac{x}{2}}\, \sin \dfrac{x}{2} = 1 \cdot 0 = 0.$

4. $\lim\limits_{x \to 0} \dfrac{\sin \alpha x}{\sin \beta x} = \lim\limits_{x \to 0} \dfrac{\alpha}{\beta} \cdot \dfrac{\dfrac{\sin \alpha x}{\alpha x}}{\dfrac{\sin \beta x}{\beta x}} = \dfrac{\alpha}{\beta}\, \dfrac{\lim\limits_{x \to 0} \dfrac{\sin \alpha x}{\alpha x}}{\lim\limits_{x \to 0} \dfrac{\sin \beta x}{\beta x}} = \dfrac{\alpha}{\beta} \cdot \dfrac{1}{1} = \dfrac{\alpha}{\beta}$

$(\alpha = \text{const}, \quad \beta = \text{const}).$

2.7. THE NUMBER e

Let us consider the variable

$$\left(1 + \frac{1}{n}\right)^n$$

where n is an increasing variable that takes on the values 1, 2, 3, ...

Theorem 1. *The variable* $\left(1 + \dfrac{1}{n}\right)^n$, *as* $n \to \infty$, *has a limit between the numbers 2 and 3.*

Proof. By Newton's binomial formula we have

$$\left(1+\frac{1}{n}\right)^n = 1 + \frac{n}{1}\frac{1}{n} + \frac{n(n-1)}{1\cdot 2}\cdot\left(\frac{1}{n}\right)^2 + \frac{n(n-1)(n-2)}{1\cdot 2\cdot 3}\left(\frac{1}{n}\right)^3$$

$$\cdots + \frac{n(n-1)(n-2)\ldots[n-(n-1)]}{1\cdot 2\cdot\ldots\cdot n}\left(\frac{1}{n}\right)^n \qquad (1)$$

Carrying out the obvious algebraic manipulations in (1), we get

$$\left(1+\frac{1}{n}\right)^n = 1 + 1 + \frac{1}{1\cdot 2}\left(1-\frac{1}{n}\right) + \frac{1}{1\cdot 2\cdot 3}\left(1-\frac{1}{n}\right)\left(1-\frac{2}{n}\right)$$

$$\cdots + \frac{1}{1\cdot 2\cdot\ldots\cdot n}\left(1-\frac{1}{n}\right)\left(1-\frac{2}{n}\right)\cdots\left(1-\frac{n-1}{n}\right) \qquad (2)$$

From the latter equality it follows that the variable $\left(1+\frac{1}{n}\right)^n$ is an increasing variable as n increases.

Indeed, when passing from the value n to the value $n+1$, each term in the latter sum increases,

$$\frac{1}{1\cdot 2}\left(1-\frac{1}{n}\right) < \frac{1}{1\cdot 2}\left(1-\frac{1}{n+1}\right) \text{ and so forth,}$$

and another term is added. (All terms of the expansion are positive.)

We shall show that the variable $\left(1+\frac{1}{n}\right)^n$ is bounded. Noting that $\left(1-\frac{1}{n}\right) < 1$, $\left(1-\frac{1}{n}\right)\left(1-\frac{2}{n}\right) < 1$, etc., we obtain from expression (2) the inequality

$$\left(1+\frac{1}{n}\right)^n < 1 + 1 + \frac{1}{1\cdot 2} + \frac{1}{1\cdot 2\cdot 3} + \cdots + \frac{1}{1\cdot 2\cdot 3\cdot\ldots\cdot n}$$

Further noting that

$$\frac{1}{1\cdot 2\cdot 3} < \frac{1}{2^2}, \quad \frac{1}{1\cdot 2\cdot 3\cdot 4} < \frac{1}{2^3}, \quad \ldots, \quad \frac{1}{1\cdot 2\cdot\ldots\cdot n} < \frac{1}{2^{n-1}}$$

we can write the inequality

$$\left(1+\frac{1}{n}\right)^n < 1 + \underbrace{1 + \frac{1}{2} + \frac{1}{2^2} + \cdots + \frac{1}{2^{n-1}}}$$

The grouped terms on the right-hand side of this inequality form a geometric progression with common ratio $q=\frac{1}{2}$ and the first term $a=1$, and so

$$\left(1+\frac{1}{n}\right)^n < 1 + \left[1 + \frac{1}{2} + \frac{1}{2^2} + \cdots + \frac{1}{2^{n-1}}\right]$$

$$= 1 + \frac{a-aq^n}{1-q} = 1 + \frac{1-\left(\frac{1}{2}\right)^n}{1-\frac{1}{2}} = 1 + \left[2-\left(\frac{1}{2}\right)^{n-1}\right] < 3$$

Consequently, for all n we get

$$\left(1+\frac{1}{n}\right)^n<3$$

From (2) it follows that

$$\left(1+\frac{1}{n}\right)^n\geqslant 2$$

Thus, we get the inequality

$$2\leqslant\left(1+\frac{1}{n}\right)^n<3 \tag{3}$$

This proves that the variable $\left(1+\frac{1}{n}\right)^n$ is bounded.

Thus, the variable $\left(1+\frac{1}{n}\right)^n$ is an increasing and bounded variable; therefore, by Theorem 7, Sec. 2.5, it has a limit. This limit is denoted by the letter e.

Definition. The limit of the variable $\left(1+\frac{1}{n}\right)^n$ as $n\longrightarrow\infty$ is the *number e*:

$$e=\lim_{n\to\infty}\left(1+\frac{1}{n}\right)^{n*}$$

By Theorem 6, Sec. 2.5, it follows from inequality (3) that the number e satisfies the inequality $2\leqslant e\leqslant 3$. The theorem is thus proved.

The number e is an irrational number. Later on, a method will be shown that permits calculating e to any degree of accuracy. Its value to ten decimal places is

$$e=2.7182818284\ldots$$

Theorem 2. *The function* $\left(1+\frac{1}{x}\right)^x$ *approaches the limit e as x approaches infinity,* $\lim\limits_{x\to\infty}\left(1+\frac{1}{x}\right)^x=e$.

Proof. It has been shown that $\left(1+\frac{1}{n}\right)^n\longrightarrow e$ as $n\longrightarrow\infty$, if n takes on positive integral values. Now let x approach infinity while taking on both fractional and negative values.

(1) Let $x\longrightarrow+\infty$. Each of its values lies between two positive integers,

$$n\leqslant x<n+1$$

---

* It may be shown that $\left(1+\frac{1}{n}\right)^n\longrightarrow e$ as $n\longrightarrow+\infty$ even if n is not an increasing variable quantity.

The following inequalities will be fulfilled:

$$\frac{1}{n} \geqslant \frac{1}{x} > \frac{1}{n+1}$$

$$1 + \frac{1}{n} \geqslant 1 + \frac{1}{x} > 1 + \frac{1}{n+1}$$

$$\left(1 + \frac{1}{n}\right)^{n+1} > \left(1 + \frac{1}{x}\right)^x > \left(1 + \frac{1}{n+1}\right)^n$$

If $x \to \infty$, it is obvious that $n \to \infty$. Let us find the limits of the variables between which the variable $\left(1 + \frac{1}{x}\right)^x$ lies:

$$\lim_{n \to +\infty} \left(1 + \frac{1}{n}\right)^{n+1} = \lim_{n \to \infty} \left(1 + \frac{1}{n}\right)^n \left(1 + \frac{1}{n}\right)$$

$$= \lim_{n \to +\infty} \left(1 + \frac{1}{n}\right)^n \cdot \lim_{n \to +\infty} \left(1 + \frac{1}{n}\right) = e \cdot 1 = e$$

$$\lim_{n \to +\infty} \left(1 + \frac{1}{n+1}\right)^n = \lim_{n \to +\infty} \frac{\left(1 + \frac{1}{n+1}\right)^{n+1}}{1 + \frac{1}{n+1}}$$

$$= \frac{\lim\limits_{n \to +\infty} \left(1 + \frac{1}{n+1}\right)^{n+1}}{\lim\limits_{n \to +\infty} \left(1 + \frac{1}{n+1}\right)} = \frac{e}{1} = e$$

Hence, by Theorem 4, Sec. 2.5,

$$\lim_{x \to +\infty} \left(1 + \frac{1}{x}\right)^x = e \tag{4}$$

(2) Let $x \to -\infty$. We introduce a new variable $t = -(x+1)$ or $x = -(t+1)$. When $t \to +\infty$, then $x \to -\infty$. We can write

$$\lim_{x \to -\infty} \left(1 + \frac{1}{x}\right)^x = \lim_{t \to +\infty} \left(1 - \frac{1}{t+1}\right)^{-t-1} = \lim_{t \to +\infty} \left(\frac{t}{t+1}\right)^{-t-1}$$

$$= \lim_{t \to +\infty} \left(\frac{t+1}{t}\right)^{t+1} = \lim_{t \to +\infty} \left(1 + \frac{1}{t}\right)^{t+1}$$

$$= \lim_{t \to +\infty} \left(1 + \frac{1}{t}\right)^t \left(1 + \frac{1}{t}\right) = e \cdot 1 = e$$

The theorem is proved. The graph of the function $y = \left(1 + \frac{1}{x}\right)^x$ is shown in Fig. 45.

If in (4) we put $\frac{1}{x} = \alpha$, then as $x \to \infty$ we have $\alpha \to 0$ (but $\alpha \neq 0$) and we get

$$\lim_{\alpha \to 0} (1 + \alpha)^{\frac{1}{\alpha}} = e$$

Examples:

(1) $\lim\limits_{n \to \infty} \left(1+\dfrac{1}{n}\right)^{n+5} = \lim\limits_{n \to \infty} \left(1+\dfrac{1}{n}\right)^n \left(1+\dfrac{1}{n}\right)^5$

$\qquad = \lim\limits_{n \to \infty} \left(1+\dfrac{1}{n}\right)^n \cdot \lim\limits_{n \to \infty} \left(1+\dfrac{1}{n}\right)^5 = e \cdot 1 = e.$

(2) $\lim\limits_{x \to \infty} \left(1+\dfrac{1}{x}\right)^{3x} = \lim\limits_{x \to \infty} \left(1+\dfrac{1}{x}\right)^x \left(1+\dfrac{1}{x}\right)^x \left(1+\dfrac{1}{x}\right)^x$

$\qquad = \lim\limits_{x \to \infty} \left(1+\dfrac{1}{x}\right)^x \cdot \lim\limits_{x \to \infty} \left(1+\dfrac{1}{x}\right)^x \cdot \lim\limits_{x \to \infty} \left(1+\dfrac{1}{x}\right)^x = e \cdot e \cdot e = e^3.$

(3) $\lim\limits_{x \to \infty} \left(1+\dfrac{2}{x}\right)^x = \lim\limits_{y \to \infty} \left(1+\dfrac{1}{y}\right)^{2y} = e^2.$

(4) $\lim\limits_{x \to \infty} \left(\dfrac{x+3}{x-1}\right)^{x+3} = \lim\limits_{x \to \infty} \left(\dfrac{x-1+4}{x-1}\right)^{x+3} = \lim\limits_{x \to \infty} \left(1+\dfrac{4}{x-1}\right)^{x+3}$

$\qquad = \lim\limits_{x \to \infty} \left(1+\dfrac{4}{x-1}\right)^{(x-1)+4} = \lim\limits_{y \to \infty} \left(1+\dfrac{4}{y}\right)^{y+4}$

$\qquad = \lim\limits_{y \to \infty} \left(1+\dfrac{4}{y}\right)^y \cdot \lim\limits_{y \to \infty} \left(1+\dfrac{4}{y}\right)^4 = e^4 \cdot 1 = e^4.$

Note. The exponential function e^x plays a very important role in mathematics, mechanics (oscillation theory), electrical and radio

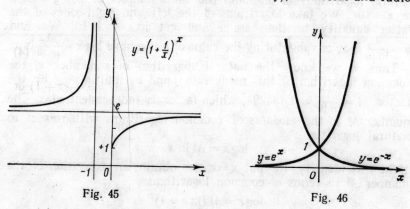

Fig. 45   Fig. 46

engineering, radiochemistry, etc. The graphs of the functions $y = e^x$ and $y = e^{-x}$ are shown in Fig. 46.

2.8 NATURAL LOGARITHMS

In Sec. 1.8 we defined the logarithmic function $y = \log_a x$. The number a is called the base of the logarithms. If $a = 10$, then y is the base-10 (common) logarithm of the number x and is denoted $y = \log x$. In school courses of mathematics we have tables of common logarithms, which are called Briggs' logarithms after the English mathematician Briggs (1561-1630).

Logarithms to the base $e = 2.71828\ldots$ are called *natural* or *Napierian logarithms* after one of the first inventors of logarithmic tables, the Scotch mathematician Napier (1550-1617).* Therefore, if $e^y = x$, then y is called the natural logarithm of the number x. In writing we have $y = \ln x$ (after the initial letters of *logarithmus naturalis*) in place of $y = \log_e x$. Graphs of the function $y = \ln x$ and $y = \log x$ are plotted in Fig. 47.

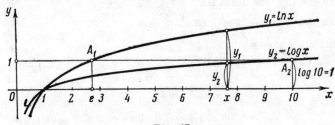

Fig. 47

Let us now establish a relationship between common and natural logarithms of one and the same number x. Let $y = \log x$ or $x = 10^y$. We take logarithms of the left and right sides of the latter equality to the base e and get $\ln x = y \ln 10$. We find $y = \frac{1}{\ln 10} \ln x$, or substituting the value of y, we have $\log x = \frac{1}{\ln 10} \ln x$.

Thus, if we know the natural logarithm of a number x, the common logarithm of this number is found by multiplying by the factor $M = \frac{1}{\ln 10} \approx 0.434294$, which factor is independent of x. The number M is the *modulus* of common logarithms with respect to natural logarithms:

$$\log x = M \ln x$$

If in this identity we put $x = e$, we obtain an expression of the number M in terms of common logarithms:

$$\log e = M \; (\ln e = 1)$$

Natural logarithms are expressed in terms of common logarithms as follows:

$$\ln x = \frac{1}{M} \log x$$

where

$$\frac{1}{M} \approx 2.302585$$

---

* The first logarithmic tables were constructed by the Swiss mathematician Bürgi (1552-1632) to a base close to the number e.

2.9 CONTINUITY OF FUNCTIONS

Let a function $y = f(x)$ be defined for some value x_0 and in some neighbourhood with centre at x_0. Let $y_0 = f(x_0)$.

If x receives some positive or negative (it is immaterial which) increment Δx and assumes the value $x = x_c + \Delta x$, then the function y too will receive an increment Δy.
The new increased value of the function will be $y_0 + \Delta y = f(x_0 + \Delta x)$ (Fig. 48). The increment of the function Δy will be expressed by the formula

$$\Delta y = f(x_0 + \Delta x) - f(x_0)$$

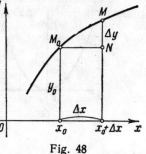

Fig. 48

Definition 1. A function $y = f(x)$ is called *continuous for the value* $x = x_0$ (or *at the point* x_0) if it is defined in some neighbourhood of the point x_0 (obviously, at the point x_0 as well) and if

$$\lim_{\Delta x \to 0} \Delta y = 0 \tag{1}$$

or, which is the same thing,

$$\lim_{\Delta x \to 0} [f(x_0 + \Delta x) - f(x_0)] = 0 \tag{2}$$

The continuity condition (2) may also be written as follows:

$$\lim_{\Delta x \to 0} f(x_0 + \Delta x) = f(x_0)$$

or

$$\lim_{x \to x_0} f(x) = f(x_0) \tag{3}$$

but

$$x_0 = \lim_{x \to x_0} x$$

Hence, (3) may be written thus:

$$\lim_{x \to x_0} f(x) = f(\lim_{x \to x_0} x) \tag{4}$$

In other words, in order to find the limit of a continuous function as $x \to x_0$, it is sufficient, in the expression of the function, to put the value x_0 in place of the argument x.

In descriptive geometrical terms, the continuity of a function at a given point signifies that the difference of the ordinates on the graph of the function $y = f(x)$ at the points $x_0 + \Delta x$ and x_0 will, in absolute value, be arbitrarily small, provided $|\Delta x|$ is sufficiently small.

Example 1. We shall prove that the function $y = x^2$ is continuous at an arbitrary point x_0. Indeed,

$$y_0 = x_0^2, \quad y_0 + \Delta y = (x_0 + \Delta x)^2, \quad \Delta y = (x_0 + \Delta x)^2 - x_0^2 = 2x_0 \Delta x + \Delta x^2,$$

$$\lim_{\Delta x \to 0} \Delta y = \lim_{\Delta x \to 0} (2x_0 \Delta x + \Delta x^2) = 2x_0 \lim_{\Delta x \to 0} \Delta x + \lim_{\Delta x \to 0} \Delta x \cdot \lim_{\Delta x \to 0} \Delta x = 0$$

for any way that Δx may approach zero (Figs. 49a and 49b).

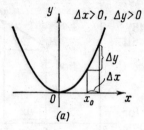 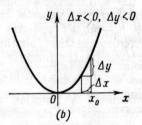

Fig. 49

Example 2. We shall prove that the function $y = \sin x$ is continuous at an arbitrary point x_0. Indeed,

$$y_0 = \sin x_0, \quad y_0 + \Delta y = \sin (x_0 + \Delta x),$$

$$\Delta y = \sin (x_0 + \Delta x) - \sin x_0 = 2 \sin \frac{\Delta x}{2} \cdot \cos \left(x_0 + \frac{\Delta x}{2} \right)$$

It has been shown that $\lim\limits_{\Delta x \to 0} \sin \dfrac{\Delta x}{2} = 0$ (Example 7, Sec. 2.5). The function $\cos \left(x + \dfrac{\Delta x}{2} \right)$ is bounded. Therefore, $\lim\limits_{\Delta x \to 0} \Delta y = 0$.

In similar fashion, by considering each basic elementary function, it is possible to prove that each basic elementary function is continuous at every point at which it is defined.

We will now prove the following theorem.

Theorem 1. *If the functions $f_1(x)$ and $f_2(x)$ are continuous at a point x_0, then the sum $\psi(x) = f_1(x) + f_2(x)$ is also a function continuous at the point x_0.*

Proof. Since $f_1(x)$ and $f_2(x)$ are continuous, on the basis of (3) we can write

$$\lim_{x \to x_0} f_1(x) = f_1(x_0) \quad \text{and} \quad \lim_{x \to x_0} f_2(x) = f_2(x_0)$$

By Theorem 1 on limits, we can write

$$\lim_{x \to x_0} \psi(x) = \lim_{x \to x_0} [f_1(x) + f_2(x)]$$

$$= \lim_{x \to x_0} f_1(x) + \lim_{x \to x_0} f_2(x) = f_1(x_0) + f_2(x_0) = \psi(x_0)$$

Thus, the sum $\psi(x) = f_1(x) + f_2(x)$ is a continuous function. The proof is complete.

Note, as a corollary, that the theorem holds true for any finite number of terms.

Using the properties of limits, we can also prove the following theorems:

(a) *The product of two continuous functions is a continuous function.*

(b) *The quotient of two continuous functions is a continuous function if the denominator does not vanish at the point under consideration.*

(c) *If $u = \varphi(x)$ is continuous at $x = x_0$ and $f(u)$ is continuous at the point $u_0 = \varphi(x_0)$, then the composite function $f[\varphi(x)]$ is continuous at the point x_0.*

Using these theorems, we can prove the following theorem.

Theorem 2. *Every elementary function is continuous at every point at which it is defined.**

Example 3. The function $y = x^2$ is continuous at every point x_0 and therefore

$$\lim_{x \to x_0} x^2 = x_0^2$$
$$\lim_{x \to 3} x^2 = 3^2 = 9$$

Example 4. The function $y = \sin x$ is continuous at every point and therefore

$$\lim_{x \to \frac{\pi}{4}} \sin x = \sin \frac{\pi}{4} = \frac{\sqrt{2}}{2}$$

Example 5. The function $y = e^x$ is continuous at every point and therefore $\lim_{x \to a} e^x = e^a$.

Example 6. $\lim_{x \to 0} \dfrac{\ln(1+x)}{x} = \lim_{x \to 0} \dfrac{1}{x} \ln(1+x) = \lim_{x \to 0} \ln \left[(1+x)^{\frac{1}{x}} \right]$. Since

$\lim_{x \to 0} (1+x)^{\frac{1}{x}} = e$ and the function $\ln z$ is continuous for $z > 0$ and, consequently, for $z = e$,

$$\lim_{x \to 0} \ln \left[(1+x)^{\frac{1}{x}} \right] = \ln \left[\lim_{x \to 0} (1+x)^{\frac{1}{x}} \right] = \ln e = 1$$

Definition 2. If a function $y = f(x)$ is continuous at each point of a certain interval (a, b), where $a < b$, then it is said that the function *is continuous in this interval.*

If the function is also defined for $x = a$ and $\lim_{x \to a+0} f(x) = f(a)$, it is said that $f(x)$ at the point $x = a$ is *continuous on the right.*

---

* This problem is discussed in detail in G. M. Fikhtengolts' *Fundamentals of Mathematical Analysis*, Vol. 1, Fizmatgiz, Moscow, 1968 (in Russian).

If $\lim\limits_{x \to b-0} f(x) = f(b)$, it is said that the function $f(x)$ at the point $x = b$ *is continuous on the left.*

If the function $f(x)$ is continuous at each point of the interval (a, b) and is continuous at the end points of the interval, on the right and left, respectively, then we say that the function $f(x)$ *is continuous over the closed interval* $[a, b]$.

Example 7. The function $y = x^2$ is continuous in any closed interval $[a, b]$. This follows from Example 1.

If at some point $x = x_0$ at least one of the conditions of continuity is not fulfilled for the function $y = f(x)$, that is, if for $x = x_0$ the function is not defined or there does not exist a limit $\lim\limits_{x \to x_0} f(x)$ or $\lim\limits_{x \to x_0} f(x) \neq f(x_0)$ in the arbitrary approach of $x \to x_0$, although the expressions on the right and left exist, then at $x = x_0$ the function $y = f(x)$ is *discontinuous*. In this case, the point $x = x_0$ is called the *point of discontinuity* of the function.

Example 8. The function $y = \dfrac{1}{x}$ is discontinuous at $x = 0$. Indeed, the function is not defined at $x = 0$.

$$\lim_{x \to 0+0} \frac{1}{x} = +\infty, \qquad \lim_{x \to 0-0} \frac{1}{x} = -\infty$$

It is easy to show that this function is continuous for any value $x \neq 0$.

Example 9. The function $y = 2^{\frac{1}{x}}$ is discontinuous at $x = 0$. Indeed, $\lim\limits_{x \to 0+0} 2^{\frac{1}{x}} = \infty$, $\lim\limits_{x \to 0-0} 2^{\frac{1}{x}} = 0$. The function is not defined at $x = 0$ (Fig. 50).

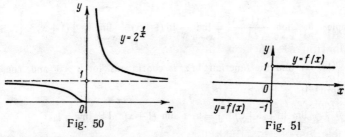

Fig. 50   Fig. 51

Example 10. Consider the function $f(x) = \dfrac{x}{|x|}$. For $x < 0$, $\dfrac{x}{|x|} = -1$, for $x > 0$, $\dfrac{x}{|x|} = 1$. Hence,

$$\lim_{x \to 0-0} f(x) = \lim_{x \to 0-0} \frac{x}{|x|} = -1,$$

$$\lim_{x \to 0+0} f(x) = \lim_{x \to 0+0} \frac{x}{|x|} = 1$$

the function is not defined at $x=0$. We have thus established the fact that the function $f(x)=\dfrac{x}{|x|}$ is discontinuous at $x=0$ (Fig. 51).

Example 11. The earlier examined function (Example 4, Sec. 2.3) $y=\sin(1/x)$ is discontinuous at $x=0$.

Definition 3. If the function $f(x)$ is such that there exist finite limits $\lim\limits_{x\to x_0+0} f(x)=f(x_0+0)$ and $\lim\limits_{x\to x_0-0} f(x)=f(x_0-0)$, but either $\lim\limits_{x\to x_0+0} f(x)\neq \lim\limits_{x\to x_0-0} f(x)$ or the value of the function $f(x)$ at $x=x_0$ is not defined, then $x=x_0$ is called a *point of discontinuity of the first kind*. (For example, for the function considered in Example 10, the point $x=0$ is a point of discontinuity of the first kind.)

2.10 CERTAIN PROPERTIES OF CONTINUOUS FUNCTIONS

In this section we shall consider a number of properties of functions that are continuous on an interval. These properties will be stated in the form of theorems given without proof. *

Theorem 1. *If a function $y=f(x)$ is continuous on some interval $[a, b]$ $(a\leqslant x\leqslant b)$, there will be, on this interval, at least one point $x=x_1$ such that the value of the function at that point will satisfy the relation*

$$f(x_1)\geqslant f(x)$$

where x is any other point of the interval, and there will be at least one point x_2 such that the value of the function at that point will satisfy the relation

$$f(x_2)\leqslant f(x)$$

We shall call the value of the function $f(x_1)$ the *greatest value* of the function $y=f(x)$ on the interval $[a, b]$, and the value of the function $f(x_2)$ the *smallest (least) value* of the function on the interval $[a, b]$.

This theorem is briefly stated as follows:

A function continuous on the interval $a\leqslant x\leqslant b$ attains on this interval (at least once) a greatest value M and a smallest value m.

The meaning of this theorem is clearly illustrated in Fig. 52.

Note. The assertion that there exists a greatest value of the function may prove incorrect if one considers the values of the function in the interval $a<x<b$. For instance, if we consider the function $y=x$ in the interval $0<x<1$, there will be no greatest and no least values among them. Indeed, there is no least

---

* These theorems are proved in G. M. Fikhtengolts' *Principles of Mathematical Analysis*, Vol. 1, Fizmatgiz, 1968 (in Russian).

value or greatest value of x in the interval. (There is no extreme left point, since no matter what point x^* we take there will be a point to the left of it, for instance, the point $\frac{x^*}{2}$; likewise,

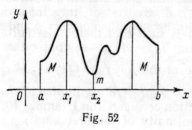

Fig. 52

there is no extreme right point; consequently, there is no least and no greatest value of the function $y = x$.)

Theorem 2. *Let the function $y = f(x)$ be continuous on the interval $[a, b]$ and at the end points of this interval let it take on values of different signs; then between the points a and b there will be at least one point $x = c$, at which the function becomes zero:*

$$f(c) = 0, \ a < c < b$$

This theorem has a simple geometrical meaning. The graph of a continuous function $y = f(x)$ joining the points $M_1 [a, f(a)]$ and $M_2 [b, f(b)]$, where $f(a) < 0$ and $f(b) > 0$ or $f(a) > 0$ and $f(b) < 0$, cuts the x-axis in at least one point (Fig. 53).

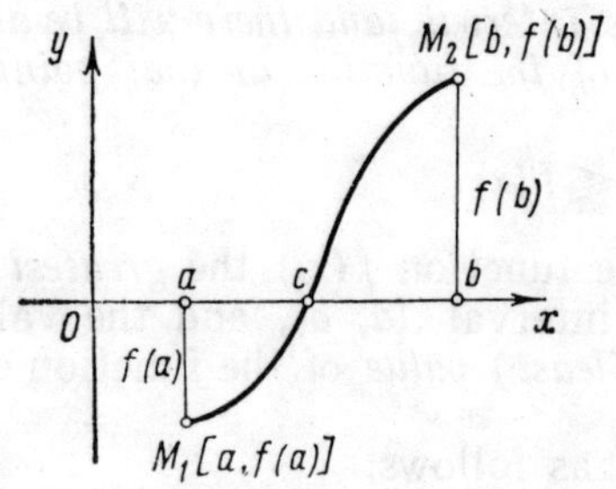

Fig. 53

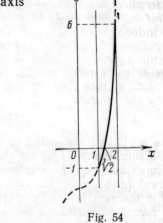

Fig. 54

Example. Given the function $y = x^3 - 2$; $y_{x=1} = -1$, $y_{x=2} = 6$. It is continuous in the interval $[1, 2]$. Hence, in this interval there is a point where $y = x^3 - 2$ becomes zero. Indeed, $y = 0$ when $x = \sqrt[3]{2}$ (Fig. 54).

Theorem 3. *Let a function $y = f(x)$ be defined and continuous in the interval $[a, b]$. If at the end points of this interval the function takes on unequal values $f(a) = A$, $f(b) = B$, then no matter what the number μ between numbers A and B, there will be a point $x = c$ between a and b such that $f(c) = \mu$.*

The meaning of this theorem is clearly illustrated in Fig. 55. In the given case, any straight line $y = \mu$ cuts the graph of the function $y = f(x)$.

Note. It will be noted that Theorem 2 is a particular case of this theorem, for if A and B have different signs, then for μ one can take 0, and then $\mu = 0$ will lie between the numbers A and B.

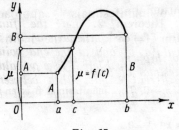

Fig. 55

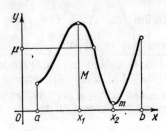

Fig. 56

Corollary of Theorem 3. *If a function $y = f(x)$ is continuous in some interval and takes on a greatest value and a least value, then in this interval it takes on, at least once, any value lying between the greatest and least values.*

Indeed, let $f(x_1) = M$, $f(x_2) = m$. Consider the interval $[x_1, x_2]$. By Theorem 3, in this interval the function $y = f(x)$ takes on any value μ lying between M and m. But the interval $[x_1, x_2]$ lies inside the interval under consideration in which the function $f(x)$ is defined (Fig. 56).

2.11 COMPARING INFINITESIMALS

Let several infinitesimal quantities

$$\alpha, \ \beta, \ \gamma, \ \ldots$$

be at the same time functions of one and the same argument x and let them approach zero as x approaches some limit a or infinity. We shall describe the approach of these variables to zero when we consider their ratios.*

We shall, in future, make use of the following definitions.

Definition 1. If the ratio $\dfrac{\beta}{\alpha}$ has a finite nonzero limit, that is, if $\lim \dfrac{\beta}{\alpha} = A \neq 0$, and therefore, $\lim \dfrac{\alpha}{\beta} = \dfrac{1}{A} \neq 0$, the infinitesimals β and α are called *infinitesimals of the same order.*

---

* We assume that the infinitesimal in the denominator does not vanish in some neighbourhood of the point a.

Example 1. Let $\alpha = x$, $\beta = \sin 2x$, where $x \to 0$. The infinitesimals α and β are of the same order because

$$\lim_{x \to 0} \frac{\beta}{\alpha} = \lim_{x \to 0} \frac{\sin 2x}{x} = 2$$

Example 2. When $x \to 0$, the infinitesimals x, $\sin 3x$, $\tan 2x$, $7 \ln(1 + x)$ are infinitesimals of the same order. The proof is similar to that given in Example 1.

Definition 2. If the ratio of two infinitesimals $\frac{\beta}{\alpha}$ approaches zero, that is, if $\lim \frac{\beta}{\alpha} = 0$ $\left(\text{and } \lim \frac{\alpha}{\beta} = \infty \right)$, then the infinitesimal β is called *an infinitesimal of higher order than* α, and the infinitesimal α is called *an infinitesimal of lower order than* β.

Example 3. Let $\alpha = x$, $\beta = x^n$, $n > 1$, $x \to 0$. The infinitesimal β is an infinitesimal of higher order than the infinitesimal α since

$$\lim_{x \to 0} \frac{x^n}{x} = \lim_{x \to 0} x^{n-1} = 0$$

Here, the infinitesimal α is an infinitesimal of lower order than β.

Definition 3. An infinitesimal β is called *an infinitesimal of the kth order relative to an infinitesimal* α, if β and α^k are infinitesimals of the same order, that is, if $\lim \frac{\beta}{\alpha^k} = A \neq 0$.

Example 4. If $\alpha = x$, $\beta = x^3$, then as $x \to 0$ the infinitesimal β is an infinitesimal of the third order relative to the infinitesimal α, since

$$\lim_{x \to 0} \frac{\beta}{\alpha^3} = \lim_{x \to 0} \frac{x^3}{x^3} = 1$$

Definition 4. If the ratio of two infinitesimals $\frac{\beta}{\alpha}$ approaches unity, that is, if $\lim \frac{\beta}{\alpha} = 1$, the infinitesimals β and α are called *equivalent infinitesimals* and we write $\alpha \sim \beta$.

Example 5. Let $\alpha = x$ and $\beta = \sin x$, where $x \to 0$. The infinitesimals α and β are equivalent, since

$$\lim_{x \to 0} \frac{\sin x}{x} = 1$$

Example 6. Let $\alpha = x$, $\beta = \ln(1 + x)$, where $x \to 0$. The infinitesimals α and β are equivalent, since

$$\lim_{x \to 0} \frac{\ln(1 + x)}{x} = 1$$

(see Example 6, Sec. 2.9).

Theorem 1. *If* α *and* β *are equivalent infinitesimals, their difference* $\alpha - \beta$ *is an infinitesimal of higher order than* α *and than* β.

Proof. Indeed,

$$\lim \frac{\alpha - \beta}{\alpha} = \lim \left(1 - \frac{\beta}{\alpha} \right) = 1 - \lim \frac{\beta}{\alpha} = 1 - 1 = 0$$

Theorem 2. *If the difference of two infinitesimals* $\alpha - \beta$ *is an infinitesimal of higher order than* α *and than* β, *then* α *and* β *are equivalent infinitesimals.*

Proof. Let $\lim \frac{\alpha - \beta}{\alpha} = 0$, then $\lim \left(1 - \frac{\beta}{\alpha} \right) = 0$, or $1 - \lim \frac{\beta}{\alpha} = 0$, or $1 = \lim \frac{\beta}{\alpha}$, i.e., $\alpha \sim \beta$. If $\lim \frac{\alpha - \beta}{\beta} = 0$, then $\lim \left(\frac{\alpha}{\beta} - 1 \right) = 0$, $\lim \frac{\alpha}{\beta} = 1$, that is, $\alpha \sim \beta$.

Example 7. Let $\alpha = x$, $\beta = x + x^3$, where $x \longrightarrow 0$.
The infinitesimals α and β are equivalent, since their difference $\beta - \alpha = x^3$ is an infinitesimal of higher order than α and than β. Indeed,

$$\lim_{x \to 0} \frac{\beta - \alpha}{\alpha} = \lim_{x \to 0} \frac{x^3}{x} = \lim_{x \to 0} x^2 = 0$$

$$\lim_{x \to 0} \frac{\beta - \alpha}{\beta} = \lim_{x \to 0} \frac{x^3}{x + x^3} = \lim_{x \to 0} \frac{x^2}{1 + x^2} = 0$$

Example 8. For $x \longrightarrow \infty$ the infinitesimals $\alpha = \frac{x+1}{x^2}$ and $\beta = \frac{1}{x}$ are equivalent infinitesimals, since their difference $\alpha - \beta = \frac{x+1}{x^2} - \frac{1}{x} = \frac{1}{x^2}$ is an infinitesimal of higher order than α and than β. The limit of the ratio of α and β is unity:

$$\lim_{x \to \infty} \frac{\alpha}{\beta} = \lim_{x \to \infty} \frac{\frac{x+1}{x^2}}{\frac{1}{x}} = \lim_{x \to \infty} \frac{x+1}{x} = \lim_{x \to \infty} \left(1 + \frac{1}{x} \right) = 1$$

Note. If the ratio of two infinitesimals $\frac{\beta}{\alpha}$ has no limit and does not approach infinity, then β and α are not comparable in the above sense.

Example 9. Let $\alpha = x$, $\beta = x \sin \frac{1}{x}$, where $x \longrightarrow 0$. The infinitesimals α and β cannot be compared because their ratio $\frac{\beta}{\alpha} = \sin \frac{1}{x}$ as $x \longrightarrow 0$ does not approach either a finite limit or infinity (see Example 4, Sec. 2.3).

Exercises on Chapter 2

Find the indicated limits:

1. $\lim\limits_{x \to 1} \frac{x^2 + 2x + 5}{x^2 + 1}$.   *Ans.* 4.   2. $\lim\limits_{x \to \frac{\pi}{2}} [2 \sin x - \cos x + \cot x]$.   *Ans.* 2.

3. $\lim\limits_{x \to 2} \dfrac{x-2}{\sqrt{2+x}}$. *Ans.* 0. 4. $\lim\limits_{x \to \infty} \left(2 - \dfrac{1}{x} + \dfrac{4}{x^2}\right)$. *Ans.* 2. 5. $\lim\limits_{x \to \infty} \dfrac{4x^3 - 2x^2 + 1}{3x^3 - 5}$.

Ans. $\dfrac{4}{3}$. 6. $\lim\limits_{x \to \infty} \dfrac{x+1}{x}$. *Ans.* 1. 7. $\lim\limits_{n \to \infty} \dfrac{1 + 2 + \ldots + n}{n^2}$. *Ans.* $\dfrac{1}{2}$.

8. $\lim\limits_{n \to \infty} \dfrac{1^2 + 2^2 + 3^2 + \ldots + n^2}{n^3}$. *Ans.* $\dfrac{1}{3}$.

Hint. Write the formula $(k+1)^3 - k^3 = 3k^2 + 3k + 1$ for $k = 0, 1, 2, \ldots, n$.

$$1^3 = 1,$$
$$2^3 - 1^3 = 3 \cdot 1^2 + 3 \cdot 1 + 1,$$
$$3^3 - 2^3 = 3 \cdot 2^2 + 3 \cdot 2 + 1,$$
$$\cdots\cdots\cdots\cdots\cdots\cdots$$
$$(n+1)^3 - n^3 = 3n^2 + 3n + 1$$

Adding the left and right sides, we get

$$(n+1)^3 = 3(1^2 + 2^2 + \ldots + n^2) + 3(1 + 2 + \ldots + n) + (n+1),$$
$$(n+1)^3 = 3(1^2 + 2^2 + \ldots + n^2) + 3\dfrac{n(n+1)}{2} + (n+1),$$

whence

$$1^2 + 2^2 + \ldots + n^2 = \dfrac{n(n+1)(2n+1)}{6}$$

9. $\lim\limits_{x \to \infty} \dfrac{x^2 + x - 1}{2x + 5}$. *Ans.* ∞. 10. $\lim\limits_{x \to \infty} \dfrac{3x^2 - 2x - 1}{x^3 + 4}$. *Ans.* 0. 11. $\lim\limits_{x \to 0} \dfrac{4x^3 - 2x^2 + x}{3x^2 + 2x}$.

Ans. $\dfrac{1}{2}$. 12. $\lim\limits_{x \to 2} \dfrac{x^2 - 4}{x - 2}$. *Ans.* 4. 13. $\lim\limits_{x \to 1} \dfrac{x^3 - 1}{x - 1}$. *Ans.* 3. 14. $\lim\limits_{x \to 2} \dfrac{x^2 - 5x + 6}{x^2 - 12x + 20}$.

Ans. $\dfrac{1}{8}$. 15. $\lim\limits_{x \to 2} \dfrac{x^2 + 3x - 10}{3x^2 - 5x - 2}$. *Ans.* 1. 16. $\lim\limits_{y \to -2} \dfrac{y^3 + 3y^2 + 2y}{y^2 - y - 6}$. *Ans.* $-\dfrac{2}{5}$.

17. $\lim\limits_{u \to -2} \dfrac{u^3 + 4u^2 + 4u}{(u+2)(u-3)}$. *Ans.* 0. 18. $\lim\limits_{h \to 0} \dfrac{(x+h)^3 - x^3}{h}$. *Ans.* $3x^2$.

19. $\lim\limits_{x \to 1} \left[\dfrac{1}{1-x} - \dfrac{3}{1-x^3}\right]$. *Ans.* -1. 20. $\lim\limits_{x \to 1} \dfrac{x^n - 1}{x - 1}$. *Ans.* n (n is a positive

integer). 21. $\lim\limits_{x \to 0} \dfrac{\sqrt{1+x} - 1}{x}$. *Ans.* $\dfrac{1}{2}$. 22. $\lim\limits_{x \to 4} \dfrac{\sqrt{2x+1} - 3}{\sqrt{x-2} - \sqrt{2}}$. *Ans.* $\dfrac{2\sqrt{2}}{3}$.

23. $\lim\limits_{x \to 0} \dfrac{\sqrt{x^2 + p^2} - p}{\sqrt{x^2 + q^2} - q}$. *Ans.* $\dfrac{q}{p}$ 24. $\lim\limits_{x \to 1} \dfrac{\sqrt[3]{x} - 1}{\sqrt{x} - 1}$. *Ans.* $\dfrac{2}{3}$.

25. $\lim\limits_{x \to a} \dfrac{\sqrt[m]{x} - \sqrt[m]{a}}{x - a}$. *Ans.* $\dfrac{\sqrt[m]{a}}{ma}$. 26. $\lim\limits_{x \to 0} \dfrac{\sqrt{1 + x + x^2} - 1}{x}$. *Ans.* $\dfrac{1}{2}$.

27. $\lim\limits_{x \to +\infty} \dfrac{\sqrt{x^2 - 3}}{\sqrt[3]{x^3 + 1}}$. *Ans.* 1. 28. $\lim\limits_{x \to \infty} \dfrac{\sqrt{x^2 + 1}}{x + 1}$. *Ans.* 1 as $x \longrightarrow +\infty$, -1 as

$x \to -\infty$. 29. $\lim\limits_{x \to \infty} (\sqrt{x^2 + 1} - \sqrt{x^2 - 1})$. *Ans.* 0. 30. $\lim\limits_{x \to \infty} x(\sqrt{x^2 + 1} - x)$.

Ans. $\dfrac{1}{2}$ as $x \longrightarrow +\infty$, $-\infty$ as $x \longrightarrow -\infty$. **31.** $\lim\limits_{x \to 0} \dfrac{\sin x}{\tan x}$. *Ans.* 1.

32. $\lim\limits_{x \to 0} \dfrac{\sin 4x}{x}$. *Ans.* 4. **33.** $\lim\limits_{x \to 0} \dfrac{\sin^2 \dfrac{x}{3}}{x^2}$. *Ans.* $\dfrac{1}{9}$. **34.** $\lim\limits_{x \to +0} \dfrac{x}{\sqrt{1 - \cos x}}$.

Ans. $\sqrt{2}$. **35.** $\lim\limits_{x \to 0} x \cot x$. *Ans.* 1. **36.** $\lim\limits_{v \to \frac{\pi}{3}} \dfrac{1 - 2 \cos v}{\sin \left(v - \dfrac{\pi}{3} \right)}$. *Ans.* $\sqrt{3}$.

37. $\lim\limits_{z \to 1} (1 - z) \tan \dfrac{\pi z}{2}$. *Ans.* $\dfrac{2}{\pi}$. **38.** $\lim\limits_{x \to 0} \dfrac{2 \arcsin x}{3x}$. *Ans.* $\dfrac{2}{3}$.

39. $\lim\limits_{x \to 0} \dfrac{\sin (a + x) - \sin (a - x)}{x}$. *Ans.* $2 \cos a$. **40.** $\lim\limits_{x \to 0} \dfrac{\tan x - \sin x}{x^3}$. *Ans.* $\dfrac{1}{2}$.

41. $\lim\limits_{x \to 0} \left(1 + \dfrac{2}{x} \right)^x$. *Ans.* e^2. **42.** $\lim\limits_{x \to \infty} \left(1 - \dfrac{1}{x} \right)^x$. *Ans.* $\dfrac{1}{e}$. **43.** $\lim\limits_{x \to \infty} \left(\dfrac{x}{1 + x} \right)^x$.

Ans. $\dfrac{1}{e}$. **44.** $\lim\limits_{n \to \infty} \left(1 + \dfrac{1}{n} \right)^{n + 5}$ *Ans.* e. **45.** $\lim\limits_{n \to \infty} \{ n \left[\ln (n + 1) - \ln n \right] \}$. *Ans.* 1.

46. $\lim\limits_{x \to \frac{\pi}{2}} (1 + \cos x)^{3 \sec x}$. *Ans.* e^3. **47.** $\lim\limits_{x \to 0} \dfrac{\ln (1 + \alpha x)}{x}$. *Ans.* α. **48.** $\lim\limits_{x \to \infty} \left(\dfrac{2x + 3}{2x + 1} \right)^{x + 1}$.

Ans. e. **49.** $\lim\limits_{x \to 0} (1 + 3 \tan^2 x)^{\cot^2 x}$. *Ans.* e^3. **50.** $\lim\limits_{m \to \infty} \left(\cos \dfrac{x}{m} \right)^m$. *Ans.* 1.

51. $\lim\limits_{\alpha \to \infty} \dfrac{\ln(1 + e^\alpha)}{\alpha}$. *Ans.* 1 as $\alpha \longrightarrow + \infty$, 0 as $\alpha \longrightarrow - \infty$. **52.** $\lim\limits_{x \to 0} \dfrac{\sin \alpha x}{\sin \beta x}$.

Ans. $\dfrac{\alpha}{\beta}$. **53.** $\lim\limits_{x \to \infty} \dfrac{a^x - 1}{x} \, (a > 1)$. *Ans.* $+\infty$ as $x \longrightarrow + \infty$, 0 as $x \longrightarrow - \infty$.

54. $\lim\limits_{n \to \infty} n \left[a^{\frac{1}{n}} - 1 \right]$. *Ans.* $\ln a$. **55.** $\lim\limits_{x \to 0} \dfrac{e^{\alpha x} - e^{\beta x}}{x}$. *Ans.* $\alpha - \beta$.

56. $\lim\limits_{x \to 0} \dfrac{e^{\alpha x} - e^{\beta x}}{\sin \alpha x - \sin \beta x}$. *Ans.* 1.

Determine the points of discontinuity of the functions:

57. $y = \dfrac{x - 1}{x (x + 1) (x^2 - 4)}$. *Ans.* Discontinuities at $x = -2, -1, 0, 2$. **58.** $y = \tan \dfrac{1}{x}$.

Ans. Discontinuities at $x = 0$ and $x = \pm \dfrac{2}{\pi}$, $\pm \dfrac{2}{3\pi}$, $\cdots$, $\pm \dfrac{2}{(2n + 1) \pi}$, $\cdots$.

59. Find the points of discontinuity of the function $y = 1 + 2^{\frac{1}{x}}$ and construct the graph of this function. *Ans.* Discontinuity at $x = 0 \, (y \longrightarrow + \infty$ as $x \longrightarrow 0 + 0$, $y \longrightarrow 1$ as $x \longrightarrow 0 - 0)$.

60. From among the following infinitesimals (as $x \longrightarrow 0$): x^2, $\sqrt{x(1 - x)}$, $\sin 3x$, $2x \cos x \sqrt[3]{\tan^2 x}$, xe^{2x}, select infinitesimals of the same order as x, and also of higher and lower order than x. *Ans.* Infinitesimals of the same order as x are $\sin 3x$ and xe^{2x}; infinitesimals of higher order than x, x^2 and $2x \cos x \sqrt[3]{\tan^2 x}$, infinitesimals of lower order than x, $\sqrt{x(1 - x)}$.

61. Choose from among the same infinitesimals (as $x \to 0$) such that are equivalent to the infinitesimal x: $2 \sin x$, $\frac{1}{2} \tan 2x$, $x - 3x^2$, $\sqrt{2x^2 + x^3}$, $\ln(1 + x)$, $x^3 + 3x^4$. *Ans.* $\frac{1}{2} \tan 2x$, $x - 3x^2$, $\ln(1 + x)$.

62. Check to see that as $x \to 1$, the infinitesimals $1 - x$ and $1 - \sqrt[3]{x}$ are of the same order. Are they equivalent? *Ans.* $\lim\limits_{x \to 1} \dfrac{1 - x}{1 - \sqrt[3]{x}} = 3$; hence, these infinitesimals are of the same order, but they are not equivalent.

CHAPTER 3

DERIVATIVE AND DIFFERENTIAL

3.1 VELOCITY OF MOTION

Let us consider the rectilinear motion of some solid, say a stone, thrown vertically upwards, or the motion of a piston in the cylinder of an engine, etc. Idealizing the situation and disregarding dimensions and shapes, we shall always represent such a body in the form of a moving point M. The distance s of the moving point reckoned from some initial position M_0 will depend on the time t; in other words, s will be a function of time t:

$$s = f(t) \qquad (1)$$

At some instant of time * t, let the moving point M be at a distance s from the initial position M_0, and at some later instant $t + \Delta t$ let the point be at M_1, a distance $s + \Delta s$ from the initial position (Fig. 57). Thus, during the interval of time Δt the distance s changed by the quantity Δs. In such cases, one says that during the time Δt the quantity s received an increment Δs.

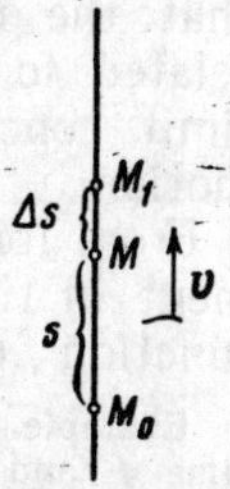

Fig. 57

Let us consider the ratio $\dfrac{\Delta s}{\Delta t}$; it gives us the average velocity of motion of the point during the time Δt:

$$v_{av} = \frac{\Delta s}{\Delta t} \qquad (2)$$

The average velocity cannot in all cases give an exact picture of the rate of translation of the point M at time t. If, for example, the body moved very fast at the beginning of the interval Δt and very slow at the end, the average velocity obviously cannot reflect these peculiarities in the motion of the point and give us a correct idea of the true velocity of motion at time t. In order to express more precisely this true velocity in terms of the average velocity, one has to take a smaller interval of time Δt. The most complete description of the rate of motion of the point at time t is given

---

* Here and henceforward we shall denote the specific value of a variable and the variable itself by the same letter.

by the limit which the average velocity approaches as $\Delta t \rightarrow 0$. This limit is called the **rate of motion at a given instant**:

$$v = \lim_{\Delta t \to 0} \frac{\Delta s}{\Delta t} \qquad (3)$$

Thus, the *rate (velocity) of motion at a given instant* is the limit of the ratio of increment in path Δs to increment in time Δt, as the time increment approaches zero.

Let us write equation (3) in full. Since

$$\Delta s = f(t + \Delta t) - f(t),$$

it follows that

$$v = \lim_{\Delta t \to 0} \frac{f(t + \Delta t) - f(t)}{\Delta t} \qquad (3')$$

This is the velocity of nonuniform motion. It is thus obvious that the notion of velocity of nonuniform motion is intimately related to the concept of a limit. It is only with the aid of the limit concept that we can determine the velocity of nonuniform motion.

From formula (3′) it follows that v is independent of the increment in time Δt, but depends on the value of t and the type of function $f(t)$.

Example. Find the velocity of uniformly accelerated motion at an arbitrary time t and at $t = 2$ sec if the relation of the path traversed to the time is expressed by the formula

$$s = \frac{1}{2} g t^2$$

Solution. At time t we have $s = \frac{1}{2} g t^2$; at time $t + \Delta t$ we get

$$s + \Delta s = \frac{1}{2} g (t + \Delta t)^2 = \frac{1}{2} g (t^2 + 2t \, \Delta t + \Delta t^2)$$

We find Δs:

$$\Delta s = \frac{1}{2} g (t^2 + 2t \, \Delta t + \Delta t^2) - \frac{1}{2} g t^2 = g t \, \Delta t + \frac{1}{2} g \, \Delta t^2$$

We form the ratio $\frac{\Delta s}{\Delta t}$:

$$\frac{\Delta s}{\Delta t} = \frac{g t \, \Delta t + \frac{1}{2} g \, \Delta t^2}{\Delta t} = g t + \frac{1}{2} g \, \Delta t$$

By definition we have

$$v = \lim_{\Delta t \to 0} \frac{\Delta s}{\Delta t} = \lim_{\Delta t \to 0} \left(g t + \frac{1}{2} g \, \Delta t \right) = g t$$

Thus, the velocity at an arbitrary time t is $v = g t$.
At $t = 2$ we have $(v)_{t=2} = g \cdot 2 = 9.8 \cdot 2 = 19.6$ m/sec.

3.2 THE DEFINITION OF A DERIVATIVE

Let there be a function

$$y = f(x) \tag{1}$$

defined in a certain interval. The function $y = f(x)$ has a definite value for each value of the argument x in this interval.

Let the argument x receive a certain increment Δx (it is immaterial whether it is positive or negative). Then the function y will receive a certain increment Δy. Thus, for the value of the argument x we will have $y = f(x)$, for the value of the argument $x + \Delta x$ we will have $y + \Delta y = f(x + \Delta x)$.

Let us find the increment of the function Δy:

$$\Delta y = f(x + \Delta x) - f(x) \tag{2}$$

Forming the ratio of the increment of the function to the increment of the argument, we get

$$\frac{\Delta y}{\Delta x} = \frac{f(x + \Delta x) - f(x)}{\Delta x} \tag{3}$$

We then find the limit of this ratio as $\Delta x \to 0$. If this limit exists, it is called the **derivative** of the given function $f(x)$ and is denoted $f'(x)$. Thus, by definition,

$$f'(x) = \lim_{\Delta x \to 0} \frac{\Delta y}{\Delta x}$$

or

$$f'(x) = \lim_{\Delta x \to 0} \frac{f(x + \Delta x) - f(x)}{\Delta x} \tag{4}$$

Consequently, the *derivative* of a given function $y = f(x)$ with respect to the argument x is the limit of the ratio of the increment in the function Δy to the increment in the argument Δx, when the latter approaches zero in arbitrary fashion.

It will be noted that in the general case, the derivative $f'(x)$ has a definite value for each value of x, which means that the derivative is also a **function** of x.

The designation $f'(x)$ is not the only one used for a derivative. Alternative symbols are

$$y', \ y'_x, \ \frac{dy}{dx}$$

The specific value of the derivative for $x = a$ is denoted $f'(a)$ or $y'|_{x=a}$.

The operation of finding the derivative of a function $f(x)$ is called *differentiation* of the function.

Example 1. Given the function $y = x^2$, find its derivative y':
(1) at an arbitrary point x,
(2) at $x = 3$.
Solution. (1) For the value of the argument x, we have $y = x^2$. When the value of the argument is $x + \Delta x$, we have $y + \Delta y = (x + \Delta x)^2$.
Find the increment of the function:

$$\Delta y = (x + \Delta x)^2 - x^2 = 2x\Delta x + (\Delta x)^2$$

Forming the ratio $\dfrac{\Delta y}{\Delta x}$, we have

$$\frac{\Delta y}{\Delta x} = \frac{2x\Delta x + (\Delta x)^2}{\Delta x} = 2x + \Delta x$$

Passing to the limit, we get the derivative of the given function:

$$y' = \lim_{\Delta x \to 0} \frac{\Delta y}{\Delta x} = \lim_{\Delta x \to 0} (2x + \Delta x) = 2x$$

Hence, the derivative of the function $y = x^2$ at an arbitrary point is $y' = 2x$.
(2) When $x = 3$ we have

$$y'|_{x=3} = 2 \cdot 3 = 6$$

Example 2. $y = \dfrac{1}{x}$; find y'.
Solution. Reasoning as before, we get

$$y = \frac{1}{x}, \quad y + \Delta y = \frac{1}{x + \Delta x},$$

$$\Delta y = \frac{1}{x + \Delta x} - \frac{1}{x} = \frac{x - x - \Delta x}{x(x + \Delta x)} = -\frac{\Delta x}{x(x + \Delta x)},$$

$$\frac{\Delta y}{\Delta x} = -\frac{1}{x(x + \Delta x)},$$

$$y' = \lim_{\Delta x \to 0} \frac{\Delta y}{\Delta x} = \lim_{\Delta x \to 0}\left[-\frac{1}{x(x + \Delta x)} \right] = -\frac{1}{x^2}$$

Note. In the preceding section it was established that if the dependence upon time t of the distance s of a moving point is expressed by the formula

$$s = f(t)$$

the velocity v at time t is expressed by the formula

$$v = \lim_{\Delta t \to 0} \frac{\Delta s}{\Delta t} = \lim_{\Delta t \to 0} \frac{f(t + \Delta t) - f(t)}{\Delta t}$$

Hence

$$v = s'_t = f'(t)$$

or, the velocity is equal to the derivative * of the distance with respect to the time.

---

* When we say "the derivative with respect to x" or "the derivative with respect to t" we mean that in computing the derivative we consider the variable x (or the time t, etc.) the argument (independent variable).

3.3 GEOMETRIC MEANING OF THE DERIVATIVE

We approached the notion of a derivative by regarding the velocity of a moving body (point), that is to say, by proceeding from **mechanical** concepts. We shall now give a no less important **geometric** interpretation of the derivative. To do this we must first define a **tangent line** to a curve at a given point.

We take a curve with a fixed point M_0 on it. Taking a point M_1 on the curve we draw the secant M_0M_1 (Fig. 58). If the point M_1 approaches the point M_0 without limit, the secant M_0M_1 will occupy various positions M_0M_1', M_0M_1'', and so on.

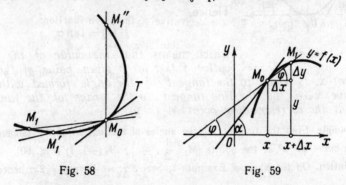

Fig. 58   Fig. 59

If, in the unbounded approach of the point M_1 (along the curve) to the point M_0 **from either side,** the secant tends to occupy the position of a definite straight line M_0T, this line is called the *tangent* to the curve at the point M_0 (the concept "tends to occupy" will be explained later on).

Let us consider the function $f(x)$ and the corresponding curve

$$y = f(x)$$

in a rectangular coordinate system (Fig. 59). At a certain value of x the function has the value $y = f(x)$. Corresponding to these values of x and y on the curve we have the point $M_0(x, y)$. Let us increase the argument x by Δx. Corresponding to the new value of the argument, $x + \Delta x$, we have an increased value of the function, $y + \Delta y = f(x + \Delta x)$. The corresponding point on the curve will be $M_1(x + \Delta x, y + \Delta y)$. Draw the secant M_0M_1 and denote by φ the angle formed by the secant and the positive x-axis. Form the ratio $\frac{\Delta y}{\Delta x}$. From Fig. 59 it follows immediately that

$$\frac{\Delta y}{\Delta x} = \tan \varphi \tag{1}$$

Now if Δx approaches zero, the point M_1 will move along the curve always approaching M_0. The secant $M_0 M_1$ will turn about M_0 and the angle φ will change with Δx. If as $\Delta x \to 0$ the angle φ approaches a certain limit α, the straight line passing through M_0 and forming an angle α with the positive x-axis will be the sought-for tangent line. It is easy to find its slope:

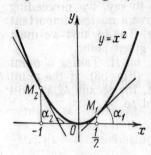

$$\tan \alpha = \lim_{\Delta x \to 0} \ \tan \varphi = \lim_{\Delta x \to 0} \frac{\Delta y}{\Delta x} = f'(x)$$

Hence,

$$f'(x) = \tan \alpha \qquad (2)$$

Fig. 60

which means that *the value of the derivative $f'(x)$, for a given value of the argument x, is equal to the tangent of the angle formed with the positive x-axis by the line tangent to the graph of the function $f(x)$ at the corresponding point $M_0(x, y)$*.

Example. Find the tangents of the angles of inclination of the tangent line to the curve $y = x^2$ at the points $M_1 \left(\dfrac{1}{2}, \dfrac{1}{4} \right)$, $M_2 (-1, 1)$ (Fig. 60).

Solution. On the basis of Example 1, Sec. 3.2, we have $y' = 2x$; hence,

$$\tan \alpha_1 = y' \Big|_{x=\frac{1}{2}} = 1, \ \ \tan \alpha_2 = y' \Big|_{x=-1} = -2$$

3.4 DIFFERENTIABILITY OF FUNCTIONS

Definition. If the function

$$y = f(x) \qquad (1)$$

has a derivative at the point $x = x_0$, that is, if there exists

$$\lim_{\Delta x \to 0} \frac{\Delta y}{\Delta x} = \lim_{\Delta x \to 0} \frac{f(x_0 + \Delta x) - f(x_0)}{\Delta x} \qquad (2)$$

we say that for the given value $x = x_0$ the function is *differentiable* or (which is the same thing) has a derivative.

If a function is differentiable **at every point** of some interval $[a, b]$ or (a, b), we say that it is *differentiable over the interval*.

Theorem. *If a function $y = f(x)$ is differentiable at some point $x = x_0$, it is continuous at that point.*

Indeed, if

$$\lim_{\Delta x \to 0} \frac{\Delta y}{\Delta x} = f'(x_0)$$

then

$$\frac{\Delta y}{\Delta x} = f'(x_0) + \gamma$$

where γ is a quantity that approaches zero as $\Delta x \to 0$. But then

$$\Delta y = f'(x_0)\,\Delta x + \gamma \Delta x$$

whence it follows that $\Delta y \to 0$ as $\Delta x \to 0$; and this means that the function $f(x)$ is continuous at the point x_0 (see Sec. 2.9).

In other words, **a function cannot have a derivative at points of discontinuity.** The converse is not true; from the fact that at some point $x = x_0$ the function $y = f(x)$ is continuous, it does not yet follow that it is differentiable at that point: the function $f(x)$ may not have a derivative at the point x_0. To convince ourselves of this, let us examine several cases.

Example 1. A function $f(x)$ is defined on an interval [0, 2] as follows (see Fig. 61):

$$f(x) = x \qquad \text{when } 0 \leqslant x \leqslant 1,$$
$$f(x) = 2x - 1 \quad \text{when } 1 < x \leqslant 2$$

At $x = 1$ the function has no derivative, although it is continuous at this point. Indeed, when $\Delta x > 0$ we have

$$\lim_{\Delta x \to 0} \frac{f(1 + \Delta x) - f(1)}{\Delta x} = \lim_{\Delta x \to 0} \frac{[2(1 + \Delta x) - 1] - [2 \cdot 1 - 1]}{\Delta x} = \lim_{\Delta x \to 0} \frac{2\Delta x}{\Delta x} = 2$$

when $\Delta x < 0$ we get

$$\lim_{\Delta x \to 0} \frac{f(1 + \Delta x) - f(1)}{\Delta x} = \lim_{\Delta x \to 0} \frac{(1 + \Delta x) - 1}{\Delta x} = \lim_{\Delta x \to 0} \frac{\Delta x}{\Delta x} = 1$$

Thus, this limit depends on the sign of Δx, and this means that the function has no derivative* at the point $x = 1$. Geometrically, this is in accord with the fact that at the point $x = 1$ the given "curve" does not have a definite tangent line.

Now the continuity of the function at the point $x = 1$ follows from the fact that

$$\Delta y = \Delta x \qquad \text{when } \Delta x < 0,$$
$$\Delta y = 2\Delta x \qquad \text{when } \Delta x > 0$$

and, therefore, in both cases $\Delta y \to 0$ as $\Delta x \to 0$.

---

* The definition of a derivative requires that the ratio $\frac{\Delta y}{\Delta x}$ should (as $\Delta x \to 0$) approach one and the same limit regardless of *the way* in which Δx approaches zero.

Example 2. A function $y = \sqrt[3]{x}$, the graph of which is shown in Fig. 62, is defined and continuous for all values of the independent variable.

Let us try to find out whether this function has a derivative at $x = 0$; to do this, we find the values of the function at $x = 0$ and at $x = 0 + \Delta x$: at $x = 0$ we have $y = 0$. at $x = 0 + \Delta x$ we have $y + \Delta y = \sqrt[3]{\Delta x}$.

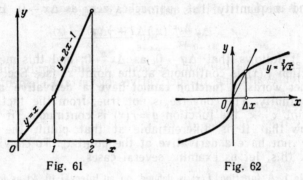

Fig. 61   Fig. 62

Therefore,

$$\Delta y = \sqrt[3]{\Delta x}$$

Find the limit of the ratio of the increment of the function to the increment of the argument:

$$\lim_{\Delta x \to 0} \frac{\Delta y}{\Delta x} = \lim_{\Delta x \to 0} \frac{\sqrt[3]{\Delta x}}{\Delta x} = \lim_{\Delta x \to 0} \frac{1}{\sqrt[3]{\Delta x^2}} = +\infty$$

Thus, the ratio of the increment of the function to the increment of the argument at the point $x = 0$ approaches infinity as $\Delta x \to 0$ (hence there is no limit). Consequently, this function is not differentiable at the point $x = 0$. The tangent to the curve at this point forms, with the x-axis, an angle $\frac{\pi}{2}$, which means that it coincides with the y-axis.

3.5 THE DERIVATIVE OF THE FUNCTION $y = x^n$, n A POSITIVE INTEGER

To find the derivative of a given function $y = f(x)$, it is necessary to carry out the following operations (on the basis of the general definition of a derivative):

(1) increase the argument x by Δx, calculate the increased value of the function:

$$y + \Delta y = f(x + \Delta x)$$

(2) find the corresponding increment in the function:

$$\Delta y = f(x + \Delta x) - f(x)$$

(3) form the ratio of the increment in the function to the increment in the argument:

$$\frac{\Delta y}{\Delta x} = \frac{f(x+\Delta x)-f(x)}{\Delta x}$$

(4) find the limit of this ratio as $\Delta x \to 0$:

$$y' = \lim_{\Delta x \to 0} \frac{\Delta y}{\Delta x} = \lim_{\Delta x \to 0} \frac{f(x+\Delta x)-f(x)}{\Delta x}$$

Here and in the following sections, we shall apply this general method for evaluating the derivatives of certain elementary functions.

Theorem. *The derivative of the function* $y=x^n$, *where n is a positive integer, is equal to* nx^{n-1}; *that is,*

$$if \ y=x^n, \ then \ y'=nx^{n-1} \tag{I}$$

Proof. We have the function

$$y = x^n$$

(1) If x receives an increment Δx, then

$$y + \Delta y = (x+\Delta x)^n$$

(2) Applying Newton's binomial theorem, we get

$$\Delta y = (x+\Delta x)^n - x^n =$$
$$= x^n + \frac{n}{1}x^{n-1}\Delta x + \frac{n(n-1)}{1\cdot2}x^{n-2}(\Delta x)^2 + \ldots + (\Delta x)^n - x^n$$

or

$$\Delta y = nx^{n-1}\Delta x + \frac{n(n-1)}{1\cdot2}x^{n-2}(\Delta x)^2 + \ldots + (\Delta x)^n$$

(3) We find the ratio

$$\frac{\Delta y}{\Delta x} = nx^{n-1} + \frac{n(n-1)}{1\cdot2}x^{n-2}\Delta x + \ldots + (\Delta x)^{n-1}$$

(4) Then we find the limit of this ratio:

$$y' = \lim_{\Delta x \to 0} \frac{\Delta y}{\Delta x}$$
$$= \lim_{\Delta x \to 0} \left[nx^{n-1} + \frac{n(n-1)}{1\cdot2}x^{n-2}\Delta x + \ldots + (\Delta x)^{n-1} \right] = nx^{n-1}$$

consequently, $y'=nx^{n-1}$, and the theorem is proved.

Example 1. $y=x^5$, $y'=5x^{5-1}=5x^4$.

Example 2. $y=x$, $y'=1x^{1-1}$, $y'=1$. The latter result has a simple geometric interpretation: the tangent to the straight line $y=x$ for any value of

x coincides with this line and, consequently, forms with the positive x-axis an angle, whose tangent is 1.

Note that formula (I) also holds true when n is fractional or negative. (This will be proved in Sec. 3.12).

Example 3. $y = \sqrt{x}$.
Let us represent the function in the form of a power:

$$y = x^{\frac{1}{2}}$$

Then by formula (I), taking into consideration what we have just said, we get

$$y' = \frac{1}{2} x^{\frac{1}{2} - 1}$$

or

$$y' = \frac{1}{2\sqrt{x}}$$

Example 4. $y = \dfrac{1}{x\sqrt{x}}$.
Represent y in the form of a power function:

$$y = x^{-\frac{3}{2}}$$

Then

$$y' = -\frac{3}{2} x^{-\frac{3}{2} - 1} = -\frac{3}{2} x^{-\frac{5}{2}} = -\frac{3}{2x^2 \sqrt{x}}$$

3.6 DERIVATIVES OF THE FUNCTIONS
$y = \sin x$, $y = \cos x$

Theorem 1. *The derivative of* $\sin x$ *is* $\cos x$, *or*

$$\text{if } y = \sin x, \text{ then } y' = \cos x. \tag{II}$$

Proof. Increase the argument x by Δx; then

(1) $y + \Delta y = \sin (x + \Delta x)$;

(2) $\Delta y = \sin (x + \Delta x) - \sin x = 2 \sin \dfrac{x + \Delta x - x}{2} \cos \dfrac{x + \Delta x + x}{2}$

$$= 2 \sin \frac{\Delta x}{2} \cdot \cos \left(x + \frac{\Delta x}{2} \right);$$

(3) $\dfrac{\Delta y}{\Delta x} = \dfrac{2 \sin \dfrac{\Delta x}{2} \cos \left(x + \dfrac{\Delta x}{2} \right)}{\Delta x} = \dfrac{\sin \dfrac{\Delta x}{2}}{\dfrac{\Delta x}{2}} \cos \left(x + \dfrac{\Delta x}{2} \right)$;

(4) $y' = \lim\limits_{\Delta x \to 0} \dfrac{\Delta y}{\Delta x} = \lim\limits_{\Delta x \to 0} \dfrac{\sin \dfrac{\Delta x}{2}}{\dfrac{\Delta x}{2}} \cdot \lim\limits_{\Delta x \to 0} \cos \left(x + \dfrac{\Delta x}{2} \right)$.

But since

$$\lim_{\Delta x \to 0} \frac{\sin \frac{\Delta x}{2}}{\frac{\Delta x}{2}} = 1$$

we get

$$y' = \lim_{\Delta x \to 0} \cos \left(x + \frac{\Delta x}{2} \right) = \cos x$$

This latter equation is obtained on the grounds that $\cos x$ is a continuous function.

Theorem 2. *The derivative of* $\cos x$ *is* $-\sin x$, *or*

$$\textit{if } y = \cos x, \textit{ then } y' = -\sin x. \tag{III}$$

Proof. Increase the argument x by Δx, then

$$y + \Delta y = \cos (x + \Delta x)$$

$$\Delta y = \cos (x + \Delta x) - \cos x = -2 \sin \frac{x + \Delta x - x}{2} \sin \frac{x + \Delta x + x}{2}$$

$$= -2 \sin \frac{\Delta x}{2} \sin \left(x + \frac{\Delta x}{2} \right)$$

$$\frac{\Delta y}{\Delta x} = - \frac{\sin \frac{\Delta x}{2}}{\frac{\Delta x}{2}} \cdot \sin \left(x + \frac{\Delta x}{2} \right)$$

$$y' = \lim_{\Delta x \to 0} \frac{\Delta y}{\Delta x} = \lim_{\Delta x \to 0} - \frac{\sin \frac{\Delta x}{2}}{\frac{\Delta x}{2}} \sin \left(x + \frac{\Delta x}{2} \right) = - \lim_{\Delta x \to 0} \sin \left(x + \frac{\Delta x}{2} \right)$$

Taking into account the fact that $\sin x$ is a continuous function, we finally get

$$y' = -\sin x$$

3.7 DERIVATIVES OF:
A CONSTANT, THE PRODUCT OF A CONSTANT BY A FUNCTION, A SUM, A PRODUCT, AND A QUOTIENT

Theorem 1. *The derivative of a constant is equal to zero; that is,*

$$\textit{if } y = C, \textit{ where } C = \text{const}, \textit{ then } y' = 0. \tag{IV}$$

Proof. $y = C$ is a function of x such that the values of it are equal to C for all x.

Hence, for any value of x,

$$y = f(x) = C$$

We increase the argument x by Δx ($\Delta x \neq 0$). Since the function y retains the value C for all values of the argument, we have

$$y + \Delta y = f(x + \Delta x) = C$$

Therefore, the increment of the function is

$$\Delta y = f(x + \Delta x) - f(x) = 0$$

the ratio of the increment of the function to the increment of the argument

$$\frac{\Delta y}{\Delta x} = 0$$

and, consequently,

$$y' = \lim_{\Delta x \to 0} \frac{\Delta y}{\Delta x} = 0$$

that is,

$$y' = 0$$

The latter result has a simple geometric interpretation. The graph of the function $y = C$ is a straight line parallel to the x-axis. Obviously, the tangent to the graph at any one of its points coincides with this straight line and, therefore, forms with the x-axis an angle whose tangent y' is zero.

Theorem 2. *A constant factor may be taken outside the derivative sign, i.e.,*

$$\text{if } y = Cu(x) \ (C = \text{const}), \text{ then } y' = Cu'(x). \tag{V}$$

Proof. Reasoning as in the proof of the preceding theorem, we have

$$y = Cu(x)$$
$$y + \Delta y = Cu(x + \Delta x)$$
$$\Delta y = Cu(x + \Delta x) - Cu(x) = C[u(x + \Delta x) - u(x)]$$
$$\frac{\Delta y}{\Delta x} = C\frac{u(x + \Delta x) - u(x)}{\Delta x}$$
$$y' = \lim_{\Delta x \to 0} \frac{\Delta y}{\Delta x} = C \lim_{\Delta x \to 0} \frac{u(x + \Delta x) - u(x)}{\Delta x}, \text{ i.e., } y' = Cu'(x)$$

Example 1. $y = 3\dfrac{1}{\sqrt{x}}$.

$$y' = 3\left(\frac{1}{\sqrt{x}}\right)' = 3\left(x^{-\frac{1}{2}}\right)' = 3\left(-\frac{1}{2}\right)x^{-\frac{1}{2}-1} = -\frac{3}{2}x^{-\frac{3}{2}}$$

or

$$y' = -\frac{3}{2x\sqrt{x}}$$

3.7 Derivatives of Some Expressions

Theorem 3. *The derivative of the sum of a finite number of differentiable functions is equal to the corresponding sum of the derivatives of these functions.* *

For the case of three terms, for example, we have

$$y = u(x) + v(x) + w(x), \quad y' = u'(x) + v'(x) + w'(x) \qquad \text{(VI)}$$

Proof. For the values of the argument x

$$y = u + v + w$$

(for the sake of brevity we drop the argument x in denoting the function).

For the value of the argument $x + \Delta x$ we have

$$y + \Delta y = (u + \Delta u) + (v + \Delta v) + (w + \Delta w)$$

where Δy, Δu, Δv, and Δw are increments of the functions y, u, v and w, which correspond to the increment Δx in the argument x. Hence,

$$\Delta y = \Delta u + \Delta v + \Delta w, \quad \frac{\Delta y}{\Delta x} = \frac{\Delta u}{\Delta x} + \frac{\Delta v}{\Delta x} + \frac{\Delta w}{\Delta x}$$

$$y' = \lim_{\Delta x \to 0} \frac{\Delta y}{\Delta x} = \lim_{\Delta x \to 0} \frac{\Delta u}{\Delta x} + \lim_{\Delta x \to 0} \frac{\Delta v}{\Delta x} + \lim_{\Delta x \to 0} \frac{\Delta w}{\Delta x}$$

or

$$y' = u'(x) + v'(x) + w'(x)$$

Example 2. $y = 3x^4 - \dfrac{1}{\sqrt[3]{x}}$.

$$y' = 3(x^4)' - \left(x^{-\frac{1}{3}}\right)' = 3 \cdot 4x^3 - \left(-\frac{1}{3}\right)x^{-\frac{1}{3}-1}$$

and so

$$y' = 12x^3 + \frac{1}{3} \frac{1}{x\sqrt[3]{x}}$$

Theorem 4. *The derivative of a product of two differentiable functions is equal to the product of the derivative of the first function by the second function plus the product of the first function by the derivative of the second function; that is,*

$$\text{if } y = uv, \text{ then } y' = u'v + uv'. \qquad \text{(VII)}$$

---

* The expression $y = u(x) - v(x)$ is equivalent to $y = u(x) + (-1)v(x)$ and $y' = [u(x) + (-1)v(x)]' = u'(x) + [-v(x)]' = u'(x) - v'(x)$.

Proof. Reasoning as in the proof of the preceding theorem, we get

$$y = uv$$

$$y + \Delta y = (u + \Delta u)(v + \Delta v)$$

$$\Delta y = (u + \Delta u)(v + \Delta v) - uv = \Delta u v + u \Delta v + \Delta u \, \Delta v$$

$$\frac{\Delta y}{\Delta x} = \frac{\Delta u}{\Delta x} v + u \frac{\Delta v}{\Delta x} + \Delta u \frac{\Delta v}{\Delta x}$$

$$y' = \lim_{\Delta x \to 0} \frac{\Delta y}{\Delta x} = \lim_{\Delta x \to 0} \frac{\Delta u}{\Delta x} v + \lim_{\Delta x \to 0} u \frac{\Delta v}{\Delta x} + \lim_{\Delta x \to 0} \Delta u \frac{\Delta v}{\Delta x}$$

$$= \left(\lim_{\Delta x \to 0} \frac{\Delta u}{\Delta x} \right) v + u \lim_{\Delta x \to 0} \frac{\Delta v}{\Delta x} + \lim_{\Delta x \to 0} \Delta u \lim_{\Delta x \to 0} \frac{\Delta v}{\Delta x}$$

(since u and v are independent of Δx).

Let us consider the last term on the right-hand side:

$$\lim_{\Delta x \to 0} \Delta u \lim_{\Delta x \to 0} \frac{\Delta v}{\Delta x}$$

Since $u(x)$ is a differentiable function, it is continuous. Consequently, $\lim_{\Delta x \to 0} \Delta u = 0$. Also,

$$\lim_{\Delta x \to 0} \frac{\Delta v}{\Delta x} = v' \neq \infty$$

Thus, the term under consideration is zero and we finally get

$$y' = u'v + uv'$$

The theorem just proved readily gives us the rule for differentiating the product of any number of functions.

Thus, if we have a product of three functions

$$y = uvw$$

then, by representing the right-hand side as the product of u and (vw), we get $y' = u'(vw) + u(vw)' = u'vw + u(v'w + vw') = u'vw + uv'w + uvw'$.

In this way we can obtain a similar formula for the derivative of the product of any (finite) number of functions. Namely, if $y = u_1 u_2 \ldots u_n$, then

$$y' = u_1' u_2 \ldots u_{n-1} u_n + u_1 u_2' \ldots u_{n-1} u_n + \ldots + u_1 u_2 \ldots u_{n-1} u_n'$$

Example 3. If $y = x^2 \sin x$, then

$$y' = (x^2)' \sin x + x^2 (\sin x)' = 2x \sin x + x^2 \cos x$$

Example 4. If $y = \sqrt{x} \sin x \cos x$, then

$$y' = (\sqrt{x})' \sin x \cos x + \sqrt{x} (\sin x)' \cos x + \sqrt{x} \sin x (\cos x)'$$

$$= \frac{1}{2\sqrt{x}} \sin x \cos x + \sqrt{x} \cos x \cos x + \sqrt{x} \sin x (-\sin x)$$

$$= \frac{1}{2\sqrt{x}} \sin x \cos x + \sqrt{x} (\cos^2 x - \sin^2 x) = \frac{\sin 2x}{4\sqrt{x}} + \sqrt{x} \cos 2x$$

Theorem 5. *The derivative of a fraction (that is, the quotient obtained by the division of two functions) is equal to a fraction whose denominator is the square of the denominator of the given fraction, and the numerator is the difference between the product of the denominator by the derivative of the numerator, and the product of the numerator by the derivative of the denominator; i.e.,*

$$\text{if } y = \frac{u}{v}, \quad \text{then } y' = \frac{u'v - uv'}{v^2}. \tag{VIII}$$

Proof. If Δy, Δu, and Δv are increments of the functions y, u, and v, corresponding to the increment Δx of the argument x, then

$$y + \Delta y = \frac{u + \Delta u}{v + \Delta v}$$

$$\Delta y = \frac{u + \Delta u}{v + \Delta v} - \frac{u}{v} = \frac{v \, \Delta u - u \, \Delta v}{v(v + \Delta v)}$$

$$\frac{\Delta y}{\Delta x} = \frac{\dfrac{v \, \Delta u - u \, \Delta v}{\Delta x}}{v(v + \Delta v)} = \frac{\dfrac{\Delta u}{\Delta x}v - u\dfrac{\Delta v}{\Delta x}}{v(v + \Delta v)}$$

$$y' = \lim_{\Delta x \to 0} \frac{\Delta y}{\Delta x} = \lim_{\Delta x \to 0} \frac{\dfrac{\Delta u}{\Delta x}v - u\dfrac{\Delta v}{\Delta x}}{v(v + \Delta v)} = \frac{v \lim\limits_{\Delta x \to 0} \dfrac{\Delta u}{\Delta x} - u \lim\limits_{\Delta x \to 0} \dfrac{\Delta v}{\Delta x}}{v \lim\limits_{\Delta x \to 0}(v + \Delta v)}$$

Whence, noting that $\Delta v \to 0$ as $\Delta x \to 0$, * we get

$$y' = \frac{u'v - uv'}{v^2}$$

Example 5. If $y = \dfrac{x^3}{\cos x}$, then

$$y' = \frac{(x^3)' \cos x - x^3 (\cos x)'}{\cos^2 x} = \frac{3x^2 \cos x + x^3 \sin x}{\cos^2 x}$$

Note. If we have a function of the form

$$y = \frac{u(x)}{C}$$

where the denominator C is a constant, then in differentiating this function we do not need to use formula (VIII); it is better to make use of formula (V):

$$y' = \left(\frac{1}{C} u\right)' = \frac{1}{C} u' = \frac{u'}{C}$$

Of course, the same result is obtained if formula (VIII) is applied.

---

*$\lim\limits_{\Delta x \to 0} \Delta v = 0$ since $v(x)$ is a differentiable and, consequently, continuous function.

Example 6. If $y = \dfrac{\cos x}{7}$, then

$$y' = \frac{(\cos x)'}{7} = -\frac{\sin x}{7}$$

3.8 THE DERIVATIVE OF A LOGARITHMIC FUNCTION

Theorem. *The derivative of the function* $\log_a x$ *is* $\dfrac{1}{x} \log_a e$, *that is,*

$$\text{if } y = \log_a x, \text{ then } y' = \frac{1}{x} \log_a e \qquad \text{(IX)}$$

Proof. If Δy is an increment in the function $y = \log_a x$ that corresponds to the increment Δx in the argument x, then

$$y + \Delta y = \log_a (x + \Delta x)$$

$$\Delta y = \log_a (x + \Delta x) - \log_a x = \log_a \frac{x + \Delta x}{x} = \log_a \left(1 + \frac{\Delta x}{x}\right)$$

$$\frac{\Delta y}{\Delta x} = \frac{1}{\Delta x} \log_a \left(1 + \frac{\Delta x}{x}\right)$$

Multiply and divide by x the expression on the right-hand side of the latter equation:

$$\frac{\Delta y}{\Delta x} = \frac{1}{x} \frac{x}{\Delta x} \log_a \left(1 + \frac{\Delta x}{x}\right) = \frac{1}{x} \log_a \left(1 + \frac{\Delta x}{x}\right)^{\frac{x}{\Delta x}}$$

We denote the quantity $\dfrac{\Delta x}{x}$ by α. Obviously, $\alpha \to 0$ for the given x, and as $\Delta x \to 0$. Consequently,

$$\frac{\Delta y}{\Delta x} = \frac{1}{x} \log_a (1 + \alpha)^{\frac{1}{\alpha}}$$

But, as we know from Sec. 2.7,

$$\lim_{\alpha \to \infty} (1 + \alpha)^{\frac{1}{\alpha}} = e$$

But if the expression under the sign of the logarithm approaches the number e, then the logarithm of this expression approaches $\log_a e$ (in virtue of the continuity of the logarithmic function). We therefore finally get

$$y' = \lim_{\Delta x \to 0} \frac{\Delta y}{\Delta x} = \lim_{\alpha \to 0} \frac{1}{x} \log_a (1 + \alpha)^{\frac{1}{\alpha}} = \frac{1}{x} \log_a e$$

Noting that $\log_a e = \dfrac{1}{\ln a}$, we can rewrite the formula as follows:

$$y' = \frac{1}{x} \frac{1}{\ln a}$$

The following is an important particular case of this formula: if $a = e$, then $\ln a = \ln e = 1$; that is,

$$\text{if } y = \ln x, \text{ then } y' = \frac{1}{x}. \tag{X}$$

3.9 THE DERIVATIVE OF A COMPOSITE FUNCTION

Given a composite function $y = f(x)$, that is, such that it may be represented in the following form:

$$y = F(u), \quad u = \varphi(x)$$

or $y = F[\varphi(x)]$ (see Sec. 1.8). In the expression $y = F(u)$, u called the *intermediate argument*.

Let us establish a rule for differentiating composite function:

Theorem. *If a function $u = \varphi(x)$ has, at some point x, a derivative $u'_x = \varphi'(x)$, and the function $y = F(u)$ has, at the corresponding value of u, the derivative $y'_u = F'(u)$, then the composite function $y = F[\varphi(x)]$ at the given point x also has a derivative, which is equal to*

$$y'_x = F'_u(u)\,\varphi'(x)$$

where for u we must substitute the expression $u = \varphi(x)$. Briefly,

$$y'_x = y'_u u'_x$$

In other words, the derivative of a composite function is equal to the product of the derivative of the given function with respect to the intermediate argument u by the derivative of the intermediate argument with respect to x.

Proof. For a definite value of x we will have

$$u = \varphi(x), \quad y = F(u)$$

For the increased value of the argument $x + \Delta x$,

$$u + \Delta u = \varphi(x + \Delta x), \quad y + \Delta y = F(u + \Delta u)$$

Thus, to the increment Δx there corresponds an increment Δu, to which corresponds an increment Δy, whereby $\Delta u \to 0$ and $\Delta y \to 0$ as $\Delta x \to 0$. It is given that

$$\lim_{\Delta u \to 0} \frac{\Delta y}{\Delta u} = y'_u$$

From this relation (taking advantage of the definition of a limit) we get (for $\Delta u \neq 0$)

$$\frac{\Delta y}{\Delta u} = y'_u + \alpha \tag{1}$$

where $\alpha \to 0$ as $\Delta u \to 0$. We rewrite (1) as

$$\Delta y = y'_u \Delta u + \alpha \, \Delta u \tag{2}$$

Equation (2) also holds true when $\Delta u = 0$ for an arbitrary α, since it turns into an identity, $0 = 0$. For $\Delta u = 0$ we shall assume $\alpha = 0$. Divide all terms of (2) by Δx:

$$\frac{\Delta y}{\Delta x} = y'_u \frac{\Delta u}{\Delta x} + \alpha \frac{\Delta u}{\Delta x} \tag{3}$$

It is given that

$$\lim_{\Delta x \to 0} \frac{\Delta u}{\Delta x} = u'_x, \quad \lim_{\Delta x \to 0} \alpha = 0$$

Passing to the limit as $\Delta x \to 0$ in (3), we get

$$y'_x = y'_u u'_x \tag{4}$$

Example 1. Given a function $y = \sin (x^2)$. Find y'_x. Represent the given function as a function of a function as follows:

$$y = \sin u, \quad u = x^2$$

We find

$$y'_u = \cos u, \quad u'_x = 2x$$

Hence, by formula (4),

$$y'_x = y'_u u'_x = \cos u \cdot 2x$$

Replacing u by its expression, we finally get

$$y'_x = 2x \cos (x^2)$$

Example 2. Given the function $y = (\ln x)^3$. Find y'_x. Represent this function as follows:

$$y = u^3, \quad u = \ln x$$

We find

$$y'_u = 3u^2, \quad u'_x = \frac{1}{x}$$

Hence,

$$y'_x = 3u^2 \frac{1}{x} = 3 (\ln x)^2 \frac{1}{x}$$

If a function $y = f(x)$ is such that it may be represented in the form

$$y = F(u), \quad u = \varphi(v), \quad v = \psi(x)$$

the derivative y'_x, is found by a successive application of the foregoing theorem.

Applying the proved rule, we have

$$y'_x = y'_u u'_x$$

Applying the same theorem to find u'_x, we have

$$u'_x = u'_v v'_x$$

Substituting the expression of u'_x into the preceding equation, we get

$$y'_x = y'_u u'_v v'_x \tag{5}$$

or

$$y'_x = F'_u (u) \, \varphi'_v (v) \, \psi'_x (x)$$

Example 3. Given the function $y = \sin [(\ln x)^3]$. Find y'_x. Represent the function as follows:

$$y = \sin u, \quad u = v^3, \quad v = \ln x$$

We then find

$$y'_u = \cos u, \quad u'_v = 3v^2, \quad v'_x = \frac{1}{x}$$

In this way, by formula (5), we get

$$y'_x = y'_u u'_v v'_x = 3 \, (\cos u) \, v^2 \, \frac{1}{x}$$

or, finally,

$$y'_x = \cos [(\ln x)^3] \cdot 3 \, (\ln x)^2 \, \frac{1}{x}$$

It is to be noted that the function considered is defined only for $x > 0$.

3.10 DERIVATIVES OF THE FUNCTIONS $y = \tan x$, $y = \cot x$, $y = \ln |x|$

Theorem 1. *The derivative of the function* $\tan x$ *is* $\dfrac{1}{\cos^2 x}$, *i. e.,*

$$\text{if } y = \tan x, \quad \text{then } y' = \frac{1}{\cos^2 x}. \tag{XI}$$

Proof. Since

$$y = \frac{\sin x}{\cos x}$$

by the rule for differentiating a fraction [see formula (VIII), Sec. 3.7] we get

$$y' = \frac{(\sin x)' \cos x - \sin x \, (\cos x)'}{\cos^2 x} = \frac{\cos x \cos x - \sin x \, (- \sin x)}{\cos^2 x}$$

$$= \frac{\cos^2 x + \sin^2 x}{\cos^2 x} = \frac{1}{\cos^2 x}$$

Theorem 2. *The derivative of the function* $\cot x$ *is* $-\dfrac{1}{\sin^2 x}$, *i. e.,*

$$\text{if } y = \cot x, \text{ then } y' = -\frac{1}{\sin^2 x}. \tag{XII}$$

Proof. Since $y = \dfrac{\cos x}{\sin x}$, we have

$$y' = \frac{(\cos x)' \sin x - \cos x (\sin x)'}{\sin^2 x} = \frac{-\sin x \sin x - \cos x \cos x}{\sin^2 x}$$
$$= -\frac{\sin^2 x + \cos^2 x}{\sin^2 x} = -\frac{1}{\sin^2 x}$$

Example 1. If $y = \tan \sqrt{x}$, then

$$y' = \frac{1}{\cos^2 \sqrt{x}} (\sqrt{x})' = \frac{1}{2 \sqrt{x}} \frac{1}{\cos^2 \sqrt{x}}$$

Example 2. If $y = \ln \cot x$, then

$$y' = \frac{1}{\cot x} (\cot x)' = \frac{1}{\cot x} \left(-\frac{1}{\sin^2 x} \right) = -\frac{1}{\cos x \sin x} = -\frac{2}{\sin 2x}$$

Theorem 3. *The derivative of the function* $\ln |x|$ (Fig. 63) *is* $\dfrac{1}{x}$, *i.e.*,

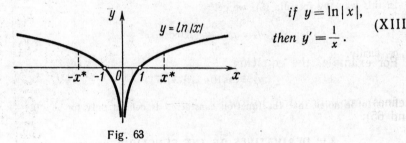

$$\text{if } y = \ln |x|,$$
$$\text{then } y' = \frac{1}{x}. \qquad \text{(XIII)}$$

Fig. 63

Proof. (a) If $x > 0$, then $|x| = x$, $\ln |x| = \ln x$, and therefore

$$y' = \frac{1}{x}$$

(b) Let $x < 0$. Then $|x| = -x$. But

$$\ln |x| = \ln (-x)$$

(It will be noted that if $x < 0$, then $-x > 0$.) Let us represent the function $y = \ln (-x)$ as a composite function by putting

$$y = \ln u, \quad u = -x$$

Then

$$y'_x = y'_u u'_x = \frac{1}{u} (-1) = \frac{1}{-x} (-1) = \frac{1}{x}$$

And so for negative values of x we also have the equation

$$y'_x = \frac{1}{x}$$

Hence, formula (XIII) has been proved for any value of $x \neq 0$. (For $x = 0$ the function $\ln |x|$ is not defined.)

3.11 AN IMPLICIT FUNCTION AND ITS DIFFERENTIATION

Let the values of two variables x and y be related by some equation, which we can symbolize as follows:

$$F(x, \ y) = 0 \qquad (1)$$

If the function $y = f(x)$, defined on some interval (a, b), is such that equation (1) becomes an identity in x when the expression $f(x)$ is substituted into it in place of y, the function $y = f(x)$ is an *implicit function* defined by equation (1).

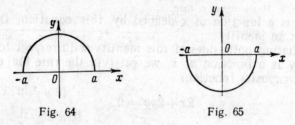

Fig. 64   Fig. 65

For example, the equation

$$x^2 + y^2 - a^2 = 0 \qquad (2)$$

defines implicitly the following elementary functions (Figs. 64 and 65):

$$y = \sqrt{a^2 - x^2} \qquad (3)$$
$$y = -\sqrt{a^2 - x^2} \qquad (4)$$

Indeed, substitution into equation (2) yields the identity

$$x^2 + (a^2 - x^2) - a^2 = 0$$

Expressions (3) and (4) were obtained by solving equation (2) for y. But not every implicitly defined function may be represented explicitly, that is, in the form $y = f(x)$, * where $f(x)$ is an elementary function.

For instance, functions defined by the equations

$$y^6 - y - x^2 = 0$$

or

$$y - x - \frac{1}{4} \sin y = 0$$

are not expressible in terms of elementary functions; that is, these equations cannot be solved for y.

---

* If a function is defined by an equation of the form $y = f(x)$, one says that the function is *defined explicitly* or is *explicit*.

Note 1. Observe that the terms "explicit function" and "implicit function" do not characterize the nature of the function but merely the way it is defined. Every explicit function $y = f(x)$ may also be represented as an implicit function $y - f(x) = 0$.

We shall now give the rule for finding the derivative of an implicit function without transforming it into an explicit one, that is, without representing it in the form $y = f(x)$.

Assume the function is defined by the equation

$$x^2 + y^2 - a^2 = 0$$

Here, if y is a function of x defined by this equation, then the equation is an identity.

Differentiating both sides of this identity with respect to x, and regarding y as a function of x, we get (via the rule for differentiating a composite function)

$$2x + 2yy' = 0$$

whence

$$y' = -\frac{x}{y}$$

Observe that if we were to differentiate the corresponding explicit function

$$y = \sqrt{a^2 - x^2}$$

we would obtain

$$y' = -\frac{x}{\sqrt{a^2 - x^2}} = -\frac{x}{y}$$

which is the same result.

Let us consider another case of an implicit function y of x:

$$y^6 - y - x^2 = 0$$

Differentiate with respect to x:

$$6y^5 y' - y' - 2x = 0$$

whence

$$y' = \frac{2x}{6y^5 - 1}$$

Note 2. From the foregoing examples it follows that to find the value of the derivative of an implicit function for a given value of the argument x, one also has to know the value of the function y for the given value of x.

3.12 DERIVATIVES OF A POWER FUNCTION FOR AN ARBITRARY REAL EXPONENT, OF A GENERAL EXPONENTIAL FUNCTION, AND OF A COMPOSITE EXPONENTIAL FUNCTION

Theorem 1. *The derivative of the function* x^n, *where* n *is any real number, is equal to* nx^{n-1}; *that is,*

$$\text{if } y = x^n, \text{ then } y' = nx^{n-1}. \tag{I'}$$

Proof. Let $x > 0$. Taking logarithms of this function, we get

$$\ln y = n \ln x$$

Differentiate, with respect to x, both sides of the equation obtained, taking y to be a function of x:

$$\frac{y'}{y} = n \frac{1}{x}, \quad y' = yn\frac{1}{x}$$

Substituting into this equation the value $y = x^n$, we finally get

$$y' = nx^{n-1}$$

It is easy to show that this formula holds true also for $x < 0$ provided x^n is meaningful. *

Theorem 2. *The derivative of the function* a^x, *where* $a > 0$, *is* $a^x \ln a$; *that is,*

$$\text{if } y = a^x, \text{ then } y' = a^x \ln a. \tag{XIV}$$

Proof. Taking logarithms of the equation $y = a^x$, we get

$$\ln y = x \ln a$$

Differentiate the equation obtained regarding y as a function of x:

$$\frac{1}{y} y' = \ln a, \quad y' = y \ln a$$

or

$$y' = a^x \ln a$$

If the base is $a = e$, then $\ln e = 1$ and we have the formula

$$y = e^x, \quad y' = e^x \tag{XIV'}$$

Example 1. Given the function

$$y = e^{x^2}$$

Represent it as a composite function by introducing the intermediate argument u:

$$y = e^u, \quad u = x^2$$

then

$$y'_u = e^u, \quad u'_x = 2x$$

---

* This formula was proved in Sec. 3.5, for the case when n is a *positive integer*. Formula (1) has now been proved for the general case (for any constant number n).

and, therefore,

$$y'_x = e^u \cdot 2x = e^{x^2} \cdot 2x$$

A *composite exponential function* is a function in which both the base and the exponent are functions of x, for instance, $(\sin x)^{x^2}$, $x^{\tan x}$, x^x, $(\ln x)^x$; generally, any function of the form

$$y = [u(x)]^{v(x)} \equiv u^v$$

is a composite exponential function. *

Theorem 3.

> If $y = u^v$, then $y' = vu^{v-1}u' + u^v v' \ln u$.   (XV)

Proof. Taking logarithms of the function y, we have

$$\ln y = v \ln u$$

Differentiating the resultant equation with respect to x, we get

$$\frac{1}{y}y' = v\frac{1}{u}u' + v' \ln u$$

whence

$$y' = y\left(v\frac{u'}{u} + v' \ln u\right)$$

Substituting into this equation the expression $y = u^v$, we obtain

$$y' = vu^{v-1}u' + u^v v' \ln u$$

Thus, the derivative of a composite exponential function consists of two terms: the first term is obtained by assuming, when differentiating, that u is a function of x and v is a **constant** (that is to say, if we regard u^v as a **power** function); the second term is obtained on the assumption that v is a function of x, and $u = \text{const}$ (i. e., if we regard u^v as an **exponential** function).

Example 2. If $y = x^x$, then $y' = xx^{x-1}(x') + x^x (x') \ln x$ or

$$y' = x^x + x^x \ln x = x^x (1 + \ln x)$$

Example 3. If $y = (\sin x)^{x^2}$, then

$$y' = x^2 (\sin x)^{x^2-1} (\sin x)' + (\sin x)^{x^2} (x^2)' \ln \sin x$$
$$= x^2 (\sin x)^{x^2-1} \cos x + (\sin x)^{x^2} 2x \ln \sin x$$

The procedure applied in this section for finding derivatives **(first finding the derivative of the logarithm of the given function)** is widely used in differentiating functions. Very often the use of this method greatly simplifies calculations.

---

* In the Soviet mathematical literature this function is also called an expo-nential-power function or a power-exponential function.

Example 4. Find the derivative of the function

$$y = \frac{(x+1)^2 \sqrt{x-1}}{(x+4)^3 e^x}$$

Solution. Taking logarithms we get

$$\ln y = 2 \ln (x+1) + \frac{1}{2} \ln (x-1) - 3 \ln (x+4) - x$$

Differentiate both sides of this equation:

$$\frac{y'}{y} = \frac{2}{x+1} + \frac{1}{2(x-1)} - \frac{3}{x+4} - 1$$

Multiplying by y and substituting, in place of y, the expression $\frac{(x+1)^2 \sqrt{x-1}}{(x+4)^3 e^x}$, we get

$$y' = \frac{(x+1)^2 \sqrt{x-1}}{(x+4)^3 e^x} \left[\frac{2}{x+1} + \frac{1}{2(x-1)} - \frac{3}{x+4} - 1 \right]$$

Note. The expression $\frac{y'}{y} = (\ln y)'$, which is the derivative, with respect to x, of the natural logarithm of the given function $y = y(x)$, is called the *logarithmic derivative*.

3.13 AN INVERSE FUNCTION AND ITS DIFFERENTIATION

Take an increasing or decreasing function (Fig. 66)

$$y = f(x) \tag{1}$$

defined in some interval (a, b) $(a < b)$ (see Sec. 1.6). Let $f(a) = c$, $f(b) = d$. For definiteness we shall henceforward consider an increasing function.

Let us consider two different values x_1 and x_2 in the interval (a, b). From the definition of an increasing function it follows that if $x_1 < x_2$ and $y_1 = f(x_1)$, $y_2 = f(x_2)$, then $y_1 < y_2$. Hence, to two different values x_1 and x_2 there correspond two different values of the function, y_1 and y_2. The converse is also true: if $y_1 < y_2$, $y_1 = f(x_1)$, and $y_2 = f(x_2)$, then from the definition of an increasing function it follows that $x_1 < x_2$. Thus, a one-to-one correspondence is established between the values of x and the corresponding values of y.

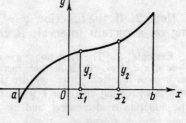

Fig. 66

Regarding these values of y as values of the argument and the values of x as values of the function, we get x as a function of y:

$$x = \varphi(y) \tag{2}$$

This function is called the *inverse function* of $y = f(x)$. It is obvious too that the function $y = f(x)$ is the inverse of $x = \varphi(y)$. With similar reasoning it is possible to prove that a decreasing function also has an inverse.

Note 1. We state, without proof, that *if an increasing (or decreasing) function $y = f(x)$ is continuous on an interval $[a, b]$, where $f(a) = c$, $f(b) = d$, then the inverse function is defined and is continuous on the interval $[c, d]$.*

Example 1. Given the function $y = x^3$. This function is increasing on the infinite interval $-\infty < x < +\infty$; it has an inverse function $x = \sqrt[3]{y}$ (Fig. 67).

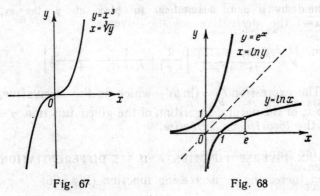

Fig. 67   Fig. 68

It will be noted that the inverse function $x = \varphi(y)$ is found by solving the equation $y = f(x)$ for x.

Example 2. Given the function $y = e^x$. This function is increasing on the infinite interval $-\infty < x < +\infty$. It has an inverse $x = \ln y$. The domain of definition of the inverse function is $0 < y < +\infty$ (Fig. 68).

Note 2. If the function $y = f(x)$ is neither increasing nor decreasing on a certain interval, it can have several inverse functions. *

Example 3. The function $y = x^2$ is defined on an infinite interval $-\infty < x < +\infty$. It is neither increasing nor decreasing and does not have an inverse function. If we consider the interval $0 \leqslant x < +\infty$, then the function here is increasing and $x = \sqrt{y}$ is its inverse. But in the interval $-\infty < x < 0$ the function is decreasing and its inverse is $x = -\sqrt{y}$ (Fig. 69).

Note 3. If the functions $y = f(x)$ and $x = \varphi(y)$ are inverses of each other, their graphs are represented by a single curve. But if

---

* Let it be noted once again that when speaking of y as a function of x we have in mind that y is a single-valued function of x.

we again denote the argument of the inverse function by x, and the function by y, and then construct them in a single coordinate system, we will get two different graphs.

It will readily be seen that the graphs will be symmetric about the bisector of the first quadrantal angle.

Example 4. Fig. 68 gives the graphs of the function $y = e^x$ (or $x = \ln y$) and its inverse $y = \ln x$, which are considered in Example 2.

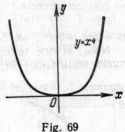

Fig. 69

Let us now prove a theorem that permits finding the derivative of a function $y = f(x)$ if we know the derivative of the inverse function.

Theorem. *If for the function*

$$y = f(x) \tag{1}$$

there exists an inverse function

$$x = \varphi(y) \tag{2}$$

which at the point under consideration y has a nonzero derivative $\varphi'(y)$, then at the corresponding point x the function $y = f(x)$ has a derivative $f'(x)$ equal to $\frac{1}{\varphi'(y)}$; that is, the following formula is true:

$$f'(x) = \frac{1}{\varphi'(y)} \tag{XVI}$$

Thus, the derivative of one of two inverse functions is equal to unity divided by the derivative of the second function for corresponding values of x and y.*

Proof. Take the increment Δy. Then, by (2), we have

$$\Delta x = \varphi(y + \Delta y) - \varphi(y)$$

Since $\varphi(y)$ is a monotonic function, it follows that $\Delta x \neq 0$. We write the identity

$$\frac{\Delta y}{\Delta x} = \frac{1}{\dfrac{\Delta x}{\Delta y}} \tag{3}$$

---

* When we write $f'(x)$ or y'_x we regard x as the independent variable when evaluating the derivative; but when we write $\varphi'(y)$ or x'_y we assume that y is the independent variable when evaluating the derivative. It should be noted that **after differentiating with respect to y, as indicated on the right side of formula (XVI), $f(x)$ must be substituted for y.**

Since the function $\varphi(y)$ is continuous, then $\Delta x \to 0$ as $\Delta y \to 0$. Passing to the limit as $\Delta y \to 0$ in both members of (3), we get

$$y'_x = \frac{1}{x'_y} \quad \text{or} \quad f'(x) = \frac{1}{\varphi'(y)}$$

In other words, we obtain formula XVI.

Note. If one takes advantage of the theorem on differentiating a composite function, then formula XVI may be obtained in the following manner.

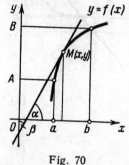

Fig. 70

Differentiate both members of (2) with respect to x, taking y to be a function of x. This yields $1 = \varphi'(y) y'_x$, whence

$$y'_x = \frac{1}{\varphi'(y)}$$

The result obtained is clearly illustrated geometrically. Consider the graph of the function $y = f(x)$ (Fig. 70). This curve will also be the graph of the function $x = \varphi(y)$, where x is now regarded as the function and y as the independent variable. Take some point $M(x, y)$ on this curve. Draw a tangent to the curve at this point. Denote by α and β the angles formed by the given tangent and the positive x- and y-axes. On the basis of the results of Sec. 3.3 concerning the geometrical meaning of a derivative we have

$$\left. \begin{array}{l} f'(x) = \tan \alpha \\ \varphi'(y) = \tan \beta \end{array} \right\} \qquad (4)$$

From Fig. 70 it follows directly that if $\alpha < \frac{\pi}{2}$, then $\beta = \frac{\pi}{2} - \alpha$. But if $\alpha > \frac{\pi}{2}$, then, as is readily seen, $\beta = \frac{3\pi}{2} - \alpha$. Hence, in any case $\tan \beta = \cot \alpha$, whence $\tan \alpha \tan \beta = \tan \alpha \cot \alpha = 1$, or $\tan \alpha = \frac{1}{\tan \beta}$. Substituting the expressions for $\tan \alpha$ and $\tan \beta$ from formula (4), we get

$$f'(x) = \frac{1}{\varphi'(y)}$$

3.14 INVERSE TRIGONOMETRIC FUNCTIONS AND THEIR DIFFERENTIATION

(1) The function $y = \arcsin x$.
Let us consider the function

$$x = \sin y \qquad (1)$$

and construct its graph by directing the y-axis vertically upwards (Fig. 71). This function is defined in the infinite interval $-\infty < < y < +\infty$. Over the interval $-\frac{\pi}{2} \leqslant y \leqslant \frac{\pi}{2}$, the function $x = \sin y$ is increasing and its values fill the interval $-1 \leqslant x \leqslant 1$. For this reason, the function $x = \sin y$ has an inverse which is denoted by

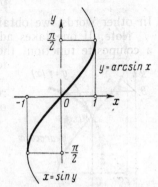

Fig. 71

$$y = \arcsin x \,*$$

This function is defined on the interval $-1 \leqslant x \leqslant 1$, and its values fill the interval $-\frac{\pi}{2} \leqslant y \leqslant \frac{\pi}{2}$. In Fig. 71, the graph of $y = \arcsin x$ is shown by the heavy line.

Theorem 1. *The derivative of the function* $\arcsin x$ *is equal to* $\frac{1}{\sqrt{1-x^2}}$; *i. e.,*

$$if \ y = \arcsin x, \ then \ y' = \frac{1}{\sqrt{1-x^2}}. \tag{XVII}$$

Proof. On the basis of (1) we have

$$x'_y = \cos y$$

By the rule for differentiating an inverse function,

$$y'_x = \frac{1}{x'_y} = \frac{1}{\cos y}$$

but

$$\cos y = \sqrt{1 - \sin^2 y} = \sqrt{1-x^2}$$

therefore,

$$y'_x = \frac{1}{\sqrt{1-x^2}}$$

The sign in front of the radical is plus because the function $y = \arcsin x$ takes on values in the interval $-\frac{\pi}{2} \leqslant y \leqslant \frac{\pi}{2}$, and, consequently, $\cos y \geqslant 0$.

Example 1. $y = \arcsin e^x$,

$$y' = \frac{1}{\sqrt{1-(e^x)^2}}(e^x)' = \frac{e^x}{\sqrt{1-e^{2x}}}.$$

---

* It may be noted that the familiar equation $y = \text{Arcsin } x$ of trigonometry is another way of writing (1). Here (for a given x) y denotes the set of values of angles whose sine is equal to x.

Example 2. $y = \left(\arcsin \dfrac{1}{x} \right)^2.$

$$y' = 2 \arcsin \frac{1}{x} \cdot \frac{1}{\sqrt{1 - \dfrac{1}{x^2}}} \left(\frac{1}{x} \right)' = -2 \arcsin \frac{1}{x} \cdot \frac{1}{x \cdot x \sqrt{x^2 - 1}}$$

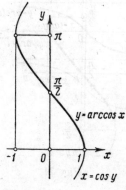

Fig. 72

(2) The function $y = \arccos x.$

As before, we consider the function

$$x = \cos y \qquad (2)$$

and construct its graph with the y-axis extending upwards (Fig. 72). This function is defined on the infinite interval $-\infty < y < +\infty$. On the interval $0 \leqslant y \leqslant \pi$, the function $x = \cos y$ is decreasing and has an inverse that we denote

$$y = \arccos x$$

This function is defined on the interval $-1 \leqslant x \leqslant 1$. The values of the function fill the interval $\pi \geqslant y \geqslant 0$. In Fig. 72, the function $y = \arccos x$ is depicted by the heavy line.

Theorem 2. *The derivative of the function* $\arccos x$ *is* $-\dfrac{1}{\sqrt{1-x^2}}$; *i. e.,*

$$if\ y = \arccos x,\ then\ y' = -\frac{1}{\sqrt{1-x^2}}. \qquad \text{(XVIII)}$$

Proof. From (2) we have

$$x'_y = -\sin y$$

Hence

$$y'_x = \frac{1}{x'_y} = -\frac{1}{\sin y} = -\frac{1}{\sqrt{1-\cos^2 y}}$$

But $\cos y = x$, and so

$$y'_x = -\frac{1}{\sqrt{1-x^2}}$$

In $\sin y = \sqrt{1-\cos^2 y}$ the radical is taken with the plus sign, since the function $y = \arccos x$ is defined on the interval $0 \leqslant y \leqslant \pi$ and, consequently, $\sin y \geqslant 0$.

Example 3. $y = \arccos (\tan x),$

$$y' = -\frac{1}{\sqrt{1-\tan^2 x}} (\tan x)' = -\frac{1}{\sqrt{1-\tan^2 x}} \cdot \frac{1}{\cos^2 x}.$$

(3) The function $y = \arctan x$.
We consider the function

$$x = \tan y \qquad (3)$$

and construct its graph (Fig. 73). This function is defined for all values of y except $y = (2k+1)\dfrac{\pi}{2}$ ($k = 0$, ± 1, ± 2, ...). On the interval $-\dfrac{\pi}{2} < y < \dfrac{\pi}{2}$ the function $x = \tan y$ is increasing and has an inverse:

$$y = \arctan x$$

This function is defined on the interval $-\infty < x < +\infty$. The values of the function fill the interval $-\dfrac{\pi}{2} < y < \dfrac{\pi}{2}$. In Fig. 73, the

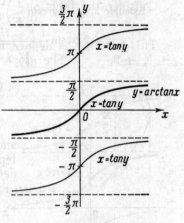

Fig. 73

graph of the function $y = \arctan x$ is shown as a heavy line.

Theorem 3. *The derivative of the function* $\arctan x$ *is* $\dfrac{1}{1+x^2}$; *i.e.*,

$$if \ y = \arctan x, \quad then \ y' = \frac{1}{1+x^2}. \qquad \textbf{(XIX)}$$

Proof. From (3) we have

$$x'_y = \frac{1}{\cos^2 y}$$

Hence

$$y'_x = \frac{1}{x'_y} = \cos^2 y$$

but

$$\cos^2 y = \frac{1}{\sec^2 y} = \frac{1}{1 + \tan^2 y}$$

since $\tan y = x$, we get, finally,

$$y' = \frac{1}{1+x^2}$$

Example 4. $y = (\arctan x)^4$,

$$y' = 4 (\arctan x)^3 (\arctan x)' = 4 (\arctan x)^3 \frac{1}{1+x^2}$$

(4) The function $y = \text{arccot } x$.

Consider the function

$$x = \cot y \qquad (4)$$

This function is defined for all values of y except $y = k\pi$ ($k = 0$, ± 1, ± 2, ...). The graph of this function is shown in Fig. 74.

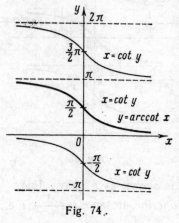

On the interval $0 < y < \pi$, the function $x = \cot y$ is decreasing and has an inverse:

$$y = \text{arccot } y$$

Consequently, this function is defined on the infinite interval $-\infty < < x < +\infty$, and its values fill the interval $\pi > y > 0$.

Theorem 4. *The derivative of the function* arccot x *is* $-\dfrac{1}{1+x^2}$; *i.e.,*

if $y = \text{arccot } x$, *then* $y' = -\dfrac{1}{1+x^2}$.

$$(XX)$$

Fig. 74.

Proof. From (4) we have

$$x'_y = -\frac{1}{\sin^2 y}$$

Hence

$$y'_x = -\sin^2 y = -\frac{1}{\csc^2 y} = -\frac{1}{1 + \cot^2 y}$$

But

$$\cot y = x$$

Therefore

$$y'_x = -\frac{1}{1 + x^2}$$

3.15 BASIC DIFFERENTIATION FORMULAS

Let us now bring together into a single table all the basic formulas and rules of differentiation derived in the preceding sections.

$$y = \text{const}, \ y' = 0$$

Power function:

$$y = x^\alpha, \ y' = \alpha x^{\alpha - 1}$$

particular instances:

$$y = \sqrt{x}, \ y' = \frac{1}{2\sqrt{x}}$$

$$y = \frac{1}{x}, \ y' = -\frac{1}{x^2}$$

Trigonometric functions:

$$y = \sin x, \quad y' = \cos x$$
$$y = \cos x, \quad y' = -\sin x$$
$$y = \tan x, \quad y' = \frac{1}{\cos^2 x}$$
$$y = \cot x, \quad y' = -\frac{1}{\sin^2 x}$$

Inverse trigonometric functions:

$$y = \arcsin x, \quad y' = \frac{1}{\sqrt{1-x^2}}$$
$$y = \arccos x, \quad y' = -\frac{1}{\sqrt{1-x^2}}$$
$$y = \arctan x, \quad y' = \frac{1}{1+x^2}$$
$$y = \operatorname{arccot} x, \quad y' = -\frac{1}{1+x^2}$$

Exponential function:

$$y = a^x, \quad y' = a^x \ln a$$

in particular,

$$y = e^x, \quad y' = e^x$$

Logarithmic function:

$$y = \log_a x, \quad y' = \frac{1}{x} \log_a e$$

in particular,

$$y = \ln x, \quad y' = \frac{1}{x}$$

General rules for differentiation:

$$y = Cu(x), \qquad y' = Cu'(x) \quad (C = \text{const})$$
$$y = u + v - w, \quad y' = u' + v' - w'$$
$$y = uv, \qquad y' = u'v + uv'$$
$$y = \frac{u}{v}, \qquad y' = \frac{u'v - uv'}{v^2}$$
$$\left.\begin{array}{l} y = f(u), \\ u = \varphi(x), \end{array}\right\} \qquad y'_x = f'_u(u)\,\varphi'_x(x)$$
$$y = u^v, \qquad\qquad y' = vu^{v-1}u' + u^v v' \ln u$$

If $y = f(x)$, $x = \varphi(y)$, where f and φ are inverse functions, then

$$f'(x) = \frac{1}{\varphi'(y)}, \quad \text{where } y = f(x)$$

7—2081

3.16 PARAMETRIC REPRESENTATION OF A FUNCTION

Given two equations:

$$\begin{cases} x = \varphi(t) \\ y = \psi(t) \end{cases} \tag{1}$$

where t assumes values that lie in the interval $[T_1, T_2]$. To each value of t there correspond values of x and y (the functions φ and ψ are assumed to be single-valued). If one regards the values of x and y as coordinates of a point in a coordinate xy-plane, then to each value of t there will correspond a definite point in the plane. And when t varies from T_1 to T_2, this point will de-

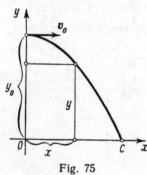

Fig. 75

scribe a certain curve. Equations (1) are called *parametric equations* of this curve, t is the *parameter*, and *parametric* is the way the curve is represented by equations (1).

Let us further assume that the function $x = \varphi(t)$ has an inverse, $t = \Phi(x)$. Then, obviously, y is a function of x;

$$y = \psi[\Phi(x)] \tag{2}$$

Thus, equations (1) define y as a function of x, and we say that the function y of x is represented parametrically.

The explicit expression of the dependence of y on x, $y = f(x)$, is obtained by eliminating the parameter t from equations (1).

Parametric representation of curves is widely used in mechanics. If in the xy-plane there is a certain material point in motion and if we know the laws of motion of the projections of this point on the coordinate axes, then

$$\begin{cases} x = \varphi(t) \\ y = \psi(t) \end{cases} \tag{1'}$$

where the parameter t is the time. Then equations (1') are parametric equations of the trajectory of the moving point. Eliminating from these equations the parameter t, we get the equation of the trajectory in the form $y = f(x)$ or $F(x, y) = 0$. By way of illustration, let us take the following problem.

Problem. Determine the trajectory and point of impact of a load dropped from an airplane moving horizontally with a velocity v_0 at an altitude y_0 (air resistance is disregarded).

Solution. Taking a coordinate system as shown in Fig. 75, we assume that the airplane drops the load at the instant it cuts the y-axis. It is obvious that the horizontal translation of the load will be uniform and with constant velocity v_0:

$$x = v_0 t$$

Vertical displacement of the falling load due to the force of gravity will be expressed by the formula

$$s = \frac{gt^2}{2}$$

Hence the distance of the load from the ground at any instant will be

$$y = y_0 - \frac{gt^2}{2}$$

The two equations

$$x = v_0 t$$
$$y = y_0 - \frac{gt^2}{2}$$

are the parametric equations of the trajectory. To eliminate the parameter t, we find the value $t = \frac{x}{v_0}$ from the first equation and substitute it into the second equation. Then we get the equation of the trajectory in the form

$$y = y_0 - \frac{g}{2v_0^2} x^2$$

This is the equation of a parabola with vertex at the point $M(0, y_0)$, the y-axis serving as the axis of symmetry of the parabola.

We determine the length of OC. Denote the abscissa of C by X, and note that the ordinate of this point is $y = 0$. Putting these values into the preceding formula, we get

$$0 = y_0 - \frac{g}{2v_0^2} X^2$$

whence

$$X = v_0 \sqrt{\frac{2y_0}{g}}$$

3.17 THE EQUATIONS OF SOME CURVES IN PARAMETRIC FORM

Circle. Given a circle with centre at the coordinate origin and with radius r (Fig. 76).

Denote by t the angle formed by the x-axis and the radius to some point $M(x, y)$ of the circle. Then the coordinates of any point on the circle will be expressed in terms of the parameter t as follows:

$$\left. \begin{array}{l} x = r \cos t, \\ y = r \sin t, \end{array} \right\} \quad 0 \leqslant t \leqslant 2\pi$$

These are the parametric equations of the circle. If we eliminate the parameter t from these equations, we will have an equation of the circle containing only x and y. Squaring the parametric equations and adding, we get

$$x^2 + y^2 = r^2 (\cos^2 t + \sin^2 t)$$

or

$$x^2 + y^2 = r^2$$

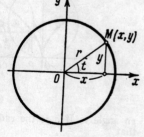

Fig. 76

Ellipse. Given the equation of the ellipse

$$\frac{x^2}{a^2}+\frac{y^2}{b^2}=1 \qquad (1)$$

Set

$$x=a\cos t \qquad (2')$$

Putting this expression into equation (1) and performing the necessary manipulations, we get

$$y=b\sin t \qquad (2'')$$

The equations

$$\left.\begin{array}{l} x=a\cos t, \\ y=b\sin t, \end{array}\right\} 0\leqslant t\leqslant 2\pi \qquad (2)$$

are the parametric equations of the ellipse.

Let us find out the geometrical meaning of the parameter t. Draw two circles with centres at the coordinate origin and with radii a and b (Fig. 77).

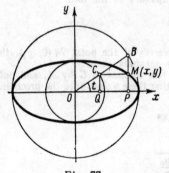

Let the point M (x, y) lie on the ellipse, and let B be a point of the large circle with the same abscissas as M. Denote by t the angle formed by the radius OB with the x-axis. From the figure it follows directly that

$$x=OP=a\cos t \qquad (2')$$
$$CQ=b\sin t$$

From (2″) we conclude that $CQ=y$; in other words, the straight line CM is parallel to the x-axis.

Consequently, in equations (2) t is an angle formed by the radius OB and the axis of abscissas. The angle t is sometimes called an *eccentric angle*.

Cycloid. The *cycloid* is a curve described by a point lying on the circumference of a circle if the circle rolls upon a straight line without sliding (Fig. 78). Suppose that when motion began the point M of the rolling circle lay at the origin. Let us determine the coordinates of M after the circle has turned through

Fig. 77

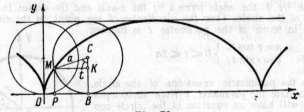

Fig. 78

an angle t. If a is the radius of the rolling circle, it will be seen from Fig. 78 that

$$x=OP=OB-PB$$

but since the circle rolls without sliding, we have

$$OB = \widehat{MB} = at, \quad PB = MK = a \sin t$$

Hence, $x = at - a \sin t = a(t - \sin t)$.

Further,

$$y = MP = KB = CB - CK = a - a \cos t = a(1 - \cos t)$$

The equations

$$\left. \begin{array}{l} x = a(t - \sin t) \\ y = a(1 - \cos t) \end{array} \right\} \quad 0 \leqslant t \leqslant 2\pi \tag{3}$$

are the parametric equations of the cycloid. As t varies between 0 and 2π, the point M will describe one arch of the cycloid.

Eliminating the parameter t from the latter equations, we get x as a function of y directly. In the interval $0 \leqslant t \leqslant \pi$, the function $y = a(1 - \cos t)$ has an inverse:

$$t = \arccos \frac{a - y}{a}$$

Substituting the expression for t into the first of equations (3), we get

$$x = a \arccos \frac{a - y}{a} - a \sin \left(\arccos \frac{a - y}{a} \right)$$

or

$$x = a \arccos \frac{a - y}{a} - \sqrt{2ay - y^2} \quad \text{when } 0 \leqslant x \leqslant \pi a$$

Examining the figure we note that when $\pi a \leqslant x \leqslant 2\pi a$

$$x = 2\pi a - \left(a \arccos \frac{a - y}{a} - \sqrt{2ay - y^2} \right)$$

It will be noted that the function

$$x = a(t - \sin t)$$

has an inverse, but it is not expressible in terms of elementary functions. And so the function $y = f(x)$ is not expressible in terms of elementary functions either.

Note 1. The cycloid clearly shows that in certain cases it is more convenient to use the parametric equations for studying functions and curves than the direct relationship of y and x (y as a function of x or x as a function of y).

Astroid. The *astroid* is a curve represented by the following parametric equations:

$$\left. \begin{array}{l} x = a \cos^3 t \\ y = a \sin^3 t \end{array} \right\} \quad 0 \leqslant t \leqslant 2\pi \tag{4}$$

Raising the terms of both equations to the power 2/3 and adding, we get the following relationship between x and y:

$$x^{\frac{2}{3}} + y^{\frac{2}{3}} = a^{\frac{2}{3}} (\cos^2 t + \sin^2 t)$$

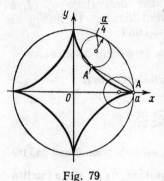

Fig. 79

or

$$x^{\frac{2}{3}} + y^{\frac{2}{3}} = a^{\frac{2}{3}} \qquad (5)$$

Later on (Sec. 5.12) it will be shown that this curve is of the form shown in Fig. 79. It can be obtained as the trajectory of a certain point on the circumference of a circle of radius $a/4$ rolling (without sliding) upon another circle of radius a (the smaller circle always remains inside the larger one, see Fig. 79).

Note 2. It will be noted that equations (4) and equation (5) define more than one function $y = f(x)$. They define two continuous functions on the interval $-a \leqslant x \leqslant +a$. One takes on nonnegative values, the other nonpositive values.

3.18 THE DERIVATIVE OF A FUNCTION REPRESENTED PARAMETRICALLY

Let a function y of x be represented by the parametric equations

$$\left. \begin{array}{l} x = \varphi(t) \\ y = \psi(t) \end{array} \right\} \ t_0 \leqslant t \leqslant T \qquad (1)$$

Let us assume that these functions have derivatives and that the function $x = \varphi(t)$ has an inverse, $t = \Phi(x)$, which also has a derivative. Then the function $y = f(x)$ defined by the parametric equations may be regarded as a composite function:

$$y = \psi(t), \quad t = \Phi(x)$$

t being the intermediate argument.

By the rule for differentiating a composite function we get

$$y'_x = y'_t t'_x = \psi'_t(t) \Phi'_x(x) \qquad (2)$$

From the theorem for the differentiation of an inverse function, it follows that

$$\Phi'_x(x) = \frac{1}{\varphi'_t(t)}$$

Putting this expression into (2), we have

$$y'_x = \frac{\psi'(t)}{\varphi'(t)}$$

or

$$y'_x = \frac{y'_t}{x'_t} \qquad (XXI)$$

The derived formula permits finding the derivative y'_x of a function represented parametrically without having to find y as a function of x.

Example 1. The function y of x is given by the parametric equations

$$\left. \begin{array}{l} x = a \cos t \\ y = a \sin t \end{array} \right\} \quad (0 \leqslant t \leqslant \pi)$$

Find the derivative $\dfrac{dy}{dx}$: (1) for any value of t; (2) for $t = \dfrac{\pi}{4}$.

Solution.

(1) $\quad y'_x = \dfrac{(a \sin t)'}{(a \cos t)'} = \dfrac{a \cos t}{-a \sin t} = -\cot t;$

(2) $\quad (y'_x)_{t=\frac{\pi}{4}} = -\cot \dfrac{\pi}{4} = -1.$

Example 2. Find the slope of the tangent to the cycloid

$$x = a \, (t - \sin t)$$
$$y = a \, (1 - \cos t)$$

at an arbitrary point $(0 \leqslant t \leqslant 2\pi)$.

Solution. The slope of the tangent at each point is equal to the value of the derivative y'_x at that point; i. e., it is

$$y'_x = \frac{y'_t}{x'_t}$$

But

$$x'_t = a \, (1 - \cos t), \quad y'_t = a \sin t$$

Consequently,

$$y'_x = \frac{a \sin t}{a \, (1 - \cos t)} = \frac{2 \sin \dfrac{t}{2} \cos \dfrac{t}{2}}{2 \sin^2 \dfrac{t}{2}} = \cot \frac{t}{2} = \tan \left(\frac{\pi}{2} - \frac{t}{2} \right)$$

Hence, the slope of the tangent to a cycloid at every point is equal to $\tan \left(\dfrac{\pi}{2} - \dfrac{t}{2} \right)$, where t is the value of the parameter corresponding to this point. But this means that the angle α of inclination of the tangent to the x-axis is equal to $\dfrac{\pi}{2} - \dfrac{t}{2}$ (for values of t lying between $-\pi$ and π) *.

---

* Indeed, the slope is equal to the tangent of the angle of inclination α of the tangent to the x-axis. And so $\tan \alpha = \tan \left(\dfrac{\pi}{2} - \dfrac{t}{2} \right)$ and $\alpha = \dfrac{\pi}{2} - \dfrac{t}{2}$ for those values of t for which $\dfrac{\pi}{2} - \dfrac{t}{2}$ lies between 0 and π.

3.19 HYPERBOLIC FUNCTIONS

In many applications of mathematical analysis we encounter combinations of exponential functions of the form $\frac{1}{2}(e^x - e^{-x})$ and $\frac{1}{2}(e^x + e^{-x})$. These combinations are regarded as new functions and are designated as follows:

$$\left.\begin{aligned} \sinh x &= \frac{e^x - e^{-x}}{2} \\ \cosh x &= \frac{e^x + e^{-x}}{2} \end{aligned}\right\} \tag{1}$$

The first of these functions is called the *hyperbolic sine*, the second, the *hyperbolic cosine*. These functions may be used to define two more functions: $\tanh x = \frac{\sinh x}{\cosh x}$ and $\coth x = \frac{\cosh x}{\sinh x}$:

$$\left.\begin{aligned} \tanh x &= \frac{e^x - e^{-x}}{e^x + e^{-x}}, \text{ the hyperbolic tangent,} \\ \coth x &= \frac{e^x + e^{-x}}{e^x - e^{-x}}, \text{ the hyperbolic cotangent} \end{aligned}\right\} \tag{1'}$$

The functions $\sinh x$, $\cosh x$, $\tanh x$ are obviously defined for all values of x. But the function $\coth x$ is defined everywhere, except at the point $x = 0$. The graphs of the hyperbolic functions are given in Figs. 80, 81, 82.

From the definitions of the functions $\sinh x$ and $\cosh x$ [formulas (1)] there follow relationships similar to those between the appropriate trigonometric functions:

$$\cosh^2 x - \sinh^2 x = 1 \tag{2}$$
$$\cosh(a+b) = \cosh a \cosh b + \sinh a \sinh b \tag{3}$$
$$\sinh(a+b) = \sinh a \cosh b + \cosh a \sinh b \tag{3'}$$

Indeed,

$$\cosh^2 x - \sinh^2 x = \left(\frac{e^x + e^{-x}}{2}\right)^2 - \left(\frac{e^x - e^{-x}}{2}\right)^2$$
$$= \frac{e^{2x} + 2 + e^{-2x} - e^{2x} + 2 - e^{-2x}}{4} = 1$$

Further, noting that

$$\cosh(a+b) = \frac{e^{a+b} + e^{-a-b}}{2}$$

we get

$$\cosh a \cosh b + \sinh a \sinh b = \frac{e^a + e^{-a}}{2} \frac{e^b + e^{-b}}{2} + \frac{e^a - e^{-a}}{2} \frac{e^b - e^{-b}}{2}$$

$$= \frac{e^{a+b} + e^{-a+b} + e^{a-b} + e^{-a-b} + e^{a+b} - e^{-a+b} - e^{a-b} + e^{-a-b}}{4}$$

$$= \frac{e^{a+b} + e^{-a-b}}{2} = \cosh (a+b)$$

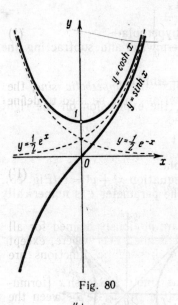

Fig. 80

The proof is similar for relation (3').

The name "hyperbolic functions" comes from the fact that the functions sinh t and cosh t play the same role in the parametric representation of the hyperbola.

$$x^2 - y^2 = 1$$

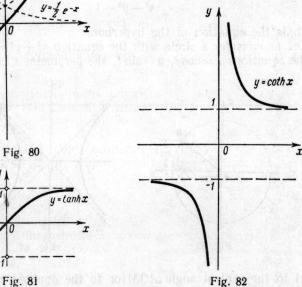

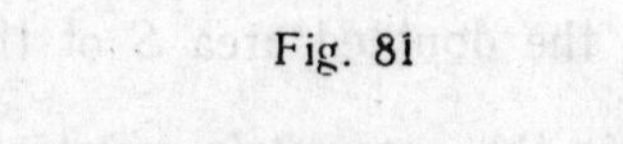

Fig. 81

Fig. 82

as the trigonometric functions sin t and cos t do in the parametric representation of the circle

$$x^2 + y^2 = 1$$

Indeed, eliminating the parameter t from the equations

$$x = \cos t, \quad y = \sin t$$

we get

$$x^2 + y^2 = \cos^2 t + \sin^2 t$$

or

$$x^2 + y^2 = 1 \text{ (the equation of the circle)}$$

Similarly, the equations

$$x = \cosh t$$
$$y = \sinh t$$

are the parametric equations of the hyperbola.

Indeed, squaring these equations termwise and subtracting the second from the first, we get

$$x^2 - y^2 = \cosh^2 t - \sinh^2 t$$

Since, on the basis of formula (2), the expression on the right is equal to unity, we have

$$x^2 - y^2 = 1$$

which is the equation of the hyperbola.

Let us consider a circle with the equation $x^2 + y^2 = 1$ (Fig. 83). In the equations $x = \cos t$, $y = \sin t$, the parameter t is numerically

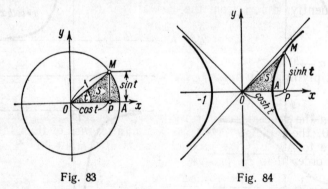

Fig. 83   Fig. 84

equal to the central angle AOM or to the doubled area S of the sector AOM, since $t = 2S$.

Let it be noted, without proof, that in the parametric equations of the hyperbola,

$$x = \cosh t$$
$$y = \sinh t$$

the parameter t is also numerically equal to twice the area of the "hyperbolic sector" AOM (Fig. 84).

The derivatives of the hyperbolic functions are defined by the formulas

$$(\sinh x)' = \cosh x, \quad (\tanh x)' = \frac{1}{\cosh^2 x},$$

$$(\cosh x)' = \sinh x, \quad (\coth x)' = -\frac{1}{\sinh^2 x}$$

(XXII)

which follow from the very definition of hyperbolic functions; for instance, for the function $\sinh x = \frac{e^x - e^{-x}}{2}$ we have

$$(\sinh x)' = \left(\frac{e^x - e^{-x}}{2}\right)' = \frac{e^x + e^{-x}}{2} = \cosh x$$

3.20 THE DIFFERENTIAL

Let a function $y = f(x)$ be differentiable on an interval $[a, b]$. The derivative of this function at some point x of $[a, b]$ is determined by the equation

$$\lim_{\Delta x \to 0} \frac{\Delta y}{\Delta x} = f'(x)$$

As $\Delta x \to 0$, the ratio $\frac{\Delta y}{\Delta x}$ approaches a definite number $f'(x)$ and, consequently, differs from the derivative $f'(x)$ by an infinitesimal:

$$\frac{\Delta y}{\Delta x} = f'(x) + \alpha$$

where $\alpha \to 0$ as $\Delta x \to 0$.

Multiplying all terms by Δx, we get

$$\Delta y = f'(x)\,\Delta x + \alpha \Delta x \tag{1}$$

Since in the general case $f'(x) \neq 0$, for a constant x and a variable $\Delta x \to 0$, the product $f'(x)\,\Delta x$ is an infinitesimal of the first order relative to Δx. But the product $\alpha \Delta x$ is always an infinitesimal of higher order than Δx because

$$\lim_{\Delta x \to 0} \frac{\alpha \Delta x}{\Delta x} = \lim_{\Delta x \to 0} \alpha = 0$$

Thus, the increment Δy of the function consists of two terms, of which the first is [when $f'(x) \neq 0$] the so-called **principal part** of the increment, and is **linear** in Δx. The product $f'(x)\,\Delta x$ is called the **differential** of the function and is denoted by dy or $df(x)$.

And so if a function $y = f(x)$ has a derivative $f'(x)$ at the point x, the product of the derivative $f'(x)$ by the increment Δx in the argument is called the *differential* of the function and is denoted by the symbol dy:

$$dy = f'(x)\,\Delta x \tag{2}$$

Find the differential of the function $y = x$; here,

$$y' = (x)' = 1$$

and, consequently, $dy = dx = \Delta x$ or $dx = \Delta x$. Thus, **the differential dx of the independent variable x coincides with its increment Δx.** The equation $dx = \Delta x$ might be regarded likewise as a definition of the differential of the independent variable, and then the foregoing example would indicate that this does not contradict the definition of the differential of the function. In any case, we can write formula (2) as

$$dy = f'(x)\,dx$$

But from this relationship it follows that

$$f'(x) = \frac{dy}{dx}$$

Hence, **the derivative $f'(x)$ may be regarded as the ratio of the differential of the function to the differential of the independent variable.**

Let us return to expression (1), which, taking (2) into account, may be rewritten thus:

$$\Delta y = dy + \alpha \Delta x \qquad (3)$$

Thus, the increment of a function differs from the differential of a function by an infinitesimal of higher order than Δx. If $f'(x) \neq 0$, then $\alpha \Delta x$ is an infinitesimal of higher order than dy and

$$\lim_{\Delta x \to 0} \frac{\Delta y}{dy} = 1 + \lim_{\Delta x \to 0} \frac{\alpha \Delta x}{f'(x)\,\Delta x} = 1 + \lim_{\Delta x \to 0} \frac{\alpha}{f'(x)} = 1$$

For this reason, in approximate calculations one sometimes uses the approximate equation

$$\Delta y \approx dy \qquad (4)$$

or, in expanded form,

$$f(x + \Delta x) - f(x) \approx f'(x)\,\Delta x \qquad (5)$$

thus reducing the amount of computation.

Example 1. Find the differential dy and the increment Δy of the function $y = x^2$:
  (1) for arbitrary values of x and Δx,
  (2) for $x = 20$, $\Delta x = 0.1$.
  Solution. (1) $\Delta y = (x + \Delta x)^2 - x^2 = 2x\Delta x + \Delta x^2$,

$$dy = (x^2)'\,\Delta x = 2x\Delta x.$$

  (2) If $x = 20$, $\Delta x = 0.1$, then $\Delta y = 2 \cdot 20 \cdot 0.1 + (0.1)^2 = 4.01$,

$$dy = 2 \cdot 20 \cdot 0.1 = 4.00.$$

Replacing Δy by dy yields an error of 0.01. In many cases, it may be considered small compared with $\Delta y = 4.01$ and therefore disregarded.

Fig. 85 gives a clear picture of the above problem.

In approximate calculations, one also makes use of the following equation, which is obtained from (5):

$$f(x + \Delta x) \approx f(x) + f'(x)\, \Delta x \qquad (6)$$

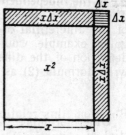

Fig. 85

Example 2. Let $f(x) = \sin x$, then $f'(x) = \cos x$. In this case the approximate equation (6) takes the form

$$\sin(x + \Delta x) \approx \sin x + \cos x\, \Delta x \qquad (7)$$

Let us calculate the approximate value of $\sin 46^\circ$. Put $x = 45^\circ = \dfrac{\pi}{4}$, $\Delta x = 1^\circ = \dfrac{\pi}{180}$, $x + \Delta x = \dfrac{\pi}{4} + \dfrac{\pi}{180}$. Substituting into (7) we get

$$\sin 46^\circ = \sin\left(\frac{\pi}{4} + \frac{\pi}{180}\right) \approx \sin\frac{\pi}{4} + \cos\frac{\pi}{4}\,\frac{\pi}{180}$$

or

$$\sin 46^\circ \approx \frac{\sqrt{2}}{2} + \frac{\sqrt{2}}{2}\,\frac{\pi}{180} = 0.7071 + 0.7071 \cdot 0.0175 = 0.7191$$

Example 3. If in (7) we put $x = 0$, $\Delta x = \alpha$, we get the following approximate equation:

$$\sin \alpha \approx \alpha$$

Example 4. If $f(x) = \tan x$, then by (6) we get the following approximate equation:

$$\tan(x + \Delta x) \approx \tan x + \frac{1}{\cos^2 x}\,\Delta x$$

for $x = 0$, $\Delta x = \alpha$, we get

$$\tan \alpha \approx \alpha$$

Example 5. If $f(x) = \sqrt{x}$, then (6) yields

$$\sqrt{x + \Delta x} \approx \sqrt{x} + \frac{1}{2\sqrt{x}}\,\Delta x$$

Putting $x = 1$, $\Delta x = \alpha$, we get the approximate equation

$$\sqrt{1 + \alpha} \approx 1 + \frac{1}{2}\,\alpha$$

The problem of finding the differential of a function is equivalent to that of finding the derivative, since, by multiplying the latter into the differential of the argument we get the differential of the function. Consequently, most theorems and formulas pertaining to derivatives are also valid for differentials. Let us illustrate this.

The differential of the sum of two differentiable functions u and v is equal to the sum of the differentials of these functions:

$$d(u + v) = du + dv$$

The differential of the product of two differentiable functions u and v is determined by the formula

$$d(uv) = u\,dv + v\,du$$

By way of illustration, let us prove the latter formula. If $y = uv$, then

$$dy = y'\,dx = (uv' + vu')\,dx = uv'\,dx + vu'\,dx$$

but

$$v'\,dx = dv, \quad u'\,dx = du$$

therefore

$$dy = u\,dv + v\,du$$

Other formulas (for instance, the formula defining the differential of a quotient) are proved in similar fashion:

$$\text{if} \quad y = \frac{u}{v}, \quad \text{then} \quad dy = \frac{v\,du - u\,dv}{v^2}$$

Let us solve some examples in calculating the differential of a function.

Example 6. $y = \tan^2 x$, $dy = 2\tan x \dfrac{1}{\cos^2 x}\,dx$.

Example 7. $y = \sqrt{1 + \ln x}$, $dy = \dfrac{1}{2\sqrt{1 + \ln x}} \cdot \dfrac{1}{x}\,dx$.

We find the expression for the differential of a composite function. Let

$$y = f(u), \quad u = \varphi(x), \quad \text{or} \quad y = f[\varphi(x)]$$

Then by the rule for differentiating a composite function,

$$\frac{dy}{dx} = f'_u(u)\,\varphi'(x)$$

Hence,

$$dy = f'_u(u)\,\varphi'(x)\,dx$$

but $\varphi'(x)\,dx = du$, therefore

$$dy = f'(u)\,du$$

Thus, *the differential of a composite function has the same form as it would have if the intermediate argument were the independent variable.* In other words, *the form of the differential does not depend on whether the argument of the function is an independent variable or the function of another argument.* This important property of a differential, called *the preservation of the form of the differential,* will be widely used later on.

Example 8. Given a function $y = \sin \sqrt{x}$. Find dy.
Solution. Representing the given function as a composite one:

$$y = \sin u, \quad u = \sqrt{x}$$

we find

$$dy = \cos u \, \frac{1}{2\sqrt{x}} \, dx$$

but $\dfrac{1}{2\sqrt{x}} \, dx = du$, so we can write

$$dy = \cos u \, du$$

or

$$dy = \cos(\sqrt{x}) \, d(\sqrt{x}).$$

3.21 THE GEOMETRIC MEANING OF THE DIFFERENTIAL

Let us consider the function

$$y = f(x)$$

and the curve it represents (Fig. 86).

On the curve $y = f(x)$, take an arbitrary point $M(x, y)$, draw a line tangent to the curve at this point and denote by α the angle* which the tangent line forms with the positive x-axis. Increase the independent variable by Δx; then the function will change by $\Delta y = NM_1$. To the values $x + \Delta x$, $y + \Delta y$ on the curve $y = f(x)$ there will correspond the point $M_1(x + \Delta x, y + \Delta y)$.

From the triangle MNT we find

$$NT = MN \tan \alpha$$

Since

$$\tan \alpha = f'(x), \quad MN = \Delta x$$

we get

$$NT = f'(x) \, \Delta x$$

But by the definition of a differential $f'(x) \, \Delta x = dy$. Thus,

$$NT = dy$$

The equation signifies that *the differential of a function $f(x)$, which corresponds to the given values x and Δx, is equal to the increment in the ordinate of the line tangent to the curve $y = f(x)$ at the given point x.*

---

* Assuming that the function $f(x)$ has a finite derivative at the point x, we get $\alpha \neq \dfrac{\pi}{2}$.

From Fig. 86 it follows directly that

$$M_1T = \Delta y - dy$$

By what has already been proved, $\dfrac{M_1T}{NT} \to 0$ as $\Delta x \to 0$.

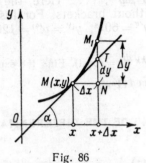

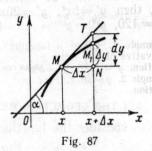

Fig. 86   Fig. 87

One should not think that the increment Δy is always greater than dy. For instance, in Fig. 87,

$$\Delta y = M_1N, \quad dy = NT, \quad \text{and} \quad \Delta y < dy.$$

3.22 DERIVATIVES OF DIFFERENT ORDERS

Let a function $y = f(x)$ be differentiable on some interval $[a, b]$. Generally speaking, the values of the derivative $f'(x)$ depend on x, which is to say that **the derivative $f'(x)$ is also a function of x.** Differentiating this function, we obtain the so-called second derivative of the function $f(x)$.

The derivative of a first derivative is called a *derivative of the second order* or the *second derivative* of the original function and is denoted by the symbol y'' or $f''(x)$:

$$y'' = (y')' = f''(x)$$

For example, if $y = x^5$, then

$$y' = 5x^4, \quad y'' = (5x^4)' = 20x^3$$

The derivative of the second derivative is called a *derivative of the third order* or the *third derivative* and is denoted by y''' or $f'''(x)$.

Generally, a *derivative of the nth order* of a function $f(x)$ is called the derivative (first-order) of the derivative of the $(n-1)$th order and is denoted by the symbol $y^{(n)}$ or $f^{(n)}(x)$:

$$y^{(n)} = (y^{(n-1)})' = f^{(n)}(x)$$

(The order of the derivative is taken in parentheses so as to avoid confusion with the exponent of a power.)

Derivatives of the fourth, fifth, and higher orders are also denoted by Roman numerals: y^{IV}, y^V, y^{VI}, ... Here, the order of the derivative may be written without brackets. For instance, if $y = x^5$, then $y' = 5x^4$, $y'' = 20x^3$, $y''' = 60x^2$, $y^{IV} = y^{(4)} = 120x$, $y^V = y^{(5)} = 120$, $y^{(6)} = y^{(7)} = \ldots = 0$.

Example 1. Given a function $y = e^{kx}$ ($k = $ const). Find the expression of its derivative of any order n.

Solution. $y' = ke^{kx}$, $y'' = k^2 e^{kx}$, ..., $y^{(n)} = k^n e^{kx}$.

Example 2. $y = \sin x$. Find $y^{(n)}$.

Solution.

$$y' = \cos x = \sin\left(x + \frac{\pi}{2}\right)$$

$$y'' = -\sin x = \sin\left(x + 2\frac{\pi}{2}\right)$$

$$y''' = -\cos x = \sin\left(x + 3\frac{\pi}{2}\right)$$

$$y^{IV} = \sin x = \sin\left(x + 4\frac{\pi}{2}\right)$$

$$\cdots\cdots\cdots\cdots\cdots\cdots$$

$$y^{(n)} = \sin\left(x + n\frac{\pi}{2}\right)$$

In similar fashion we can also derive the formulas for the derivatives of any order of certain other elementary functions. The reader himself can find the formulas for derivatives of the nth order of the functions $y = x^k$, $y = \cos x$, $y = \ln x$.

The rules given in theorems 2 and 3, Sec. 3.7, are readily generalized to the case of derivatives of any order.

In this case we have obvious formulas:

$$(u + v)^{(n)} = u^{(n)} + v^{(n)}, \quad (Cu)^{(n)} + Cu^{(n)}$$

Let us derive a formula (called the *Leibniz rule*, or *Leibniz formula*) that will enable us to calculate the nth derivative of the product of two functions $u(x)$ $v(x)$. To obtain this formula, let us first find several derivatives and then establish the general rule for finding the derivative of any order:

$$y = uv$$
$$y' = u'v + uv'$$
$$y'' = u''v + u'v' + u'v' + uv'' = u''v + 2u'v' + uv''$$
$$y''' = u'''v - u''v' + 2u''v' + 2u'v'' + u'v'' + uv'''$$
$$= u'''v + 3u''v' + 3u'v'' + uv'''$$
$$y^{IV} = u^{IV}v + 4u'''v' + 6u''v'' + 4u'v''' + uv^{IV}$$

The rule for forming derivatives holds for the derivative of any order and obviously consists in the following.

The expression $(u+v)^n$ is expanded by the binomial theorem, and in the expansion obtained the exponents of the powers of u and v are replaced by indices that are the orders of the derivatives, and the zero powers $(u^0 = v^0 = 1)$ in the end terms of the expansion are replaced by the functions themselves (that is, "derivatives of zero order"):

$$y^{(n)} = (uv)^{(n)} = u^{(n)}v + nu^{(n-1)}v' + \frac{n(n-1)}{1 \cdot 2} u^{(n-2)}v'' + \ldots + uv^{(n)}$$

This is the *Leibniz rule.*

A rigorous proof of this formula may be carried out by the method of complete mathematical induction (in other words, to prove that if this formula holds for the nth order it will hold for the order $n+1$).

Example 3. $y = e^{ax}x^2$. Find the derivative $y^{(n)}$.
Solution.

$$u = e^{ax}, \qquad v = x^2$$
$$u' = ae^{ax}, \qquad v' = 2x$$
$$u'' = a^2 e^{ax}, \qquad v'' = 2$$
$$\cdots \cdots \cdots \qquad \cdots \cdots$$
$$u^{(n)} = a^n e^{ax}, \qquad v''' = v^{IV} = \ldots = 0$$
$$y^{(n)} = a^n e^{ax} x^2 + n a^{n-1} e^{ax} \cdot 2x + \frac{n(n-1)}{1 \cdot 2} a^{n-2} e^{ax} \cdot 2$$

or

$$y^{(n)} = e^{ax} [a^n x^2 + 2n a^{n-1} x + n(n-1) a^{n-2}]$$

3.23 DIFFERENTIALS OF DIFFERENT ORDERS

Suppose we have a function $y = f(x)$, where x is the independent variable. The differential of this function

$$dy = f'(x) dx$$

is some function of x, but only the first factor, $f'(x)$, can depend on x; the second factor, dx, is an increment of the independent variable x and is independent of the value of this variable. Since dy is a function of x we have the right to speak of the differential of this function.

The differential of the differential of a function is called the *second differential* or the *second-order differential* of the function and is denoted by $d^2 y$:

$$d(dy) = d^2 y$$

Let us find the expression for the second differential. By virtue of the general definition of a differential we have

$$d^2y = [f'(x)\,dx]'\,dx$$

Since dx is independent of x, dx is taken outside the sign of the derivative upon differentiation, and we get

$$d^2y = f''(x)\,(dx)^2$$

When writing the degree of a differential it is common to drop the brackets; in place of $(dx)^2$ we write dx^2 to mean the square of the expression dx; in place of $(dx)^3$ we write dx^3, etc.

The *third differential* or the *third-order differential* of a function is the differential of its second differential:

$$d^3y = d\,(d^2y) = [f''(x)\,dx^2]'\,dx = f'''(x)\,dx^3$$

Generally, the *nth differential* is the first differential of a differential of the $(n-1)$th order:

$$d^ny = d\,(d^{n-1}y) = [f^{(n-1)}(x)\,dx^{n-1}]'\,dx$$
$$d^ny = f^{(n)}(x)\,dx^n \qquad (1)$$

Using differentials of different orders, we can represent the derivative of any order as a ratio of differentials of the appropriate orders:

$$f'(x) = \frac{dy}{dx}, \quad f''(x) = \frac{d^2y}{dx^2}, \quad \ldots, \quad f^{(n)}(x) = \frac{d^ny}{dx^n} \qquad (2)$$

Note. Equations (1) and (2) are true (for $n > 1$) solely in the case where x is an independent variable. Indeed, suppose we have the composite function

$$y = F(u), \quad u = \varphi(x) \qquad (3)$$

We have seen that the first-order differential preserves its form irrespective of whether u is an independent variable or a function of x:

$$dy = F'_u(u)\,du \qquad (4)$$

The second and higher differentials do not have that property. Indeed, by (3) and (4), we get

$$d^2y = d\,(F'_u(u)\,du)$$

But here $du = \varphi'(x)\,dx$ is dependent on x and so we get

$$d^2y = d\,(F'_u(u))\,du + F'_u(u)\,d\,(du)$$

or

$$d^2y = F''_{uu}(u)\,(du)^2 + F'_u(u)\,d^2u, \text{ where } d^2u = \varphi''(x)\,(dx)^2 \qquad (5)$$

In similar fashion, we find d^3y and so on.

Example 1. Find dy and d^2y of the composite function

$$y = \sin u, \quad u = \sqrt{x}$$

Solution.

$$dy = \cos u \cdot \frac{1}{2\sqrt{x}} \quad dx = \cos u \, du$$

'urthermore, by formula (5), we obtain

$$d^2y = -\sin u \,(du)^2 + \cos u \, d^2u = -\sin u \,(du)^2 + \cos u \cdot u'' \,(dx)^2$$

$$= -\sin u \left(\frac{1}{2\sqrt{x}}\right)^2 (dx)^2 + \cos u \left(-\frac{1}{4x^{3/2}}\right)(dx)^2$$

3.24 DERIVATIVES (OF VARIOUS ORDERS)
OF IMPLICIT FUNCTIONS
AND OF FUNCTIONS REPRESENTED PARAMETRICALLY

1. An example will illustrate the finding of derivatives of different orders of *implicit functions*.

Let an implicit function y of x be defined by the equation

$$\frac{x^2}{a^2} + \frac{y^2}{b^2} - 1 = 0 \tag{1}$$

Differentiate all terms of the equation, with respect to x, and remember that y is a function of x:

$$\frac{2x}{a^2} + \frac{2y}{b^2} \frac{dy}{dx} = 0$$

From this we get

$$\frac{dy}{dx} = -\frac{b^2x}{a^2y} \tag{2}$$

Again differentiate with respect to x (having in view that y is a function of x):

$$\frac{d^2y}{dx^2} = -\frac{b^2}{a^2} \cdot \frac{y - x\dfrac{dy}{dx}}{y^2}$$

Substituting, in place of the derivative $\frac{dy}{dx}$, its expression from (2), we get

$$\frac{d^2y}{dx^2} = -\frac{b^2}{a^2} \cdot \frac{y + x \dfrac{b^2}{a^2} \dfrac{x}{y}}{y^2}$$

or, after simplifying.

$$\frac{d^2y}{dx^2} = -\frac{b^2 \,(a^2y^2 + b^2x^2)}{a^4y^3}.$$

From equation (1) it follows that

$$a^2y^2 + b^2x^2 = a^2b^2$$

Therefore the second derivative may be represented as

$$\frac{d^2y}{dx^2} = -\frac{b^4}{a^2y^3}.$$

Differentiating the latter equation with respect to x, we find $\frac{d^3y}{dx^3}$, etc.

2. Let us now consider the problem of finding the derivatives of higher orders **of a function represented parametrically.**

Let the function y of x be represented by parametric equations:

$$\left. \begin{array}{c} x = \varphi(t) \\ y = \psi(t) \end{array} \right\} \quad t_0 \leqslant t \leqslant T \qquad (3)$$

The function $x = \varphi(t)$ has an inverse function $t = \Phi(x)$ on the interval $[t_0, T]$.

In Sec 3.18 it was proved that in this case the derivative $\frac{dy}{dx}$ is defined by the equation

$$\frac{dy}{dx} = \frac{\dfrac{dy}{dt}}{\dfrac{dx}{dt}} \qquad (4)$$

To find the second derivative, $\frac{d^2y}{dx^2}$, differentiate (4) with respect to x, bearing in mind that t is a function of x:

$$\frac{d^2y}{dx^2} = \frac{d}{dx}\left(\frac{\dfrac{dy}{dt}}{\dfrac{dx}{dt}}\right) = \frac{d}{dt}\left(\frac{\dfrac{dy}{dt}}{\dfrac{dx}{dt}}\right)\frac{dt}{dx} \qquad (5)$$

but

$$\frac{d}{dt}\left(\frac{\dfrac{dy}{dt}}{\dfrac{dx}{dt}}\right) = \frac{\dfrac{dx}{dt}\dfrac{d}{dt}\left(\dfrac{dy}{dt}\right) - \dfrac{dy}{dt}\dfrac{d}{dt}\left(\dfrac{dx}{dt}\right)}{\left(\dfrac{dx}{dt}\right)^2} = \frac{\dfrac{dx}{dt}\dfrac{d^2y}{dt^2} - \dfrac{dy}{dt}\dfrac{d^2x}{dt^2}}{\left(\dfrac{dx}{dt}\right)^2}$$

$$\frac{dt}{dx} = \frac{1}{\dfrac{dx}{dt}}$$

Substituting the latter expressions into (5), we get

$$\frac{d^2y}{dx^2} = \frac{\dfrac{dx}{dt}\dfrac{d^2y}{dt^2} - \dfrac{dy}{dt}\dfrac{d^2x}{dt^2}}{\left(\dfrac{dx}{dt}\right)^3}$$

This formula may be written in more compact form as follows:

$$\frac{d^2y}{dx^2} = \frac{\varphi'(t)\,\psi''(t) - \psi'(t)\,\varphi''(t)}{[\varphi'(t)]^3}$$

In similar fashion we can find the derivatives $\frac{d^3y}{dx^3}$, $\frac{d^4y}{dx^4}$ and so forth.

Example. A function y of x is represented parametrically:

$$x = a\cos t, \quad y = b\sin t$$

Find the derivatives $\frac{dy}{dx}$, $\frac{d^2y}{dx^2}$.

Solution.

$$\frac{dx}{dt} = -a\sin t, \quad \frac{d^2x}{dt^2} = -a\cos t$$

$$\frac{dy}{dt} = b\cos t, \quad \frac{d^2y}{dt^2} = -b\sin t$$

$$\frac{dy}{dx} = \frac{b\cos t}{-a\sin t} = -\frac{b}{a}\cot t$$

$$\frac{d^2y}{dx^2} = \frac{(-a\sin t)(-b\sin t) - (b\cos t)(-a\cos t)}{(-a\sin t)^3} = -\frac{b}{a^2}\frac{1}{\sin^3 t}$$

3.25 THE MECHANICAL MEANING OF THE SECOND DERIVATIVE

Let s be the path covered by a body in translation as a function of the time; it is expressed as

$$s = f(t) \qquad (1)$$

As we already know (see Sec. 3.1.), the velocity v of a body at any time is equal to the first derivative of the path with respect to time:

$$v = \frac{ds}{dt} \qquad (2)$$

At some time t, let the velocity of the body be v. If the motion is not uniform, then during an interval of time Δt that has elapsed since t the velocity will change by the increment Δv.

The *average acceleration* during time Δt is the ratio of the increment in velocity Δv to the increment in time:

$$a_{av} = \frac{\Delta v}{\Delta t}$$

Acceleration at a given instant is the limit of the ratio of the increment in velocity to the increment in time as the latter approaches zero:

$$a = \lim_{\Delta t \to 0} \frac{\Delta v}{\Delta t}$$

In other words, acceleration (at a given instant) is equal to the derivative of the velocity with respect to time:

$$a = \frac{dv}{dt}$$

but since $v = \frac{ds}{dt}$, consequently,

$$a = \frac{d}{dt}\left(\frac{ds}{dt}\right) = \frac{d^2s}{dt^2}$$

or *the acceleration of linear motion is equal to the second derivative of the path covered with respect to time.* Reverting to equation (1), we get

$$a = f''(t)$$

Example. Find the velocity v and the acceleration a of a freely falling body, if the dependence of distance s upon time t is given by the formula

$$s = \frac{1}{2} gt^2 + v_0 t + s_0 \qquad (3)$$

where $g = 9.8$ m/sec^2 is the acceleration of gravity and $s_0 = s_{t=0}$ is the value of s at $t = 0$.

Solution. Differentiating, we find

$$v = \frac{ds}{dt} = gt + v_0 \qquad (4)$$

from this formula it follows that $v_0 = (v)_{t=0}$.

Differentiating again, we find

$$a = \frac{dv}{dt} = \frac{d^2s}{dt^2} = g$$

Let it be noted that, conversely, if the acceleration of some motion is constant and equal to g, the velocity will be expressed by equation (4), and the distance by equation (3) provided that $(v)_{t=0} = v_0$ and $(s)_{t=0} = s_0$.

3.26 THE EQUATIONS OF A TANGENT AND OF A NORMAL. THE LENGTHS OF A SUBTANGENT AND A SUBNORMAL

Let us consider a curve whose equation is

$$y = f(x)$$

On this curve take a point $M(x_1, y_1)$ (Fig. 88) and write the equation of the tangent line to the given curve at the point M, assuming that this tangent is not parallel to the axis of ordinates.

The equation of a straight line with slope k passing through the point M is of the form

$$y - y_1 = k(x - x_1)$$

For the tangent line (see Sec. 3.3)

$$k = f'(x_1)$$

and so the **equation of the tangent** is of the form

$$y - y_1 = f'(x_1)(x - x_1)$$

In addition to the tangent to a curve at a given point, one often has to consider the normal.

Definition. The *normal* to a curve at a given point is a straight line passing through the given point perpendicular to the tangent at that point.

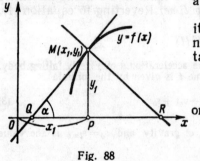

Fig. 88

From the definition of a normal it follows that its slope k_n is connected with the slope k_t of the tangent by the equation

$$k_n = -\frac{1}{k_t}$$

or

$$k_n = -\frac{1}{f'(x_1)}$$

Hence, the **equation of a normal** to a curve $y = f(x)$ at a point $M(x_1, y_1)$ is of the form

$$y - y_1 = -\frac{1}{f'(x_1)}(x - x_1)$$

Example 1. Write the equations of the tangent and the normal to the curve $y = x^3$ at the point $M(1, 1)$.
Solution. Since $y' = 3x^2$, the slope of the tangent is $(y')_{x=1} = 3$.
Therefore, the equation of the tangent is

$$y - 1 = 3(x - 1) \text{ or } y = 3x - 2$$

The equation of the normal is

$$y - 1 = -\frac{1}{3}(x - 1)$$

or

$$y = -\frac{1}{3}x + \frac{4}{3}$$

(see Fig. 89).

The length T of the segment QM (Fig. 88) of the tangent between the point of tangency and the x-axis is called the *length of the tangent*. The projection of this segment on the x-axis, that is,

QP, is called the *subtangent*; the length of the subtangent is denoted by S_T. The length N of the segment MR is called the *length of the normal*, while the projection RP of the segment RM on the x-axis is called the *subnormal*; the length of the subnormal is denoted by S_N.

Let us find the quantities T, S_T, N, S_N for the curve $y = f(x)$ and the point $M(x_1, y_1)$.

From Fig. 88 it will be seen that

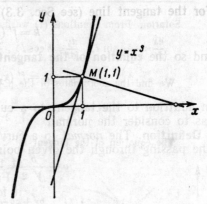

Fig. 89

$$QP = |y_1 \cot \alpha| = \left|\frac{y_1}{\tan \alpha}\right| = \left|\frac{y_1}{y_1'}\right|$$

therefore

$$S_T = \left|\frac{y_1}{y_1'}\right|$$

$$T = \sqrt{y_1^2 + \frac{y_1^2}{y_1'^2}} = \left|\frac{y_1}{y_1'}\sqrt{y_1'^2 + 1}\right|$$

It is further clear from this same figure that

$$PR = |y_1 \tan \alpha| = |y_1 y_1'|$$

and so

$$S_N = |y_1 y_1'|$$

$$N = \sqrt{y_1^2 + (y_1 y_1')^2} = |y_1 \sqrt{1 + y_1'^2}|$$

These formulas are derived on the assumption that $y_1 > 0$, $y_1' > 0$. However, they hold in the general case as well.

Example 2. Find the equations of the tangent and normal, the lengths of the tangent and the subtangent, the lengths of the normal and subnormal for

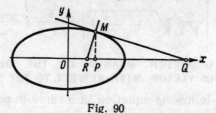

Fig. 90

the ellipse

$$x = a \cos t, \quad y = b \sin t \tag{1}$$

at the point $M(x_1, y_1)$ for which $t = \frac{\pi}{4}$ (Fig. 90).

Solution. From equations (1) we find

$$\frac{dx}{dt} = -a\sin t, \quad \frac{dy}{dt} = b\cos t, \quad \frac{dy}{dx} = -\frac{b}{a}\cot t, \quad \left(\frac{dy}{dx}\right)_{t=\frac{\pi}{4}} = -\frac{b}{a}$$

We find the coordinates of the point of tangency M:

$$x_1 = (x)_{t=\frac{\pi}{4}} = \frac{a}{\sqrt{2}}, \quad y_1 = (y)_{t=\frac{\pi}{4}} = \frac{b}{\sqrt{2}}$$

The equation of the tangent is

$$y - \frac{b}{\sqrt{2}} = -\frac{b}{a}\left(x - \frac{a}{\sqrt{2}}\right)$$

or

$$bx + ay - ab\sqrt{2} = 0$$

The equation of the normal is

$$y - \frac{b}{\sqrt{2}} = \frac{a}{b}\left(x - \frac{a}{\sqrt{2}}\right)$$

or

$$(ax - by)\sqrt{2} - a^2 + b^2 = 0$$

The lengths of the subtangent and subnormal are

$$S_T = \left|\frac{\dfrac{b}{\sqrt{2}}}{-\dfrac{b}{a}}\right| = \frac{a}{\sqrt{2}}$$

$$S_N = \left|\frac{b}{\sqrt{2}}\left(-\frac{b}{a}\right)\right| = \frac{b^2}{a\sqrt{2}}$$

The lengths of the tangent and the normal are

$$T = \left|\frac{\dfrac{b}{\sqrt{2}}}{-\dfrac{b}{a}}\right|\sqrt{\left(-\frac{b}{a}\right)^2 + 1} = \frac{1}{\sqrt{2}}\sqrt{a^2 + b^2}$$

$$N = \left|\frac{b}{\sqrt{2}}\right|\sqrt{1 + \left(-\frac{b}{a}\right)^2} = \frac{b}{a\sqrt{2}}\sqrt{a^2 + b^2}$$

3.27 THE GEOMETRIC MEANING OF THE DERIVATIVE OF THE RADIUS VECTOR WITH RESPECT TO THE POLAR ANGLE

We have the following equation of a curve in polar coordinates:

$$\rho = f(\theta) \tag{1}$$

Let us write the formulas for changing from polar coordinates to rectangular Cartesian coordinates:

$$x = \rho\cos\theta, \quad y = \rho\sin\theta$$

Substituting, in place of ρ, its expression in terms of θ from equation (1), we get

$$x = f(\theta) \cos \theta, \quad y = f(\theta) \sin \theta \tag{2}$$

Equations (2) are parametric equations of the given curve, the parameter being the polar angle θ (Fig. 91).

If we denote by φ the angle formed by the tangent to the curve at some point $M(\rho, \theta)$ with the positive x-axis, we will have

$$\tan \varphi = \frac{dy}{dx} = \frac{\dfrac{dy}{d\theta}}{\dfrac{dx}{d\theta}}$$

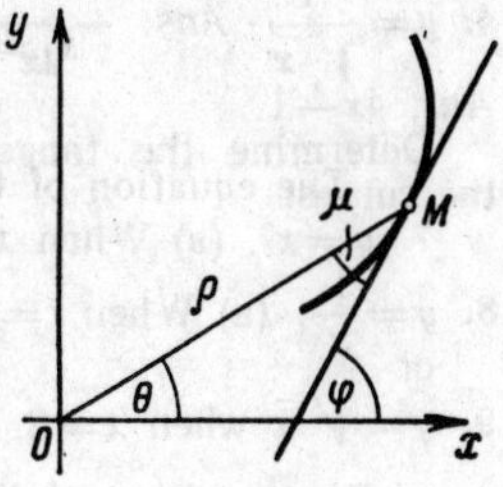

Fig. 91

or

$$\tan \varphi = \frac{\dfrac{d\rho}{d\theta} \sin \theta + \rho \cos \theta}{\dfrac{d\rho}{d\theta} \cos \theta - \rho \sin \theta} \tag{3}$$

Denote by μ the angle between the direction of the radius vector and the tangent. It is obvious that $\mu = \varphi - \theta$,

$$\tan \mu = \frac{\tan \varphi - \tan \theta}{1 + \tan \varphi \tan \theta}$$

Substituting, in place of $\tan \varphi$, its expression (3) and making the necessary changes, we get

$$\tan \mu = \frac{(\rho' \sin \theta + \rho \cos \theta) \cos \theta - (\rho' \cos \theta - \rho \sin \theta) \sin \theta}{(\rho' \cos \theta - \rho \sin \theta) \cos \theta + (\rho' \sin \theta + \rho \cos \theta) \sin \theta} = \frac{\rho}{\rho'}$$

or

$$\rho'_\theta = \rho \cot \mu \tag{4}$$

Thus, the derivative of the radius vector with respect to the polar angle is equal to the length of the radius vector multiplied by the cotangent of the angle between the radius vector and the tangent to the curve at the given point.

Example. Show that the tangent to the logarithmic spiral

$$\rho = e^{a\theta}$$

intersects the radius vector at a constant angle.

Solution. From the equation of the spiral we get

$$\rho' = a e^{a\theta}$$

From formula (4) we have

$$\cot \mu = \frac{\rho'}{\rho} = a, \text{ that is, } \mu = \text{arccot } a = \text{const}$$

Exercises on Chapter 3

Find the derivatives of the following functions using the definition of a derivative:

1. $y = x^2$. *Ans.* $3x^2$.   **2.** $y = \dfrac{1}{x}$. *Ans.* $-\dfrac{1}{x^2}$.   **3.** $y = \sqrt{x}$. *Ans.* $\dfrac{1}{2\sqrt{x}}$.

4. $y = \dfrac{1}{\sqrt{x}}$. *Ans.* $-\dfrac{1}{2x\sqrt{x}}$.   **5.** $y = \sin^2 x$. *Ans.* $2\sin x \cos x$.   **6.** $y = 2x^2 - x$. *Ans.* $4x - 1$.

Determine the tangents of the angles of inclination of the tangent line to the curves:

7. $y = x^3$. (a) When $x = 1$. *Ans.* 3. (b) When $x = -1$. *Ans.* 3. Make a drawing.

8. $y = \dfrac{1}{x}$. (a) When $x = \dfrac{1}{2}$. *Ans.* -4. (b) When $x = 1$. *Ans.* -1. Make a drawing.

9. $y = \sqrt{x}$ when $x = 2$. *Ans.* $\dfrac{1}{2\sqrt{2}}$.

Find the derivatives of the following functions:

10. $y = x^4 + 3x^2 - 6$.   *Ans.* $y' = 4x^3 + 6x$.   **11.** $y = 6x^3 - x^2$.

Ans. $y' = 18x^2 - 2x$.   **12.** $y = \dfrac{x^5}{a+b} - \dfrac{x^2}{a-b} - x$. *Ans.* $y' = \dfrac{5x^4}{a+b} - \dfrac{2x}{a-b} - 1$.

13. $y = \dfrac{x^3 - x^2 + 1}{5}$.   *Ans.* $y' = \dfrac{3x^2 - 2x}{5}$.   **14.** $y = 2ax^3 - \dfrac{x^2}{b} + c$.

Ans. $y' = 6ax^2 - \dfrac{2x}{b}$.   **15.** $y = 6x^{\frac{7}{2}} + 4x^{\frac{5}{2}} + 2x$. *Ans.* $y' = 21x^{\frac{5}{2}} + 10x^{\frac{3}{2}} + 2$.

16. $y = \sqrt{3x} + \sqrt[3]{x} + \dfrac{1}{x}$. *Ans.* $y' = \dfrac{\sqrt{3}}{2\sqrt{x}} + \dfrac{1}{3\sqrt[3]{x^2}} - \dfrac{1}{x^2}$ **17.** $y = \dfrac{(x+1)^3}{x^{\frac{3}{2}}}$.

Ans. $y' = \dfrac{3(x+1)^2(x-1)}{2x^{\frac{5}{2}}}$.   **18.** $y = \dfrac{x}{m} + \dfrac{m}{x} + \dfrac{x^2}{n^2} + \dfrac{n^2}{x^2}$. *Ans.* $y' = \dfrac{1}{m} - \dfrac{m}{x^2} +$

$+ \dfrac{2x}{n^2} - \dfrac{2n^2}{x^3}$.   **19.** $y = \sqrt[3]{x^2} - 2\sqrt{x} + 5$. *Ans.* $y' = \dfrac{2}{3} \dfrac{1}{\sqrt[3]{x}} - \dfrac{1}{\sqrt{x}}$.   **20.** $y =$

$= \dfrac{ax^2}{\sqrt[3]{x}} + \dfrac{b}{x\sqrt{x}} - \dfrac{\sqrt[3]{x}}{\sqrt{x}}$. *Ans.* $y' = \dfrac{5}{3}ax^{\frac{2}{3}} - \dfrac{3}{2}bx^{-\frac{5}{2}} + \dfrac{1}{6}x^{-\frac{7}{6}}$.   **21.** $y =$

$= (1 + 4x^3)(1 + 2x^2)$. *Ans.* $y' = 4x(1 + 3x + 10x^3)$.   **22.** $y = x(2x-1)(3x+2)$. *Ans.* $y' = 2(9x^2 + x - 1)$.   **23.** $y = (2x-1)(x^2 - 6x + 3)$. *Ans.* $y' = 6x^2 - 26x + 12$.

24. $y = \dfrac{2x^4}{b^2 - x^2}$. *Ans.* $y' = \dfrac{4x^3(2b^2 - x^2)}{(b^2 - x^2)^2}$.   **25.** $y = \dfrac{a-x}{a+x}$. *Ans.* $y' = -\dfrac{2a}{(a+x)^2}$.

26. $f(t) = \dfrac{t^3}{1+t^2}$. *Ans.* $f'(t) = \dfrac{t^2(3+t^2)}{(1+t^2)^2}$.   **27.** $f(s) = \dfrac{(s+4)^2}{s+3}$. *Ans.* $f'(s) =$

$= \dfrac{(s+2)(s+4)}{(s+3)^2}$.   **28.** $y = \dfrac{x^3 + 2}{x^2 - x - 2}$. *Ans.* $y' = \dfrac{x^4 - 2x^3 - 6x^2 - 4x + 2}{(x^2 - x - 2)^2}$.

29. $y = \dfrac{x^p}{x^m - a^m}$. *Ans.* $y' = \dfrac{x^{p-1}[(p-m)x^m - pa^m]}{(x^m - a^m)^2}$.   **30.** $y = (2x^2 - 3)^2$. *Ans.*

$y' = 8x(2x^2 - 3)$.   **31.** $y = (x^2 + a^2)^5$. *Ans.* $y = 10x(x^2 + a^2)^4$.   **32.** $y = \sqrt{x^2 + a^2}$.

Ans. $y' = \dfrac{x}{\sqrt{x^2+a^2}}$. **33.** $y=(a+x)\sqrt{a-x}$. Ans. $y'=\dfrac{a-3x}{2\sqrt{a-x}}$. **34.** $y=$

$= \sqrt{\dfrac{1+x}{1-x}}$. Ans. $y'=\dfrac{1}{(1-x)\sqrt{1-x^2}}$. **35.** $y=\dfrac{2x^2-1}{x\sqrt{1+x^2}}$. Ans. $y'=$

$= \dfrac{1+4x^2}{x^2(1+x^2)^{\frac{3}{2}}}$. **36.** $y=\sqrt[3]{x^2+x+1}$. Ans. $y'=\dfrac{2x+1}{3\sqrt[3]{(x^2+x+1)^2}}$. **37.** $y=$

$=(1+\sqrt[3]{x})^3$. Ans. $y'=\left(1+\dfrac{1}{\sqrt[3]{x}}\right)^2$. **38.** $y=\sqrt{x+\sqrt{x+\sqrt{x}}}$. Ans.

$y'=\dfrac{1}{2\sqrt{x+\sqrt{x+\sqrt{x}}}}\left[1+\dfrac{1}{2\sqrt{x+\sqrt{x}}}\left(1+\dfrac{1}{2\sqrt{x}}\right)\right]$. **39.** $y=\sin^2 x$.

Ans. $y'=\sin 2x$. **40.** $y=2\sin x+\cos 3x$. Ans. $y'=2\cos x-3\sin 3x$. **41.** $y=$

$=\tan(ax+b)$. Ans. $y'=\dfrac{a}{\cos^2(ax+b)}$. **42.** $y=\dfrac{\sin x}{1+\cos x}$. Ans. $y'=\dfrac{1}{1+\cos x}$.

43. $y=\sin 2x\cos 3x$. Ans. $y'=2\cos 2x\cos 3x-3\sin 2x\sin 3x$. **44.** $y=\cot^2 5x$. Ans.

$y'=-10\cot 5x\csc^2 5x$. **45.** $y=t\sin t+\cos t$. Ans. $y'=t\cos t$. **46.** $y=\sin^3 t\cos t$.

Ans. $y'=\sin^2 t(3\cos^2 t-\sin^2 t)$. **47.** $y=a\sqrt{\cos 2x}$. Ans. $y'=-\dfrac{a\sin 2x}{\sqrt{\cos 2x}}$.

48. $r=a\sin^3\dfrac{\varphi}{3}$. Ans. $r'_\varphi=a\sin^2\dfrac{\varphi}{3}\cos\dfrac{\varphi}{3}$. **49.** $y=\dfrac{\tan\dfrac{x}{2}+\cot\dfrac{x}{2}}{x}$.

Ans. $y'=-\dfrac{2(x\cos x+\sin x)}{x^2\sin^2 x}$. **50.** $y=a\sin^4\dfrac{x}{2}$. Ans. $y'=2a\sin^3\dfrac{x}{2}\cos\dfrac{x}{2}$.

51. $y=\dfrac{1}{2}\tan^2 x$. Ans. $y'=\tan x\sec^2 x$. **52.** $y=\ln\cos x$. Ans. $y'=-\tan x$.

53. $y=\ln\tan x$. Ans. $y'=\dfrac{2}{\sin 2x}$. **54.** $y=\ln\sin^2 x$. Ans. $y'=2\cot x$.

55. $y=\dfrac{\tan x-1}{\sec x}$. Ans. $y'=\sin x+\cos x$. **56.** $y=\ln\sqrt{\dfrac{1+\sin x}{1-\sin x}}$.

Ans. $y'=\dfrac{1}{\cos x}$. **57.** $y=\ln\tan\left(\dfrac{\pi}{4}+\dfrac{x}{2}\right)$. Ans. $y'=\dfrac{1}{\cos x}$.

58. $y=\sin(x+a)\cos(x+a)$. Ans. $y'=\cos 2(x+a)$. **59.** $f(x)=\sin(\ln x)$.

Ans. $f'(x)=\dfrac{\cos(\ln x)}{x}$. **60.** $f(x)=\tan(\ln x)$. Ans. $f'(x)=\dfrac{\sec^2(\ln x)}{x}$.

61. $f(x)=\sin(\cos x)$. Ans. $f'(x)=-\sin x\cos(\cos x)$. **62.** $r=\dfrac{1}{3}\tan^3\varphi-\tan\varphi+\varphi$.

Ans. $\dfrac{dr}{d\varphi}=\tan^4\varphi$. **63.** $f(x)=(x\cot x)^2$. Ans. $f'(x)=2x\cot x(\cot x-x\csc^2 x)$.

64. $y=\ln(ax+b)$. Ans. $y'=\dfrac{a}{ax+b}$. **65.** $y=\log_a(x^2+1)$. Ans. $y'=\dfrac{2x}{(x^2+1)\ln a}$.

66. $y=\ln\dfrac{1+x}{1-x}$. Ans. $y'=\dfrac{2}{1-x^2}$. **67.** $y=\log_3(x^2-\sin x)$.

Ans. $y'=\dfrac{2x-\cos x}{(x^2-\sin x)\ln 3}$. **68.** $y=\ln\dfrac{1+x^2}{1-x^2}$. Ans. $y'=\dfrac{4x}{1-x^4}$.

69. $y=\ln(x^2+x)$. Ans. $y'=\dfrac{2x+1}{x^2+x}$. **70.** $y=\ln(x^3-2x+5)$.

Ans. $y'=\dfrac{3x^2-2}{x^3-2x+5}$. **71.** $y=x\ln x$. **Ans.** $y'=\ln x+1$. **72.** $y=\ln^3 x$.

Ans. $y'=\dfrac{3\ln^2 x}{x}$. **73.** $y=\ln(x+\sqrt{1+x^2})$. **Ans.** $y'=\dfrac{1}{\sqrt{1+x^2}}$.

74. $y=\ln(\ln x)$. **Ans.** $y'=\dfrac{1}{x\ln x}$. **75.** $f(x)=\ln\sqrt{\dfrac{1+x}{1-x}}$. **Ans.** $f'(x)=\dfrac{1}{1-x^2}$.

76. $f(x)=\ln\dfrac{\sqrt{x^2+1}-x}{\sqrt{x^2+1}+x}$. **Ans.** $f'(x)=-\dfrac{2}{\sqrt{1+x^2}}$ **77.** $y=\sqrt{a^2+x^2}-$

$-a\ln\dfrac{a+\sqrt{a^2+x^2}}{x}$. **Ans.** $y'=\dfrac{\sqrt{a^2+x^2}}{x}$. **78.** $y=\ln(x+\sqrt{x^2+a^2})-$

$-\dfrac{\sqrt{x^2+a^2}}{x}$. **Ans.** $y'=\dfrac{\sqrt{x^2+a^2}}{x^2}$. **79.** $y=-\dfrac{\cos x}{2\sin^2 x}+\dfrac{1}{2}\ln\tan\dfrac{x}{2}$. **Ans.**

$y'=\dfrac{1}{\sin^3 x}$. **80.** $y=\dfrac{\sin x}{2\cos^2 x}$. **Ans.** $y'=\dfrac{1+\sin^2 x}{2\cos^3 x}$. **81.** $y=\dfrac{1}{2}\tan^2 x+\ln\cos x$.

Ans. $y'=\tan^3 x$. **82.** $y=e^{ax}$. **Ans.** $y'=ae^{ax}$. **83.** $y=e^{4x+5}$. **Ans.** $y'=4e^{4x+5}$.

84. $y=a^{x^2}$. **Ans.** $y'=2xa^{x^2}\ln a$. **85.** $y=7^{x^2+2x}$. **Ans.** $y'=2(x+1)7^{x^2+2x}\ln 7$.

86. $y=c^{a^2-x^2}$. **Ans.** $y'=-2xc^{a^2-x^2}\ln c$. **87.** $y=ae^{\sqrt{x}}$. **Ans.** $y'=\dfrac{a}{2\sqrt{x}}e^{\sqrt{x}}$.

88. $r=a^\theta$. **Ans.** $r'=a^\theta\ln a$. **89.** $r=a^{\ln\theta}$. **Ans.** $\dfrac{dr}{d\theta}=\dfrac{a^{\ln\theta}\ln a}{\theta}$. **90.** $y=e^x(1-x^2)$.

Ans. $y'=e^x(1-2x-x^2)$. **91.** $y=\dfrac{e^x-1}{e^x+1}$. **Ans.** $y'=\dfrac{2e^x}{(e^x+1)^2}$ **92.** $y=\ln\dfrac{e^x}{1+e^x}$.

Ans. $y'=\dfrac{1}{1+e^x}$. **93.** $y=\dfrac{a}{2}\left(e^{\frac{x}{a}}-e^{-\frac{x}{a}}\right)$. **Ans.** $y'=\dfrac{1}{2}\left(e^{\frac{x}{a}}+e^{-\frac{x}{a}}\right)$.

94. $y=e^{\sin x}$. **Ans.** $y'=e^{\sin x}\cos x$. **95.** $y=a^{\tan nx}$. **Ans.** $y'=na^{\tan nx}\sec^2 nx\ln a$.

96. $y=e^{\cos x}\sin x$. **Ans.** $y'=e^{\cos x}(\cos x-\sin^2 x)$. **97.** $y=e^x\ln\sin x$.

Ans. $y'=e^x(\cot x+\ln\sin x)$. **98.** $y=x^n e^{\sin x}$. **Ans.** $y'=x^{n-1}e^{\sin x}(n+x\cos x)$.

99. $y=x^x$. **Ans.** $y'=x^x(\ln x+1)$. **100.** $y=x^{\frac{1}{x}}$. **Ans.** $y'=x^{\frac{1}{x}}\left(\dfrac{1-\ln x}{x^2}\right)$.

101. $y=x^{\ln x}$. **Ans.** $y'=x^{\ln x-1}\ln x^2$. **102.** $y=e^{x^x}$. **Ans.** $y'=e^{x^x}(1+\ln x)x^x$.

103. $y=\left(\dfrac{x}{n}\right)^{nx}$ **Ans.** $y'=n\left(\dfrac{x}{n}\right)^{nx}\left(1+\ln\dfrac{x}{n}\right)$. **104.** $y=x^{\sin x}$.

Ans. $y'=x^{\sin x}\left(\dfrac{\sin x}{x}+\ln x\cos x\right)$. **105.** $y=(\sin x)^x$. **Ans.** $y'=(\sin x)^x\times$

$\times(\ln\sin x+x\cot x)$. **106.** $y=(\sin x)^{\tan x}$. **Ans.** $y'=(\sin x)^{\tan x}(1+\sec^2 x\ln\sin x)$.

107. $y=\tan\dfrac{1-e^x}{1+e^x}$. **Ans.** $y'=-\dfrac{2e^x}{(1+e^x)^2}\dfrac{1}{\cos^2\dfrac{1-e^x}{1+e^x}}$. **108.** $y=\sin\sqrt{1-2^x}$.

Ans. $y'=-\dfrac{\cos\sqrt{1-2^x}}{2\sqrt{1-2^x}}2^x\ln 2$. **109.** $y=10^{x\tan x}$. **Ans.** $y'=10^{x\tan x}\ln 10\times$

$\times\left(\tan x+\dfrac{x}{\cos^2 x}\right)$.

Find the derivatives of the following functions after first taking logarithms of the functions:

110. $y=\sqrt[3]{\dfrac{x(x^2+1)}{(x-1)^2}}$. **Ans.** $y'=\dfrac{1}{3}\sqrt[3]{\dfrac{x(x^2+1)}{(x-1)^2}}\left(\dfrac{1}{x}+\dfrac{2x}{x^2+1}+\dfrac{2}{x-1}\right)$.

111. $y = \dfrac{(x+1)^3 \sqrt[4]{(x-2)^3}}{\sqrt[5]{(x-3)^2}}$. *Ans.* $y' = \dfrac{(x+1)^3 \sqrt[4]{(x-2)^3}}{\sqrt[5]{(x-3)^2}} \left(\dfrac{3}{x+1} + \dfrac{3}{4(x-2)} - \right.$

$\left. - \dfrac{2}{5(x-3)} \right)$. **112.** $y = \dfrac{(x+1)^2}{(x+2)^3 (x+3)^4}$. *Ans.* $y' = -\dfrac{(x+1)(5x^2+14x+5)}{(x+2)^4(x+3)^5}$.

113. $y = \dfrac{\sqrt[5]{(x-1)^2}}{\sqrt[4]{(x-2)^3} \sqrt[3]{(x-3)^7}}$. *Ans.* $y' = \dfrac{-161x^2+480x-271}{60 \sqrt[5]{(x-1)^3} \sqrt[4]{(x-2)^7} \sqrt[3]{(x-3)^{10}}}$.

114. $y = \dfrac{x(1+x^2)}{\sqrt{1-x^2}}$. *Ans.* $y' = \dfrac{1+3x^2-2x^4}{(1-x^2)^{\frac{3}{2}}}$ **115.** $y = x^5(a+3x)^3(a-2x)^2$.

Ans. $y' = 5x^4(a+3x)^2(a-2x)(a^2+2ax-12x^2)$. **116.** $y = \arcsin \dfrac{x}{a}$.

Ans. $y' = \dfrac{1}{\sqrt{a^2-x^2}}$. **117.** $y = (\arcsin x)^2$. *Ans.* $y' = \dfrac{2 \arcsin x}{\sqrt{1-x^2}}$.

118. $y = \arctan(x^2+1)$. *Ans.* $y' = \dfrac{2x}{1+(x^2+1)^2}$. **119.** $y = \arctan \dfrac{2x}{1-x^2}$.

Ans. $y' = \dfrac{2}{1+x^2}$. **120.** $y = \arccos(x^2)$. *Ans.* $y' = \dfrac{-2x}{\sqrt{1-x^4}}$. **121.** $y = \dfrac{\arccos x}{x}$.

Ans. $y' = \dfrac{-(x + \sqrt{1-x^2} \arccos x)}{x^2 \sqrt{1-x^2}}$. **122.** $y = \arcsin \dfrac{x+1}{\sqrt{2}}$. *Ans.* $y' =$

$= \dfrac{1}{\sqrt{1-2x-x^2}}$ **123.** $y = x \sqrt{a^2-x^2} + a^2 \arcsin \dfrac{x}{a}$. *Ans.* $y' = 2 \sqrt{a^2-x^2}$.

124. $y = \sqrt{a^2-x^2} + a \arcsin \dfrac{x}{a}$. *Ans.* $y' = \sqrt{\dfrac{a-x}{a+x}}$. **125.** $u = \arctan \dfrac{v+a}{1-av}$

Ans. $\dfrac{du}{dv} = \dfrac{1}{1+v^2}$. **126.** $y = \dfrac{1}{\sqrt{3}} \arctan \dfrac{x\sqrt{3}}{1-x^2}$. *Ans.* $y' = \dfrac{x^2+1}{x^4+x^2+1}$. **127.**

$y = x \arcsin x$. *Ans.* $y' = \arcsin x + \dfrac{x}{\sqrt{1-x^2}}$. **128.** $f(x) = \arccos(\ln x)$. *Ans.*

$f'(x) = -\dfrac{1}{x \sqrt{1-\ln^2 x}}$. **129.** $f(x) = \arcsin \sqrt{\sin x}$. *Ans.* $f'(x) = \dfrac{\cos x}{2 \sqrt{\sin x - \sin^2 x}}$.

130. $y = \arctan \sqrt{\dfrac{1-\cos x}{1+\cos x}}$ $(0 \leqslant x < \pi)$. *Ans.* $y' = \dfrac{1}{2}$. **131.** $y = e^{\arctan x}$.

Ans. $y' = \dfrac{e^{\arctan x}}{1+x^2}$. **132.** $y = \arctan \dfrac{e^x - e^{-x}}{2}$. *Ans.* $y' = \dfrac{2}{e^x + e^{-x}}$. **133.** $y =$

$= x^{\arcsin x}$. *Ans.* $y' = x^{\arcsin x} \left(\dfrac{\arcsin x}{x} + \dfrac{\ln x}{\sqrt{1-x^2}} \right)$. **134.** $y = \arcsin(\sin x)$.

Ans. $y' = \dfrac{\cos x}{|\cos x|} = \begin{cases} +1 \text{ in 1st and 4th quadrants.} \\ -1 \text{ in 2nd and 3rd quadrants.} \end{cases}$ **135.** $y = \arctan \dfrac{4 \sin x}{3+5 \cos x}$.

Ans. $y' = \dfrac{4}{5+3 \cos x}$. **136.** $y = \arctan \dfrac{a}{x} + \ln \sqrt{\dfrac{x-a}{x+a}}$. *Ans.* $y' = \dfrac{2a^3}{x^4-a^4}$.

137. $y = \ln \left(\dfrac{1+x}{1-x} \right)^{\frac{1}{4}} - \dfrac{1}{2} \arctan x$. *Ans.* $y' = \dfrac{x^2}{1-x^4}$. **138.** $y = \dfrac{3x^2-1}{3x^3} +$

$+ \ln \sqrt{1+x^2} + \arctan x$. *Ans.* $y' = \dfrac{x^5+1}{x^6+x^4}$. **139.** $y = \dfrac{1}{3} \ln \dfrac{x+1}{\sqrt{x^2-x+1}} +$

$+\dfrac{1}{\sqrt{3}}\arctan\dfrac{2x-1}{\sqrt{3}}$. *Ans.* $y'=\dfrac{1}{x^3+1}$.   **140.** $y=\ln\dfrac{1+x\sqrt{2}+x^2}{1-x\sqrt{2}+x^2}+$

$+2\arctan\dfrac{x\sqrt{2}}{1-x^2}$. *Ans.* $y'=\dfrac{4\sqrt{2}}{1+x^4}$. **141.** $y=\arccos\dfrac{x^{2n}-1}{x^{2n}+1}$. *Ans.* $-\dfrac{2n\,|x\,|^n}{x\,(x^{2n}+1)}$.

Differentiation of Implicit Functions

Find $\dfrac{dy}{dx}$ if: **142.** $y^2=4px$. *Ans.* $\dfrac{dy}{dx}=\dfrac{2p}{y}$. **143.** $x^2+y^2=a^2$. *Ans.* $\dfrac{dy}{dx}=-\dfrac{x}{y}$.

144. $b^2x^2+a^2y^2=a^2b^2$. *Ans.* $\dfrac{dy}{dx}=-\dfrac{b^2x}{a^2y}$. **145.** $y^3-3y+2ax=0$. *Ans.* $\dfrac{dy}{dx}=$

$=\dfrac{2a}{3\,(1-y^2)}$. **146.** $x^{\frac{1}{2}}+y^{\frac{1}{2}}=a^{\frac{1}{2}}$. *Ans.* $\dfrac{dy}{dx}=-\sqrt{\dfrac{y}{x}}$. **147.** $x^{\frac{2}{3}}+y^{\frac{2}{3}}=a^{\frac{2}{3}}$.

Ans. $\dfrac{dy}{dx}=-\sqrt[3]{\dfrac{y}{x}}$. **148.** $y^2-2xy+b^2=0$. *Ans.* $\dfrac{dy}{dx}=\dfrac{y}{y-x}$. **149.** x^3+y^3-

$-3axy=0$. *Ans.* $\dfrac{dy}{dx}=\dfrac{ay-x^2}{y^2-ax}$. **150.** $y=\cos(x+y)$. *Ans.* $\dfrac{dy}{dx}=-\dfrac{\sin(x+y)}{1+\sin(x+y)}$.

151. $\cos(xy)=x$. *Ans.* $\dfrac{dy}{dx}=-\dfrac{1+y\sin(xy)}{x\sin(xy)}$.

Find $\dfrac{dy}{dx}$ of the following functions represented parametrically:

152. $x=a\cos t$, $y=b\sin t$. *Ans.* $\dfrac{dy}{dx}=-\dfrac{b}{a}\cot t$. **153.** $x=a\,(t-\sin t)$, $y=a\,(1-\cos t)$.

Ans. $\dfrac{dy}{dx}=\cot\dfrac{t}{2}$. **154.** $x=a\cos^3 t$, $y=b\sin^3 t$. *Ans.* $\dfrac{dy}{dx}=-\dfrac{b}{a}\tan t$. **155.** $x=$

$=\dfrac{3at}{1+t^2}$, $y=\dfrac{3at^2}{1+t^2}$. *Ans.* $\dfrac{dy}{dx}=\dfrac{2t}{1-t^2}$. **156.** $u=2\ln\cot s$, $v=\tan s+\cot s$.

Show that $\dfrac{du}{dv}=\tan 2s$.

Find the tangents of the angles of inclination of tangent lines to curves:

157. $x=\cos t$, $y=\sin t$ at the point $x=-\dfrac{1}{2}$, $y=\dfrac{\sqrt{3}}{2}$. Make a drawing.

Ans. $\dfrac{1}{\sqrt{3}}$. **158.** $x=2\cos t$, $y=\sin t$ at the point $x=1$, $y=-\dfrac{\sqrt{3}}{2}$. Make a

drawing. *Ans.* $\dfrac{1}{2\sqrt{3}}$. **159.** $x=a\,(t-\sin t)$, $y=a\,(1-\cos t)$ when $t=\dfrac{\pi}{2}$.

Make a drawing. *Ans.* 1. **160.** $x=a\cos^3 t$, $y=a\sin^3 t$ when $t=\dfrac{\pi}{4}$. Make a

drawing. *Ans.* −1. **161.** A body thrown at an angle α to the horizon (in airless space) described a curve parabola, under the force of gravity, whose equations are: $x=(v_0\cos\alpha)\,t$, $y=(v_0\sin\alpha)\,t-\dfrac{gt^2}{2}$ ($g=9.8$ m/sec²). Knowing that $\alpha=60°$, $v_0=50$ m/sec, determine the direction of motion when: (1) $t=2$ sec, (2) $t=7$ sec. Make a drawing. *Ans.* (1) $\tan\varphi_1=0.948$, $\varphi_1=43°30'$; (2) $\tan\varphi_2=-1.012$, $\varphi_2=+134°3'$.

Find the differentials of the following functions:

162. $y = (a^2 - x^2)^5$. *Ans.* $dy = -10x(a^2 - x^2)^4 dx$. **163.** $y = \sqrt{1 + x^2}$. *Ans.*

$dy = \dfrac{x\,dx}{\sqrt{1 + x^2}}$. **164.** $y = \dfrac{1}{3}\tan^3 x + \tan x$. *Ans.* $dy = \sec^4 x\,dx$.

165. $y = \dfrac{x \ln x}{1 - x} + \ln(1 - x)$. *Ans.* $dy = \dfrac{\ln x\,dx}{(1 - x)^2}$.

Calculate the increments and differentials of the following functions:
166. $y = 2x^2 - x$ when $x = 1$, $\Delta x = 0.01$. *Ans.* $\Delta y = 0.0302$, $dy = 0.03$. **167.** Given $y = x^3 + 2x$. Find Δy and dy when $x = -1$, $\Delta x = 0.02$. *Ans.* $\Delta y = 0.098808$, $dy = 0.1$. **168.** Given $y = \sin x$. Find dy when $x = \dfrac{\pi}{3}$, $\Delta x = \dfrac{\pi}{18}$. *Ans.* $dy = \dfrac{\pi}{36} = 0.0873$. **169.** Knowing that $\sin 60° = \dfrac{\sqrt{3}}{2} = 0.866025$, $\cos 60° = \dfrac{1}{2}$, find the approximate values of $\sin 60°3'$ and $\sin 60°18'$. Compare the results with tabular data. *Ans.* $\sin 60°3' \approx 0.866461$, $\sin 60°18' \approx 0.868643$. **170.** Find the approximate value of $\tan 45°4'30''$. *Ans.* 1.00262. **171.** Knowing that $\log_{10} 200 = 2.30103$ find the approximate value of $\log_{10} 200.2$. *Ans.* 2.30146.

Derivatives of different orders. **172.** $y = 3x^3 - 2x^2 + 5x - 1$. Find y''. *Ans.* $18x - 4$. **173.** $y = \sqrt[5]{x^3}$. Find y'''. *Ans.* $\dfrac{42}{125} x^{-\frac{12}{5}}$. **174.** $y = x^6$. Find $y^{(6)}$. *Ans.* 6!. **175.** $y = \dfrac{C}{x^n}$. Find y''. *Ans.* $\dfrac{n(n+1)C}{x^{n+2}}$. **176.** $y = \sqrt{a^2 - x^2}$. Find y''. *Ans.* $-\dfrac{a^2}{(a^2 - x^2)\sqrt{a^2 - x^2}}$. **177.** $y = 2\sqrt{x}$. Find $y^{(4)}$. *Ans.* $-\dfrac{15}{8\sqrt{x^7}}$. **178.** $y = ax^2 + bx + c$. Find y'''. *Ans.* 0. **179.** $f(x) = \ln(x + 1)$. Find $f^{(4)}(x)$. *Ans.* $-\dfrac{6}{(x+1)^4}$. **180.** $y = \tan x$. Find y'''. *Ans.* $6\sec^4 x - 4\sec^2 x$. **181.** $y = \ln \sin x$. Find y'''. *Ans.* $2\cot x \csc^2 x$. **182.** $f(x) = \sqrt{\sec 2x}$. Find $f''(x)$. *Ans.* $f''(x) = 3[f(x)]^5 - f(x)$. **183.** $y = \dfrac{x^3}{1 - x}$. Find $f^{(4)}(x)$. *Ans.* $\dfrac{4!}{(1 - x)^5}$. **184.** $p = (q^2 + a^2)\arctan \dfrac{q}{a}$. Find $\dfrac{d^3 p}{dq^3}$. *Ans.* $\dfrac{4a^3}{(a^2 + q^2)^2}$. **185.** $y = \dfrac{a}{2}\left(e^{\frac{x}{a}} + e^{-\frac{x}{a}}\right)$. Find $\dfrac{d^2 y}{dx^2}$. *Ans.* $\dfrac{y}{a^2}$. **186.** $y = \cos ax$. Find $y^{(n)}$. *Ans.* $a^n \cos\left(ax + n\dfrac{\pi}{2}\right)$. **187.** $y = a^x$. Find $y^{(n)}$. *Ans.* $(\ln a)^n a^x$. **188.** $y = \ln(1 + x)$. Find $y^{(n)}$. *Ans.* $(-1)^{n-1}\dfrac{(n-1)!}{(1 + x)^n}$. **189.** $y = \dfrac{1 - x}{1 + x}$. Find $y^{(n)}$. *Ans.* $2(-1)^n \dfrac{n!}{(1 + x)^{n+1}}$. **190.** $y = e^x x$. Find $y^{(n)}$. *Ans.* $e^x(x + n)$. **191.** $y = x^{n-1}\ln x$. Find $y^{(n)}$. *Ans.* $\dfrac{(n-1)!}{x}$. **192.** $y = \sin^2 x$. Find $y^{(n)}$. *Ans.* $-2^{n-1}\cos\left(2x + n\dfrac{\pi}{2}\right)$. **193.** $y = x\sin x$. Find $y^{(n)}$. *Ans.* $x\sin\left(x + n\dfrac{\pi}{2}\right) - n\cos\left(x + n\dfrac{\pi}{2}\right)$. **194.** If $y = e^x \sin x$, prove that $y'' - 2y' + 2y = 0$. **195.** $y^2 = 4ax$. Find $\dfrac{d^2 y}{dx^2}$. *Ans.* $-\dfrac{4a^2}{y^3}$. **196.** $b^2 x^2 + a^2 y^2 = a^2 b^2$. Find $\dfrac{d^2 y}{dx^2}$ and $\dfrac{d^3 y}{dx^3}$. *Ans.* $-\dfrac{b^4}{a^2 y^3}$; $-\dfrac{3b^6 x}{a^4 y^5}$. **197.** $x^2 + y^2 = r^2$. Find $\dfrac{d^2 y}{dx^2}$. *Ans.* $-\dfrac{r^2}{y^3}$. **198.** $y^2 - 2xy = 0$. Find $\dfrac{d^3 y}{dx^3}$. *Ans.* 0. **199.** $\rho = \tan(\varphi + \rho)$.

Find $\dfrac{d^3\rho}{d\varphi^3}$. Ans. $-\dfrac{2(5+8\rho^2+3\rho^4)}{\rho^5}$. 200. $\sec\varphi\cos\rho=C$. Find $\dfrac{d^2\rho}{d\varphi^2}$. Ans. $\dfrac{\tan^2\rho-\tan^2\varphi}{\tan^3\rho}$. 201. $e^x+x=e^y+y$. Find $\dfrac{d^2y}{dx^2}$. Ans. $\dfrac{(1-e^{x+y})(e^x-e^y)}{(e^y+1)^3}$.

202. $y^3+x^3-3axy=0$. Find $\dfrac{d^2y}{dx^2}$. Ans. $-\dfrac{2a^3xy}{(y^2-ax)^3}$. 203. $x=a(t-\sin t)$, $y=a(1-\cos t)$. Find $\dfrac{d^2y}{dx^2}$. Ans. $-\dfrac{1}{4a\sin^4\left(\dfrac{t}{2}\right)}$. 204. $x=a\cos 2t$, $y=b\sin^2 t$.

Show that $\dfrac{d^2y}{dx^2}=0$. 205. $x=a\cos t$, $y=a\sin t$. Find $\dfrac{d^3y}{dx^3}$. Ans. $-\dfrac{3\cos t}{a^2\sin^5 t}$.

206. Show that $\dfrac{d^{2n}}{dx^{2n}}(\sinh x)=\sinh x$; $\dfrac{d^{2n+1}}{dx^{2n+1}}(\sinh x)=\cosh x$.

Equations of a Tangent and a Normal.
Lengths of a Subtangent and a Subnormal

207. Write the equations of the tangent and the normal to the curve $y=x^3-3x^2-x+5$ at the point $M(3, 2)$. Ans. The tangent is $8x-y-22=0$; the normal, $x+8y-19=0$.

208. Find the equations of the tangent and normal, the lengths of the subtangent and subnormal of the circle $x^2+y^2=r^2$ at the point $M(x_1, y_1)$. Ans. The tangent is $xx_1+yy_1=r^2$; the normal is $x_1y-y_1x=0$; $S_T=\left|\dfrac{y_1^2}{x_1}\right|$; $S_N=|x_1|$.

209. Show that the subtangent of the parabola $y^2=4px$ at any point is divided into two by the vertex, and the subnormal is constant and equal to $2p$. Make a drawing.

210. Find the equation of the tangent at the point $M(x_1, y_1)$

(a) to the ellipse $\dfrac{x^2}{a^2}+\dfrac{y^2}{b^2}=1$. Ans. $\dfrac{xx_1}{a^2}+\dfrac{yy_1}{b^2}=1$;

(b) to the hyperbola $\dfrac{x^2}{a^2}-\dfrac{y^2}{b^2}=1$. Ans. $\dfrac{xx_1}{a^2}-\dfrac{yy_1}{b^2}=1$.

211. Find the equations of the tangent and normal to the Witch of Agnesi $y=\dfrac{8a^3}{4a^2+x^2}$ at the point where $x=2a$. Ans. The tangent is $x+2y=4a$; the normal is $y=2x-3a$.

212. Show that the normal to the curve $3y=6x-5x^3$ drawn to the point $M\left(1, \dfrac{1}{3}\right)$ passes through the coordinate origin.

213. Show that the tangent to the curve $\left(\dfrac{x}{a}\right)^n+\left(\dfrac{y}{b}\right)^n=2$ at the point $M(a, b)$ is $\dfrac{x}{a}+\dfrac{y}{b}=2$.

214. Find the equation of that tangent to the parabola, $y^2=20x$, which forms an angle of $45°$ with the x-axis. Ans. $y=x+5$ [at the point $(5, 10)$].

215. Find the equations of those tangents to the circle $x^2+y^2=52$ which are parallel to the straight line $2x+3y=6$. Ans. $2x+3y\pm 26=0$.

216. Find the equations of those tangents to the hyperbola $4x^2-9y^2=36$ which are perpendicular to the straight line $2y+5x=10$. Ans. There are no such tangents.

217. Show that the segment (lying between the coordinate axes) of the tangent to the hyperbola $xy=m$ is divided into two by the point of tangency.

218. Prove that the segment (between the coordinate axes) of a tangent to the astroid $x^{2/3} + y^{2/3} = a^{2/3}$ is of constant length.

219. At what angle α do the curves $y = a^x$ and $y = b^x$ intersect? *Ans.* $\tan \alpha = \dfrac{\ln a - \ln b}{1 + \ln a \cdot \ln b}$.

220. Find the lengths of the subtangent, subnormal, tangent and normal to the cycloid $x = a(\theta - \sin \theta)$, $y = a(1 - \cos \theta)$ at the point at which $\theta = \dfrac{\pi}{2}$.

Ans. $S_T = a$, $S_N = a$, $T = a\sqrt{2}$, $N = a\sqrt{2}$.

221. Find the quantities S_T, S_N, T and N for the astroid $x = 4a\cos^3 t$, $y = 4a\sin^3 t$. *Ans.* $S_T = |4a\sin^2 t \, \cos t|$; $S_N = |4a\sin^3 t \, \tan t|$; $T = 4a\sin^2 t$; $N = |4a\sin^2 t \, \tan t|$.

Miscellaneous Problems

Find the derivatives of the following functions:

222. $y = \dfrac{\sin x}{2\cos^2 x} - \dfrac{1}{2}\ln\tan\left(\dfrac{\pi}{4} - \dfrac{x}{2}\right)$. *Ans.* $y' = \dfrac{1}{\cos^3 x}$.   **223.** $y = \arcsin\dfrac{1}{x}$.

Ans. $y' = -\dfrac{1}{|x|\sqrt{x^2 - 1}}$.   **224.** $y = \arcsin(\sin x)$. *Ans.* $y' = \dfrac{\cos x}{|\cos x|}$.   **225.** $y =$

$= \dfrac{2}{\sqrt{a^2 - b^2}}\arctan\left(\sqrt{\dfrac{a - b}{a + b}}\tan\dfrac{x}{2}\right)$ $(a > 0, \ b > 0)$. *Ans.* $y' = \dfrac{1}{a + b\cos x}$.

226. $y = |x|$. *Ans.* $y' = \dfrac{x}{|x|}$.   **227.** $y = \arcsin\sqrt{1 - x^2}$. *Ans.* $y' = -\dfrac{x}{|x|} \times$

$\times \dfrac{1}{\sqrt{1 - x^2}}$.

228. From the formulas for the volume and surface of a sphere $v = \dfrac{4}{3}\pi r^3$ and $s = 4\pi r^2$ it follows that $\dfrac{dv}{dr} = s$. Explain the geometric significance of this result. Find a similar relationship between the area of a circle and the length of the circumference.

229. In a triangle ABC, the side a is expressed in terms of the other two sides b, c and the angle A between them by the formula

$$a = \sqrt{b^2 + c^2 - 2bc\cos A}$$

For b and c constant, side a is a function of the angle A. Show that $\dfrac{da}{dA} = h_a$, where h_a is the altitude of the triangle corresponding to the base a. Interpret this result geometrically.

230. Using the differential concept, determine the origin of the approximate formulas

$$\sqrt{a^2 + b} \approx a + \dfrac{b}{2a}, \quad \sqrt[3]{a^3 + b} \approx a + \dfrac{b}{3a^2}$$

where $|b|$ is a number small compared with a.

231. The period of oscillation of a pendulum is computed by the formula

$$T = \pi\sqrt{\dfrac{l}{g}}$$

In calculating the period T, how will the error be affected by an error of 1% in the measurement of: (1) the length of the pendulum l, (2) the acceleration of gravity g? *Ans.* (1) $\approx 1/2\%$, (2) $\approx 1/2\%$.

232. The tractrix has the property that for any point of it, the tangent T remains constant in iength. Prove this on the basis of: (1) the equation of the tractrix in the form

$$x = \sqrt{a^2 - y^2} + \frac{a}{2} \ln \frac{a - \sqrt{a^2 - y^2}}{a + \sqrt{a^2 - y^2}} \quad (a > 0)$$

(2) the parametric equations of the curve

$$x = a \left(\ln \tan \frac{t}{2} + \cos t \right)$$
$$y = a \sin t$$

233. Prove that the function $y = C_1 e^{-x} + C_2 e^{-2x}$ satisfies the equation $y'' + 3y' + 2y = 0$ (here C_1 and C_2 are constants).

234. Putting $y = e^x \sin x$, $z = e^x \cos x$ prove the equations $y'' = 2z$, $z'' = -2y$.

235. Prove that the function $y = \sin (m \arcsin x)$ satisfies the equation $(1 - x^2) y'' - xy' + m^2 y = 0$.

236. Prove that if $(a + bx) e^{\frac{y}{x}} = x$, then $x^3 \frac{d^2y}{dx^2} = \left(x \frac{dy}{dx} - y \right)^2$.

CHAPTER 4

SOME THEOREMS ON DIFFERENTIABLE FUNCTIONS

4.1 A THEOREM ON THE ROOTS OF A DERIVATIVE (ROLLE'S THEOREM)

Rolle's Theorem. *If a function* $f(x)$ *is continuous on an interval* $[a, b]$ *and is differentiable at all interior points of the interval, and vanishes* $[f(a) = f(b) = 0]$ *at the end points* $x = a$ *and* $x = b$, *then inside* $[a, b]$ *there exists at least one point* $x = c$, $a < c < b$, *at which the derivative* $f'(x)$ *vanishes, that is,* $f'(c) = 0$.*

Proof. Since the function $f(x)$ is continuous on the interval $[a, b]$, it has a maximum M and a minimum m on that interval.

If $M = m$ the function $f(x)$ is constant, which means that for all values of x it has a constant value $f(x) = m$. But then at any point of the interval $f'(x) = 0$, and the theorem is proved.

Suppose $M \neq m$. Then at least one of these numbers is not equal to zero.

For the sake of definiteness, let us assume that $M > 0$ and that the function takes on its maximum value at $x = c$, so that $f(c) = M$. Let it be noted that, here, c is not equal either to a or to b, since it is given that $f(a) = 0$, $f(b) = 0$. Since $f(c)$ is the maximum value of the function, it follows that $f(c + \Delta x) - f(c) \leqslant 0$, both when $\Delta x > 0$ and when $\Delta x < 0$. Whence it follows that

$$\frac{f(c + \Delta x) - f(c)}{\Delta x} \leqslant 0 \text{ when } \Delta x > 0 \qquad (1')$$

$$\frac{f(c + \Delta x) - f(c)}{\Delta x} \geqslant 0 \text{ when } \Delta x < 0 \qquad (1'')$$

Since it is given in the theorem that the derivative at $x = c$ exists, we get, upon passing to the limit as $\Delta x \rightarrow 0$,

$$\lim_{\Delta x \to 0} \frac{f(c + \Delta x) - f(c)}{\Delta x} = f'(c) \leqslant 0 \quad \text{when} \quad \Delta x > 0$$

$$\lim_{\Delta x \to 0} \frac{f(c + \Delta x) - f(c)}{\Delta x} = f'(c) \geqslant 0 \quad \text{when} \quad \Delta x < 0$$

But the relations $f'(c) \leqslant 0$ and $f'(c) \geqslant 0$ are compatible only if $f'(c) = 0$. Consequently, there is a point c inside the interval $[a, b]$ at which the derivative $f'(x)$ is equal to zero.

---

* The number c is called a *root of the function* $\varphi(x)$ if $\varphi(c) = 0$.

The theorem about the roots of a derivative has a simple geometric interpretation: if a continuous curve, which at each point
has a tangent, intersects the x-axis at points with abscissas *a*
and *b*, then on this curve there will be at least one point with
abscissa *c*, $a < c < b$, at which the tangent is parallel to the
x-axis.

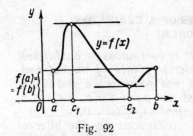

Fig. 92

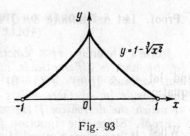

Fig. 93

Note 1. The theorem that has just been proved also holds for
a differentiable function such that does not vanish at the end
points of the interval $[a, b]$, but takes on equal values $f(a) = f(b)$
(Fig. 92). The proof in this case is exactly the same as before.

Note 2. If the function $f(x)$ is such that the derivative does
not exist at all points within the interval $[a, b]$, the assertion
of the theorem may prove erroneous (in this case there might
not be a point *c* in the interval $[a, b]$, at which the derivative
$f'(x)$ vanishes).

For example, the function

$$y = f(x) = 1 - \sqrt[3]{x^2}$$

(Fig. 93) is continuous on the interval $[-1, 1]$ and vanishes at
the end points of the interval, yet the derivative

$$f'(x) = -\frac{2}{3\sqrt[3]{x}}$$

within the interval does not vanish. This is because there is a
point $x = 0$ inside the interval at which the derivative does not
exist (becomes infinite).

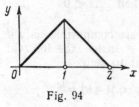

Fig. 94

The graph shown in Fig. 94 is another
instance of a function whose derivative
does not vanish in the interval $[0, 2]$.

The conditions of the Rolle theorem are
not fulfilled for this function either,
because at the point $x = 1$ the function
has no derivative.

4.2 THE MEAN-VALUE THEOREM (LAGRANGE'S THEOREM)

Lagrange's Theorem. *If a function $f(x)$ is continuous on the interval $[a, b]$ and differentiable at all interior points of the interval, there will be, within $[a, b]$, at least one point c, $a < c < b$, such that*

$$f(b) - f(a) = f'(c)(b - a) \tag{1}$$

Proof. Let us denote by Q the number $\dfrac{f(b) - f(a)}{b - a}$ that is, set:

$$Q = \frac{f(b) - f(a)}{b - a} \tag{2}$$

and let us consider the auxiliary function $F(x)$ defined by the equation

$$F(x) = f(x) - f(a) - (x - a)Q \tag{3}$$

What is the geometric significance of the function $F(x)$? First write the equation of the chord AB (Fig. 95), taking into account that its slope is $\dfrac{f(b) - f(a)}{b - a} = Q$ and that it passes through the point $(a, f(a))$:

$$y - f(a) = Q(x - a)$$

whence

$$y = f(a) + Q(x - a)$$

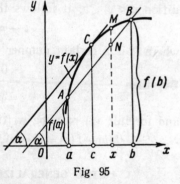

Fig. 95

But $F(x) = f(x) - [f(a) + Q(x - a)]$. Thus, for each value of x, $F(x)$ is equal to the difference between the ordinates of the curve $y = f(x)$ and the chord $y = f(a) + Q(x - a)$ for points with the same abscissa.

It will readily be seen that $F(x)$ is continuous on the interval $[a, b]$, is differentiable within the interval, and vanishes at the end points of the interval; in other words, $F(a) = 0$, $F(b) = 0$. Hence, the Rolle theorem is applicable to the function $F(x)$. By this theorem, there exists within the interval a point $x = c$ such that

$$F'(c) = 0$$

But

$$F'(x) = f'(x) - Q$$

and so

$$F'(c) = f'(c) - Q = 0$$

whence

$$Q = f'(c)$$

Substituting the value of Q in (2), we get

$$\frac{f(b)-f(a)}{b-a}=f'(c) \tag{1'}$$

whence follows formula (1) directly. The theorem is thus proved.

See Fig. 95 for an explanation of the geometric significance of the Lagrange theorem. From the figure it is immediately clear that the quantity $\frac{f(b)-f(a)}{b-a}$ is the tangent of the angle of inclination α of the chord passing through the points A and B with abscissas a and b.

On the other hand, $f'(c)$ is the tangent of the angle of inclination of the tangent line to the curve at the point with abscissa c. Thus, the geometric significance of (1') or its equivalent (1) consists in the following: if at all points of the arc AB there is a tangent line, then there will be, on this arc, a point C between A and B at which the **tangent is parallel to the chord** connecting points A and B.

Now note the following. Since the value of c satisfies the condition $a < c < b$, it follows that $c - a < b - a$, or

$$c - a = \theta(b - a)$$

where θ is a certain number between 0 and 1, that is,

$$0 < \theta < 1$$

But then

$$c = a + \theta(b - a)$$

and formula (1) may be written as follows:

$$f(b)-f(a)=(b-a)f'[a+\theta(b-a)], \quad 0 < \theta < 1 \tag{1''}$$

4.3 THE GENERALIZED MEAN-VALUE THEOREM (CAUCHY'S THEOREM)

Cauchy's Theorem. *If $f(x)$ and $\varphi(x)$ are two functions continuous on an interval $[a, b]$ and differentiable within it, and $\varphi'(x)$ does not vanish anywhere inside the interval, there will be, in $[a, b]$, a point $x = c$, $a < c < b$, such that*

$$\frac{f(b)-f(a)}{\varphi(b)-\varphi(a)}=\frac{f'(c)}{\varphi'(c)} \tag{1}$$

Proof. Let us define the number Q by the equation

$$Q=\frac{f(b)-f(a)}{\varphi(b)-\varphi(a)} \tag{2}$$

It will be noted that $\varphi(b)-\varphi(a)\neq 0$, since otherwise $\varphi(b)$ would be equal to $\varphi(a)$, and then, by the Rolle theorem, the derivative

$\varphi'(x)$ would vanish in the interval; but this contradicts the statement of the theorem.

Let us construct an auxiliary function

$$F(x) = f(x) - f(a) - Q\left[\varphi(x) - \varphi(a)\right]$$

It is obvious that $F(a) = 0$ and $F(b) = 0$ (this follows from the definition of the function $F(x)$ and the definition of the number Q). Noting that the function $F(x)$ satisfies all the hypotheses of the Rolle theorem on the interval $[a, b]$, we conclude that there exists between a and b a value $x = c$ $(a < c < b)$ such that $F'(c) = 0$. But $F'(x) = f'(x) - Q\varphi'(x)$, hence

$$F'(c) = f'(c) - Q\varphi'(c) = 0$$

whence

$$Q = \frac{f'(c)}{\varphi'(c)}$$

Substituting the value of Q into (2) we get (1).

Note. The Cauchy theorem cannot be proved (as it might appear at first glance) by applying the Lagrange theorem to the numerator and denominator of the fraction

$$\frac{f(b) - f(a)}{\varphi(b) - \varphi(a)}$$

Indeed, in this case we would (after cancelling out $b - a$) get the formula

$$\frac{f(b) - f(a)}{\varphi(b) - \varphi(a)} = \frac{f'(c_1)}{\varphi'(c_2)}$$

in which $a < c_1 < b$, $a < c_2 < b$. But since, generally, $c_1 \neq c_2$, the result obtained obviously does not yet yield the Cauchy theorem.

4.4 THE LIMIT OF A RATIO OF TWO INFINITESIMALS $\left(\text{EVALUATING INDETERMINATE FORMS OF THE TYPE } \frac{0}{0}\right)$

Let the functions $f(x)$ and $\varphi(x)$, on a certain interval $[a, b]$, satisfy the Cauchy theorem and vanish at the point $x = a$ of this interval, $f(a) = 0$ and $\varphi(a) = 0$.

The ratio $\frac{f(x)}{\varphi(x)}$ is not defined for $x = a$, but has a very definite meaning for values of $x \neq a$. Hence, we can raise the question of searching for the limit of this ratio as $x \to a$. Evaluating limits of this type is usually known as evaluating indeterminate forms of the type $\frac{0}{0}$.

We have already encountered such problems, for instance when considering the limit $\lim\limits_{x \to 0} \dfrac{\sin x}{x}$ and when finding derivatives of elementary functions. For $x = 0$, the expression $\dfrac{\sin x}{x}$ is meaningless; the function $F(x) = \dfrac{\sin x}{x}$ is not defined for $x = 0$, but we have seen that the limit of the expression $\dfrac{\sin x}{x}$ as $x \to 0$ exists and is equal to unity.

L'Hospital's Theorem (Rule). *Let the functions $f(x)$ and $\varphi(x)$, in $[a, b]$, satisfy the Cauchy theorem and vanish at the point $x = a$, that is, $f(a) = \varphi(a) = 0$; then, if the ratio $\dfrac{f'(x)}{\varphi'(x)}$ has a limit as $x \to a$, there also exists $\lim\limits_{x \to a} \dfrac{f(x)}{\varphi(x)}$, and*

$$\lim_{x \to a} \frac{f(x)}{\varphi(x)} = \lim_{x \to a} \frac{f'(x)}{\varphi'(x)}$$

Proof. On the interval $[a, b]$ take some point $x \neq a$. Applying the Cauchy formula we have

$$\frac{f(x) - f(a)}{\varphi(x) - \varphi(a)} = \frac{f'(\xi)}{\varphi'(\xi)}$$

where ξ lies between a and x. But it is given that $f(a) = \varphi(a) = 0$, and so

$$\frac{f(x)}{\varphi(x)} = \frac{f'(\xi)}{\varphi'(\xi)} \tag{1}$$

If $x \to a$, then $\xi \to a$ also, since ξ lies between x and a. And if $\lim\limits_{x \to a} \dfrac{f'(x)}{\varphi'(x)} = A$, then $\lim\limits_{\xi \to a} \dfrac{f'(\xi)}{\varphi'(\xi)}$ exists and is equal to A. Whence it is clear that

$$\lim_{x \to a} \frac{f(x)}{\varphi(x)} = \lim_{x \to a} \frac{f'(\xi)}{\varphi'(\xi)} = \lim_{\xi \to a} \frac{f'(\xi)}{\varphi'(\xi)} = \lim_{x \to a} \frac{f'(x)}{\varphi'(x)} = A$$

and, finally,

$$\lim_{x \to a} \frac{f(x)}{\varphi(x)} = \lim_{x \to a} \frac{f'(x)}{\varphi'(x)}$$

Note 1. The theorem holds also for the case where the functions $f(x)$ or $\varphi(x)$ are **not defined** at $x = a$, but

$$\lim_{x \to a} f(x) = 0, \quad \lim_{x \to a} \varphi(x) = 0$$

In order to reduce this case to the earlier considered case, we **redefine** the functions $f(x)$ and $\varphi(x)$ at the point $x = a$ so that they become **continuous at the point** a. To do this, it is sufficient to put

$$f(a) = \lim_{x \to a} f(x) = 0, \quad \varphi(a) = \lim_{x \to a} \varphi(x) = 0$$

since it is obvious that the limit of the ratio $\frac{f(x)}{\varphi(x)}$ as $x \to a$ does not depend on whether the functions $f(x)$ and $\varphi(x)$ are defined at $x = a$.

Note 2. If $f'(a) = \varphi'(a) = 0$ and the derivatives $f'(x)$ and $\varphi'(x)$ satisfy the conditions that were imposed by the theorem on the functions $f(x)$ and $\varphi(x)$, then applying the l'Hospital rule to the ratio $\frac{f'(x)}{\varphi'(x)}$, we arrive at the formula $\lim_{x \to a} \frac{f'(x)}{\varphi'(x)} = \lim_{x \to a} \frac{f''(x)}{\varphi''(x)}$, and so forth.

Note 3. If $\varphi'(a) = 0$, but $f'(x) \neq 0$, then the theorem is applicable to the reciprocal ratio $\frac{\varphi(x)}{f(x)}$, which tends to zero as $x \to a$. Hence, the ratio $\frac{f(x)}{\varphi(x)}$ tends to infinity.

Example 1.

$$\lim_{x \to 0} \frac{\sin 5x}{3x} = \lim_{x \to 0} \frac{(\sin 5x)'}{(3x)'} = \lim_{x \to 0} \frac{5\cos 5x}{3} = \frac{5}{3}$$

Example 2.

$$\lim_{x \to 0} \frac{\ln(1+x)}{x} = \lim_{x \to 0} \frac{\frac{1}{1+x}}{1} = \frac{1}{1} = 1$$

Example 3.

$$\lim_{x \to 0} \frac{e^x - e^{-x} - 2x}{x - \sin x} = \lim_{x \to 0} \frac{e^x + e^{-x} - 2}{1 - \cos x} = \lim_{x \to 0} \frac{e^x - e^{-x}}{\sin x} = \lim_{x \to 0} \frac{e^x + e^{-x}}{\cos x} = \frac{2}{1} = 2$$

Here, we had to apply the l'Hospital rule three times because the ratios of the first, second and third derivatives at $x = 0$ yield the indeterminate form $\frac{0}{0}$.

Note 4. The l'Hospital rule is also applicable if

$$\lim_{x \to \infty} f(x) = 0 \quad \text{and} \quad \lim_{x \to \infty} \varphi(x) = 0$$

Indeed, putting $x = \frac{1}{z}$, we see that $z \to 0$ as $x \to \infty$ and therefore

$$\lim_{z \to 0} f\left(\frac{1}{z}\right) = 0, \quad \lim_{z \to 0} \varphi\left(\frac{1}{z}\right) = 0$$

Applying the l'Hospital rule to the ratio $\dfrac{f\left(\dfrac{1}{z}\right)}{\varphi\left(\dfrac{1}{z}\right)}$, we find

$$\lim_{x \to \infty} \frac{f(x)}{\varphi(x)} = \lim_{z \to 0} \frac{f\left(\dfrac{1}{z}\right)}{\varphi\left(\dfrac{1}{z}\right)} = \lim_{z \to 0} \frac{f'\left(\dfrac{1}{z}\right)\left(-\dfrac{1}{z^2}\right)}{\varphi'\left(\dfrac{1}{z}\right)\left(-\dfrac{1}{z^2}\right)}$$

$$= \lim_{z \to 0} \frac{f'\left(\dfrac{1}{z}\right)}{\varphi'\left(\dfrac{1}{z}\right)} = \lim_{x \to \infty} \frac{f'(x)}{\varphi'(x)}$$

which is what we wanted to prove.

Example 4.

$$\lim_{x \to \infty} \frac{\sin\dfrac{k}{x}}{\dfrac{1}{x}} = \lim_{x \to \infty} \frac{k\cos\dfrac{k}{x}\left(-\dfrac{1}{x^2}\right)}{-\dfrac{1}{x^2}} = \lim_{x \to \infty} k\cos\frac{k}{x} = k$$

4.5 THE LIMIT OF A RATIO OF TWO INFINITELY LARGE QUANTITIES
$$\left(\text{EVALUATING INDETERMINATE FORMS OF THE TYPE } \frac{\infty}{\infty}\right)$$

Let us now consider the question of the limit of a ratio of two functions $f(x)$ and $\varphi(x)$ approaching infinity as $x \to a$ (or as $x \to \infty$).

Theorem. *Let the functions $f(x)$ and $\varphi(x)$ be continuous and differentiable for all $x \neq a$ in the neighbourhood of the point a, the derivative $\varphi'(x)$ does not vanish; further, let*

$$\lim_{x \to a} f(x) = \infty, \quad \lim_{x \to a} \varphi(x) = \infty$$

and let there.be a limit

$$\lim_{x \to a} \frac{f'(x)}{\varphi'(x)} = A \tag{1}$$

Then there is a limit $\lim\limits_{x \to a} \dfrac{f(x)}{\varphi(x)}$ *and*

$$\lim_{x \to a} \frac{f(x)}{\varphi(x)} = \lim_{x \to a} \frac{f'(x)}{\varphi'(x)} = A \tag{2}$$

Proof. In the given neighbourhood of the point a, take two points α and x such that $\alpha < x < a$ (or $a < x < \alpha$). By Cauchy's theorem we have

$$\frac{f(x) - f(\alpha)}{\varphi(x) - \varphi(\alpha)} = \frac{f'(c)}{\varphi'(c)} \tag{3}$$

where $\alpha < c < x$. We transform the left side of (3) as follows:

$$\frac{f(x) - f(\alpha)}{\varphi(x) - \varphi(\alpha)} = \frac{f(x)}{\varphi(x)} \cdot \frac{1 - \dfrac{f(\alpha)}{f(x)}}{1 - \dfrac{\varphi(\alpha)}{\varphi(x)}} \tag{4}$$

From relations (3) and (4) we have

$$\frac{f'(c)}{\varphi'(c)} = \frac{f(x)}{\varphi(x)} \cdot \frac{1 - \dfrac{f(\alpha)}{f(x)}}{1 - \dfrac{\varphi(\alpha)}{\varphi(x)}}$$

Whence we find

$$\frac{f(x)}{\varphi(x)} = \frac{f'(c)}{\varphi'(c)} \cdot \frac{1 - \dfrac{\varphi(\alpha)}{\varphi(x)}}{1 - \dfrac{f(\alpha)}{f(x)}} \tag{5}$$

From condition (1) it follows that for an arbitrarily small $\varepsilon > 0$, α may be chosen so close to a that for all $x = c$ where $\alpha < c < a$, the following inequality will be fulfilled:

$$\left| \frac{f'(c)}{\varphi'(c)} - A \right| < \varepsilon$$

or

$$A - \varepsilon < \frac{f'(c)}{\varphi'(c)} < A + \varepsilon \tag{6}$$

Let us further consider the fraction

$$\frac{1 - \dfrac{\varphi(\alpha)}{\varphi(x)}}{1 - \dfrac{f(\alpha)}{f(x)}}$$

Fixing α so that inequality (6) holds, we allow x to approach a. Since $f(x) \to \infty$ and $\varphi(x) \to \infty$ as $x \to a$, we have

$$\lim_{x \to a} \frac{1 - \dfrac{\varphi(\alpha)}{\varphi(x)}}{1 - \dfrac{f(\alpha)}{f(x)}} = 1$$

and, consequently, for the earlier chosen $\varepsilon > 0$ (for x sufficiently close to a) we will have

$$\left| \frac{1 - \dfrac{\varphi(\alpha)}{\varphi(x)}}{1 - \dfrac{f(\alpha)}{f(x)}} - 1 \right| < \varepsilon$$

or

$$1-\varepsilon < \frac{1-\dfrac{\varphi(\alpha)}{\varphi(x)}}{1-\dfrac{f(\alpha)}{f(x)}} < 1+\varepsilon \qquad (7)$$

Multiplying together the appropriate terms of inequalities (6) and (7), we get

$$(A-\varepsilon)(1-\varepsilon) < \frac{f'(c)}{\varphi'(c)} \frac{1-\dfrac{\varphi(\alpha)}{\varphi(x)}}{1-\dfrac{f(\alpha)}{f(x)}} < (A+\varepsilon)(1+\varepsilon)$$

or, from (5),

$$(A-\varepsilon)(1-\varepsilon) < \frac{f(x)}{\varphi(x)} < (A+\varepsilon)(1+\varepsilon)$$

Since ε is an arbitrarily small number for x sufficiently close to a, it follows from the latter inequalities that

$$\lim_{x \to a} \frac{f(x)}{\varphi(x)} = A$$

or, by (1),

$$\lim_{x \to a} \frac{f(x)}{\varphi(x)} = \lim_{x \to a} \frac{f'(x)}{\varphi'(x)} = A$$

which completes the proof.

Note 1. If in condition (1) $A = \infty$, that is,

$$\lim_{x \to a} \frac{f'(x)}{\varphi'(x)} = \infty$$

then (2) holds in this case as well. Indeed, from the preceding expression it follows that

$$\lim_{x \to a} \frac{\varphi'(x)}{f'(x)} = 0$$

Then by the theorem just proved

$$\lim_{x \to a} \frac{\varphi(x)}{f(x)} = \lim_{x \to a} \frac{\varphi'(x)}{f'(x)} = 0$$

whence

$$\lim_{x \to a} \frac{f(x)}{\varphi(x)} = \infty$$

Note 2. The theorem just proved is readily extended to the case where $x \to \infty$. If $\lim\limits_{x \to \infty} f(x) = \infty$, $\lim\limits_{x \to \infty} \varphi(x) = \infty$ and $\lim\limits_{x \to \infty} \dfrac{f'(x)}{\varphi'(x)}$

exists, then

$$\lim_{x \to \infty} \frac{f(x)}{\varphi(x)} = \lim_{x \to \infty} \frac{f'(x)}{\varphi'(x)} \qquad (8)$$

The proof is carried out by the substitution $x = \frac{1}{z}$, as was done under similar conditions in the case of the indeterminate form $\frac{0}{0}$ (see Sec. 4.4, Note 4).

Example 1.

$$\lim_{x \to \infty} \frac{e^x}{x} = \lim_{x \to \infty} \frac{(e^x)'}{(x)'} = \lim_{x \to \infty} \frac{e^x}{1} = \infty$$

Note 3. Once again note that formulas (2) and (8) hold only if the limit on the right (finite or infinite) exists. It may happen that the limit on the left exists while there is no limit on the right. To illustrate, let it be required to find

$$\lim_{x \to \infty} \frac{x + \sin x}{x}$$

This limit exists and is equal to 1. Indeed,

$$\lim_{x \to \infty} \frac{x + \sin x}{x} = \lim_{x \to \infty} \left(1 + \frac{\sin x}{x}\right) = 1$$

But the ratio of derivatives

$$\frac{(x + \sin x)'}{(x')} = \frac{1 + \cos x}{1} = 1 + \cos x$$

as $x \to \infty$ does not approach any limit, it oscillates between 0 and 2.

Example 2.

$$\lim_{x \to \infty} \frac{ax^2 + b}{cx^2 - d} = \lim_{x \to \infty} \frac{2ax}{2cx} = \frac{a}{c}$$

Example 3.

$$\lim_{x \to \frac{\pi}{2}} \frac{\tan x}{\tan 3x} = \lim_{x \to \frac{\pi}{2}} \frac{\dfrac{1}{\cos^2 x}}{\dfrac{3}{\cos^2 3x}} = \lim_{x \to \frac{\pi}{2}} \frac{1}{3} \frac{\cos^2 3x}{\cos^2 x} = \lim_{x \to \frac{\pi}{2}} \frac{1}{3} \frac{2 \cdot 3 \cos 3x \sin 3x}{2 \cos x \sin x}$$

$$= \lim_{x \to \frac{\pi}{2}} \frac{\cos 3x}{\cos x} \lim_{x \to \frac{\pi}{2}} \frac{\sin 3x}{\sin x} = \lim_{x \to \frac{\pi}{2}} \frac{3 \sin 3x}{\sin x} \cdot \frac{(-1)}{(1)} = 3 \frac{(-1)}{(1)} \cdot \frac{(-1)}{(1)} = 3$$

Example 4.

$$\lim_{x \to \infty} \frac{x}{e^x} = \lim_{x \to \infty} \frac{1}{e^x} = 0$$

Generally, for any integral $n > 0$,

$$\lim_{x \to \infty} \frac{x^n}{e^x} = \lim_{x \to \infty} \frac{nx^{n-1}}{e^x} = \ldots = \lim_{x \to \infty} \frac{n(n-1)\ldots 1}{e^x} = 0$$

The other indeterminate forms reduce to the foregoing cases. These forms may be written symbolically as follows:

(a) $0 \cdot \infty$, (b) 0^0, (c) ∞^0, (d) 1^∞, (e) $\infty - \infty$

They have the following meaning.

(a) Let $\lim_{x \to a} f(x) = 0$; $\lim_{x \to a} \varphi(x) = \infty$; it is required to find

$$\lim_{x \to a} [f(x)\, \varphi(x)]$$

that is, the indeterminate form $0 \cdot \infty$.

If the required expression is rewritten as follows:

$$\lim_{x \to a} [f(x)\, \varphi(x)] = \lim_{x \to a} \frac{f(x)}{\dfrac{1}{\varphi(x)}}$$

or in the form

$$\lim_{x \to a} [f(x)\, \varphi(x)] = \lim_{x \to a} \frac{\varphi(x)}{\dfrac{1}{f(x)}}$$

then as $x \to a$ we obtain the indeterminate form $\dfrac{0}{0}$ or $\dfrac{\infty}{\infty}$.

Example 5.

$$\lim_{x \to 0} x^n \ln x = \lim_{x \to 0} \frac{\ln x}{\dfrac{1}{x^n}} = \lim_{x \to 0} \frac{\dfrac{1}{x}}{-\dfrac{n}{x^{n+1}}} = -\lim_{x \to 0} \frac{x^n}{n} = 0$$

(b) Let

$$\lim_{x \to a} f(x) = 0, \quad \lim_{x \to a} \varphi(x) = 0$$

it is required to find

$$\lim_{x \to a} [f(x)]^{\varphi(x)}$$

or, as we say, to evaluate the indeterminate form 0^0.

Putting

$$y = [f(x)]^{\varphi(x)}$$

take logarithms of both sides of the equation:

$$\ln y = \varphi(x) [\ln f(x)]$$

As $x \to a$ we obtain (on the right) the indeterminate form $0 \cdot \infty$. Finding $\lim\limits_{x \to a} \ln y$, it is easy to get $\lim\limits_{x \to a} y$. Indeed, by virtue of the continuity of the logarithmic function, $\lim\limits_{x \to a} \ln y = \ln \lim\limits_{x \to a} y$ and if $\ln \lim\limits_{x \to a} y = b$, it is obvious that $\lim\limits_{x \to a} y = e^b$. If, in particular, $b = +\infty$ or $-\infty$, then we will have $\lim y = +\infty$ or 0, respectively.

Example 6. It is required to find $\lim\limits_{x \to 0} x^x$. Putting $y = x^x$ we find $\ln \lim y =$ $= \lim \ln y = \lim \ln (x^x) = \lim (x \ln x)$;

$$\lim_{x \to 0} (x \ln x) = \lim_{x \to 0} \frac{\ln x}{\frac{1}{x}} = \lim_{x \to 0} \frac{\frac{1}{x}}{-\frac{1}{x^2}} = -\lim_{x \to 0} x = 0$$

Consequently, $\ln \lim y = 0$, whence $\lim y = e^0 = 1$, or

$$\lim_{x \to 0} x^x = 1$$

The technique is similar for finding limits in other cases.

4.6 TAYLOR'S FORMULA

Let us assume that the function $y = f(x)$ has all derivatives up to the $(n+1)$th order, inclusive, in some interval containing the point $x = a$. Let us find a polynomial $y = P_n(x)$ of degree not above n, the value of which at $x = a$ is equal to the value of the function $f(x)$ at this point, and the values of its derivatives up to the nth order at $x = a$ are equal to the values of the corresponding derivatives of the function $f(x)$ at this point:

$$P_n(a) = f(a), \ P_n'(a) = f'(a), \ P_n''(a) = f''(a), \ \ldots, P_n^{(n)}(a) = f^{(n)}(a) \quad (1)$$

It is natural to expect that, in a certain sense, such a polynomial is "close" to the function $f(x)$.

Let us look for this polynomial in the form of a polynomial in powers of $(x-a)$ with undetermined coefficients:

$$P_n(x) = C_0 + C_1(x-a) + C_2(x-a)^2 + C_3(x-a)^3$$
$$+ \ldots + C_n(x-a)^n \quad (2)$$

We define the undetermined coefficients $C_1, C_2, \ldots, C_n$ so that conditions (1) are satisfied,

10—2081

Let us first find the derivatives of $P_n(x)$:

$$\left.\begin{array}{l} P'_n(x) = C_1 + 2C_2(x-a) + 3C_3(x-a)^2 + \ldots + nC_n(x-a)^{n-1} \\ P''_n(x) = 2\cdot 1 C_2 + 3\cdot 2 C_3(x-a) + \ldots + n(n-1)C_n(x-a)^{n-2} \\ \cdot\ \cdot\ \cdot\ \cdot\ \cdot\ \cdot\ \cdot\ \cdot\ \cdot\ \cdot\ \cdot\ \cdot\ \cdot\ \cdot\ \cdot\ \cdot\ \cdot\ \cdot\ \cdot \\ P_n^{(n)}(x) = \qquad\qquad\qquad\qquad n(n-1)\ldots 2\cdot 1\cdot C_n \end{array}\right\} \quad (3)$$

Substituting, into the left and right sides of (2) and (3), the value of a in place of x and replacing, by (1), $P_n(a)$ by $f(a)$, $P'_n(a) = f'(a)$, etc., we get

$$f(a) = C_0$$
$$f'(a) = C_1$$
$$f''(a) = 2\cdot 1 C_2$$
$$f'''(a) = 3\cdot 2\cdot 1 C_3$$
$$\cdot\ \cdot\ \cdot\ \cdot\ \cdot\ \cdot\ \cdot\ \cdot\ \cdot\ \cdot\ \cdot$$
$$f^{(n)}(a) = n(n-1)(n-2)\ldots 2\cdot 1 C_n$$

whence we find

$$\left.\begin{array}{l} C_0 = f(a), \quad C_1 = f'(a), \quad C_2 = \dfrac{1}{1\cdot 2} f''(a), \\ C_3 = \dfrac{1}{1\cdot 2\cdot 3} f'''(a), \quad \ldots, \quad C_n = \dfrac{1}{1\cdot 2\ \ldots\ n} f^{(n)}(a) \end{array}\right\} \quad (4)$$

Substituting into (2) the values of $C_1, C_2, \ldots, C_n$ that have been found, we get the required polynomial:

$$P_n(x) = f(a) + \frac{x-a}{1} f'(a) + \frac{(x-a)^2}{1\cdot 2} f''(a) + \frac{(x-a)^3}{1\cdot 2\cdot 3} f'''(a)$$
$$+ \ldots + \frac{(x-a)^n}{1\cdot 2\ ..\ n} f^{(n)}(a) \qquad (5)$$

Designate by $R_n(x)$ the difference between the values of the given function $f(x)$ and the constructed polynomial $P_n(x)$ (Fig. 96):

$$R_n(x) = f(x) - P_n(x)$$

whence

$$f(x) = P_n(x) + R_n(x)$$

or, in expanded form,

$$f(x) = f(a) + \frac{x-a}{1!} f'(a) + \frac{(x-a)^2}{2!} f''(a)$$
$$+ \ldots + \frac{(x-a)^n}{n!} f^{(n)}(a) + R_n(x) \qquad (6)$$

$R_n(x)$ is called the *remainder*. For those values of x, for which the remainder $R_n(x)$ is small, the polynomial $P_n(x)$ yields an approximate representation of the function $f(x)$.

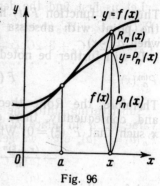

Fig. 96

Thus, formula (6) enables one to replace the function $y = f(x)$ by the polynomial $y = P_n(x)$ to an appropriate degree of accuracy equal to the value of the remainder $R_n(x)$.

Our next problem is to evaluate the quantity $R_n(x)$ for various values of x.

Let us write the remainder in the form

$$R_n(x) = \frac{(x-a)^{n+1}}{(n+1)!} Q(x) \qquad (7)$$

where $Q(x)$ is a certain function to be defined, and accordingly rewrite (6):

$$f(x) = f(a) + \frac{x-a}{1} f'(a) + \frac{(x-a)^2}{2!} f''(a)$$
$$+ \ldots + \frac{(x-a)^n}{n!} f^{(n)}(a) + \frac{(x-a)^{n+1}}{(n+1)!} Q(x) \qquad (6')$$

For fixed x and a, the function $Q(x)$ has a definite value; denote it by Q.

Let us further examine the auxiliary function of t (t lying between a and x):

$$F(t) = f(x) - f(t) - \frac{x-t}{1} f'(t) - \frac{(x-t)^2}{2!} f''(t) - \ldots$$
$$- \frac{(x-t)^n}{n!} f^{(n)}(t) - \frac{(x-t)^{n+1}}{(n+1)!} Q$$

where Q has the value defined by the relation (6'); here we consider a and x to be definite numbers.

We find the derivative $F'(t)$:

$$F'(t) = -f'(t) + f'(t) - \frac{x-t}{1} f''(t) + \frac{2(x-t)}{2!} f''(t)$$
$$- \frac{(x-t)^2}{2!} f'''(t) + \ldots + \frac{(x-t)^{n-1}}{(n-1)!} f^{(n)}(t) + \frac{n(x-t)^{n-1}}{n!} f^{(n)}(t)$$
$$- \frac{(x-t)^n}{n!} f^{(n+1)}(t) + \frac{(n+1)(x-t)^n}{(n+1)!} Q$$

or, on cancelling,

$$F'(t) = -\frac{(x-t)^n}{n!} f^{(n+1)}(t) + \frac{(x-t)^n}{n!} Q \qquad (8)$$

Thus, the function $F(t)$ has a derivative at all points t lying near the point with abscissa a ($a \leqslant t \leqslant x$ when $a < x$ and $a \geqslant t \geqslant x$ when $a > x$).

It will further be noted that, on the basis of (6'),

$$F(x) = 0, \quad F(a) = 0$$

Therefore, the Rolle theorem is applicable to the function $F(t)$ and, consequently, there exists a value $t = \xi$ lying between a and x such that $F'(\xi) = 0$. Whence, on the basis of relation (8), we get

$$-\frac{(x-\xi)^n}{n!} f^{(n+1)}(\xi) + \frac{(x-\xi)^n}{n!} Q = 0$$

and from this

$$Q = f^{(n+1)}(\xi)$$

Substituting this expression into (7), we get

$$R_n(x) = \frac{(x-a)^{n+1}}{(n+1)!} f^{(n+1)}(\xi)$$

This is the so-called *Lagrange form* of the remainder.

Since ξ lies between x and a, it may be represented in the form [*]

$$\xi = a + \theta(x-a)$$

where θ is a number lying between 0 and 1, that is, $0 < \theta < 1$; then the formula of the remainder takes the form

$$R_n(x) = \frac{(x-a)^{n+1}}{(n+1)!} f^{(n+1)}[a + \theta(x-a)]$$

The formula

$$f(x) = f(a) + \frac{x-a}{1!} f'(a) + \frac{(x-a)^2}{2!} f''(a) + \cdots$$
$$+ \frac{(x-a)^n}{n!} f^{(n)}(a) + \frac{(x-a)^{n+1}}{(n+1)!} f^{(n+1)}[a + \theta(x-a)] \quad (9)$$

is called *Taylor's formula* of the function $f(x)$.

If in the Taylor formula we put $a = 0$ we will have

$$f(x) = f(0) + \frac{x}{1!} f'(0) + \frac{x^2}{2!} f''(0) + \cdots$$
$$+ \frac{x^n}{n!} f^{(n)}(0) + \frac{x^{n+1}}{(n+1)!} f^{(n+1)}(\theta x) \quad (10)$$

where θ lies between 0 and 1. This special case of the Taylor formula is sometimes called *Maclaurin's formula*.

---

[*] See end of Sec. 4.2.

4.7 EXPANSION OF THE FUNCTIONS e^x, $\sin x$, AND $\cos x$ IN A TAYLOR SERIES

1. Expansion of the function $f(x) = e^x$. Finding the successive derivatives of $f(x)$, we have

$$f(x) = e^x, \quad f(0) = 1$$
$$f'(x) = e^x, \quad f'(0) = 1$$
$$\cdots \cdots \cdots \cdots \cdots$$
$$f^{(n)}(x) = e^x, \quad f^{(n)}(0) = 1$$

Substituting the expressions obtained into formula (10) (Sec. 4.6), we get

$$e^x = 1 + \frac{x}{1!} + \frac{x^2}{2!} + \frac{x^3}{3!} + \ldots + \frac{x^n}{n!} + \frac{x^{n+1}}{(n+1)!} e^{\theta x}, \quad 0 < \theta < 1$$

If $|x| \leqslant 1$, then, taking $n = 8$, we obtain an estimate of the remainder:

$$R_8 < \frac{1}{9!} 3 < 10^{-5}$$

For $x = 1$ we get a formula that permits approximating the number e:

$$e = 1 + 1 + \frac{1}{2!} + \frac{1}{3!} + \ldots + \frac{1}{8!}$$

Calculating to the sixth decimal place,* and then rounding to five decimals, we have

$$e = 2.71828$$

Here the error does not exceed $\frac{3}{9!}$, or 0.00001.

Observe that no matter what x is, the remainder

$$R_n = \frac{x^{n+1}}{(n+1)!} e^{\theta x} \to 0 \quad \text{as} \quad n \to \infty$$

Indeed, since $\theta < 1$, the quantity $e^{\theta x}$ for fixed x is bounded (it is less than e^x for $x > 0$ and less than 1 for $x < 0$).

We shall prove that, no matter what the fixed number x,

$$\frac{x^{n+1}}{(n+1)!} \to 0 \quad \text{as} \quad n \to \infty$$

Indeed,

$$\left| \frac{x^{n+1}}{(n+1)!} \right| = \left| \frac{x}{1} \cdot \frac{x}{2} \cdot \frac{x}{3} \cdots \frac{x}{n} \cdot \frac{x}{n+1} \right|$$

---

* Otherwise the overall rounding error may considerably exceed R_8 (for instance, for 10 terms, this error can exceed $5 \cdot 10^{-5}$).

If x is a fixed number, there will be a positive integer N such that

$$|x| < N$$

We introduce the notation $\dfrac{|x|}{N} = q$; then, noting that $0 < q < 1$, we can write for $n = N+1,\ N+2,\ N+3$, etc.

$$\left|\frac{x^{n+1}}{(n+1)!}\right| = \left|\frac{x}{1} \cdot \frac{x}{2} \cdot \frac{x}{3} \cdots \frac{x}{n} \cdot \frac{x}{n+1}\right|$$

$$= \left|\frac{x}{1}\right|\left|\frac{x}{2}\right|\left|\frac{x}{3}\right| \cdots \left|\frac{x}{N-1}\right| \cdot \left|\frac{x}{N}\right| \cdots \left|\frac{x}{n}\right| \cdot \left|\frac{x}{n+1}\right|$$

$$< \frac{x}{1} \cdot \frac{x}{2} \cdot \frac{x}{3} \cdots \frac{x}{N-1} \cdot q \cdot q \cdots q = \frac{x^{N-1}}{(N-1)!} q^{n-N+2}$$

for the reason that

$$\left|\frac{x}{N}\right| = q, \quad \left|\frac{x}{N+1}\right| < q, \quad \ldots, \quad \left|\frac{x}{n+1}\right| < q$$

But $\dfrac{x^{N-1}}{(N-1)!}$ is a constant quantity; that is to say, it is independent of n, while q^{n-N+2} approaches zero as $n \to \infty$. And so

$$\lim_{n \to \infty} \frac{x^{n+1}}{(n+1)!} = 0 \tag{1}$$

Consequently, $R_n(x) = e^{\theta x} \dfrac{x^{n+1}}{(n+1)!}$ also approaches zero as n approaches infinity.

From the foregoing it follows that for any x (if a sufficient number of terms is taken) we can evaluate e^x to any degree of accuracy.

2. Expansion of the function $f(x) = \sin x$. We find the successive derivatives of $f(x) = \sin x$:

$$f(x) \quad = \sin x \qquad\qquad\qquad f(0) = 0$$

$$f'(x) \quad = \cos x = \sin\left(x + \frac{\pi}{2}\right), \qquad f'(0) = 1$$

$$f''(x) \quad = -\sin x = \sin\left(x + 2\frac{\pi}{2}\right), \qquad f''(0) = 0$$

$$f'''(x) = -\cos x = \sin\left(x + 3\frac{\pi}{2}\right), \qquad f'''(0) = -1$$

$$f^{IV}(x) \ = \sin x = \sin\left(x + 4\frac{\pi}{2}\right), \qquad f^{IV}(0) = 0.$$

$$\cdots\cdots\cdots\cdots\cdots\cdots\cdots\cdots\cdots$$

$$f^{(n)}(x) = \sin\left(x + n\frac{\pi}{2}\right), \qquad\qquad f^{(n)}(0) = \sin n\frac{\pi}{2}$$

$$f^{(n+1)}(x) = \sin\left(x + (n+1)\frac{\pi}{2}\right), \quad f^{(n+1)}(\xi) = \sin\left[\xi + (n+1)\frac{\pi}{2}\right]$$

Substituting the values obtained into (10), Sec. 4.6, we get an expansion of the function $f(x) = \sin x$ by the Taylor formula:

$$\sin x = x - \frac{x^3}{3!} + \frac{x^5}{5!} - \ldots + \frac{x^n}{n!} \sin n \frac{\pi}{2} + \frac{x^{n+1}}{(n+1)!} \sin \left[\xi + (n+1) \frac{\pi}{2} \right]$$

Since $\left| \sin \left[\xi + (n+1) \frac{\pi}{2} \right] \right| \leqslant 1$, we have $\lim\limits_{n \to \infty} R_n(x) = 0$ for all values of x.

Let us apply the formula in order to approximate sin 20°. Put $n = 3$, thus restricting ourselves to the first two terms of the expansion:

$$\sin 20° = \sin \frac{\pi}{9} \approx \frac{\pi}{9} - \frac{1}{3!} \left(\frac{\pi}{9} \right)^3 = 0.342$$

Let us estimate the error, which is equal to the remainder:

$$|R_3| = \left| \left(\frac{\pi}{9} \right)^4 \frac{1}{4!} \sin (\xi + 2\pi) \right| \leqslant \left(\frac{\pi}{9} \right)^4 \frac{1}{4!} \approx 0.00062 < 0.001$$

Hence, the error is less than 0.001, and so sin 20° = 0.342 to three places of decimals.

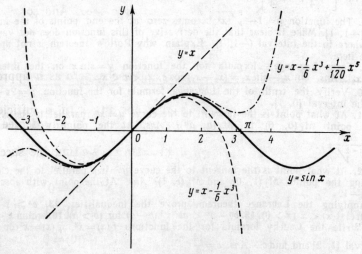

Fig. 97

Fig. 97 shows the graphs of the function $f(x) = \sin x$ and the first three approximations: $S_1(x) = x$, $S_2(x) = x - \frac{x^3}{3!}$, $S_3(x) = x - \frac{x^3}{3!} + \frac{x^5}{5!}$.

3. **Expansion of the function $f(x) = \cos x$.** Finding the values of the successive derivatives for $x = 0$ of the function $f(x) = \cos x$

and substituting them into the Maclaurin formula, we get the expansion

$$\cos x = 1 - \frac{x^2}{2!} + \frac{x^4}{4!} - \ldots + \frac{x^n}{n!}\cos\left(n\,\frac{\pi}{2}\right) + \frac{x^{n+1}}{(n+1)!}\cos\left[\xi + (n+1)\,\frac{\pi}{2}\right],$$
$$|\xi| < |x|$$

Here again, $\lim\limits_{n \to \infty} R_n(x) = 0$ for all values of x.

Exercises on Chapter 4

Verify the truth of Rolle's theorem for the functions: **1.** $y = x^2 - 3x + 2$ on the interval $[1, 2]$. **2.** $y = x^3 + 5x^2 - 6x$ on the interval $[0, 1]$. **3.** $y = (x - 1) \times (x - 2)(x - 3)$ on the interval $[1, 3]$. **4.** $y = \sin^2 x$ on the interval $[0, \pi]$.
5. The function $f(x) = 4x^3 + x^2 - 4x - 1$ has roots 1 and -1. Find the root of the derivative $f'(x)$ mentioned in Rolle's theorem.

6. Verify that between the roots of the function $y = \sqrt[3]{x^2 - 5x + 6}$ lies the root of its derivative.

7. Verify the truth of Rolle's theorem for the function $y = \cos^2 x$ on the interval $\left[-\frac{\pi}{4}, +\frac{\pi}{4}\right]$.

8. The function $y = 1 - \sqrt[5]{x^4}$ becomes zero at the end points of the interval $[-1, 1]$. Make it clear that the derivative of this function does not vanish anywhere in the interval $(-1, 1)$. Explain why Rolle's theorem is not applicable here.

9. Form Lagrange's formula for the function $y = \sin x$ on the interval $[x_1, x_2]$. *Ans.* $\sin x_2 - \sin x_1 = (x_2 - x_1)\cos c$, $x_1 < c < x_2$.

10. Verify the truth of the Lagrange formula for the function $y = 2x - x^2$ on the interval $[0, 1]$.

11. At what point is the tangent to the curve $y = x^n$ parallel to the chord from point $M_1(0, 0)$ to $M_2(a, a^n)$? *Ans.* At the point with abscissa $c = \dfrac{a}{\sqrt[n-1]{n}}$.

12. At what point is the tangent to the curve $y = \ln x$ parallel to the chord linking the points $M_1(1, 0)$ and $M_2(e, 1)$? *Ans.* At the point with abscissa $c = e - 1$.

Applying the Lagrange theorem, prove the inequalities: **13.** $e^x \geqslant 1 + x$. **14.** $\ln(1 + x) < x\ (x > 0)$. **15.** $b^n - a^n < nb^{n-1}(b - a)$ for $(b > a)$. **16.** $\arctan x < x$. **17.** Write the Cauchy formula for the functions $f(x) = x^2$, $\varphi(x) = x^3$ on the interval $[1, 2]$ and find c. *Ans.* $c = \dfrac{14}{9}$.

Evaluate the following limits:

18. $\lim\limits_{x \to 1} \dfrac{x - 1}{x^n - 1}$. *Ans.* $\dfrac{1}{n}$. **19.** $\lim\limits_{x \to 0} \dfrac{e^x - e^{-x}}{\sin x}$. *Ans.* 2. **20.** $\lim\limits_{x \to 0} \dfrac{\tan x - x}{x - \sin x}$. *Ans.* 2.

21. $\lim\limits_{x \to 0} \dfrac{e^{x^2} - 1}{\cos x - 1}$. *Ans.* -2. **22.** $\lim\limits_{x \to 0} \dfrac{\sin x}{\sqrt{1 - \cos x}}$. *Ans.* There is no limit

($\sqrt{2}$ as $x \to +0$, $-\sqrt{2}$ as $x \to -0$). **23.** $\lim\limits_{x \to \frac{\pi}{2}} \dfrac{\ln \sin x}{(\pi - 2x)^2}$. *Ans.* $-\dfrac{1}{8}$.

24. $\lim\limits_{x \to 0} \dfrac{a^x - b^x}{x}$. *Ans.* $\ln \dfrac{a}{b}$. **25.** $\lim\limits_{x \to 0} \dfrac{x - \arcsin x}{\sin^3 x}$. *Ans.* $-\dfrac{1}{6}$.

26. $\lim\limits_{x \to a} \dfrac{\sin x - \sin a}{x - a}$. *Ans.* $\cos a$. **27.** $\lim\limits_{y \to 0} \dfrac{e^y + \sin y - 1}{\ln (1 + y)}$. *Ans.* 2.

28. $\lim\limits_{x \to 0} \dfrac{e^x \sin x - x}{3x^2 + x^5}$. *Ans.* $\dfrac{1}{3}$. **29.** $\lim\limits_{x \to \infty} \dfrac{3x - 1}{2x + 5}$. *Ans.* $\dfrac{3}{2}$. **30.** $\lim\limits_{x \to \infty} \dfrac{\ln x}{x^n}$

(where $n > 0$). *Ans.* 0. **31.** $\lim\limits_{x \to \infty} \dfrac{\ln \left(1 + \dfrac{1}{x}\right)}{\arctan x}$. *Ans.* 1. **32.** $\lim\limits_{x \to \infty} \dfrac{\ln \dfrac{x+1}{x}}{\ln \dfrac{x-1}{x}}$.

Ans. -1. **33.** $\lim\limits_{y \to +\infty} \dfrac{y}{e^{ay}}$. *Ans.* 0 for $a > 0$, ∞ for $a \leqslant 0$. **34.** $\lim\limits_{x \to +\infty} \dfrac{e^x + e^{-x}}{e^x - e^{-x}}$.

Ans. 1. **35.** $\lim\limits_{x \to 0} \dfrac{\ln \sin 3x}{\ln \sin x}$. *Ans.* 1. **36.** $\lim\limits_{x \to 0} \dfrac{\ln \tan 7x}{\ln \tan 2x}$. *Ans.* 1.

37. $\lim\limits_{x \to 1} \dfrac{\ln (x - 1) - x}{\tan \dfrac{\pi}{2x}}$. *Ans.* 0. **38.** $\lim\limits_{x \to 1} (1 - x) \tan \dfrac{\pi x}{2}$. *Ans.* $\dfrac{2}{\pi}$.

39. $\lim\limits_{x \to 1} \left[\dfrac{2}{x^2 - 1} - \dfrac{1}{x - 1}\right]$. *Ans.* $-\dfrac{1}{2}$. **40.** $\lim\limits_{x \to 1} \left[\dfrac{1}{\ln x} - \dfrac{x}{\ln x}\right]$. *Ans.* -1.

41. $\lim\limits_{\varphi \to \frac{\pi}{2}} (\sec \varphi - \tan \varphi)$. *Ans.* 0. **42.** $\lim\limits_{x \to 1} \left[\dfrac{x}{x - 1} - \dfrac{1}{\ln x}\right]$. *Ans.* $\dfrac{1}{2}$. **43.** $\lim\limits_{x \to 0} x \cot 2x$.

Ans. $\dfrac{1}{2}$. **44.** $\lim\limits_{x \to 0} x^2 e^{\frac{1}{x^2}}$. *Ans.* ∞. **45.** $\lim\limits_{x \to 1} x^{\frac{1}{1 - x}}$ *Ans.* $\dfrac{1}{e}$. **46.** $\lim\limits_{t \to \infty} \sqrt[t]{t^2}$. *Ans.* 1.

47. $\lim\limits_{x \to 0} \left(\dfrac{1}{x}\right)^{\tan x}$. *Ans.* 1. **48.** $\lim\limits_{x \to \infty} \left(1 + \dfrac{a}{x}\right)^x$. *Ans.* e^a. **49.** $\lim\limits_{x \to 0} (\cot x)^{\frac{1}{\ln x}}$

Ans. $\dfrac{1}{e}$. **50.** $\lim\limits_{x \to \frac{\pi}{2}} (\cos x)^{\frac{\pi}{2} - x}$. *Ans.* 1. **51.** $\lim\limits_{\varphi \to 0} \left(\dfrac{\sin \varphi}{\varphi}\right)^{\frac{1}{\varphi^2}}$. *Ans.* $\dfrac{1}{\sqrt[6]{e}}$.

52. $\lim\limits_{x \to 1} \left(\tan \dfrac{\pi x}{4}\right)^{\tan \frac{\pi x}{2}}$. *Ans.* $\dfrac{1}{e}$. **53.** Expand, in powers of $x - 2$, the polyno-

mial $x^4 - 5x^3 + 5x^2 + x + 2$. *Ans.* $-7(x - 2) - (x - 2)^2 + 3(x - 2)^3 + (x - 2)^4$.

54. Expand, in powers of $x + 1$, the polynomial $x^5 + 2x^4 - x^2 + x + 1$. *Ans.*
$(x + 1)^2 + 2(x + 1)^3 - 3(x + 1)^4 + (x + 1)^5$. **55.** Write Taylor's formula for the

function $y = \sqrt{x}$ when $a = 1$, $n = 3$. *Ans.* $\sqrt{x} = 1 + \dfrac{x - 1}{1} \cdot \dfrac{1}{2} - \dfrac{(x - 1)^2}{1 \cdot 2} \cdot \dfrac{1}{4} +$

$+ \dfrac{(x - 1)^3}{1 \cdot 2 \cdot 3} \cdot \dfrac{3}{8} - \dfrac{(x - 1)^4}{4!} \cdot \dfrac{15}{16} \cdot [1 + \theta(x - 1)]^{-\frac{7}{2}}$, $0 < \theta < 1$. **56.** Write the Mac-

laurin formula for the function $y = \sqrt{1 + x}$ when $n = 2$. *Ans.* $\sqrt{1 + x} = 1 +$

$+ \dfrac{1}{2} x - \dfrac{1}{8} x^2 + \dfrac{x^3}{16(1 + \theta x)^{\frac{5}{2}}}$, $0 < \theta < 1$. **57.** Using the results of the preceding exercise, estimate the error of the approximate equation $\sqrt{1+x} \approx$ $\approx 1+\frac{1}{2}x-\frac{1}{8}x^2$ when $x=0.2$. *Ans.* Less than $\frac{1}{2 \cdot 10^3}$.

Determine the origin of the approximate equations for small values of x and estimate the errors of these equations: **58.** $\ln \cos x \approx -\frac{x^2}{2}-\frac{x^4}{12}$.

59. $\tan x \approx x+\frac{x^3}{3}+\frac{2x^5}{15}$. **60.** $\arcsin x \approx x+\frac{x^3}{6}$. **61.** $\arctan x \approx x-\frac{x^3}{3}$.

62. $\frac{e^x+e^{-x}}{2} \approx 1+\frac{x^2}{2}+\frac{x^4}{24}$. **63.** $\ln\left(x+\sqrt{1-x^2}\right) \approx x-x^2+\frac{5x^3}{6}$.

Using Taylor's formula, compute the limits of the following expressions:

64. $\lim\limits_{x \to 0} \dfrac{x-\sin x}{e^x-1-x-\dfrac{x^2}{2}}$. *Ans.* 1. **65.** $\lim\limits_{x \to 0} \dfrac{\ln^2(1+x)-\sin^2 x}{1-e^{-x^2}}$. *Ans.* 0.

66. $\lim\limits_{x \to 0} \dfrac{2(\tan x-\sin x)-x^3}{x^5}$. *Ans.* $\dfrac{1}{4}$. **67.** $\lim\limits_{x \to 0}\left[x-x^2\ln\left(1+\dfrac{1}{x}\right)\right]$. *Ans.* 0.

68. $\lim\limits_{x \to 0}\left(\dfrac{1}{x^2}-\dfrac{\cot x}{x}\right)$. *Ans.* $\dfrac{1}{3}$. **69.** $\lim\limits_{x \to 0}\left(\dfrac{1}{x^2}-\cot^2 x\right)$. *Ans.* $\dfrac{2}{3}$.

CHAPTER 5

INVESTIGATING THE BEHAVIOUR OF FUNCTIONS

5.1. STATEMENT OF THE PROBLEM

A study of the quantitative aspect of natural phenomena leads to the establishment and study of functional relations between the variables involved. If such a functional relationship can be expressed analytically, that is, in the form of one or more formulas, we are then in a position to investigate it with the tools of mathematical analysis. For instance, a study of the flight of a shell in empty space yields a formula that gives the dependence of the range R upon the angle of elevation α and the initial velocity v_0:

$$R = \frac{v_0^2 \sin 2\alpha}{g}$$

(g is the acceleration of gravity).

With this formula we can determine at what angle α the range R will be greatest, or least, and what the conditions must be for the range to increase as the angle α is increased, etc.

Let us consider another instance. Studies of oscillations of a load on a spring (of a railway car or automobile) yielded a formula showing how the deviation y of the load from a position of equilibrium depends on the time t:

$$y = e^{-kt} (A \cos \omega t + B \sin \omega t)$$

For a given oscillatory system the quantities k, A, B, ω that enter into this formula have a very definite meaning (they depend upon the elasticity of the spring, the load, etc., but do not change with time t) and for this reason are considered constant.

On the basis of this formula we can find out at what values of t the deviation y will increase with increasing t, how the maximum deviation varies as a function of time, for what values of t we observe these maximum deviations, for what values of t we obtain maximum velocities of motion of the load, and a number of other things.

All these questions are embraced by the concept "investigating the behaviour of a function". It is obviously very difficult to determine all these questions by calculating the values of a function at specific points (like we did in Chapter 2). The purpose of this chapter is to establish more general techniques for investigating the behaviour of functions.

5.2 INCREASE AND DECREASE OF A FUNCTION

In Sec. 1.6 we gave a definition of an increasing and a decreasing function. We will now apply the concept of the derivative to investigate the increase and decrease of a function.

Theorem. (1) *If a function* $f(x)$, *which has a derivative on an interval* $[a, b]$, *increases on this interval, then its derivative on* $[a, b]$ *is not negative, that is,* $f'(x) \geqslant 0$.

(2) *If the function* $f(x)$ *is continuous on the interval* $[a, b]$ *and is differentiable on* (a, b), *where* $f'(x) > 0$ *for* $a < x < b$, *then the function increases on the interval* $[a, b]$.

Proof. We start by proving the first part of the theorem. Let $f(x)$ increase on the interval $[a, b]$. Increase the argument x by Δx and consider the ratio

$$\frac{f(x + \Delta x) - f(x)}{\Delta x} \tag{1}$$

Since $f(x)$ is an increasing function,

$$f(x + \Delta x) > f(x) \quad \text{for} \quad \Delta x > 0$$

and

$$f(x + \Delta x) < f(x) \quad \text{for} \quad \Delta x < 0$$

In both cases

$$\frac{f(x + \Delta x) - f(x)}{\Delta x} > 0 \tag{2}$$

and consequently

$$\lim_{\Delta x \to 0} \frac{f(x + \Delta x) - f(x)}{\Delta x} \geqslant 0$$

which means $f'(x) \geqslant 0$, which is what we set out to prove. [If we had $f'(x) < 0$, then for sufficiently small values of Δx, ratio (1) would be negative, but this would contradict relation (2).]

Let us now prove the second part of the theorem. Let $f'(x) > 0$ for all values of x on the interval (a, b).

Let us consider any two values x_1 and x_2, $x_1 < x_2$, on the interval $[a, b]$.

By Lagrange's mean-value theorem we have

$$f(x_2) - f(x_1) = f'(\xi)(x_2 - x_1), \quad x_1 < \xi < x_2$$

It is given that $f'(\xi) > 0$, hence $f(x_2) - f(x_1) > 0$, and this means that $f(x)$ is an increasing function.

There is a similar theorem for a decreasing (differentiable) function as well, namely:

If $f(x)$ *decreases on an interval* $[a, b]$, *then* $f'(x) \leqslant 0$ *on this interval. If* $f'(x) < 0$ *on* (a, b), *then* $f(x)$ *decreases on* $[a, b]$. [Of course, we again assume that the function is continuous at all points of $[a, b]$ and is differentiable everywhere on (a, b).]

Note. The foregoing theorem expresses the following geometric fact. If on an interval $[a, b]$ a function $f(x)$ increases, then the tangent to the curve $y = f(x)$ at each point on this interval forms an **acute** angle φ with the x-axis or (at certain points) is horizontal; the tangent of this angle is not negative: $f'(x) = \tan \varphi \geqslant 0$ (Fig. 98a). If the function $f(x)$ decreases on the interval $[a, b]$, then the angle of inclination of the tangent line forms an obtuse angle (or, at some

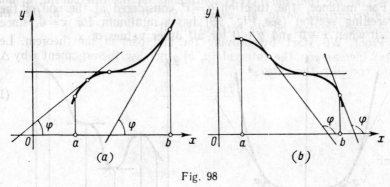

(a)   (b)

Fig. 98

points, the tangent line is horizontal)· the tangent of this angle is not positive (Fig. 98b). We can illustrate the second part of the theorem in similar fashion. This theorem permits judging the increase or decrease of a function by the sign of its derivative.

Example. Determine the domains of increase and decrease of the function

$$y = x^4$$

Solution. The derivative is equal to

$$y' = 4x^3$$

For $x > 0$ we have $y' > 0$ and the function increases; for $x < 0$ we have $y' < 0$ and the function decreases (Fig. 99).

5.3 MAXIMA AND MINIMA OF FUNCTIONS

Definition of a maximum. A function $f(x)$ has a *maximum* at the point x_1 if the value of the function $f(x)$ at the point x_1 is greater than its values at all points of a certain interval containing the point x_1. In other words, the function $f(x)$ has a *maximum* when $x = x_1$ if $f(x_1 + \Delta x) < f(x_1)$ for any Δx (positive and negative) that are sufficiently small in absolute value.*

---

* This definition is sometimes formulated as follows: a function $f(x)$ has a *maximum* at x_1 if it is possible to find a neighbourhood (α, β) of x_1 $(\alpha < x_1 < \beta)$ such that for all points of this neighbourhood different from x_1 the inequality $f(x) < f(x_1)$ is fulfilled.

For example, the function $y = f(x)$, whose graph is given in Fig. 100, has a maximum at $x = x_1$.

Definition of a minimum. A function $f(x)$ has a *minimum* at $x = x_2$ if

$$f(x_2 + \Delta x) > f(x_2)$$

for any Δx (positive and negative) that are sufficiently small in absolute value (Fig. 100).

For instance, the function $y = x^4$ considered at the end of the preceding section (see Fig. 99) has a minimum for $x = 0$, since $y = 0$ when $x = 0$ and $y > 0$ for all other values of x.

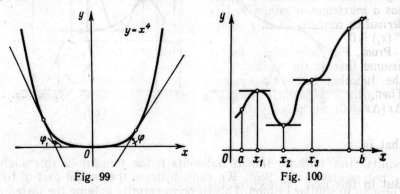

Fig. 99   Fig. 100

In connection with the definitions of maximum and minimum, note the following.

1. A function defined on an interval can reach maximum and minimum values only for values of x that lie *within* the given interval.

2. One should not think that the maximum and minimum of a function are its respective largest and smallest values over a given interval: at a point of maximum, a function has the largest value only in comparison with those values that it has at all points *sufficiently close* to the point of maximum, and the smallest value only in comparison with those that it has at all points *sufficiently close* to the minimum point.

To illustrate, take Fig. 101. Here is a function, defined on the interval $[a, b]$, which

$$\text{at } x = x_1 \text{ and } x = x_3 \text{ has a maximum,}$$
$$\text{at } x = x_2 \text{ and } x = x_4 \text{ has a minimum,}$$

but the minimum of the function at $x = x_4$ is greater than the maximum of the function at $x = x_1$. At $x = b$, the value of the function is greater than any maximum of the function on the interval under consideration.

The generic terms for maxima and minima of a function are *extremum* (pl. *extrema*) or *extreme values* of the function.

To some extent, the extrema of a function and their positions on the interval [*a*, *b*] characterize the variation of the function versus changes in the argument.

Below we give a method for finding extrema.

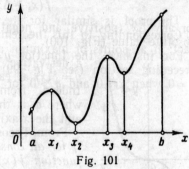

Fig. 101

Theorem 1. (A necessary condition for the existence of an extremum). *If at a point $x = x_1$ a differentiable function $y = f(x)$ has a maximum or minimum, its derivative vanishes at this point:* $f'(x_1) = 0$.

Proof. For definiteness, let us assume that at the point $x = x_1$ the function has a maximum.

Then, for sufficiently small (in absolute value) increments $\Delta x (\Delta x \neq 0)$ we have

$$f(x_1 + \Delta x) < f(x_1)$$

that is,

$$f(x_1 + \Delta x) - f(x_1) < 0$$

But in this case the sign of the ratio

$$\frac{f(x_1 + \Delta x) - f(x_1)}{\Delta x}$$

is determined by the sign of Δx, namely:

$$\frac{f(x_1 + \Delta x) - f(x_1)}{\Delta x} > 0 \text{ when } \Delta x < 0$$

$$\frac{f(x_1 + \Delta x) - f(x_1)}{\Delta x} < 0 \text{ when } \Delta x > 0$$

By the definition of a derivative we have

$$f'(x_1) = \lim_{\Delta x \to 0} \frac{f(x_1 + \Delta x) - f(x_1)}{\Delta x}$$

If $f(x_1)$ has a derivative at $x = x_1$, the limit on the right is independent of how Δx approaches zero (remaining positive or negative).

But if $\Delta x \to 0$ and remains negative, then

$$f'(x_1) \geqslant 0$$

But if $\Delta x \to 0$ and remains positive, then

$$f'(x_1) \leqslant 0$$

Since $f'(x_1)$ is a definite number that is independent of the way in which Δx approaches zero, the latter two inequalities are consistent only if

$$f'(x_1) = 0$$

The proof is similar for the case of a minimum of a function. Corresponding to this theorem is the following obvious geometric fact: if at points of maximum and minimum, a function $f(x)$ has

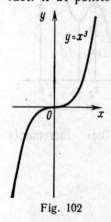

a derivative, the tangent line to the curve $y = f(x)$ at each point is parallel to the x-axis. Indeed, from the fact that $f'(x_1) = \tan \varphi = 0$, where φ is the angle between the tangent line and the x-axis, it follows that $\varphi = 0$ (Fig. 100).

From Theorem 1 it follows immediately that *if for all considered values of the argument x the function $f(x)$ has a derivative, then it can have an extremum (maximum or minimum) only at those values for which the derivative vanishes.* The converse does not hold: *it cannot be said that there definitely exists a maximum or minimum for every value at which the derivative vanishes.* For instance, in Fig. 100 we have a function for

Fig. 102

which the derivative at $x = x_3$ vanishes (the tangent line is horizontal), yet the function at this point is neither a maximum nor a minimum.

In exactly the same way, the function $y = x^3$ (Fig. 102) at $x = 0$ has a derivative equal to zero:

$$(y')_{x=0} = (3x^2)_{x=0} = 0$$

but at this point the function has neither a maximum nor a minimum. Indeed, no matter how close the point x is to 0, we will always have

$$x^3 < 0 \text{ when } x < 0$$

and

$$x^3 > 0 \text{ when } x > 0$$

We have investigated the case where a function has a derivative at all points on some closed interval. Now what about those points at which there is no derivative? The following examples will show that at these points there can only be a maximum or a minimum, but there may not be either one or the other.

Example 1. The function $y = |x|$ has no derivative at the point $x = 0$ (at this point the curve does not have a definite tangent line), but the function has a minimum at this point: $y = 0$ when $x = 0$, whereas for any other point x different from zero we have $y > 0$ (Fig. 103).

Example 2. The function $y = \left(1 - x^{\frac{2}{3}}\right)^{3/2}$ has no derivative at $x = 0$, since $y' = -\left(1 - x^{\frac{2}{3}}\right)^{\frac{1}{2}} x^{-\frac{1}{3}}$ becomes infinite at $x = 0$, but the function has a maximum at this point: $f(0) = 1$, $f(x) < 1$ for x different from zero (Fig. 104).

Example 3. The function $y = \sqrt[3]{x}$ has no derivative at $x = 0$ ($y' \longrightarrow \infty$ as $x \longrightarrow 0$). At this point the function has neither a maximum nor a minimum: $f(0) = 0$, $f(x) < 0$ for $x < 0$, $f(x) > 0$ for $x > 0$ (Fig. 105).

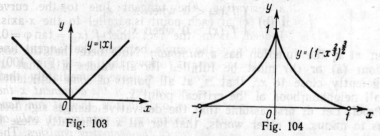

Fig. 103   Fig. 104

Thus, a function can have an extremum only in two cases: either at points where the derivative exists and is zero, or at points where the derivative does not exist.

It must be noted that if the derivative does not exist at some point (but exists at nearby points), then at this point the derivative is **discontinuous**.

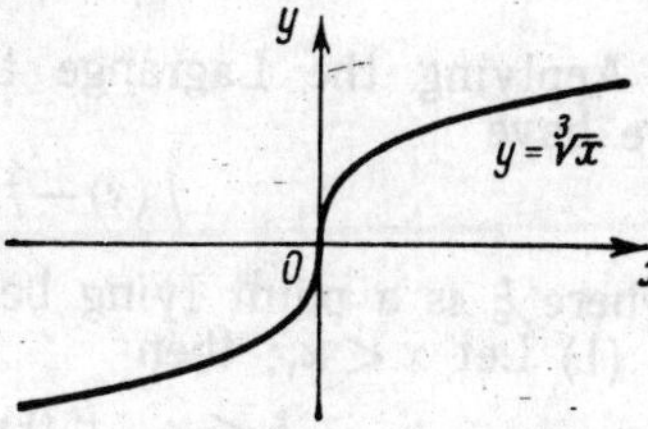

The values of the argument for which the derivative vanishes or is discontinuous are called *critical points* or *critical values*.

Fig. 105

From what has been said it follows that not for every critical value does a function have a maximum or a minimum. However, if at some point the function attains a maximum or a minimum, this point is definitely critical. And so to find the extrema of a function do as follows: find all the critical points, and then, investigating separately each critical point, find out whether the function will have a maximum or a minimum at that point, or whether there will be neither maximum nor minimum.

Investigation of a function at critical points is based on the following theorem.

Theorem 2. (Sufficient conditions for the existence of an extremum). *Let there be a function $f(x)$ continuous on some interval containing a critical point x_1 and differentiable at all points of the interval (with the exception, possibly, of the point x_1 itself). If in moving from left to right through this point the derivative changes sign from plus to minus, then at $x = x_1$ the function has a maximum.*

But if in moving through the point x_1 from left to right the derivative changes sign from minus to plus, the function has a minimum at this point.

And so

if (a) $\begin{cases} f'(x) > 0 \text{ when } x < x_1 \\ f'(x) < 0 \text{ when } x > x_1 \end{cases}$

then at x_1 the function has a *maximum*;

if (b) $\begin{cases} f'(x) < 0 \text{ when } x < x_1 \\ f'(x) > 0 \text{ when } x > x_1 \end{cases}$

then at x_1 the function has a *minimum*. Note here that the conditions (a) or (b) must be fulfilled for all values of x that are sufficiently close to x_1, that is, at all points of some sufficiently small neighbourhood of the critical point x_1.

Proof. Let us first assume that the derivative changes sign from plus to minus, in other words, that for all x sufficiently close to x_1 we have

$$f'(x) > 0 \text{ when } x < x_1$$
$$f'(x) < 0 \text{ when } x > x_1$$

Applying the Lagrange theorem to the difference $f(x) - f(x_1)$ we have

$$f(x) - f(x_1) = f'(\xi)(x - x_1)$$

where ξ is a point lying between x and x_1.

(1) Let $x < x_1$; then

$$\xi < x_1, \ f'(\xi) > 0, \ f'(\xi)(x - x_1) < 0$$

and, consequently,

$$f(x) - f(x_1) < 0$$

or

$$f(x) < f(x_1) \tag{1}$$

(2) Let $x > x_1$; then

$$\xi > x_1, \ f'(\xi) < 0, \ f'(\xi)(x - x_1) < 0$$

and, consequently,

$$f(x) - f(x_1) < 0$$

or

$$f(x) < f(x_1) \tag{2}$$

The relations (1) and (2) show that for all values of x sufficiently close to x_1 the values of the function are less than those at x_1. Hence, the function $f(x)$ has a maximum at the point x_1.

The second part of the theorem on the sufficient condition for a minimum is proved in similar fashion.

Fig. 106 illustrates the meaning of Theorem 2.

At $x = x_1$, suppose $f'(x_1) = 0$ and let the following inequalities be fulfilled for all x sufficiently close to x_1:

$$f'(x) > 0 \text{ when } x < x_1$$
$$f'(x) < 0 \text{ when } x > x_1$$

Then for $x < x_1$ the tangent to the curve forms with the x-axis an acute angle, and the function increases, but for $x > x_1$ the tangent forms with the x-axis an obtuse angle, and the function decreases; at $x = x_1$ the function passes from increasing to decreasing values, which means it has a maximum.

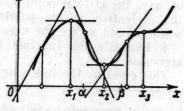

If at x_2 we have $f'(x_2) = 0$ and for all values of x sufficiently close to x_2 the following inequalities hold:

$$f'(x) < 0 \text{ when } x < x_2$$
$$f'(x) > 0 \text{ when } x > x_2$$

Fig. 106

then at $x < x_2$ the tangent to the curve forms with the x-axis an obtuse angle, the function decreases, and at $x > x_2$ the tangent to the curve forms an acute angle, and the function increases. At $x = x_2$ the function passes from decreasing to increasing values, which means it has a minimum.

If at $x = x_3$ we have $f'(x_3) = 0$ and for all values of x sufficiently close to x_3 the following inequalities hold:

$$f'(x) > 0 \text{ when } x < x_3$$
$$f'(x) > 0 \text{ when } x > x_3$$

then the function increases both for $x < x_3$ and for $x > x_3$. Therefore, at $x = x_3$ the function has neither a maximum nor a minimum. Such is the case with the function $y = x^3$ at $x = 0$.

Indeed, the derivative $y' = 3x^2$, hence,

$$(y')_{x=0} = 0$$
$$(y')_{x<0} > 0$$
$$(y')_{x>0} > 0$$

and this means that at $x = 0$ the function has neither a maximum nor a minimum (see Fig. 102).

11*

5.4 TESTING A DIFFERENTIABLE FUNCTION FOR MAXIMUM AND MINIMUM WITH A FIRST DERIVATIVE

The preceding section permits us to formulate a rule for testing a differentiable function, $y = f(x)$, for maximum and minimum.

1. Find the first derivative of the function, i.e., $f'(x)$.
2. Find the critical values of the argument x; to do this:
(a) equate the first derivative to zero and find the real roots of the equation $f'(x) = 0$ obtained;
(b) find the values of x at which the derivative $f'(x)$ becomes discontinuous.
3. Investigate the sign of the derivative on the left and right of the critical point. Since the sign of the derivative remains constant on the interval between two critical points, it is sufficient, for investigating the sign of the derivative on the left and right of, say, the critical point x_2 (Fig. 106), to determine the sign of the derivative at the points α and β ($x_1 < \alpha < x_2$, $x_2 < \beta < x_3$, where x_1 and x_3 are the closest critical points).
4. Evaluate the function $f(x)$ for every critical value of the argument.

This gives us the following diagram of possible cases:

Signs of derivative $f'(x)$ when passing through critical point x_1:			Character of critical point
$x < x_1$	$x = x_1$	$x > x_1$	
$+$	$f'(x_1) = 0$ or is discontinuous	$-$	Maximum point
$-$	$f'(x_1) = 0$ or is discontinuous	$+$	Minimum point
$+$	$f'(x_1) = 0$ or is discontinuous	$+$	Neither maximum nor minimum (function increases)
$-$	$f'(x_1) = 0$ or is discontinuous	$-$	Neither maximum nor minimum (function decreases)

Example 1. Test the following function for maximum and minimum:

$$y = \frac{x^3}{3} - 2x^2 + 3x + 1$$

Solution. 1. Find the first derivative:

$$y' = x^2 - 4x + 3$$

2. Find the real roots of the derivative:

$$x^2 - 4x + 3 = 0$$

Consequently,

$$x_1 = 1, \quad x_2 = 3$$

The derivative is everywhere continuous and so there are no other critical points.

3. Investigate the critical values and record the results in Fig. 107.
Investigate the first critical point $x_1 = 1$. Since $y' = (x-1)(x-3)$,

$$\text{for } x < 1 \quad \text{we have } y' = (-) \cdot (-) > 0$$
$$\text{for } x > 1 \quad \text{we have } y' = (+) \cdot (-) < 0$$

Thus, when passing (from left to right) through the value $x_1 = 1$ the derivative changes sign from plus to minus. Hence, at $x = 1$ the function has a maximum, namely,

$$(y)_{x=1} = \frac{7}{3}$$

Investigate the second critical point $x_2 = 3$:

$$\text{when } x < 3 \quad \text{we have } y' = (+) \cdot (-) < 0$$
$$\text{when } x > 3 \quad \text{we have } y' = (+) \cdot (+) > 0$$

Thus, when passing through the value $x = 3$ the derivative changes sign from minus to plus. Therefore, at $x = 3$ the function has a minimum, namely:

$$(y)_{x=3} = 1$$

This investigation yields the graph of the function (Fig. 107).

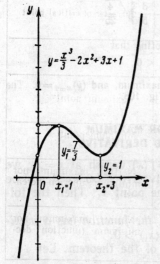

$$y = \frac{x^3}{3} - 2x^2 + 3x + 1$$

$$y_1 = \frac{7}{3}$$

$$y_2 = 1$$

$$0 \quad x_1 = 1 \quad x_2 = 3 \quad x$$

Fig. 107

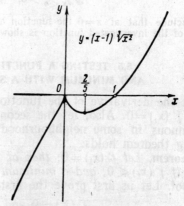

$$y = (x-1)\sqrt[3]{x^2}$$

$$0 \quad \frac{2}{5} \quad 1 \quad x$$

Fig. 108

Example 2. Test for maximum and minimum the function

$$y = (x-1)\sqrt[3]{x^2}$$

Solution. 1. Find the first derivative:

$$y' = \sqrt[3]{x^2} + \frac{2(x-1)}{3\sqrt[3]{x}} = \frac{5x-2}{3\sqrt[3]{x}}$$

2. Find the critical values of the argument: (a) find the points at which the derivative vanishes:

$$y' = \frac{5x-2}{3\sqrt[3]{x}} = 0, \quad x_1 = \frac{2}{5}$$

(b) find the points at which the derivative becomes discontinuous (in this instance, it becomes infinite). Obviously, that point is

$$x_2 = 0$$

(It will be noted that for $x_2 = 0$ the function is defined and continuous.)
There are no other critical points.

3. Investigate the character of the critical points obtained. Investigate the point $x_1 = \frac{2}{5}$. Noting that

$$(y')_{x < \frac{2}{5}} < 0, \quad (y')_{x > \frac{2}{5}} > 0$$

we conclude that at $x = \frac{2}{5}$ the function has a minimum. The value of the function at the minimum point is

$$(y)_{x = \frac{2}{5}} = \left(\frac{2}{5} - 1\right)\sqrt[3]{\frac{4}{25}} = -\frac{3}{5}\sqrt[3]{\frac{4}{25}}$$

Investigate the second critical point $x = 0$. Noting that

$$(y')_{x < 0} > 0, \quad (y')_{x > 0} < 0$$

we conclude that at $x = 0$ the function has a maximum, and $(y)_{x=0} = 0$. The graph of the investigated function is shown in Fig. 108.

5.5 TESTING A FUNCTION FOR MAXIMUM AND MINIMUM WITH A SECOND DERIVATIVE

Let the derivative of the function $y = f(x)$ vanish at $x = x_1$; we have $f'(x_1) = 0$. Also, let the second derivative $f''(x)$ exist and be continuous in some neighbourhood of the point x_1. Then the following theorem holds.

Theorem. *Let $f'(x_1) = 0$; then at $x = x_1$ the function has a maximum if $f''(x_1) < 0$, and a minimum if $f''(x_1) > 0$.*

Proof. Let us first prove the first part of the theorem. Let

$$f'(x_1) = 0 \text{ and } f''(x_1) < 0$$

Since it is given that $f''(x)$ is continuous in some small interval about the point $x = x_1$, there will obviously be some small closed interval about the point $x = x_1$, at all points of which the second derivative $f''(x)$ will be negative.

Since $f''(x)$ is the first derivative of the first derivative, $f''(x) = = (f'(x))'$, it follows from the condition $(f'(x))' < 0$ that $f'(x)$ decreases on the closed interval containing $x = x_1$ (Sec. 5.2). But $f'(x_1) = 0$, and so on this interval we have $f'(x) > 0$ when $x < x_1$, and when $x > x_1$ we have $f'(x) < 0$; in other words, the derivative $f'(x)$ changes sign from plus to minus when passing through the point $x = x_1$, and this means that at the point x_1 the function $f(x)$ has a maximum. The first part of the theorem is proved.

The second part of the theorem is proved in similar fashion: if $f''(x_1) > 0$, then $f''(x) > 0$ at all points of some closed interval about the point x_1, but then on this interval $f''(x) = (f'(x))' > 0$ and, hence, $f'(x)$ increases. Since $f'(x_1) = 0$ the derivative $f'(x)$ changes sign from minus to plus when passing through the point x_1, i.e., the function $f(x)$ has a minimum at $x = x_1$.

If at the critical point $f''(x_1) = 0$, then at this point there may be either a maximum or a minimum or neither maximum nor minimum. In this case, investigate by the first method (see Sec. 5.4).

The scheme for investigating extrema with a second derivative is shown in the following table.

$f'(x_1)$	$f''(x_1)$	Character of critical point
0	—	Maximum point
0	+	Minimum point
0	0	Unknown

Example 1. Examine the following function for maximum and minimum

$$y = 2 \sin x + \cos 2x$$

Solution. Since the function is periodic with period 2π, it is sufficient to investigate the function in the interval $[0, 2\pi]$.

1. Find the derivative:

$$y' = 2 \cos x - 2 \sin 2x = 2 (\cos x - 2 \sin x \cos x) = 2 \cos x (1 - 2 \sin x)$$

2. Find the critical values of the argument:

$$2 \cos x (1 - 2 \sin x) = 0$$

$$x_1 = \frac{\pi}{6}; \quad x_2 = \frac{\pi}{2}; \quad x_3 = \frac{5\pi}{6}, \quad x_4 = \frac{3\pi}{2}$$

3. Find the second derivative:

$$y'' = -2 \sin x - 4 \cos 2x$$

4. Investigate the character of each critical point:

$$(y'')_{x_1 = \frac{\pi}{6}} = -2 \cdot \frac{1}{2} - 4 \cdot \frac{1}{2} = -3 < 0$$

Hence, at the point $x_1 = \frac{\pi}{6}$ we have a maximum:

$$(y)_{x=\frac{\pi}{6}} = 2 \cdot \frac{1}{2} + \frac{1}{2} = \frac{3}{2}$$

Further,

$$(y'')_{x=\frac{\pi}{2}} = -2 \cdot 1 + 4 \cdot 1 = 2 > 0$$

And so at the point $x_2 = \frac{\pi}{2}$ we have a minimum:

$$(y)_{x=\frac{\pi}{2}} = 2 \cdot 1 - 1 = 1$$

At $x_3 = \frac{5\pi}{6}$ we have

$$(y'')_{x=\frac{5\pi}{6}} = -2 \cdot \frac{1}{2} - 4 \cdot \frac{1}{2} = -3 < 0$$

Thus, at $x_3 = \frac{5\pi}{6}$ the function has a maximum:

$$(y)_{x_3=\frac{5\pi}{6}} = 2 \cdot \frac{1}{2} + \frac{1}{2} = \frac{3}{2}$$

Finally,

$$(y'')_{x=\frac{3\pi}{2}} = -2(-1) - 4(-1) = 6 > 0$$

Consequently, at $x_4 = \frac{3\pi}{2}$ we have a minimum:

$$(y)_{x=\frac{3\pi}{2}} = 2(-1) - 1 = -3$$

The graph of the function under investigation is shown in Fig. 109.

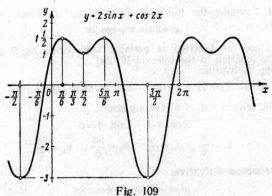

Fig. 109

The following examples will show that if at a certain point $x = x_1$ we have $f'(x_1) = 0$ and $f''(x_1) = 0$, then at this point the function $f(x)$ can have either a maximum or a minimum or neither.

Example 2. Test the following function for maximum and minimum:

$$y = 1 - x^4$$

Solution. 1. Find the critical points:

$$y' = -4x^3, \quad -4x^3 = 0, \quad x = 0$$

2. Determine the sign of the second derivative at $x = 0$.

$$y'' = -12x^2, \quad (y'')_{x=0} = 0$$

It is thus impossible here to determine the character of the critical point by means of the sign of the second derivative.

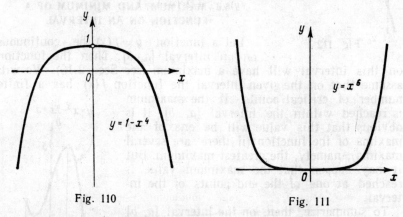

Fig. 110   Fig. 111

3. Investigate the character of the critical point by the first method (see Sec. 5.4):

$$(y')_{x<0} > 0, \quad (y')_{x>0} < 0$$

Consequently, at $x = 0$ the function has a maximum, namely,

$$(y)_{x=0} = 1$$

The graph of this function is given in Fig. 110.

Example 3. Test for maximum and minimum the function

$$y = x^6$$

Solution. By the second method we find

1. $y' = 6x^5, \quad y' = 6x^5 = 0, \quad x = 0,$
2. $y'' = 30x^4, \quad (y'')_{x=0} = 0$

Thus, the second method does not yield anything. Resorting to the first method, we get

$$(y')_{x<0} < 0, \quad (y')_{x>0} > 0$$

Therefore, at $x = 0$ the function has a minimum (Fig. 111).

Example 4. Test for maximum and minimum the function

$$y = (x - 1)^3$$

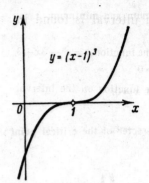

$y = (x-1)^3$

Fig. 112

Solution. By the second method we find:

$$y' = 3(x-1)^2, \quad 3(x-1)^2 = 0, \quad x = 1$$
$$y'' = 6(x-1), \quad (y'')_{x=1} = 0$$

Thus, the second method does not yield an answer. By the first method we get

$$(y')_{x<1} > 0, \quad (y')_{x>1} > 0$$

Consequently, at $x = 1$ the function has neither a maximum nor a minimum (Fig. 112).

5.6 MAXIMUM AND MINIMUM OF A FUNCTION ON AN INTERVAL

Let a function $y = f(x)$ be continuous on an interval $[a, b]$. Then the function on this interval will have a maximum (see Sec. 2.10). We will assume that on the given interval the function $f(x)$ has a finite number of critical points. If the maximum is reached within the interval $[a, b]$, it is obvious that this value will be one of the maxima of the function (if there are several maxima), namely, the greatest maximum. But it may happen that the maximum value is reached at one of the end points of the interval.

To summarize, then, on the interval $[a, b]$ the function reaches its greatest value either at one of the end points of the interval, or at such an interior point as is the maximum point.

The same may be said about the minimum value of the function: it is attained either at one of the end points of the interval or at an interior point such that the latter is the minimum point.

From the foregoing we get the following rule: if it is required to find the maximum of a continuous function on an interval $[a, b]$, do the following:

1. Find all maxima of the function on the interval.

2. Determine the values of the function at the end points of the interval; that is, evaluate $f(a)$ and $f(b)$.

3. Of all the values of the function obtained choose the greatest; it will be the maximum value of the function on the interval.

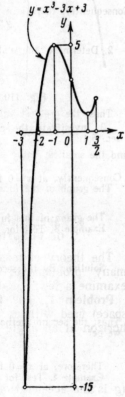

$y = x^3 - 3x + 3$

Fig. 113

The minimum value of a function on an interval is found in similar fashion.

Example. Determine the maximum and minimum of the function $y = x^3 - 3x + 3$ on the interval $\left[-3, \dfrac{3}{2}\right]$.

Solution. 1. Find the maxima and minima of the function on the interval $\left[-3, \dfrac{3}{2}\right]$:

$$y' = 3x^2 - 3, \ 3x^2 - 3 = 0, \ x_1 = 1, \ x_2 = -1,$$
$$y'' = 6x$$

then

$$(y'')_{x=1} = 6 > 0$$

Hence, there is a minimum at the point $x = 1$:

$$(y)_{x=1} = 1$$

Furthermore

$$(y'')_{x=-1} = -6 < 0$$

Consequently, there is a maximum at the point $x = -1$:

$$(y)_{x=-1} = 5$$

2. Determine the value of the function at the end points of the interval:

$$(y)_{x=\frac{3}{2}} = \frac{15}{8}, \ (y)_{x=-3} = -15$$

Thus, the greatest value of this function on the interval $\left[-3, \dfrac{3}{2}\right]$ is

$$(y)_{x=-1} = 5$$

and the smallest value is

$$(y)_{x=-3} = -15$$

The graph of the function is shown in Fig. 113.

5.7 APPLYING THE THEORY OF MAXIMA AND MINIMA OF FUNCTIONS TO THE SOLUTION OF PROBLEMS

The theory of maxima and minima is applied in the solution of many problems of geometry, mechanics, and so forth. Let us examine a few.

Problem 1. The range $R = OA$ (Fig. 114) of a shell (in empty space) fired with an initial velocity v_0 from a gun inclined to the horizon at an angle φ is determined by the formula

$$R = \frac{v_0^2 \sin 2\varphi}{g}$$

(g is the acceleration of gravity). Determine the angle φ at which the range R will be a maximum for a given initial velocity v_0.

Solution. The quantity R is a function of the variable angle φ. Test this function for a maximum on the interval $0 \leqslant \varphi \leqslant \dfrac{\pi}{2}$:

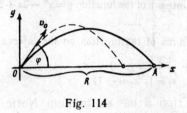

Fig. 114

$$\frac{dR}{d\varphi} = \frac{2v_0^2 \cos 2\varphi}{g} \; ; \quad \frac{2v_0^2 \cos 2\varphi}{g} = 0;$$

critical value $\varphi = \dfrac{\pi}{4}$;

$$\frac{d^2R}{d\varphi^2} = -\frac{4v_0^2 \sin 2\varphi}{g}$$

$$\left(\frac{d^2R}{d\varphi^2}\right)_{\varphi = \pi/4} = -\frac{4v_0^2}{g} < 0$$

Hence, for the value $\varphi = \dfrac{\pi}{4}$ the range R has a maximum:

$$(R)_{\varphi = \pi/4} = \frac{v_0^2}{g}$$

The values of the function R at the end points of the interval $\left[0, \dfrac{\pi}{2}\right]$ are

$$(R)_{\varphi = 0} = 0, \quad (R)_{\varphi = \pi/2} = 0$$

Thus, the maximum obtained is the sought-for greatest value of R.

Problem 2. What should the dimensions of a cylinder be so that for a given volume v its total surface area S is a minimum?

Solution. Denoting by r the radius of the base of the cylinder and by h the altitude, we have

$$S = 2\pi r^2 + 2\pi rh$$

Since the volume of the cylinder is given, for a given r the quantity h is determined by the formula

$$v = \pi r^2 h$$

whence

$$h = \frac{v}{\pi r^2}$$

Substituting this expression of h into the formula for S, we have

$$S = 2\pi r^2 + 2\pi r \frac{v}{\pi r^2}$$

or

$$S = 2\left(\pi r^2 + \frac{v}{r}\right)$$

Here v is given, so we have represented S as a function of a single independent variable r.

Find the minimum value of this function on the interval $0 < r < \infty$:

$$\frac{dS}{dr} = 2\left(2\pi r - \frac{v}{r^2}\right)$$

$$2\pi r - \frac{v}{r^2} = 0, \quad r_1 = \sqrt[3]{\frac{v}{2\pi}}$$

$$\left(\frac{d^2 S}{dr^2}\right)_{r=r_1} = 2\left(2\pi + \frac{2v}{r^3}\right)_{r=r_1} > 0$$

Thus, at the point $r = r_1$ the function S has a minimum. Noticing that $\lim_{r \to 0} S = \infty$ and $\lim_{r \to \infty} S = \infty$, that is, that as r approaches zero or infinity the surface S increases without bound, we arrive at the conclusion that at $r = r_1$ the function S has a **minimum**. But if $r = \sqrt[3]{\frac{v}{2\pi}}$, then

$$h = \frac{v}{\pi r^2} = 2\sqrt[3]{\frac{v}{2\pi}} = 2r$$

Therefore, for the total surface area S of a cylinder to be a minimum for a given volume v, the altitude of the cylinder must be equal to its diameter.

5.8 TESTING A FUNCTION FOR MAXIMUM AND MINIMUM BY MEANS OF TAYLOR'S FORMULA

In Sec. 5.5, it was noted that if at a certain point $x = a$ we have $f'(a) = 0$ and $f''(a) = 0$, then at this point there may be either a maximum or a minimum or neither. And it was noted that in this instance the problem is solved by investigating by the first method; in other words, by testing the sign of the first derivative on the left and on the right of the point $x = a$.

Now we will show that it is possible in this case to investigate by means of Taylor's formula, which was derived in Sec. 4.6.

For greater generality, we assume that not only $f''(x)$, but also all derivatives of the function $f(x)$ up to the nth order inclusive vanish at $x = a$:

$$f'(a) = f''(a) = \ldots = f^{(n)}(a) = 0 \tag{1}$$

and

$$f^{(n+1)}(a) \neq 0$$

Further, we assume that $f(x)$ has continuous derivatives up to the $(n+1)$th order inclusive in the neighbourhood of the point $x = a$.

Write the Taylor formula for $f(x)$, taking account of equalities (1):

$$f(x) = f(a) + \frac{(x-a)^{n+1}}{(n+1)!} f^{(n+1)}(\xi) \qquad (2)$$

where ξ is a number that lies between a and x.

Since $f^{(n+1)}(x)$ is continuous in the neighbourhood of the point a and $f^{(n+1)}(a) \neq 0$, there will be a small positive number h such that for any x that satisfies the inequality $|x-a| < h$, it will be true that $f^{(n+1)}(x) \neq 0$. And if $f^{(n+1)}(a) > 0$, then at all points of the interval $(a-h, a+h)$ we will have $f^{(n+1)}(x) > 0$; if $f^{(n+1)}(a) < 0$, then at all points of this interval we will have $f^{(n+1)}(x) < 0$.

Rewrite formula (2) in the form

$$f(x) - f(a) = \frac{(x-a)^{n+1}}{(n+1)!} f^{(n+1)}(\xi) \qquad (2')$$

and consider various special cases.

Case 1. n is odd.

(a) Let $f^{(n+1)}(a) < 0$. Then there will be an interval $(a-h, a+h)$ at all points of which the $(n+1)$th derivative is negative. If x is a point of this interval, then ξ likewise lies between $a-h$ and $a+h$ and, consequently, $f^{(n+1)}(\xi) < 0$. Since $n+1$ is an even number, $(x-a)^{n+1} > 0$ for $x \neq a$, and therefore the right side of formula $(2')$ is negative.

Thus, for $x \neq a$ at all points of the interval $(a-h, a+h)$ we have

$$f(x) - f(a) < 0$$

and this means that at $x = a$ the function has a maximum.

(b) Let $f^{(n+1)}(a) > 0$. Then we have $f^{(n+1)}(\xi) > 0$ for a sufficiently small value of h at all points x of the interval $(a-h, a+h)$. Hence, the right side of formula $(2')$ will be positive; in other words, for $x \neq a$ we will have the following at all points in the given interval:

$$f(x) - f(a) > 0$$

and this means that at $x = a$ the function has a minimum.

Case 2. n is even.

Then $n+1$ is odd and the quantity $(x-a)^{n+1}$ has different signs for $x < a$ and $x > a$.

If h is sufficiently small in absolute value, then the $(n+1)$th derivative retains the same sign at all points of the interval $(a-h, a+h)$ as at the point a. Thus, $f(x) - f(a)$ has different signs for $x < a$ and $x > a$. But this means that there is neither maximum nor minimum at $x = a$.

It will be noted that if $f^{(n+1)}(a) > 0$ when n is even, then $f(x) < f(a)$ for $x < a$ and $f(x) > f(a)$ for $x > a$.

But if $f^{(n+1)}(a) < 0$ when n is even, then $f(x) > f(a)$ for $x < a$ and $f(x) < f(a)$ for $x > a$.

The results obtained may be formulated as follows.

If at $x = a$ we have

$$f'(a) = f''(a) = \ldots = f^{(n)}(a) = 0$$

and the first nonvanishing derivative $f^{(n+1)}(a)$ is a derivative of **even** order, then at the point a

$$f(x) \text{ has a } \textbf{maximum} \text{ if } f^{(n+1)}(a) < 0$$
$$f(x) \text{ has a } \textbf{minimum} \text{ if } f^{(n+1)}(a) > 0$$

But if the first nonvanishing derivative $f^{(n+1)}(a)$ is a derivative of **odd** order, then the function has neither maximum nor minimum at the point a. Here,

$$f(x) \text{ increases if } f^{(n+1)}(a) > 0$$
$$f(x) \text{ decreases if } f^{(n+1)}(a) < 0$$

Example. Test the following function for maximum and minimum:

$$f(x) = x^4 - 4x^3 + 6x^2 - 4x + 1$$

Solution. We find the critical values of the function

$$f'(x) = 4x^3 - 12x^2 + 12x - 4 = 4(x^3 - 3x^2 + 3x - 1)$$

From equation

$$4(x^3 - 3x^2 + 3x - 1) = 0$$

we obtain the only critical point

$$x = 1$$

(since this equation has only one real root).

Investigate the character of the critical point $x = 1$:

$$f''(x) = 12x^2 - 24x + 12 = 0 \quad \text{for } x = 1$$
$$f'''(x) = 24x - 24 = 0 \quad \text{for } x = 1$$
$$f^{IV}(x) = 24 > 0 \quad \text{for any } x$$

Consequently, for $x = 1$ the function $f(x)$ has a minimum.

5.9 CONVEXITY AND CONCAVITY OF A CURVE. POINTS OF INFLECTION

In the plane, we consider a curve $y = f(x)$, which is the graph of a single-valued differentiable function $f(x)$.

Definition 1. We say that a curve is *convex upwards* on the interval (a, b) if all points of the curve lie below any tangent to it on the interval.

We say that the curve is *convex downwards* on the interval (b, c) if all points of the curve lie above any tangent to it on the interval.

We shall call a curve convex up, a *convex curve*, and a curve convex down, a *concave curve*.

Fig. 115 shows a curve convex on the interval (a, b) and concave on the interval (b, c).

An important characteristic of the shape of a curve is its convexity or concavity. This section will be devoted to establishing the characteristics by which, when investigating a function $y = f(x)$, one can judge the convexity or concavity (direction of bulge) on various intervals.

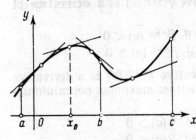

Fig. 115

We shall prove the following theorem.

Theorem 1. *If at all points of an interval (a, b) the second derivative of the function $f(x)$ is negative, i. e., $f''(x) < 0$, the curve $y = f(x)$ on this interval is convex upwards (the curve is convex).*

Proof. In the interval (a, b) take an arbitrary point $x = x_0$ (Fig. 115) and draw a tangent to the curve at the point with abscissa $x = x_0$. The theorem will be proved provided we establish that all the points of the curve on the interval (a, b) lie below this tangent; that is, that the ordinate of any point of the curve $y = f(x)$ is less than the ordinate y of the tangent line for one and the same value of x.

The equation of the curve is of the form

$$y = f(x) \tag{1}$$

But the equation of the tangent to the curve at the point $x = x_0$ is of the form

$$\overline{y} - \;\; = f'(x_0)(x - x_0)$$

or

$$\overline{y} = f(x_0) + f'(x_0)(x - x_0) \tag{2}$$

From equations (1) and (2) it follows that the difference between the ordinates of the curve and the tangent for the same value of x is

$$y - \overline{y} = f(x) - f(x_0) - f'(x_0)(x - x_0)$$

Applying the Lagrange theorem to the difference $f(x) - f(x_0)$, we get

$$y - \overline{y} = f'(c)(x - x_0) - f'(x_0)(x - x_0)$$

(where c lies between x_0 and x) or

$$y - \overline{y} = [f'(c) - f'(x_0)](x - x_0)$$

We again apply the Lagrange theorem to the expression in the square brackets; then

$$y - \bar{y} = f''(c_1)(c - x_0)(x - x_0) \qquad (3)$$

(where c_1 lies between x_0 and c).

Let us first examine the case where $x > x_0$. In this case, $x_0 < c_1 < c < x$; since

$$x - x_0 > 0, \quad c - x_0 > 0$$

and since, in addition, it is given that

$$f''(c_1) < 0$$

it follows from (3) that $y - \bar{y} < 0$.

Now let us consider the case where $x < x_0$. In this case $x < c < c_1 < x_0$ and $x - x_0 < 0$, $c - x_0 < 0$, and since it is given that $f''(c_1) < 0$, it follows from (3) that

$$y - \bar{y} < 0$$

We have thus proved that every point of the curve lies below the tangent to the curve, no matter what values x and x_0 have on the interval (a, b). And this signifies that the curve is convex. The theorem is proved.

The following theorem is proved in similar fashion.

Theorem 1'. *If at all points of the interval (b, c), the second derivative of the function $f(x)$ is positive, that is, $f''(x) > 0$, then*

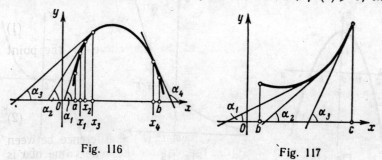

Fig. 116   Fig. 117

the curve $y = f(x)$ on this interval is convex downwards (the curve is concave).

Note. The content of Theorems 1 and 1' may be illustrated geometrically. Consider the curve $y = f(x)$, convex upwards on the interval (a, b) (Fig. 116). The derivative $f'(x)$ is equal to the tangent of the angle of inclination α of the tangent line at the point with abscissa x, or $f'(x) = \tan \alpha$. For this reason, $f''(x) = (\tan \alpha)'_x$. It $f''(x) < 0$ for all x on the interval (a, b), this means that $\tan \alpha$ decreases with increasing x. It is geometrically obvious that if $\tan \alpha$ decreases with increasing x, then the corresponding curve is convex. Theorem 1 is an analytic proof of this fact.

Theorem 1′ is illustrated geometrically in similar fashion (Fig. 117).

Example 1. Establish the intervals of convexity and concavity of a curve represented by the equation

$$y = 2 - x^2$$

Solution. The second derivative

$$y'' = -2 < 0$$

for all values of x. Hence, the curve is everywhere convex upwards (Fig. 118).

Example 2. The curve is given by the equation

$$y = e^x$$

Since

$$y'' = e^x > 0$$

for all values of x, the curve is therefore everywhere concave (bulges, or is convex downwards) (Fig. 119).

Example 3. A curve is defined by the equation

$$y = x^3$$

Since

$$y'' = 6x.$$

$y'' < 0$ for $x < 0$ and $y'' > 0$ for $x > 0$. Hence, for $x < 0$ the curve is convex upwards, and for $x > 0$, convex down (Fig. 120).

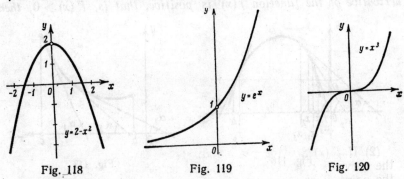

Fig. 118   Fig. 119   Fig. 120

Definition 2. The point that separates the convex part of a continuous curve from the concave part is called the *point of inflection* of the curve.

In Figs. 120, 121 and 122 the points O, A and B are points of inflection.

It is obvious that at the point of inflection the tangent line, if it exists, **cuts** the curve, because on one side the curve lies **under** the **tangent and** on the other side, **above** it.

Let us now establish sufficient conditions for a given **point of** a curve to be a point of inflection.

Theorem 2. *Let a curve be defined by an equation* $y = f(x)$. *If* $f''(a) = 0$ *or* $f''(a)$ *does not exist and if the derivative* $f''(x)$ *changes*

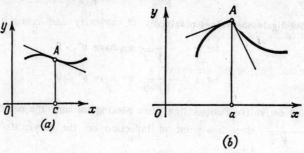

Fig. 121

sign when passing through $x = a$, *then the point of the curve with abscissa* $x = a$ *is the point of inflection.*

Proof. (1) Let $f''(x) < 0$ for $x < a$ and $f''(x) > 0$ for $x > a$.

Then for $x < a$ the curve is convex up and for $x > a$, it is convex down. Hence, the point A of the curve with abscissa $x = a$ is a point of inflection (Fig. 121).

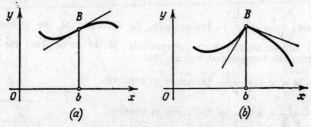

Fig. 122

(2) If $f''(x) > 0$ for $x < b$ and $f''(x) < 0$ for $x > b$, then for $x < b$ the curve is convex down, and for $x > b$, it is convex up. Hence, the point B of the curve with abscissa $x = b$ is a point of inflection (see Fig. 122).

Example 4. Find the points of inflection and determine the intervals of convexity and concavity of the curve

$$y = e^{-x^2} \quad \text{(Gaussian curve)}$$

Solution. (1) Find the first and second derivatives:

$$y' = -2xe^{-x^2}$$
$$y'' = 2e^{-x^2}(2x^2 - 1)$$

12*

(2) The first and second derivatives exist everywhere. Find the values of x for which $y'' = 0$:

$$2e^{-x^2}(2x^2 - 1) = 0$$

$$x_1 = -\frac{1}{\sqrt{2}}, \qquad x_2 = \frac{1}{\sqrt{2}}$$

(3) Investigate the values obtained:

$$\text{for } x < -\frac{1}{\sqrt{2}} \text{ we have } y'' > 0$$

$$\text{for } x > -\frac{1}{\sqrt{2}} \text{ we have } y'' < 0$$

The second derivative changes sign when passing through the point x_1. Hence, for $x_1 = -\frac{1}{\sqrt{2}}$, there is a point of inflection on the curve; its coordinates are $\left(-\frac{1}{\sqrt{2}}, e^{-\frac{1}{2}} \right)$;

$$\text{for } x < \frac{1}{\sqrt{2}} \text{ we have } y'' < 0$$

$$\text{for } x > \frac{1}{\sqrt{2}} \text{ we have } y'' > 0$$

Thus, there is also a point of inflection on the curve for $x_2 = \frac{1}{\sqrt{2}}$; its coordinates are $\left(\frac{1}{\sqrt{2}}, e^{-\frac{1}{2}} \right)$. Incidentally, the existence of the second point of inflection follows directly from the symmetry of the curve about the y-axis.

(4) From the foregoing it follows that

for $-\infty < x < -\frac{1}{\sqrt{2}}$ the curve is concave:

for $-\frac{1}{\sqrt{2}} < x < \frac{1}{\sqrt{2}}$ the curve is convex;

for $\frac{1}{\sqrt{2}} < x < +\infty$ the curve is concave

(5) From the expression of the first derivative

$$y' = -2xe^{-x^2}$$

it follows that

for $x < 0$ $y' > 0$, the function increases,
for $x > 0$ $y' < 0$, the function decreases,
for $x = 0$ $y' = 0$.

At this point the function has a maximum, namely, $y = 1$. The foregoing analysis makes it easy to construct a graph of the curve (Fig. 123).

Example 5. Test the curve $y = x^4$ for points of inflection.

Solution. (1) Find the second derivative:

$$y'' = 12x^2$$

(2) Determine the points at which $y'' = 0$:
$$12x^2 = 0, \quad x = 0$$

(3) Investigate the value $x = 0$ obtained:
for $x < 0$ $y'' > 0$, the curve is concave,

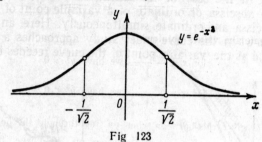

Fig 123

for $x > 0$ $y'' > 0$, the curve is concave.
Thus, the curve has no points of inflection (Fig. 124).

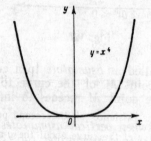 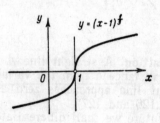

Fig. 124   Fig. 125

Example 6. Investigate the following curve for points of inflection:
$$y = (x-1)^{\frac{1}{3}}$$

Solution. (1) Find the first and second derivatives:
$$y' = \frac{1}{3}(x-1)^{-\frac{2}{3}}; \quad y'' = -\frac{2}{9}(x-1)^{-\frac{5}{3}}$$

(2) The second derivative does not vanish anywhere, but at $x = 1$ it does not exist ($y'' = \pm \infty$).
(3) Investigate the value $x = 1$:

for $x < 1$ $y'' > 0$, the curve is concave;
for $x > 1$ $y'' < 0$, the curve is convex.

Consequently, at $x = 1$ there is a point of inflection $(1, 0)$.
It will be noted that for $x = 1$ $y' = \infty$; the curve at this point has a vertical tangent (Fig. 125).

5.10 ASYMPTOTES

Very frequently one has to investigate the shape of a curve $y = f(x)$ and, consequently, the type of variation of the corresponding function **in the case of an unlimited increase** (in absolute value) of the abscissa or ordinate of a variable point of the curve, or of the abscissa and ordinate simultaneously. Here, an important special case is when the curve under study approaches a given line without bound as the variable point of the curve recedes to infinity.*

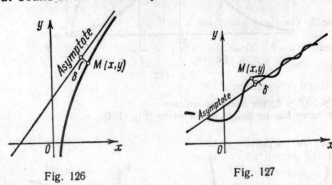

Fig. 126   Fig. 127

Definition. A straight line A is called an *asymptote* to a curve, if the distance δ from the variable point M of the curve to this straight line approaches zero as the point M recedes to infinity (Figs. 126 and 127).

In future we shall differentiate between *vertical asymptotes* (parallel to the axis of ordinates) and *inclined asymptotes* (not parallel to the axis of ordinates).

1. Vertical asymptotes. From the definition of an asymptote it follows that if $\lim\limits_{x \to a+0} f(x) = \infty$ or $\lim\limits_{x \to a-0} f(x) = \infty$ or $\lim\limits_{x \to a} f(x) = \infty$, then the straight line $x = a$ is an asymptote to the curve $y = f(x)$; and, conversely, if the straight line $x = a$ is an asymptote, then one of the foregoing equalities is fulfilled.

Consequently, to find vertical asymptotes one has to find values of $x = a$ such that when they are approached by the function $y = f(x)$ the latter approaches infinity. Then the straight line $x = a$ will be a vertical asymptote.

Example 1. The curve $y = \dfrac{2}{x-5}$ has a vertical asymptote $x = 5$, since $y \longrightarrow \infty$ as $x \longrightarrow 5$ (Fig. 128).

* We say the variable point M moves along a curve to infinity if the distance of the point from the origin increases without bound.

Example 2. The curve $y = \tan x$ has an infinite number of vertical asymptotes

$$x = \pm \frac{\pi}{2}, \quad x = \pm \frac{3\pi}{2}, \quad x = \pm \frac{5\pi}{2}, \ldots$$

This follows from the fact that $\tan x \to \infty$ as x approaches the values $\dfrac{\pi}{2}, \dfrac{3\pi}{2}, \dfrac{5\pi}{2}, \ldots,$

or $-\dfrac{\pi}{2}, -\dfrac{3\pi}{2}, -\dfrac{5\pi}{2}, \ldots$ (Fig. 129).

Example 3. The curve $y = e^{\frac{1}{x}}$ has a verti-

cal asymptote $x = 0$, since $\lim\limits_{x \to +0} e^{\frac{1}{x}} = \infty$ (Fig. 130).

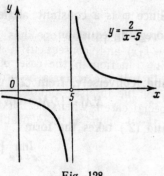

Fig. 128

2. Inclined asymptotes. Let the curve $y = f(x)$ have an inclined asymptote whose equation is

$$y = kx + b \qquad (1)$$

Determine the numbers k and b (Fig. 131). Let $M(x, y)$ be a point lying on the curve and $N(x, \bar{y})$, a point lying on the asymptote.

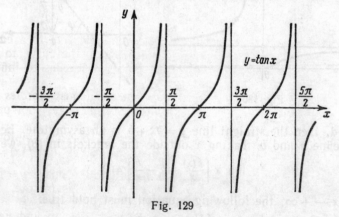

Fig. 129

The length of MP is equal to the distance from the point M to the asymptote. It is given that

$$\lim_{x \to +\infty} MP = 0 \qquad (2)$$

Designating the angle of inclination of the asymptote to the x-axis by φ, we find from $\triangle NMP$ that

$$NM = \frac{MP}{\cos \varphi}$$

Since φ is a constant angle $\left(\text{not equal to } \dfrac{\pi}{2}\right)$, by virtue of the foregoing equation

$$\lim_{x \to +\infty} NM = 0 \qquad (2')$$

and, conversely, from (2') we get (2). But

$$NM = |QM - QN| = |y - \bar{y}| = |f(x) - (kx + b)|$$

and (2') takes the form

$$\lim_{x \to +\infty} [f(x) - kx - b] = 0 \qquad (3)$$

To summarize: if the straight line (1) is an asymptote, then (3) is satisfied, and conversely, if, k and b are constant, equation (3) is

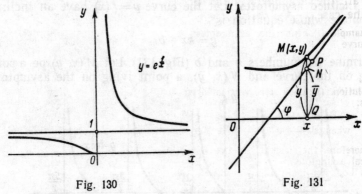

Fig. 130   Fig. 131

satisfied, then the straight line $y = kx + b$ is an asymptote. Let us now define k and b. Taking x outside the brackets in (3), we get

$$\lim_{x \to +\infty} x \left[\frac{f(x)}{x} - k - \frac{b}{x} \right] = 0$$

Since $x \to +\infty$, the following equation must hold true:

$$\lim_{x \to +\infty} \left[\frac{f(x)}{x} - k - \frac{b}{x} \right] = 0$$

For b constant, $\lim\limits_{x \to \infty} \dfrac{b}{x} = 0$. Hence,

$$\lim_{x \to +\infty} \left[\frac{f(x)}{x} - k \right] = 0$$

or

$$k = \lim_{x \to +\infty} \frac{f(x)}{x} \qquad (4)$$

Knowing k, we find b from (3):

$$b = \lim_{x \to +\infty} [f(x) - kx] \qquad (5)$$

Thus, if the straight line $y = kx + b$ is an asymptote, then k and b may be found from (4) and (5). Conversely, if the limits (4) and (5) exist, then (3) is fulfilled and the straight line $y = kx + b$ is an asymptote. If even one of the limits (4) or (5) does not exist, then the curve does not have an asymptote.

It should be noted that we carried out our investigation as applied to Fig. 131, as $x \to +\infty$, but all the arguments hold also for the case $x \to -\infty$.

Example 4. Find the asymptotes of the curve

$$y = \frac{x^2 + 2x - 1}{x}$$

Solution. (1) Look for vertical asymptotes:

$$\text{when } x \to -0 \quad y \to +\infty$$
$$\text{when } x \to +0 \quad y \to -\infty$$

Therefore, the straight line $x = 0$ is a vertical asymptote.

(2) Look for inclined asymptotes:

$$k = \lim_{x \to \pm\infty} \frac{y}{x} = \lim_{x \to \pm\infty} \frac{x^2 + 2x - 1}{x^2} =$$
$$= \lim_{x \to \pm\infty} \left[1 + \frac{2}{x} - \frac{1}{x^2} \right] = 1$$

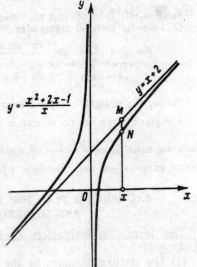

Fig. 132

that is,

$$k = 1$$

$$b = \lim_{x \to \pm\infty} [y - x] = \lim_{x \to \pm\infty} \left[\frac{x^2 + 2x - 1}{x} - x \right] = \lim_{x \to \pm\infty} \left[\frac{x^2 + 2x - 1 - x^2}{x} \right]$$
$$= \lim_{x \to \pm\infty} \left[2 - \frac{1}{x} \right] = 2$$

or, finally,

$$b = 2$$

Therefore, the straight line

$$y = x + 2$$

is an inclined asymptote to the given curve.

To investigate the mutual positions of a curve and an asymptote, let us consider the difference of the ordinates of the curve and the asymptote for one and the same value of x:

$$\frac{x^2+2x-1}{x}-(x+2)=-\frac{1}{x}$$

This difference is negative for $x > 0$ and positive for $x < 0$; and so for $x > 0$ the curve lies below the asymptote, and for $x < 0$ it lies above the asymptote (Fig. 132).

Example 5. Find the asymptotes of the curve

$$y=e^{-x}\sin x+x$$

Solution. (1) It is obvious that there are no vertical asymptotes.

(2) Look for inclined asymptotes:

$$k=\lim_{x\to+\infty}\frac{y}{x}=\lim_{x\to+\infty}\frac{e^{-x}\sin x+x}{x}=\lim_{x\to+\infty}\left[\frac{e^{-x}\sin x}{x}+1\right]=1$$

$$b=\lim_{x\to+\infty}[e^{-x}\sin x+x-x]=\lim_{x\to+\infty}e^{-x}\sin x=0$$

Hence, the straight line $y=x$ is an inclined asymptote as $x\longrightarrow+\infty$.

The given curve has no asymptote as $x\longrightarrow-\infty$. Indeed, the limit $\lim\limits_{x\to-\infty}\dfrac{y}{x}$ does not exist, since $\dfrac{y}{x}=\dfrac{e^{-x}}{x}\sin x+1$. (Here, the first term increases without bound as $x\longrightarrow-\infty$ and, therefore it has no limit.)

5.11 GENERAL PLAN FOR INVESTIGATING FUNCTIONS AND CONSTRUCTING GRAPHS

The term "investigation of a function" usually implies the finding of:

(1) the natural domain of the function;

(2) the discontinuities of the function;

(3) the intervals of increase and decrease of the function;

(4) the maximum point and the minimum point, and also the maximal and minimal values of the functions;

(5) the regions of convexity and concavity of the graph, and points of inflection;

(6) the asymptotes of the graph of the function.

The graph of the function is constructed on the basis of such an investigation (it is sometimes wise to plot certain elements of the graph in the very process of investigation).

Note 1. If the function under investigation $y=f(x)$ is *even*, that is, such that upon a change in sign of the argument the value of the function does not change, i.e., if

$$f(-x)=f(x)$$

then it is sufficient to investigate the function and construct its graph for positive values of the argument that lie within the domain of definition of the function. For negative values of the argument, the graph of the function is constructed on the gro~~ 's that the graph of an even function is symmetric about the ordinate axis.

Example 1. The function $y = x^2$ is even, since $(- x)^2 = x^2$ (see Fig. 5).

Example 2. The function $y = \cos x$ is even, since $\cos (- x) = \cos x$ (see Fig. 16).

Note 2. If the function $y = f(x)$ is *odd*, that is, such that for any change in the argument the function changes sign, i.e., if

$$f(-x) = -f(x)$$

then it is sufficient to investigate this function in the case of positive values of the argument. The graph of an odd function is symmetric about the origin.

Example 3. The function $y = x^3$ is odd, since $(- x)^3 = - x^3$ (see Fig. 7).

Example 4. The function $y = \sin x$ is odd, since $\sin (- x) = - \sin x$ (see Fig. 15).

Note 3. Since a knowledge of certain properties of a function allows us to judge of the other properties, it is sometimes advisable to choose the order of investigation on the basis of the peculiarities of the given function. For example, if we have found out that the given function is continuous and differentiable and if we have found the maximum point and the minimum point of this function, we have thus already determined also the range of increase and decrease of the function.

Example 5. Investigate the function

$$y = \frac{x}{1 + x^2}$$

and construct its graph.

Solution. (1) The domain of the function is the interval $-\infty < x < +\infty$. It will straightaway be noted that for $x < 0$ we have $y < 0$, and for $x > 0$ we have $y > 0$.

(2) The function is everywhere continuous.

(3) Test the function for maximum and minimum: from the equation

$$y' = \frac{1 - x^2}{(1 + x^2)^2} = 0$$

find the critical points:

$$x_1 = -1, \quad x_2 = 1$$

Investigate the character of the critical points:

for $x < -1$ we have $y' < 0$
for $x > -1$ we have $y' > 0$

Hence, at $x = -1$ the function has a minimum:

$$y_{\min} = (y)_{x = -1} = -0.5$$

Furthermore

for $x < 1$ we have $y' > 0$
for $x > 1$ we have $y' < 0$

Hence, at $x = 1$ the function has a maximum:

$$y_{max} = (y)_{x=1} = 0.5$$

(4) Determine the domains of increase and decrease of the function:

for $-\infty < x < -1$ we have $y' < 0$, the function decreases,

for $-1 < x < 1$ we have $y' > 0$, the function increases,

for $1 < x < +\infty$ we have $y' < 0$, the function decreases.

(5) Determine the domains of convexity and concavity of the curve and the points of inflection: from the equation

$$y'' = \frac{2x\,(x^2 - 3)}{(1 + x^2)^3} = 0$$

we get

$$x_1 = -\sqrt{3}, \ x_2 = 0, \ x_3 = \sqrt{3}$$

Investigating y'' as a function of x we find that

for $-\infty < x < -\sqrt{3}$ $y'' < 0$, the curve is convex,

for $-\sqrt{3} < x < 0$ $y'' > 0$, the curve is concave,

for $0 < x < \sqrt{3}$ $y'' < 0$, the curve is convex,

for $\sqrt{3} < x < +\infty$ $y'' > 0$, the curve is concave.

Thus, the point with coordinates $x = -\sqrt{3}$, $y = -\dfrac{\sqrt{3}}{4}$ is a point of inflection; in exactly the same way, the points $(0, 0)$ and $\left(\sqrt{3}, \dfrac{\sqrt{3}}{4}\right)$ are points of inflection.

(6) Determine the asymptotes of the curve:

for $x \longrightarrow +\infty$ $y \longrightarrow 0$

for $x \longrightarrow -\infty$ $y \longrightarrow 0$

Consequently, the straight line $y = 0$ is the only inclined asymptote. The curve has no vertical asymptotes because the function does not approach infinity for a single finite value of x.

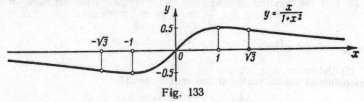

Fig. 133

The graph of the curve under study is given in Fig. 133.

Example 6. Investigate the function

$$y = \sqrt[3]{2ax^2 - x^3} \quad (a > 0)$$

and construct its graph.

Solution. (1) The function is defined for all values of x.

(2) The function is everywhere continuous.

(3) Test the function for maximum and minimum:

$$y' = \frac{4ax - 3x^2}{3\sqrt[3]{(2ax^2 - x^3)^2}} = \frac{4a - 3x}{3\sqrt[3]{x(2a-x)^2}}$$

There is a derivative everywhere except at the points

$$x_1 = 0 \quad \text{and} \quad x_2 = 2a$$

Investigate the limiting values of the derivative as $x \rightarrow -0$ and as $x \rightarrow +0$:

$$\lim_{x \to -0} \frac{4a - 3x}{3\sqrt[3]{x}\sqrt[3]{(2a-x)^2}} = -\infty, \qquad \lim_{x \to +0} \frac{4a - 3x}{3\sqrt[3]{x}\sqrt[3]{(2a-x)^2}} = +\infty$$

for $x < 0$ $y' < 0$, and for $x > 0$ $y' > 0$.

Hence, at $x = 0$ the function has a minimum. The value of the function at this point is zero.

Now investigate the function at the other critical point $x_2 = 2a$ As $x \rightarrow 2a$ the derivative also approaches infinity. However, in this case, for all values of x close to $2a$ (both on the right and left of $2a$), the derivative is negative. Therefore, at this point the function has neither a maximum nor a minimum. At and about the point $x_2 = 2a$ the function decreases; the tangent to the curve at this point is vertical.

At $x = \frac{4a}{3}$ the derivative vanishes. Let us investigate the character of this critical point. Examining the expression of the first derivative, we note that

$$\text{for } x < \frac{4a}{3} \;\; y' > 0, \quad \text{and} \quad \text{for } x > \frac{4a}{3} \;\; y' < 0$$

Thus, at $x = \frac{4a}{3}$ the function has a maximum:

$$y_{\max} = \frac{2}{3} a \sqrt[3]{4}$$

(4) On the basis of this study we get the domains of increase and decrease of the function:

for $-\infty < x < 0$ the function decreases,

for $0 < x < \frac{4a}{3}$ the function increases,

for $\frac{4a}{3} < x < +\infty$ the function decreases.

(5) Determine the domains of convexity and concavity of the curve and the points of inflection: the second derivative

$$y'' = -\frac{8a^2}{9x^{\frac{4}{3}}(2a-x)^{\frac{5}{3}}}$$

does not vanish at a single point. Yet there are two points at which the second derivative is discontinuous: $x_1 = 0$ and $x_2 = 2a$.

Let us investigate the sign of the second derivative near each of these points. For $x < 0$ we have $y'' < 0$ and the curve is convex up; for $x > 0$ we have $y'' < 0$ and the curve is convex up. Hence, the point with abscissa $x = 0$ is not a point of inflection.

For $x < 2a$ we have $y'' < 0$ and the curve is convex up; for $x > 2a$ we have $y'' > 0$ and the curve is convex down. Hence, the point $(2a, 0)$ on the curve is a point of inflection.

(6) Determine the asymptotes of the curve:

$$k = \lim_{x \to \pm\infty} \frac{y}{x} = \lim_{x \to \pm\infty} \frac{\sqrt[3]{2ax^2 - x^3}}{x} = \lim_{x \to \pm\infty} \sqrt[3]{\frac{2a}{x} - 1} = -1$$

$$b = \lim_{x \to \pm\infty} \left[\sqrt[3]{2ax^2 - x^3} + x \right] = \lim_{x \to \pm\infty} \frac{2ax^2 - x^3 + x^3}{\sqrt[3]{(2ax^2 - x^3)^2} - x\sqrt[3]{2ax^2 - x^3} + x^2} = \frac{2a}{3}$$

Thus the straight line

$$y = -x + \frac{2a}{3}$$

is an inclined asymptote to the curve $y = \sqrt[3]{2ax^2 - x^3}$. The graph of this function is shown in Fig. 134.

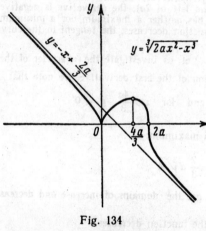

Fig. 134

5.12 INVESTIGATING CURVES REPRESENTED PARAMETRICALLY

Let a curve be given by the parametric equations

$$\left. \begin{array}{l} x = \varphi(t) \\ y = \psi(t) \end{array} \right\} \quad (1)$$

In this case the investigation and construction of the curve is carried out just as for the curve given by the equation

$$y = f(x)$$

Evaluate the derivatives

$$\left. \begin{array}{l} \dfrac{dx}{dt} = \varphi'(t) \\ \dfrac{dy}{dt} = \psi'(t) \end{array} \right\} \quad (2)$$

For those points of the curve near which it is the graph of a certain function $y = f(x)$, evaluate the derivative

$$\frac{dy}{dx} = \frac{\psi'(t)}{\varphi'(t)} \quad (3)$$

We find the values of the parameter $t = t_1, t_2, \ldots, t_k$ for which at least one of the derivatives $\varphi'(t)$ or $\psi'(t)$ vanishes or becomes discontinuous. (We shall call these values of t critical values.)

By formula (3), in each of the intervals (t_1, t_2); (t_2, t_3); ...; (t_{k-1}, t_k) and hence, in each of the intervals (x_1, x_2); (x_2, x_3); ...; (x_{k-1}, x_k) [where $x_i = \varphi(t_i)$], we determine the sign of $\frac{dy}{dx}$, in this way determining the domain of increase and decrease. This likewise enables us to determine the character of points that correspond to the values of the parameter $t_1, t_2, ..., t_k$. Next, we compute

$$\frac{d^2y}{dx^2} = \frac{\psi''(t)\,\varphi'(t) - \varphi''(t)\,\psi'(t)}{[\varphi'(t)]^3} \tag{4}$$

From this formula, we determine the direction of convexity of the curve at each point.

To find the asymptotes determine those values of t, upon approach to which either x or y approaches infinity, and those values of t upon approach to which both x and y approach infinity. Then carry out the investigation in the usual way.

The following examples will serve to illustrate some of the peculiarities that appear when investigating curves represented parametrically.

Example 1. Investigate the curve given by the equation

$$\left. \begin{array}{l} x = a\cos^3 t \\ y = a\sin^3 t \end{array} \right\} \quad (a > 0) \tag{1'}$$

Solution. The quantities x and y are defined for all values of t. But since he functions $\cos^3 t$ and $\sin^3 t$ are periodic, of a period 2π, it is sufficient to consider the variation of the parameter t in the range from 0 to 2π; here the nterval $[-a, a]$ is the range of x and the interval $[-a, a]$ is the range of y. Consequently, this curve has no asymptotes. Next, we find

$$\left. \begin{array}{l} \dfrac{dx}{dt} = -3a\cos^2 t\,\sin t \\[2mm] \dfrac{dy}{dt} = 3a\sin^2 t\,\cos t \end{array} \right\} \tag{2'}$$

These derivatives vanish at $t = 0$, $\frac{\pi}{2}$, π, $\frac{3\pi}{2}$, 2π. We determine

$$\frac{dy}{dx} = \frac{3a\sin^2 t\,\cos t}{-3a\cos^2 t\,\sin t} = -\tan t \tag{3'}$$

On the basis of (2') and (3') we compile the following table:

Range of t	Corresponding range of x	Corresponding range of y	Sign of $\dfrac{dy}{dx}$	Type of variation of y as a function of x $[y=f(x)]$
$0 < t < \dfrac{\pi}{2}$	$a > x > 0$	$0 < y < a$	$-$	Decreases
$\dfrac{\pi}{2} < t < \pi$	$0 > x > -a$	$a > y > 0$	$+$	Increases
$\pi < t < \dfrac{3\pi}{2}$	$-a < x < 0$	$0 > y > -a$	$-$	Decreases
$\dfrac{3\pi}{2} < t < 2\pi$	$0 < x < a$	$-a < y < 0$	$+$	Increases

From the table it follows that equations (1') define two continuous functions of the type $y = f(x)$, for $0 \leqslant t \leqslant \pi$ $y \geqslant 0$ (see first two lines of the table), for $\pi \leqslant t \leqslant 2\pi$ $y \leqslant 0$ (see last two lines of the table). From (3') it follows that

$$\lim_{t \to \frac{\pi}{2}} \frac{dy}{dx} = \infty$$

and

$$\lim_{x \to \frac{3\pi}{2}} \frac{dy}{dx} = \infty$$

At these points the tangent to the curve is vertical. We now find

$$\frac{dy}{dt}\bigg|_{t=0} = 0, \quad \frac{dy}{dt}\bigg|_{t=\pi} = 0, \quad \frac{dy}{dt}\bigg|_{t=2\pi} = 0$$

At these points the tangent to the curve is horizontal. We then find

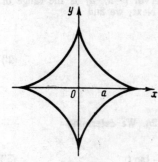

$$\frac{d^2y}{dx^2} = \frac{1}{3a \cos^4 t \sin t}$$

Whence it follows that

for $0 < t < \pi$, $\dfrac{d^2y}{dx^2} > 0$, the curve is concave,

for $\pi < t < 2\pi$, $\dfrac{d^2y}{dx^2} < 0$, the curve is convex.

On the basis of this investigation we can construct a curve (Fig. 135), which is called an *astroid*.

Example 2. Construct a curve given by the following equations (*folium of Descartes*):

Fig. 135

$$x = \frac{3at}{1+t^3}, \qquad y = \frac{3at^2}{1+t^3} \quad (a > 0) \tag{1''}$$

Solution. Both functions are defined for all values of t except at $t = -1$, and

$$\lim_{t \to -1-0} x = \lim_{t \to -1-0} \frac{3at}{1+t^3} = +\infty, \qquad \lim_{t \to -1+0} x = -\infty,$$

$$\lim_{t \to -1-0} y = \lim_{t \to -1-0} \frac{3at^2}{1+t^3} = -\infty, \qquad \lim_{t \to -1+0} y = +\infty,$$

Further note that

$$\begin{aligned}
&\text{when } t = 0 \qquad\quad x = 0, \qquad y = 0 \\
&\text{when } t \longrightarrow +\infty \quad x \longrightarrow 0, \quad y \longrightarrow 0 \\
&\text{when } t \longrightarrow -\infty \quad x \longrightarrow 0, \quad y \longrightarrow 0
\end{aligned}$$

Find $\dfrac{dx}{dt}$ and $\dfrac{dy}{dt}$:

$$\frac{dx}{dt} = \frac{6a \left(\frac{1}{2} - t^3 \right)}{(1+t^3)^2}, \quad \frac{dy}{dt} = \frac{3at(2-t^3)}{(1+t^3)^2} \qquad (2'')$$

For the parameter t we get the following four critical values:

$$t_1 = -1, \quad t_2 = 0, \quad t_3 = \frac{1}{\sqrt[3]{2}}, \quad t_4 = \sqrt[3]{2}$$

Then we find

$$\frac{dy}{dx} = \frac{\dfrac{dy}{dt}}{\dfrac{dx}{dt}} = \frac{t(2-t^3)}{2\left(\dfrac{1}{2} - t^3\right)} \qquad (3'')$$

On the basis of formulas $(1'')$, $(2'')$, and $(3'')$ we compile the following table:

Range of t	Corresponding range of x	Corresponding range of y	Sign of $\dfrac{dy}{dx}$	Type of variation of y as a function of x $[y=f(x)]$
$-\infty < t < -1$	$0 < x < +\infty$	$0 > y > -\infty$	$-$	Decreases
$-1 < t < 0$	$-\infty < x < 0$	$+\infty > y > 0$	$-$	Decreases
$0 < t < \dfrac{1}{\sqrt[3]{2}}$	$0 < x < a\sqrt[3]{4}$	$0 < y < a\sqrt[3]{2}$	$+$	Increases
$\dfrac{1}{\sqrt[3]{2}} < t < \sqrt[3]{2}$	$a\sqrt[3]{4} > x > a\sqrt[3]{2}$	$a\sqrt[3]{2} < y < a\sqrt[3]{4}$	$-$	Decreases
$\sqrt[3]{2} < t < +\infty$	$a\sqrt[3]{2} > x > 0$	$a\sqrt[3]{4} > y > 0$	$+$	Increases

From $(3'')$ we find

$$\left(\frac{dy}{dx} \right)_{\substack{t=0 \\ \binom{x=0}{y=0}}} = 0, \qquad \left(\frac{dy}{dx} \right)_{\substack{t=\infty \\ \binom{x=0}{y=0}}} = \infty$$

Thus, the curve cuts the origin twice: with the tangent parallel to the x-axis and with the tangent parallel to the y-axis. Further,

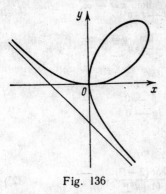

$$\left(\frac{dy}{dx}\right)_{t=\frac{1}{\sqrt[3]{2}}} = \infty$$

$$\left(\begin{matrix} x=a\sqrt[3]{4} \\ y=a\sqrt[3]{2} \end{matrix}\right)$$

At this point the tangent to the curve is vertical.

$$\left(\frac{dy}{dx}\right)_{t=\sqrt[3]{2}} = 0$$

$$\left(\begin{matrix} x=a\sqrt[3]{2} \\ y=a\sqrt[3]{4} \end{matrix}\right)$$

Fig. 136

At this point the tangent to the curve is horizontal. Let us investigate the question of the existence of an asymptote:

$$k = \lim_{x \to +\infty} \frac{y}{x} = \lim_{t \to -1-0} \frac{3at^2(1+t^3)}{3at(1+t^3)} = -1$$

$$b = \lim_{x \to +\infty}(y-kx) = \lim_{x \to -1-0}\left[\frac{3at^2}{1+t^3}-(-1)\frac{3at}{1+t^3}\right] =$$

$$= \lim_{t \to -1-0}\left[\frac{3at(t+1)}{1+t^3}\right] = \lim_{t \to -1-0}\frac{3at}{1-t+t^2} = -a$$

Hence, the straight line $y=-x-a$ is an asymptote to a branch of the curve as $x \longrightarrow +\infty$.

Similarly we find

$$k = \lim_{x \to -\infty}\frac{y}{x} = -1, \quad b = \lim_{x \to -\infty}(y-kx) = -a$$

Thus, the straight line is also an asymptote to a branch of the curve as $x \longrightarrow -\infty$.

On the basis of this investigation we construct the curve (Fig. 136).

Some problems involving investigation of curves will again be discussed in Sec. 8.20 ("Singular Points of a Curve").

Exercises on Chapter 5

Find the extrema of the functions:

1. $y=x^2-2x+3$. *Ans.* $y_{min}=2$ at $x=1$. **2.** $y=\frac{x^3}{3}-2x^2+3x+1$. *Ans.*
$y_{max}=\frac{7}{3}$ at $x=1$, $y_{min}=1$ at $x=3$. **3.** $y=x^3-9x^2+15x+3$. *Ans.* $y_{max}=10$
at $x=1$, $y_{min}=-22$ at $x=5$. **4.** $y=-x^4+2x^2$. *Ans.* $y_{max}=1$ at $x=\pm1$,
$y_{min}=0$ at $x=0$. **5.** $y=x^4-8x^2+2$. *Ans.* $y_{max}=2$ at $x=0$, $y_{min}=-14$ at
$x=\pm2$. **6.** $y=3x^5-125x^3+2160x$. *Ans.* Maximum at $x=-4$ and $x=3$, mini-

mum at $x=-3$ and $x=4$. **7.** $y=2-(x-1)^{\frac{2}{3}}$. *Ans.* $y_{max}=2$ at $x=1$.

8. $y=3-2(x+1)^{\frac{1}{3}}$. *Ans.* There is neither maximum nor minimum. **9.** $y=$ $=\dfrac{x^2-3x+2}{x^2+3x+2}$. *Ans.* Minimum at $x=\sqrt{2}$, maximum at $x=-\sqrt{2}$. **10.** $y=$ $=\dfrac{(x-2)(3-x)}{x^2}$. *Ans.* Maximum at $x=\dfrac{12}{5}$. **11.** $y=2e^x+e^{-x}$. *Ans.* Minimum at $x=-\dfrac{\ln 2}{2}$. **12.** $y=\dfrac{x}{\ln x}$. *Ans.* $y_{min}=e$ at $x=e$. **13.** $y=\cos x+$ $+\sin x \left(-\dfrac{\pi}{2}\leqslant x\leqslant \dfrac{\pi}{2}\right)$. *Ans.* $y_{max}=\sqrt{2}$ at $x=\dfrac{\pi}{4}$. **14.** $y=\sin 2x-$ $-x\left(-\dfrac{\pi}{2}\leqslant x\leqslant\dfrac{\pi}{2}\right)$. *Ans.* Maximum at $x=\dfrac{\pi}{6}$, minimum at $x=-\dfrac{\pi}{6}$.
15. $y=x+\tan x$. *Ans.* There is neither maximum nor minimum. **16.** $y=e^x \sin x$.
Ans. Minimum at $x=2k\pi-\dfrac{\pi}{4}$, maximum at $x=2k\pi+\dfrac{3}{4}\pi$. **17.** $y=x^4-$ $-2x^2+2$. *Ans.* Maximum at $x=0$, two minima when $x=-1$ and when $x=1$.
18. $y=(x-2)^3(2x+1)$. *Ans.* $y_{min}\approx-8.24$ when $x=\dfrac{1}{8}$. **19.** $y=x+\dfrac{1}{x}$. *Ans.*
Minimum when $x=1$, maximum when $x=-1$. **20.** $y=x^2(a-x)^2$. *Ans.*
$y_{max}=\dfrac{a^4}{16}$ when $x=\dfrac{a}{2}$, $y_{min}=0$ when $x=0$ and when $x=a$. **21.** $y=\dfrac{a^2}{x}+$ $+\dfrac{b^2}{a-x}$. *Ans.* Maximum when $x=\dfrac{a^2}{a-b}$, minimum when $x=\dfrac{a^2}{a+b}$. **22.** $y=$ $=x+\sqrt{1-x}$. *Ans.* $y_{max}=\dfrac{5}{4}$ when $x=\dfrac{3}{4}$, $y_{min}=1$ when $x=1$. **23.** $y=$ $=x\sqrt{1-x}$ $(x\leqslant 1)$. *Ans.* $y_{max}=\dfrac{2}{3}\sqrt{\dfrac{1}{3}}$ when $x=\dfrac{2}{3}$. **24.** $y=\dfrac{x}{1+x^2}$.
Ans. Minimum when $x=-1$, maximum when $x=1$. **25.** $y=x\ln x$. *Ans.* Minimum when $x=\dfrac{1}{e}$. **26.** $y=x\ln^2 x$. *Ans.* $y_{max}=4e^{-2}$ at $x=e^{-2}$, $y_{min}=0$ at $x=1$. **27.** $y=\ln x-\arctan x$. *Ans.* The function increases. **28.** $y=\sin 3x-3\sin x$.
Ans. Minimum when $x=\dfrac{\pi}{2}$, maximum when $x=\dfrac{3\pi}{2}$. **29.** $y=2x+\arctan x$. *Ans.*
No extrema.. **30.** $y=\sin x\cos^2 x$. *Ans.* Minimum when $x=\dfrac{\pi}{2}$, two maxima when $x=\arccos\sqrt{\dfrac{2}{3}}$ and when $x=\arccos\left(-\sqrt{\dfrac{2}{3}}\right)$. **31.** $y=\arcsin(\sin x)$.
Ans. Maximum when $x=\dfrac{(4m+1)\pi}{2}$, minimum when $x=\dfrac{(4m+3)\pi}{2}$.

Find the maximum and minimum values of the function on the indicated intervals:
32. $y=-3x^4+6x^2-1$ $(-2\leqslant x\leqslant 2)$. *Ans.* Maximum $y=2$ at $x=\pm 1$, minimum $y=-25$ at $x=\pm 2$. **33.** $y=\dfrac{x^3}{3}-2x^2+3x+1$ $(-1\leqslant x\leqslant 5)$. *Ans.* Maximum value $y=\dfrac{23}{3}$ at $x=5$, minimum value $y=-\dfrac{13}{3}$ at $x=-1$. **34.** $y=\dfrac{x-1}{x+1}$ $(0\leqslant x\leqslant 4)$. *Ans.* Maximum value $y=\dfrac{3}{5}$ at $x=4$, minimum value $y=-1$

at $x = 0$. **35.** $y = \sin 2x - x \left(-\dfrac{\pi}{2} \leqslant x \leqslant \dfrac{\pi}{2} \right)$. *Ans.* Maximum value $y = \dfrac{\pi}{2}$ at $x = -\dfrac{\pi}{2}$, minimum value $y = -\dfrac{\pi}{2}$ at $x = \dfrac{\pi}{2}$.

36. Using square tin sheet with side a, make a topless box of maximum volume by cutting equal squares at the corners and removing them and then bending the tin so as to form the sides of the box. What will the length of a side of the squares be? *Ans.* $\dfrac{a}{6}$.

37. Prove that of all rectangles that may be inscribed in a given circle, the square has the greatest area. Also show that the square will have the maximum perimeter as well.

38. Show that of all isosceles triangles inscribed in a given circle, an equilateral triangle has the largest perimeter.

39. Find a right triangle of maximum area with a hypotenuse h. *Ans.* Length of each leg, $\dfrac{h}{\sqrt{2}}$.

40. Find the height of a right cylinder with greatest volume that can be inscribed in a sphere of radius R. *Ans.* Height, $\dfrac{2R}{\sqrt{3}}$.

41. Find the height of a right cylinder with greatest lateral surface area that may be inscribed in a given sphere of radius R. *Ans.* Height, $R\sqrt{2}$.

42. Find the height of a right cone with least volume circumscribed about a given sphere of radius R. *Ans.* $4R$ (the volume of the cone is twice the volume of the sphere).

43. A reservoir with a square bottom and open top is to be lined inside with lead. What are the dimensions of the reservoir (to hold 32 litres) that will require the smallest amount of lead? *Ans.* Height, 0.2 metre, side of base, 0.4 metre (the side of the base must be twice the height).

44. A roofer wants to make an open gutter of maximum capacity with bottom and sides 10 cm in width, and with the sides inclined at the same angle to the bottom. What is the width of the gutter at the top? *Ans.* 20 cm.

45. Prove that a conical vessel of given storage capacity requires the least material when its height is $\sqrt{2}$ times the radius of the base.

46. It is required to make a cylinder, open at the top, the walls and bottom of which have a given thickness. What should the dimensions of the cylinder be so that for a given storage capacity it will require the least material? *Ans.* If R is the inner radius of the base, v the inner volume of the cylinder, then $R = \sqrt[3]{\dfrac{v}{\pi}}$.

47. It is required to build a boiler out of a cylinder topped by two hemispheres and with walls of constant thickness so that for a given volume v it should have a minimum outer surface area. *Ans.* It should have the shape of a sphere with inner radius $R = \sqrt[3]{\dfrac{3v}{4\pi}}$.

48. Construct an isosceles trapezoid, which for a given area S has a minimum perimeter; the angle at the base of the trapezoid is equal to α. *Ans.* The length of one of the nonparallel sides is $\sqrt{\dfrac{S}{\sin \alpha}}$.

49. Inscribe in a given sphere of radius R a regular triangular prism of maximum volume. *Ans.* The altitude of the prism is $\dfrac{2R}{\sqrt{3}}$.

50. It is required to circumscribe about a hemisphere of radius R a cone of minimum volume; the plane of the base of the cone coincides with that of the hemisphere; find the altitude of the cone. *Ans.* The altitude of the cone is $R\sqrt{3}$.

51. About a given cylinder of radius r circumscribe a right cone of minimum volume; we assume the planes and centres of the circular bases of the cylinder and the cone coincide. *Ans.* The radius of the base of the cone is equal to $\frac{3}{2}r$.

52. Out of sheet metal having the shape of a circle of radius R, cut a sector such that it may be bent into a funnel of maximum storage capacity. *Ans.* The central angle of the sector is $2\pi\sqrt{\dfrac{2}{3}}$.

53. Of all circular cylinders inscribed in a given cube with side a so that their axes coincide with a diagonal of the cube and the circumferences of the bases touch its faces, find the cylinder with maximum volume. *Ans.* The altitude of the cylinder is equal to $\dfrac{a\sqrt{3}}{3}$; the radius of the base is $\dfrac{a}{\sqrt{6}}$.

54. Given, in a rectangular coordinate system, a point (x_0, y_0) lying in the first quadrant. Draw a straight line through this point so that it forms a triangle of least area with the positive directions of the axes. *Ans.* The straight line intercepts on the axes the segments $2x_0$ and $2y_0$; thus, it has the equation $\dfrac{x}{2x_0}+\dfrac{y}{2y_0}=1$.

55. Given a point on the axis of the parabola $y^2=2px$ at a distance a from the vertex, find the abscissa of the point of the curve closest to it. *Ans.* $x=a-p$.

56. Assuming that the strength of a beam of rectangular cross-section is directly proportional to its width and to the cube of the altitude, find the width of a beam of maximum strength that may be cut out of a log of diameter 16 cm. *Ans.* The width is 8 cm.

57. A torpedo boat is standing at anchor 9 km from the closest point of the shore; a messenger has to be sent to a camp 15 km (along the shore) from the point of the shore closest to the boat. Where should the messenger land so as to get to the camp in the shortest possible time if he does 5 km/hr walking and 4 km/hr rowing? *Ans.* At a point 3 km from the camp.

58. A point moves rectilinearly over a plane in a medium situated outside a line MN with velocity v_1, and along the line MN with velocity v_2. What path between A and B, situated on MN, will it cover in the shortest time? The distance of A from MN is h, the distance from B of the projection α of A on the line MN is a. *Ans.* If ABC is the path of the point, then $\dfrac{\alpha C}{AC}=\dfrac{v_1}{v_2}$ for $\dfrac{\alpha B}{AB}\geq\dfrac{v_1}{v_2}$ and $\alpha C=\alpha B$ for $\dfrac{\alpha B}{AB}<\dfrac{v_1}{v_2}$.

59. A load w is hoisted by a lever; a force F is applied to one end, the point of support is at the other end of the lever. If the load is suspended from a point a centimetres from the fulcrum, and the lever rod weighs v grams per centimetre of length, what should the length of the rod be for the force (required to raise the load) to be a minimum? *Ans.* $x=\sqrt{\dfrac{2aw}{v}}$ cm.

60. For n measurements of an unknown quantity x the following readings have been obtained: $x_1, x_2, \ldots, x_n$. Show that the sum of the squares of the errors $(x-x_1)^2+(x-x_2)^2+\ldots+(x-x_n)^2$ will be least if for x we take the number $\dfrac{x_1+x_2+\ldots+x_n}{n}$.

61. To reduce the friction of a liquid against the walls of a channel, the area in contact with the liquid must be a minimum. Show that the best shape of an open rectangular channel with given cross-sectional area is that for which the width of the channel is twice its altitude.

Determine the points of inflection and the intervals of convexity and concavity of the following curves:

62. $y=x^5$. *Ans.* For $x<0$ the curve is convex; for $x>0$ the curve is concave; at $x=0$ there is a point of inflection. **63.** $y=1-x^2$. *Ans.* The curve is everywhere convex. **64.** $y=x^3-3x^2-9x+9$. *Ans.* Point of inflection at $x=1$. **65.** $y=(x-b)^3$. *Ans.* Point of inflection at $x=b$. **66.** $y=x^4$. *Ans.* The curve is everywhere concave. **67.** $y=\dfrac{1}{x^2+1}$. *Ans.* Point of inflection at $x=\pm$ $\pm\dfrac{1}{\sqrt{3}}$. **68.** $y=\tan x$. *Ans.* Point of inflection at $x=n\pi$. **69.** $y=xe^{-x}$. *Ans.* Point of inflection at $x=2$. **70.** $y=a-\sqrt[3]{x-b}$. *Ans.* Point of inflection at $x=b$. **71.** $y=a-\sqrt[5]{(x-b)^2}$. *Ans.* The curve has no point of inflection.

Find the asymptotes to the following curves:

72. $y=\dfrac{1}{x-1}$. *Ans.* $x=1$, $y=0$. **73.** $y=\dfrac{1}{(x+2)^3}$. *Ans.* $x=-2$, $y=0$. **74.** $y=c+\dfrac{a^3}{(x-b)^2}$. *Ans.* $x=b$, $y=c$. **75.** $y=e^{\frac{1}{x}}-1$. *Ans.* $x=0$, $y=0$. **76.** $y=\ln x$. *Ans.* $x=0$. **77.** $y^3=6x^2+x^3$. *Ans.* $y=x+2$. **78.** $y^3=a^3-x^3$. *Ans.* $y+x=0$. **79.** $y^2=\dfrac{x^3}{2a-x}$. *Ans.* $x=2a$. **80.** $y^2(x-2a)=x^3-a^3$. *Ans.* $x=2a$, $y=\pm(x+a)$.

Investigate the following functions and construct their graphs:

81. $y=x^4-2x+10$. **82.** $y=\dfrac{8a^3}{x^2+4a^2}$. **83.** $y=e^{-\frac{1}{x}}$. **84.** $y=\dfrac{6x}{1+x^2}$. **85.** $y=\dfrac{4+x}{x^2}$. **86.** $y=\dfrac{x}{x^2-1}$. **87.** $y=\dfrac{x+2}{x^3}$. **88.** $y=\dfrac{x^2}{1+x}$. **89.** $y^2=x^3-x$. **90.** $y=\dfrac{x^3}{3-x^2}$. **91.** $y=\sqrt[3]{x^2}+2$. **92.** $y=x-\sqrt[3]{x^3+1}$. **93.** $y=\sqrt{\dfrac{x-1}{x+1}}$. **94.** $y=xe^{-x}$. **95.** $y=x^2e^{-x^2}$. **96.** $y=x-\ln(x+1)$. **97.** $y=\ln(x^2+1)$. **98.** $y=\sin 3x$. **99.** $y=x+\sin x$. **100.** $y=x\sin x$. **101.** $y=e^{-x}\sin x$. **102.** $y=\ln\sin x$. **103.** $y=\dfrac{\ln x}{x}$. **104.** $\begin{cases} x=t^2, \\ y=\dfrac{1}{2}\,t. \end{cases}$ **105.** $\begin{cases} x=t^2, \\ y=t^3. \end{cases}$

106. $\begin{cases} x=a(t-\sin t), \\ y=a(1-\cos t). \end{cases}$ **107.** $\begin{cases} x=ae^t\cos t, \\ y=ae^t\sin t. \end{cases}$

Additional Exercises

Find the asymptotes of the following lines:

108. $y=\dfrac{x^2+1}{1+x}$. *Ans.* $x=-1$, $y=x-1$. **109.** $y=x+e^{-x}$. *Ans.* $y=x$. **110.** $2y(x+1)^2=x^3$. *Ans.* $x=-1$, $y=\dfrac{1}{2}x-1$. **111.** $y^3=a^3-x^2$. *Ans.* No asymptotes. **112.** $y = e^{-2x} \sin x$ *Ans.* $y = 0$. **113.** $y = e^{-x} \sin 2x + x$. *Ans.* $y = x$.

114. $y = x \ln \left(e + \dfrac{1}{x} \right)$. *Ans.* $x = -\dfrac{1}{e}$, $y = x + \dfrac{1}{e}$. **115.** $y = x e^{\frac{1}{x^2}}$. *Ans.* $x = 0$,

$y = x$. **116.** $x = \dfrac{2t}{1 - t^2}$, $y = \dfrac{t^2}{1 - t^2}$. *Ans.* $y = \pm \dfrac{1}{2} x - \dfrac{1}{2}$.

Investigate and graph the following functions:

117. $y = |x|$. **118.** $y = \ln|x|$. **119.** $y^2 = x^3 - x$. **120.** $y = (x + 1)^2 (x - 2)$.

121. $y = x + |x|$. **122.** $y = \sqrt[3]{x^2 - x}$. **123.** $y = x^2 \sqrt{x + 1}$. **124.** $y = \dfrac{x^2}{2} - \ln x$.

125. $y = \dfrac{x^2}{2} \ln x$. **126.** $y = \dfrac{1}{e^x - 1}$. **127.** $y = \dfrac{x}{\ln x}$. **128.** $y = x + \dfrac{\ln x}{x}$. **129.** $y =$

$= x \ln x$. **130.** $y = e^{\frac{1}{x}} - x$. **131.** $y = |\sin 3x|$. **132.** $y = \dfrac{\sin x}{x}$. **133.** $y = x \arctan x$.

134. $y = x - 2 \arctan x$. **135.** $y = e^{-2x} \sin 3x$. **136.** $y = |\sin x| + x$. **137.** $y = \sin(x^2)$.

138. $y = \cos^3 x + \sin^3 x$. **139.** $y = \dfrac{x + |x|}{2}$. **140.** $y = \dfrac{x - |x|}{2}$. **141.** $y =$

$= \sin \left(\dfrac{x + |x|}{2} \right) - \dfrac{x - |x|}{2}$ $(-\pi \leqslant x \leqslant \pi)$. **142.** $y = \cos \left(\dfrac{x - |x|}{2} \right) -$

$- \dfrac{x + |x|}{2}$ $\left(-\dfrac{\pi}{2} \leqslant x \leqslant 1 \right)$. **143.** $y = \dfrac{1}{2} (3x + |x|) + 1$. **144.** $y = \dfrac{1}{2} [3 (x - 1) +$

$+ |x - 1|] + 1$ $(0 \leqslant x \leqslant 2)$.

CHAPTER 6

THE CURVATURE OF A CURVE

6.1 ARC LENGTH AND ITS DERIVATIVE

Let the arc of a curve $M_0 M$ (Fig. 137) be the graph of a function $y = f(x)$ defined on an interval (a, b). Let us determine the arc length of the curve. On the curve $M_0 M$ take the points M_0, M_1, M_2, ..., M_{i-1}, M_i, ..., M_{n-1}, M. Connecting the points we get a broken line $M_0 M_1 M_2 ... M_{i-1} M_i ... M_{n-1} M$ inscribed in the arc $M_0 M$. Denote the length of this broken line by P_n.

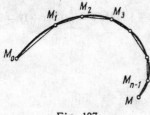

Fig. 137

The *length of the arc* $M_0 M$ is the limit (we denote it by s) approached by the length of the broken line as the largest of the lengths of the segments of the broken line $M_{i-1} M_i$ approaches zero, if this limit exists and is independent of any choice of points of the broken line $M_0 M_1 M_2 ... M_{i-1} M_i ... M_{n-1} M$.

It will be noted that this definition of the arc length of an arbitrary curve is similar to the definition of the length of the circumference of a circle.

In Ch. 12 it will be proved that if a function $f(x)$ and its derivative $f'(x)$ are continuous on an interval $[a, b]$, then the arc of the curve $y = f(x)$ lying between the points $[a, f(a)]$ and $[b, f(b)]$ has a definite length; a method will be shown for computing this length. It will also be established (as a corollary) that under the given conditions the ratio of the length of any arc of this curve to the length of its chord approaches unity when the length of the chord approaches zero, that is,

$$\lim_{M_0 M \to 0} \frac{\text{length } \widehat{M_0 M}}{\text{length } \overline{M_0 M}} = 1$$

This theorem may be readily proved for the circumference* of

---

* Consider the arc AB, the central angle of which is 2α (Fig. 138). The length of this arc is $2R\alpha$ (R is the radius of the circle), and the length of its chord is $2R \sin \alpha$. Therefore, $\lim\limits_{\alpha \to 0} \dfrac{\text{length } \widehat{AB}}{\text{length } \overline{AB}} = \lim\limits_{\alpha \to 0} \dfrac{2R\alpha}{2R \sin \alpha} = 1$.

a circle; however, in the general case we shall accept it without proof (Fig. 138).

Let us consider the following question.

On a plane we have a curve given by the equation

$$y = f(x).$$

Let $M_0(x_0, y_0)$ be some fixed point of the curve and $M(x, y)$, some variable point of the curve. Denote by s the arc length M_0M (Fig. 139).

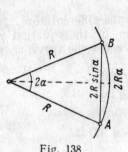

Fig. 138

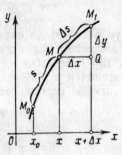

Fig. 139

The arc length s will vary with changes in the abscissa x of the point M; in other words, s is a function of x. Find the derivative of s with respect to x.

Increase x by Δx. Then the arc s will change by $\Delta s =$ the length of $\widehat{MM_1}$. Let $\overline{MM_1}$ be the chord subtending this arc. In order to find $\lim\limits_{\Delta x \to 0} \dfrac{\Delta s}{\Delta x}$ do as follows: from ΔMM_1Q find

$$\overline{MM_1^2} = (\Delta x)^2 + (\Delta y)^2$$

Multiply and divide the left-hand side by Δs^2:

$$\left(\frac{\overline{MM_1}}{\Delta s}\right)^2 \Delta s^2 = (\Delta x)^2 + (\Delta y)^2$$

Divide all terms of the equation by Δx^2:

$$\left(\frac{\overline{MM_1}}{\Delta s}\right)^2 \left(\frac{\Delta s}{\Delta x}\right)^2 = 1 + \left(\frac{\Delta y}{\Delta x}\right)^2$$

Find the limits of the left and right sides as $\Delta x \to 0$. Taking into account that $\lim\limits_{\overline{MM_1} \to 0} \dfrac{\overline{MM_1}}{\Delta s} = 1$ and that $\lim\limits_{\Delta x \to 0} \dfrac{\Delta y}{\Delta x} = \dfrac{dy}{dx}$, we get

$$\left(\frac{ds}{dx}\right)^2 = 1 + \left(\frac{dy}{dx}\right)^2$$

·or

$$\frac{ds}{dx} = \sqrt{1 + \left(\frac{dy}{dx}\right)^2} \tag{1}$$

For the *differential of the arc* we get the following expression:

$$ds = \sqrt{1 + \left(\frac{dy}{dx}\right)^2}\, dx \tag{2}$$

or *

$$ds = \sqrt{dx^2 + dy^2} \tag{2'}$$

W˙ have obtained an expression for the differential of arc length for the case when the curve is given by the equation $y = f(x)$. However, (2′) holds also for the case when the curve is represented by parametric equations.

If the curve is represented parametrically,

$$x = \varphi(t), \quad y = \psi(t)$$

then

$$dx = \varphi'(t)\, dt, \quad dy = \psi'(t)\, dt$$

and expression (2′) takes the form

$$ds = \sqrt{[\varphi'(t)]^2 + [\psi'(t)]^2}\, dt$$

6.2 CURVATURE

One of the elements that characterize the shape of a curve is the degree of its bentness, or curvature.

Let there be a curve that does not intersect itself and has a definite tangent at each point. Draw tangents to the curve at any two points A and B and denote the angle formed by these tangents by α [or, more precisely, the angle through which the tangent turns from A to B (Fig. 140)]. This angle is called the *angle of contingence* of the arc AB. Of two arcs of the same length, that arc is more curved which has a greater angle of contingence (Figs. 140 and 141).

On the other hand, when considering arcs of different length we cannot gauge the degree of their curvature solely by the appropriate angles of contingence. Whence it follows that a complete description of the curvature of a curve is given by the **ratio** of the angle of contingence to the length of the corresponding arc.

---

* Strictly speaking, (2′) holds only for the case when $dx > 0$. But if $dx < 0$, then $ds = -\sqrt{dx^2 + dy^2}$. For this reason, in the general case this formula is more correctly written as $|ds| = \sqrt{dx^2 + dy^2}$.

Definition 1. The *average curvature* K_{av} of an arc $\widehat{AB}$ is the ratio of the corresponding angle of contingence α to the length of the arc:

$$K_{av} = \frac{\alpha}{\widehat{AB}}$$

For one and the same curve, the average curvature of its different parts (arcs) may be different; for example, for the curve

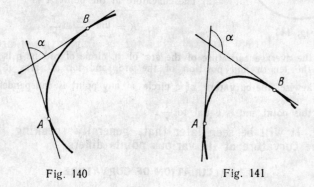

Fig. 140   Fig. 141

shown in Fig. 142, the average curvature of the arc $\widehat{AB}$ is not equal to the average curvature of the arc $\widehat{A_1B_1}$, although the lengths of their arcs are the same.
What is more, at different points the curvature of the curve differs. To characterize the degree of curvature of a given line in the immediate neighbourhood of a given point A, we introduce the concept of curvature of a curve at a given point.

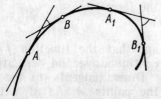

Fig. 142

Definition 2. The *curvature K_A of a line at a given point A* is the limit of the average curvature of the arc AB when the length of the arc approaches* zero (that is, when the point B approaches the point A):

$$K_A = \lim_{B \to A} K_{av} = \lim_{AB \to 0} \frac{\alpha}{\widehat{AB}}$$

Example. For a circle of radius r: (1) determine the average curvature of the arc $\widehat{AB}$ subtending the central angle α (Fig. 143); (2) determine the curvature at the point A.

* We assume that the magnitude of the limit does not depend on which side of the point A we take the variable point B on the curve.

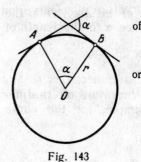

Solution. (1) Obviously the angle of contingence of the arc $\widehat{AB}$ is α, the length of the arc is αr. Hence,

$$K_{av} = \frac{\alpha}{\alpha r}$$

or

$$K_{av} = \frac{1}{r}$$

(2) The curvature at the point A is

$$K = \lim_{\alpha \to 0} \frac{\alpha}{\alpha r} = \frac{1}{r}$$

Fig. 143

Thus, the average curvature of the arc of a circle of radius r is independent of the length and position of the arc, and for all arcs it is equal to $\frac{1}{r}$. Likewise, the curvature of a circle at any point is independent of the choice of this point and is equal to $\frac{1}{r}$.

Note. It will be seen later that, generally speaking, for any curve the curvature at its various points differs.

6.3 CALCULATION OF CURVATURE

Let us develop a formula for finding the curvature of any curve at any point $M(x, y)$. We shall assume that the curve is represented in a Cartesian coordinate system by an equation of the form

$$y = f(x) \qquad (1)$$

and that the function $f(x)$ has a continuous second derivative.

Draw tangents to the curve at the points M and M_1 with abscissas x and $x + \Delta x$ and denote by φ and $\varphi + \Delta\varphi$ the angles of inclination of these tangents (Fig. 144).

We reckon the length of the arc $\widehat{M_0 M}$ from some fixed point

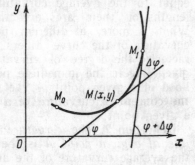

Fig. 144

M_0 and denote it by s; then $\Delta s = \widehat{M_0 M_1} - \widehat{M_0 M}$, and $|\Delta s| = \widehat{MM_1}$.

As will be seen from Fig. 144, the angle of contingence corresponding to the arc $\widehat{MM_1}$ is equal to the absolute value * of the difference of the angles φ and $\varphi + \Delta\varphi$, which means it is equal to $|\Delta\varphi|$.

---

* It is obvious that for the curve given in Fig. 144, $|\Delta\varphi| = \Delta\varphi$ since $\Delta\varphi > 0$.

According to the definition of average curvature of a curve, on the segment MM_1 we have

$$K_{av} = \frac{|\Delta\varphi|}{|\Delta s|} = \left|\frac{\Delta\varphi}{\Delta s}\right|$$

To obtain the **curvature at the point** M, it is necessary to find the limit of the expression obtained on the condition that the arc length $\widehat{MM_1}$ approaches zero:

$$K = \lim_{\Delta s \to 0}\left|\frac{d\varphi}{\Delta s}\right|$$

Since the quantities φ and s both depend on x (are functions of x), φ may thus be considered as a function of s. We may consider that this function is represented parametrically by means of the parameter x. Then

$$\lim_{\Delta s \to 0}\frac{\Delta\varphi}{\Delta s} = \frac{d\varphi}{ds}$$

and, consequently,

$$K = \left|\frac{d\varphi}{ds}\right| \qquad (2)$$

To calculate $\frac{d\varphi}{ds}$, we make use of the formula for differentiating a function represented parametrically:

$$\frac{d\varphi}{ds} = \frac{\dfrac{d\varphi}{dx}}{\dfrac{ds}{dx}}$$

To express the derivative $\frac{d\varphi}{dx}$ in terms of the function $y = f(x)$, we note that $\tan\varphi = \frac{dy}{dx}$ and, therefore,

$$\varphi = \arctan\frac{dy}{dx}$$

Differentiating this equation with respect to x, we get

$$\frac{d\varphi}{dx} = \frac{\dfrac{d^2y}{dx^2}}{1 + \left(\dfrac{dy}{dx}\right)^2}$$

As for the derivative $\frac{ds}{dx}$, we found in Sec. 6.1 that

$$\frac{ds}{dx} = \sqrt{1 + \left(\frac{dy}{dx}\right)^2}$$

Therefore,

$$\frac{d\varphi}{ds} = \frac{\dfrac{d\varphi}{dx}}{\dfrac{ds}{dx}} = \frac{\dfrac{\dfrac{d^2y}{dx^2}}{1+\left(\dfrac{dy}{dx}\right)^2}}{\sqrt{1+\left(\dfrac{dy}{dx}\right)^2}} = \frac{\dfrac{d^2u}{dx^2}}{\left[1+\left(\dfrac{dy}{dx}\right)^2\right]^{3/2}}$$

or, since $K = \left|\dfrac{d\varphi}{ds}\right|$, we finally get

$$K = \frac{\left|\dfrac{d^2y}{dx^2}\right|}{\left[1+\left(\dfrac{dy}{dx}\right)^2\right]^{3/2}} \tag{3}$$

It is thus possible to find the curvature at any point of a curve where a second derivative $\dfrac{d^2y}{dx^2}$ exists and is continuous. Calculations are done with formula (3). It should be noted that when calculating the curvature of a curve only the positive value of the root in the denominator should be taken, since the curvature of a line cannot (by definition) be negative.

Example 1. Determine the curvature of the parabola $y^2 = 2px$:
(a) at an arbitrary point $M(x, y)$;
(b) at the point $M_1(0, 0)$;
(c) at the point $M_2\left(\dfrac{p}{2}, p\right)$.

Solution. Find the first and second derivatives of the function $y = \sqrt{2px}$:

$$\frac{dy}{dx} = \frac{p}{\sqrt{2px}}; \quad \frac{d^2y}{dx^2} = -\frac{p^2}{(2px)^{3/2}}$$

Substituting the expressions obtained into (3), we get

(a) $K = \dfrac{p^2}{(2px+p^2)^{3/2}}$

(b) $K_{\substack{x=0 \\ y=0}} = \dfrac{1}{p}$

(c) $K_{\substack{x=\frac{p}{2} \\ y=p}} = \dfrac{1}{2\sqrt{2p}}$

Example 2. Determine the curvature of the straight line $y = ax+b$ at an arbitrary point (x, y).
Solution.

$$y' = a, \quad y'' = 0$$

Referring to (3) we get

$$K = 0$$

Thus, a straight line is a "line of zero curvature". This very same result is readily obtainable directly from the definition of curvature.

6.4 CALCULATING THE CURVATURE OF A CURVE REPRESENTED PARAMETRICALLY

Let a curve be represented parametrically:

$$x = \varphi(t), \quad y = \psi(t)$$

Then (see Sec. 3.24):

$$\frac{dy}{dx} = \frac{\psi'(t)}{\varphi'(t)}, \quad \frac{d^2y}{dx^2} = \frac{\psi''\varphi' - \psi'\varphi''}{(\varphi')^3}$$

Substituting the expressions obtained into formula (3) of the preceding section, we get

$$K = \frac{|\psi''\varphi' - \psi'\varphi''|}{[\varphi'^2 + \psi'^2]^{3/2}} \tag{1}$$

Example. Determine the curvature of the cycloid

$$x = a(t - \sin t), \quad y = a(1 - \cos t)$$

at an arbitrary point $(x \quad y)$.
Solution.

$$\frac{dx}{dt} = a(1 - \cos t), \quad \frac{d^2x}{dt^2} = a \sin t, \quad \frac{dy}{dt} = a \sin t, \quad \frac{d^2y}{dt^2} = a \cos t$$

Substituting the expressions obtained into (3), we get

$$K = \frac{|a(1 - \cos t) a \cos t - a \sin t \cdot a \sin t|}{[a^2(1 - \cos t)^2 + a^2 \sin^2 t]^{3/2}} = \frac{|\cos t - 1|}{2^{3/2} a (1 - \cos t)^{3/2}}$$

$$= \frac{1}{2^{3/2} a (1 - \cos t)^{1/2}} = \frac{1}{4a \left| \sin \dfrac{t}{2} \right|}$$

6.5 CALCULATING THE CURVATURE OF A CURVE GIVEN BY AN EQUATION IN POLAR COORDINATES

Given a curve represented by an equation of the form

$$\rho = f(\theta) \tag{1}$$

Write the transformation formulas from polar coordinates to Cartesian coordinates:

$$\left. \begin{array}{l} x = \rho \cos\theta \\ y = \rho \sin\theta \end{array} \right\} \tag{2}$$

If in these formulas we replace ρ by its expression in terms of θ, i.e., $f(\theta)$, we get

$$\left. \begin{array}{l} x = f(\theta) \cos\theta \\ y = f(\theta) \sin\theta \end{array} \right\} \tag{3}$$

The latter equations may be regarded as parametric equations of curve (1), the parameter being θ.

Then

$$\frac{dx}{d\theta} = \frac{d\rho}{d\theta} \cos\theta - \rho \sin\theta, \quad \frac{dy}{d\theta} = \frac{d\rho}{d\theta} \sin\theta + \rho \cos\theta$$

$$\frac{d^2x}{d\theta^2} = \frac{d^2\rho}{d\theta^2} \cos\theta - 2\frac{d\rho}{d\theta} \sin\theta - \rho\cos\theta$$

$$\frac{d^2y}{d\theta^2} = \frac{d^2\rho}{d\theta^2} \sin\theta + 2\frac{d\rho}{d\theta} \cos\theta - \rho\sin\theta$$

Substituting the latter expressions into (1) of the preceding section, we get a formula for calculating the curvature of a curve in polar coordinates:

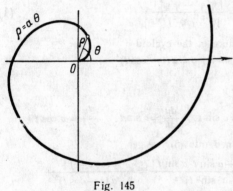

$$K = \frac{|\rho^2 + 2\rho'^2 - \rho\rho''|}{(\rho^2 + \rho'^2)^{3/2}} \quad (4)$$

Example. Determine the curvature of the spiral of Archimedes $\rho = a\theta$ ($a > 0$) at an arbitrary point (Fig. 145).

Solution.

$$\frac{d\rho}{d\theta} = a, \quad \frac{d^2\rho}{d\theta^2} = 0$$

Hence

$$K = \frac{|a^2\theta^2 + 2a^2|}{(a^2\theta^2 + a^2)^{3/2}} = \frac{1}{a}\frac{\theta^2 + 2}{(\theta^2 + 1)^{3/2}}$$

Fig. 145

It will be noted that for large values of θ we have the approximate equations $\frac{\theta^2 + 2}{\theta^2} \approx 1$, $\frac{\theta^2 + 1}{\theta^2} \approx 1$; therefore, replacing $\theta^2 + 2$ by θ^2 and $\theta^2 + 1$ by θ^2 in the foregoing formula, we get an approximate formula (for large values of θ):

$$K \approx \frac{1}{a}\frac{\theta^2}{(\theta^2)^{3/2}} = \frac{1}{a\theta}$$

Thus, for large values of θ the spiral of Archimedes has, approximately, the same curvature as a circle of radius $a\theta$.

6.6 THE RADIUS AND CIRCLE OF CURVATURE. THE CENTRE OF CURVATURE. EVOLUTE AND INVOLUTE

Definition. The quantity R, which is the reciprocal of the curvature K of a curve at a given point M, is called the *radius of curvature* of the curve at the point in question:

$$R = \frac{1}{K} \quad (1)$$

or

$$R = \frac{\left[1 + \left(\frac{dy}{dx}\right)^2\right]^{3/2}}{\left|\frac{d^2y}{dx^2}\right|} \qquad (2)$$

Draw a normal, at the point M, to a curve in the direction of the concavity of the curve, and lay off a segment MC equal to the radius R of the curvature of the curve at the point M. The

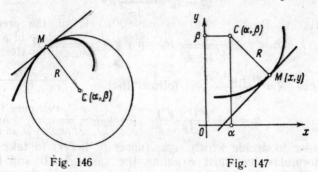

Fig. 146   Fig. 147

point C is called the *centre of curvature* of the given curve at M; the circle, of radius R, with centre at C (passing through M) is called the *circle of curvature* of the given curve at the point M (Fig. 146).

From the definition of circle of curvature it follows that at a given point the curvature of a curve and the curvature of a circle of curvature are the same.

Let us derive formulas defining the coordinates of the centre of curvature.

Let a curve be given by the equation

$$y = f(x) \qquad (3)$$

Take a point $M(x, y)$ on this curve and determine the coordinates α and β of the centre of curvature corresponding to this point (Fig. 147). To do this, write the equation of the normal to the curve at M:

$$Y - y = -\frac{1}{y'}(X - x) \qquad$$

(Here, X and Y are the moving coordinates of the point of the normal.)

Since the point $C(\alpha, \beta)$ lies on the normal, its coordinates must satisfy equation (4):

$$\beta - y = -\frac{1}{y'}(\alpha - x) \qquad (5)$$

14—2081

Further, the point $C(\alpha, \beta)$ is separated from $M(x, y)$ by a distance equal to the radius of curvature R:

$$(\alpha - x)^2 + (\beta - y)^2 = R^2 \tag{6}$$

Solving equations (5) and (6) simultaneously, we find α and β:

$$(\alpha - x)^2 + \frac{1}{y'^2}(\alpha - x)^2 = R^2$$

$$(\alpha - x)^2 = \frac{y'^2}{1 + y'^2} R^2$$

whence

$$\alpha = x \pm \frac{y'}{\sqrt{1 + y'^2}} R, \quad \beta = y \mp \frac{1}{\sqrt{1 + y'^2}} R$$

and since $R = \frac{(1 + y'^2)^{3/2}}{|y''|}$, it follows that

$$\alpha = x \pm \frac{y'(1 + y'^2)}{|y''|}, \quad \beta = y \mp \frac{1 + y'^2}{|y''|}$$

In order to decide which signs (upper or lower) to take in the latter formulas, we must examine the case $y'' > 0$ and the case $y'' < 0$. If $y'' > 0$, then at this point the curve is concave, and, hence, $\beta > y$ (Fig. 147), and for this reason we take the lower signs. Taking into account that in this case $|y''| = y''$, the formulas of the coordinates of the centre of curvature will be

$$\left. \begin{array}{l} \alpha = x - \dfrac{y'(1 + y'^2)}{y''} \\[2mm] \beta = y + \dfrac{1 + y'^2}{y''} \end{array} \right\} \tag{7}$$

Similarly, it may be shown that formulas (7) will hold for the case $y'' < 0$ as well.

If the curve is represented by the parametric equations

$$x = \varphi(t), \quad y = \psi(t)$$

then the coordinates of the centre of curvature are readily obtainable from (7) by substituting, in place of y' and y'', their expressions in terms of the parameter

$$y' = \frac{y'_t}{x'_t}, \quad y'' = \frac{x'_t y''_t - x''_t y'_t}{x_t'^3}$$

Then

$$\left. \begin{array}{l} \alpha = x - \dfrac{y'(x'^2 + y'^2)}{x'y'' - x''y'} \\[2mm] \beta = y + \dfrac{x'(x'^2 + y'^2)}{x'y'' - x''y'} \end{array} \right\} \tag{7'}$$

Example 1. To determine the coordinates of the centre of curvature of the parabola

$$y^2 = 2px$$

(a) at an arbitrary point $M(x, y)$, (b) at the point $M_0(0, 0)$, (c) at the point $M_1\left(\dfrac{p}{2}, p\right)$.

Solution. Substituting the values $\dfrac{dy}{dx}$ and $\dfrac{d^2y}{dx^2}$ into (7) we get (Fig. 148):

(a) $\alpha = 3x + p$, $\beta = -\dfrac{(2x)^{3/2}}{\sqrt{p}}$,

(b) at $x = 0$ we find $\alpha = p$, $\beta = 0$,

(c) at $x = \dfrac{p}{2}$ we have $\alpha = \dfrac{5p}{2}$, $\beta = -p$.

If at $M_1(x, y)$ of a given curve the curvature differs from zero, then a very definite centre of curvature $C_1(\alpha, \beta)$ corresponds to this point. The totality of all centres of curvature of the given curve forms a certain new line, called the evolute, with respect to the first.

Thus, the locus of centres of curvature of a given curve is called the *evolute*. As related to its evolute, the given curve is called the *evolvent* or *involute*.

If a given curve is defined by the equation $y = f(x)$, then equations (7) may be regarded as the parametric equations of the evolute with parameter x. Eliminating from these equations the parameter x (if this is possible), we get an immediate relationship between the moving coordinates of the evolute α and β. But if the curve is given by parametric equations $x = \varphi(t)$, $y = \psi(t)$, then equations (7') yield the parametric equations of the evolute (since the quantities x, y, x', y', x'', y'' are functions of t).

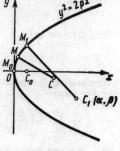

Fig. 148

Example 2. Find the equation of the evolute of the parabola

$$y^2 = 2px$$

Solution. On the basis of Example 1 we have, for any point (x, y) of the parabola,

$$\alpha = 3x + p$$

$$\beta = -\frac{(2x)^{3/2}}{\sqrt{p}}$$

Eliminating the parameter x from these equations, we get

$$\beta^2 = \frac{8}{27p}(\alpha - p)^3$$

This is the equation of a semicubical parabola (Fig. 149).

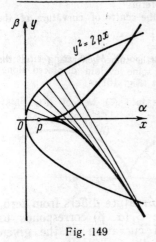

Fig. 149

Example 3. Find the equation of the evolute of an ellipse represented by the parametric equations

$$x = a \cos t, \quad y = b \sin t$$

Solution. Find the derivatives of x and y with respect to t:

$$x' = -a \sin t, \quad y' = b \cos t$$
$$x'' = -a \cos t, \quad y'' = -b \sin t$$

Substituting the expressions of the derivatives into (7'), we get

$$\alpha = a \cos t - \frac{b \cos t \,(a^2 \sin^2 t + b^2 \cos^2 t)}{ab \sin^2 t + ab \cos^2 t}$$
$$= a \cos t - a \cos t \sin^2 t - \frac{b^2}{a} \cos^3 t =$$
$$= \left(a - \frac{b^2}{a} \right) \cos^3 t$$

Thus,

$$\alpha = \left(a - \frac{b^2}{a} \right) \cos^3 t$$

Similarly we get

$$\beta = \left(b - \frac{a^2}{b} \right) \sin^3 t$$

Eliminating the parameter t, we get the equation of the evolute of the ellipse in the form

$$\left(\frac{\alpha}{b} \right)^{2/3} + \left(\frac{\beta}{a} \right)^{2/3} = \left(\frac{a^2 - b^2}{ab} \right)^{2/3}$$

Here, α and β are the coordinates of the evolute (Fig. 150).

Example 4. Find the parametric equations of the evolute of the cycloid

$$x = a\,(t - \sin t)$$
$$y = a\,(1 - \cos t)$$

Solution.

$$x' = a\,(1 - \cos t), \quad y' = a \sin t$$
$$x'' = a \sin t, \qquad\quad y'' = a \cos t$$

Substituting the expressions obtained into (7'), we get

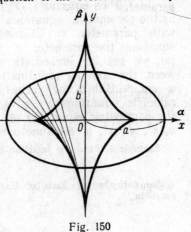

Fig. 150

$$\alpha = a\,(t + \sin t)$$
$$\beta = -a\,(1 - \cos t)$$

Make a change of variables, putting

$$\alpha = \xi - \pi a$$
$$\beta = \eta - 2a$$
$$t = \tau - \pi$$

Then the equations of the evolute will take the form

$$\xi = a\,(\tau - \sin \tau)$$
$$\eta = a\,(1 - \cos \tau)$$

They define, in coordinates ξ, η, a cycloid with the same generating circle of radius a. Thus, the evolute of a cycloid is that same cycloid displaced along the x-axis by $-\pi a$ and along the y-axis by $-2a$ (Fig. 151).

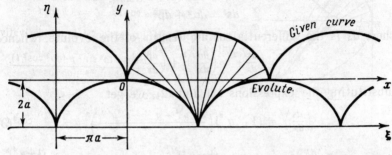

Fig. 151

6.7 THE PROPERTIES OF AN EVOLUTE

Theorem 1. *The normal to a given curve is a tangent to its evolute.*
Proof. The slope of the tangent to an evolute defined by the parametric equations (7) of the preceding section is equal to

$$\frac{d\beta}{d\alpha} = \frac{\dfrac{d\beta}{dx}}{\dfrac{d\alpha}{dx}}$$

Noting that [by virtue of the same equations (7)]

$$\frac{d\alpha}{dx} = -\frac{3y''^2 y'^2 - y'y''' - y'^3 y'''}{y''^2} = -y'\,\frac{3y'y''^2 - y''' - y'^2 y'''}{y''^2} \qquad (1)$$

$$\frac{d\beta}{dx} = \frac{3y''^2 y' - y''' - y'^2 y'''}{y''^2} \qquad (2)$$

we get the relationship

$$\frac{d\beta}{d\alpha} = -\frac{1}{y'}$$

But y' is the slope of the tangent to the curve at the corresponding point; it therefore follows from the relationship obtained that the tangent to the curve and the tangent to its evolute at the corresponding point are mutually perpendicular; that is, the normal to a curve is the tangent to the evolute.

Theorem 2. *If, over a certain segment M_1M_2 of a curve, the radius of curvature varies monotonically (i.e., either only increases or only decreases), then the increment in the arc length of the evolute on this portion of the curve is equal (in absolute value) to the corresponding increment in the radius of curvature of the given curve.*

Proof. From formula (2′), Sec. 6.1, we have

$$ds^2 = d\alpha^2 + d\beta^2$$

where ds is the differential of arc length of the evolute; whence

$$\left(\frac{ds}{dx}\right)^2 = \left(\frac{d\alpha}{dx}\right)^2 + \left(\frac{d\beta}{dx}\right)^2$$

Substituting the expressions (1) and (2), we get

$$\left(\frac{ds}{dx}\right)^2 = (1+y'^2)\left(\frac{3y'y''^2 - y''' - y'^2y'''}{y''^2}\right)^2 \tag{3}$$

Then we find $\left(\dfrac{dR}{dx}\right)^2$. Since $R = \dfrac{(1+y'^2)^{3/2}}{y''}$, it follows that $R_2 = \dfrac{(1+y'^2)^3}{y''^2}$.

Differentiating both sides of this equation with respect to x, we get the following (after appropriate manipulations):

$$2R\frac{dR}{dx} = \frac{2(1+y'^2)^2(3y'y''^2 - y''' - y'^2y''')}{(y'')^3}$$

Dividing both sides of the equation by $2R = \dfrac{2(1+y'^2)^{3/2}}{y''}$, we have

$$\frac{dR}{dx} = \frac{(1+y'^2)^{1/2}(3y'y''^2 - y''' - y'^2y''')}{y''^2}$$

Squaring, we get

$$\left(\frac{dR}{dx}\right)^2 = (1+y'^2)\left(\frac{3y'y''^2 - y''' - y'^2y'''}{y''^2}\right)^2 \tag{4}$$

Comparing (3) and (4), we find

$$\left(\frac{dR}{dx}\right)^2 = \left(\frac{ds}{dx}\right)^2$$

whence

$$\frac{dR}{dx} = \mp\frac{ds}{dx}$$

It is given that $\dfrac{dR}{dx}$ does not change sign (R only increases or only decreases); hence, $\dfrac{ds}{dx}$ does not change sign either. For the sake of definiteness, let $\frac{dR}{dx} \leqslant 0$, $\frac{ds}{dx} \geqslant 0$ (which corresponds to Fig. 152). Hence, $\frac{dR}{dx} = -\frac{ds}{dx}$.

Let the point M_1 have abscissa x_1 and M_2 have abscissa x_2. Apply the Cauchy theorem to the functions $s(x)$ and $R(x)$ on the interval $[x_1, x_2]$:

$$\frac{s(x_2)-s(x_1)}{R(x_2)-R(x_1)} = \frac{\left(\frac{ds}{dx}\right)_{x=\xi}}{\left(\frac{dR}{dx}\right)_{x=\xi}} = -1$$

where ξ is a number lying between x_1 and x_2 $(x_1 < \xi < x_2)$.

We introduce the designations (Fig. 152)

$$s(x_2) = s_2, \quad s(x_1) = s_1, \quad R(x_2) = R_2, \quad R(x_1) = R_1$$

Then $\frac{s_2 - s_1}{R_2 - R_1} = -1$ or $s_2 - s_1 = -(R_2 - R_1)$. But this means that

$$|s_2 - s_1| = |R_2 - R_1|$$

This equation is proved in exactly the same manner if the radius of curvature increases.

We have proved Theorems 1 and 2 for the case where the curve is given by an explicit function, $y = f(x)$.

If the curve is represented by parametric equations, these theorems also hold, and their proof is exactly the same.

Note. The following is a simple mechanical method for constructing an involute from its evolute.

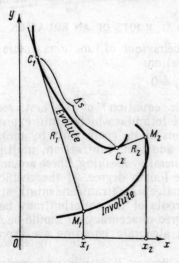

Fig. 152

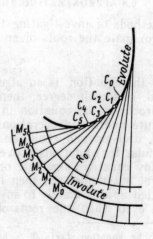

Fig. 153

Let a flexible ruler be bent into the shape of an evolute C_0C_5 (Fig. 153). Suppose one end of an unstretchable string is attached to the point C_0 and bends round the ruler. If we hold the string taut and unwind it, the end of the string will describe a curve M_5M_0, which is the involute (or evolvent, the name coming from this process of "evolving"). Proof that this curve is indeed an involute may be carried out by means of the above-established properties of the evolute.

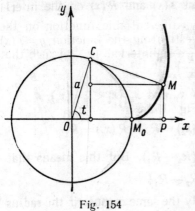

Fig. 154

It should be noted that to a single evolute there correspond an infinitude of various involutes (Fig. 153).

Example. Suppose we have a circle of radius a (Fig. 154). Take the involute of this circle that passes through the point M_0 $(a, 0)$.

Taking into account that $CM = \overgroup{CM_0} =$ $= at$, it is easy to obtain the equations of the involute of the circle:

$$OP = x = a(\cos t + t \sin t)$$
$$PM = y = a(\sin t - t \cos t)$$

It will be noted that the profile of a tooth of a gear wheel is most often in the shape of the involute of a circle.

6.8 APPROXIMATING THE REAL ROOTS OF AN EQUATION

Methods of investigating the behaviour of functions enable us to approximate the roots of an equation:

$$f(x) = 0$$

If the equation is an algebraic equation * of the first, second, third, or fourth degree, there are formulas which permit expressing the roots of the equation in terms of its coefficients by means of a finite number of operations of addition, subtraction, multiplication, division and evolution. Generally speaking, there are no such formulas for equations above the fourth degree. If the coefficients of any equation, algebraic or nonalgebraic (transcendental), are not literal but numerical, then the roots of the equation may be calculated approximately to any degree of accuracy. It should be noted that even when the roots of an algebraic equation are expressed

---

* The equation $f(x) = 0$ is called *algebraic* if $f(x)$ is a polynomial (see Sec. 7.6).

in terms of radicals, it is sometimes better to apply an approxi-mation method of solving the equation. Below we give some me-thods of approximating the roots of an equation.

1. **Method of chords.** Given an equation

$$f(x) = 0 \qquad (1)$$

where $f(x)$ is a continuous, doubly differentiable function on the interval $[a, b]$. Suppose that by investigating the function $y = f(x)$ within the interval $[a, b]$ we isolate a subinterval $[x_1, x_2]$ such that within this subinterval the func-tion is monotonic (either increas-ing or decreasing), and at the end points the values of the func-

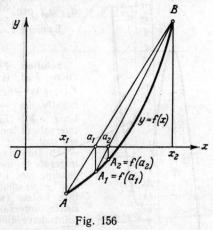

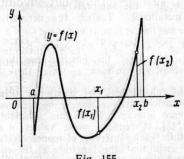

Fig. 155   Fig. 156

tion $f(x_1)$ and $f(x_2)$ have different signs. For definiteness, we say that $f(x_1) < 0$, $f(x_2) > 0$ (Fig. 155). Since the function $y = f(x)$ is continuous on the interval $[x_1, x_2]$, its graph will cut the x-axis in some one point between x_1 and x_2.

Draw a chord AB connecting the end points of the curve $y = f(x)$, which correspond to abscissas x_1 and x_2. Then the abscissa a_1 of the point of intersection of this chord with the x-axis will be the approximate value of the root (Fig. 156). In order to find this approximate value let us write the equation of the straight line AB that passes through two given points $A [x_1, f(x_1)]$ and $B [x_2, f(x_2)]$:

$$\frac{y - f(x_1)}{f(x_2) - f(x_1)} = \frac{x - x_1}{x_2 - x_1}$$

Since $y = 0$ at $x = a_1$, it follows that

$$\frac{-f(x_1)}{f(x_2) - f(x_1)} = \frac{a_1 - x_1}{x_2 - x_1}$$

whence

$$a_1 = x_1 - \frac{(x_2 - x_1) f(x_1)}{f(x_2) - f(x_1)} \qquad (2)$$

or

$$a_1 = \frac{x_1 f(x_2) - x_2 f(x_1)}{f(x_2) - f(x_1)}. \tag{2'}$$

To obtain a more exact value of the root, we determine $f(a_1)$. If $f(a_1) < 0$, then repeat the same procedure applying formula (2') to the interval $[a_1, x_2]$. If $f(a_1) > 0$, then apply this formula to the interval $[x_1, a_1]$. By repeating this procedure several times we will obviously obtain more and more precise values of the root a_2, a_3, etc.

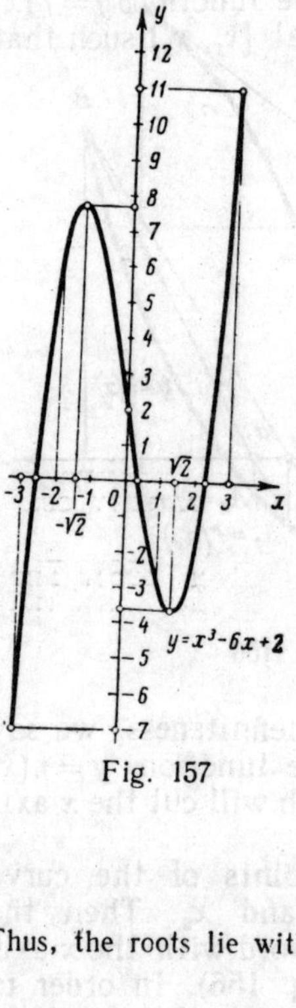

Example 1. Approximate the roots of the equation

$$f(x) = x^3 - 6x + 2 = 0$$

Solution. First find the intervals where the function $f(x)$ is monotonic. Taking the derivative $f'(x) = 3x^2 - 6$, we find that it is positive for $x < -\sqrt{2}$, negative for $-\sqrt{2} < x < +\sqrt{2}$ and again positive for $x > \sqrt{2}$ (Fig. 157). Thus, the function has three intervals of monotonicity, in each of which there is one root.

To simplify the calculations, let us narrow these intervals of monotonicity (there should be a corresponding root in each interval). To do this, substitute into expression $f(x)$, at random, some values of x, then isolate (within each interval of monotonicity) shorter intervals such that the functions at the end points have different signs:

Fig. 157

$$
\left.
\begin{array}{ll}
x_1 = 0, & f(0) = 2 \\
x_2 = 1, & f(1) = -3
\end{array}
\right\}
$$

$$
\left.
\begin{array}{ll}
x_3 = -3, & f(-3) = -7 \\
x_4 = -2, & f(-2) = 6
\end{array}
\right\}
$$

$$
\left.
\begin{array}{ll}
x_5 = 2, & f(2) = -2 \\
x_6 = 3, & f(3) = 11
\end{array}
\right\}
$$

Thus, the roots lie within the intervals

$$(-3, -2,), \quad (0, 1), \quad (2, 3)$$

Find the approximate value of the root in the interval (0, 1); from formula (2) we have

$$a_1 = 0 - \frac{(1-0) 2}{-3 - 2} = \frac{2}{5} = 0.4$$

Since

$$f(0.4) = 0.4^3 - 6 \cdot 0.4 + 2 = -0.336, \quad f(0) = 2$$

it follows that the root lies between 0 and 0.4. Again applying (2) to this interval, we get the following approximation:

$$a_2 = 0 - \frac{(0.4 - 0) \cdot 2}{-0.336 - 2} = \frac{0.8}{2.336} = 0.342, \text{ etc.}$$

We approximate the roots in the other intervals in similar fashion.

2. **Method of tangents (Newton's method).** Again, let $f(x_1) < 0$, $f(x_2) > 0$. On the interval $[x_1, x_2]$ the first derivative does not change sign. Then there is one root of the equation $f(x) = 0$ in the interval (x_1, x_2). Let us assume that the second derivative does not change sign in the interval $[x_1, x_2]$ either; this can be achieved by reducing the length of the interval within which the root lies.

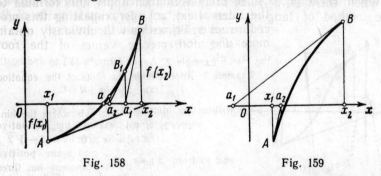

Fig. 158   Fig. 159

Preservation of the sign of the second derivative on the interval $[x_1, x_2]$ means that the curve is either only convex or only concave on $[x_1, x_2]$.

Draw a tangent to the curve at the point B (Fig. 158). The abscissa a_1 of the point of intersection of the tangent with the x-axis will be an approximate value of the root. To find this abscissa, write the equation of the tangent at the point B:

$$y - f(x_2) = f'(x_2)(x - x_2)$$

Noting that $x = a_1$ at $y = 0$, we have

$$a_1 = x_2 - \frac{f(x_2)}{f'(x_2)} \tag{3}$$

Then, drawing the tangent line at the point $B_1 [a_1, f(a_1)]$, we analogously find a more exact value of the root a_2. By repeating this procedure we can calculate the approximate value of the root to any desired degree of accuracy.

Note the following. If we drew the tangent to the curve not at the point B but at A, it might appear that the point of intersection of the tangent with the x-axis lies outside the interval (x_1, x_2).

From Figs. 158 and 159 it follows that the tangent should be drawn at the end of the arc at which the signs of the function and its second derivative coincide. Since it is given that on the interval $[x_1, x_2]$ the second derivative preserves its sign, the signs of the function and the second derivative must coincide at one of the end points. This rule also holds for the case where $f'(x) \leq 0$. If the tangent is drawn at the left end point of the interval, then in formula (3) we must put x_1 in place of x_2:

$$a_1 = x_1 - \frac{f(x_1)}{f'(x_1)} \qquad (3')$$

When there is a point of inflection C in the interval (x_1, x_2), the method of tangents can yield an approximate value of the root lying without the interval (x_1, x_2) (Fig. 160).

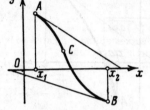

Fig. 160

Example 2. Apply formula $(3')$ to finding the root of the equation

$$f(x) = x^3 - 6x + 2 = 0$$

within the interval $(0, 1)$. We have

$$f(0) = 2, \quad f'(0) = (3x^2 - 6) \mid_{x=0} = -6,$$
$$f''(x) = 6x \geqslant 0$$

and so from $(3')$ we get

$$a_1 = 0 - \frac{2}{-6} = \frac{1}{3} = 0.333.$$

3. **Combined method** (Fig. 161). Applying at the same time on the interval $[x_1, x_2]$ the method of chords and the method of tangents, we get two points a_1 and $\bar{a}_1$ lying on either side of the desired root a, since $f(a_1)$ and $f(\bar{a}_1)$ have different signs. Then, on the interval $[a_1, \bar{a}_1]$ again apply the method of chords and the method of tangents. This yields two numbers: a_2 and $\bar{a}_2$, which are still closer to the value of the root. We continue in this manner until the difference between the approximate values found is less than the required degree of accuracy. It will be noted that in the combined method we approach the sought-for root from two sides simultaneously (i.e., at the same time we approximate the root with an excess and with a deficit).

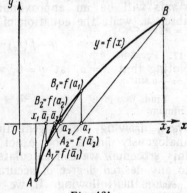

Fig. 161

To illustrate in the case we have examined it will be clear that by substitution we have

$$f(0.333) > 0, \quad f(0.342) < 0$$

Hence, the root lies between the approximate values obtained:

$$0.333 < x < 0.342$$

Exercises on Chapter 6

Find the curvature of the curves at the indicated points:

1. $b^2x^2 + a^2y^2 = a^2b^2$ at the points $(0, b)$ and $(a, 0)$. *Ans.* $\dfrac{b}{a^2}$ at $(0, b)$;

$\dfrac{a}{b^2}$ at $(a, 0)$. **2.** $xy = 12$ at the point $(3, 4)$. *Ans.* $\dfrac{24}{125}$. **3.** $y = x^3$ at the point

(x_1, y_1). *Ans.* $\dfrac{6x_1}{(1+9x_1^4)^{3/2}}$. **4.** $16y^2 = 4x^4 - x^6$ at the point $(2, 0)$. *Ans.* $\dfrac{1}{2}$.

5. $x^{\frac{2}{3}} + y^{\frac{2}{3}} = a^{\frac{2}{3}}$ at an arbitrary point. *Ans.* $\dfrac{1}{3\sqrt[3]{|axy|}}$.

Find the radius of curvature of the following curves at the indicated points; draw each curve and construct the appropriate circle of curvature:

6. $y^2 = x^3$ at the point $(4, 8)$. *Ans.* $R = \dfrac{80\sqrt{10}}{3}$. **7.** $x^2 = 4ay$ at the point $(0, 0)$.

Ans. $R = 2a$. **8.** $b^2x^2 - a^2y^2 = a^2b^2$ at the point (x_1, y_1). *Ans.* $R = \dfrac{(b^4x_1 + a^4y_1)^{3/2}}{a^4b^4}$.

9. $y = \ln x$ at the point $(1, 0)$. *Ans.* $R = 2\sqrt{2}$. **10.** $y = \sin x$ at the point

$\left(\dfrac{\pi}{2}, 1\right)$. *Ans.* $R = 1$. **11.** $\left.\begin{array}{l} x = a\cos^3 t \\ y = a\sin^3 t \end{array}\right\}$ for $t = t_1$. *Ans.* $R = 3a\sin t_1 \cos t_1$.

Find the radius of curvature of the indicated curves:

12. $\left.\begin{array}{l} x = 3t^2 \\ y = 3t - t^3 \end{array}\right\}$ for $t = 1$. *Ans.* $R = 6$. **13.** Circle $\rho = a\sin\theta$. *Ans.* $R = \dfrac{a}{2}$.

14. Spiral of Archimedes $\rho = a\theta$. *Ans.* $R = \dfrac{(\rho^2 + a^2)^{3/2}}{\rho^2 + 2a^2}$. **15.** Cardioid $\rho =$

$= a(1 - \cos\theta)$. *Ans.* $R = \dfrac{2}{3}\sqrt{2a\rho}$. **16.** Lemniscate $\rho^2 = a^2\cos 2\theta$. *Ans.* $R = \dfrac{a^2}{3\rho}$.

17. Parabola $\rho = a\sec^2\dfrac{\theta}{2}$. *Ans.* $R = 2a\sec^3\dfrac{\theta}{2}$. **18.** $\rho = a\sin^3\dfrac{\theta}{3}$. *Ans.* $R =$

$= \dfrac{3}{4}a\sin^2\dfrac{\theta}{3}$.

Find the points of the curves at which the radius of curvature is a minimum:

19. $y = \ln x$. *Ans.* $\left(\dfrac{\sqrt{2}}{2}, -\dfrac{1}{2}\ln 2\right)$. **20.** $y = e^x$. *Ans.* $\left(-\dfrac{1}{2}\ln 2, \dfrac{\sqrt{2}}{2}\right)$.

21. $\sqrt{x} + \sqrt{y} = \sqrt{a}$. *Ans.* $\left(\dfrac{a}{4}, \dfrac{a}{4}\right)$. **22.** $y = a\ln\left(1 - \dfrac{x^2}{a^2}\right)$. *Ans.* At the

point $(0, 0)$ $R = \dfrac{a}{2}$.

Find the coordinates of the centre of curvature (α, β) and the equation of the evolute for each of the following curves:

23. $\dfrac{x^2}{a^2} - \dfrac{y^2}{b^2} = 1$. *Ans.* $\alpha = \dfrac{(a^2+b^2)x^3}{a^4}$, $\beta = -\dfrac{(a^2+b^2)y^3}{b^4}$. **24.** $x^{\frac{2}{3}} + y^{\frac{2}{3}} = a^{\frac{2}{3}}$.

Ans. $\alpha = x + 3x^{\frac{1}{3}}y^{\frac{2}{3}}$, $\beta = y + 3x^{\frac{2}{3}}y^{\frac{1}{3}}$. **25.** $y^3 = a^2x$. *Ans.* $\alpha = \dfrac{a^4 + 15y^4}{6a^2y}$,

$\beta = \dfrac{a^4y - 9y^5}{2a^4}$. **26.** $\begin{cases} x = 3t, \\ y = t^2 - 6. \end{cases}$ *Ans.* $\alpha = -\dfrac{4}{3}t^3$, $\beta = 3t^2 - \dfrac{3}{2}$.

27. $\begin{cases} x = k \ln \cot \dfrac{t}{2} - k \cos t, \\ y = k \sin t. \end{cases}$ *Ans.* $y = \dfrac{k}{2}\left(e^{\frac{x}{k}} + e^{-\frac{x}{k}}\right)$ (tractrix).

28. $\begin{cases} x = a\,(\cos t + t \sin t), \\ y = a\,(\sin t - t \cos t). \end{cases}$ *Ans.* $\alpha = a \cos t$, $\beta = a \sin t$.   **29.** $\begin{cases} x = a \cos^3 t, \\ y = a \sin^3 t. \end{cases}$

Ans. $\alpha = a \cos^3 t + 3a \cos t \sin^2 t$, $\beta = a \sin^3 t + 3a \cos^2 t \sin t$.

30. Find the roots of the equation $x^3 - 4x + 2 = 0$ to three decimal places. *Ans.* $x_1 = 1.675$, $x_2 = 0.539$, $x_3 = -2.214$.

31. For the equation $f(x) = x^5 - x - 0.2 = 0$, approximate the root in the interval $(1,\ 1.1)$. *Ans.* 1.045.

32. Evaluate the roots of the equation $x^4 + 2x^2 - 6x + 2 = 0$ to two decimal places. *Ans.* $0.38 < x_1 < 0.39$, $1.24 < x_2 < 1.25$.

33. Solve the equation $x^3 - 5 = 0$ approximately. *Ans.* $x_1 \approx 1.71$, $x_{2,3} = 1.71\,\dfrac{-1 \pm i\sqrt{3}}{2}$.

34. Approximate the root of the equation $x - \tan x = 0$ lying between 0 and $\dfrac{3\pi}{2}$. *Ans.* 4.4935.

35. Compute the root of the equation $\sin x = 1 - x$ to three places of decimals. **Hint.** Reduce the equation to the form $f(x) = 0$. *Ans.* $0.5110 < x < 0.5111$.

Miscellaneous Problems

36. Show that at each point of the lemniscate $\rho^2 = a^2 \cos 2\varphi$ the curvature is proportional to the radius vector of the point.

37. Find the greatest value of the radius of curvature of the curve $\rho = a \sin^3 \dfrac{\varphi}{3}$. *Ans.* $R = \dfrac{3}{4}a$.

38. Find the coordinates of the centre of curvature of the curve $y = x \ln x$ at the point where $y' = 0$. *Ans.* $(e^{-1},\ 0)$.

39. Prove that for points of the spiral of Archimedes $\rho = a\varphi$ as $\varphi \to \infty$ the magnitude of the difference between the radius vector and the radius of curvature approaches zero.

40. Find the parabola $y = ax^2 + bx + c$, which has common tangent and curvature with the sine curve $y = \sin x$ at the point $\left(\dfrac{\pi}{2},\ 1\right)$. Make a drawing.

Ans. $y = -\dfrac{x^2}{2} + \dfrac{\pi x}{2} + 1 - \dfrac{\pi^2}{8}$.

41. The function $y = f(x)$ is defined as follows:

$$f(x) = x^3 \text{ in the interval } -\infty < x \leqslant 1$$
$$f(x) = ax^2 + bx + c \text{ in the interval } 1 < x < +\infty$$

What must a, b and c be for the curve $y = f(x)$ to have continuous curvature everywhere? Make a drawing. *Ans.* $a = 3$, $b = -3$, $c = 1$.

42. Show that the radius of curvature of a cycloid at any one of its points is twice the length of the normal at that point.

43. Write the equation of the circle of curvature of the parabola $y = x^2$ at the point $(1,\ 1)$. *Ans.* $(x + 4)^2 + \left(y - \dfrac{7}{2}\right)^2 = \dfrac{125}{4}$.

44. Write the equation of the circle of curvature of the curve $y = \tan x$ at the point $\left(\dfrac{\pi}{4},\ 1\right)$. *Ans.* $\left(x - \dfrac{\pi - 10}{4}\right)^2 + \left(y - \dfrac{9}{4}\right)^2 = \dfrac{125}{16}$.

45. Find the length of the entire evolute of an ellipse whose semi-axes are a and b. *Ans.* $\dfrac{4(a^3 - b^3)}{ab}$.

46. Find the approximate values of the roots of the equation $xe^x = 2$ to within 0.01. *Ans.* The equation has only one real root, $x \approx 0.84$.

47. Find the approximate values of the roots of the equation $x \ln x = 0.8$ to within 0.01. *Ans.* The equation has only one real root, $x \approx 1.64$.

48. Find the approximate values of the roots of the equation $x^2 \arctan x = 1$ to within 0.001. *Ans.* The equation has only one real root, $x \approx 1.096$.

CHAPTER 7

COMPLEX NUMBERS. POLYNOMIALS

7.1 COMPLEX NUMBERS. BASIC DEFINITIONS

A *complex number* is a number given by the expression

$$z = a + ib \tag{1}$$

where a and b are *real* numbers and i is the so-called *imaginary unit*, which is defined as

$$i = \sqrt{-1} \text{ or } i^2 = -1 \tag{2}$$

a is called the *real part*, and b, the *imaginary part* of the complex number. They are designated, respectively, as follows:

$$a = \text{Re}\, z, \quad b = \text{Im}\, z$$

If $a = 0$, then the number $0 + ib = ib$ is a *pure imaginary*; if $b = 0$, then we have the real number $a + i0 = a$. Two complex numbers $z = a + ib$ and $\bar{z} = a - ib$ that differ solely in the sign of the imaginary part are called *conjugate complex numbers*.

We agree upon the two following basic definitions.

(1) Two complex numbers $z_1 = a_1 + ib_1$ and $z_2 = a_2 + ib_2$ are equal, $z_1 = z_2$, if

$$a_1 = a_2, \quad b_1 = b_2$$

that is, if their real parts are equal and their imaginary parts are equal.

(2) A complex number z is equal to zero

$$z = a + ib = 0$$

if and only if $a = 0$, $b = 0$.

1. **Geometric representation of complex numbers.** Any complex number $z = a + ib$ may be represented in the xy-plane as a point $A(a, b)$ with coordinates a and b. Conversely, every point $M(x, y)$ of the plane is associated with a complex number $z = x + iy$. The plane on which complex numbers are represented is called the *plane of the complex variable z*, or the *complex plane* (Fig. 162, the encircled z symbol indicates that this is the complex plane).

Points of the plane of the complex variable z lying on the x-axis correspond to real numbers ($b = 0$). Points lying on the y-axis represent pure imaginary numbers, since $a = 0$. Therefore, in the complex plane, the y-axis is called the *imaginary axis*, or *axis of imaginaries*, and the x-axis is the *real axis*, or *axis of reals*.

Joining the point $A(a, b)$ to the origin, we get a vector $\overline{OA}$. In certain instances, it is convenient to consider the vector $\overline{OA}$ as the geometric representation of the complex number $z = a + ib$.

2. **Trigonometric form of a complex number.** Denote by φ and $r\ (r \geqslant 0)$ the polar coordinates of the point $A(a, b)$ and consider the origin as the pole and the positive direction of the x-axis, the polar axis. Then (Fig. 162) we have the familiar relationships

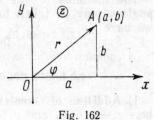

Fig. 162

$$a = r\cos\varphi, \quad b = r\sin\varphi$$

and, hence, the complex number may be given in the form

$$a + ib = r\cos\varphi + ir\sin\varphi \quad \text{or} \quad z = r(\cos\varphi + i\sin\varphi) \tag{3}$$

The expression on the right is called the *trigonometric form* (or *polar form*) *of the complex number* $z = a + ib$; r is termed the *modulus* of the complex number z, φ is the *argument* (*amplitude* or *phase*) of the complex number z. They are designated as

$$r = |z|, \quad \varphi = \arg z \tag{4}$$

The quantities r and φ are expressed in terms of a and b as follows:

$$r = \sqrt{a^2 + b^2}, \quad \varphi = \operatorname{Arctan}\frac{b}{a}$$

To summarize, then,

$$\left.\begin{array}{c} |z| = |a + ib| = \sqrt{a^2 + b^2} \\ \arg z = \arg(a + ib) = \operatorname{Arctan}\dfrac{b}{a} \end{array}\right\} \tag{5}$$

The amplitude of a complex number is considered positive if it is reckoned from the positive x-axis counterclockwise, and negative, in the opposite sense. The amplitude φ is obviously not determined uniquely but up to term $2\pi k$, where k is any integer.

Note. The conjugate complex numbers $z = a + ib$ and $\bar{z} = a - ib$ have equal moduli $|z| = |\bar{z}|$ and their arguments (amplitudes) are equal in absolute value but differ in sign: $\arg z = -\arg \bar{z}$.

It will be noted that the real number A can also be written in the form (3), namely:

$$A = |A|(\cos 0 + i \sin 0) \quad \text{for } A > 0$$
$$A = |A|(\cos \pi + i \sin \pi) \quad \text{for } A < 0$$

The modulus of the complex number 0 is zero: $|0| = 0$. Any angle φ may be taken for amplitude zero. Indeed, for any angle φ we have

$$0 = 0 (\cos \varphi + i \sin \varphi)$$

7.2 BASIC OPERATIONS ON COMPLEX NUMBERS

1. Addition of complex numbers. The *sum* of two complex numbers $z_1 = a_1 + ib_1$ and $z_2 = a_2 + ib_2$ is a complex number defined by the equation

$$z_1 + z_2 = (a_1 + ib_1) + (a_2 + ib_2) = (a_1 + a_2) + i(b_1 + b_2) \qquad (1)$$

From (1) it follows that the addition of complex numbers depicted as vectors is performed by the rule of the addition of vectors (Fig. 163a).

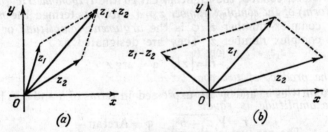

Fig. 163

2. Subtraction of complex numbers. The *difference* of two complex numbers $z_1 = a_1 + ib_1$ and $z_2 = a_2 + ib_2$ is a complex number such that when it is added to z_2 it yields z_1.

It is easy to see that

$$z_1 - z_2 = (a_1 + ib_1) - (a_2 + ib_2) = (a_1 - a_2) + i(b_1 - b_2) \qquad (2)$$

It will be noted that the modulus of the difference of two complex numbers is equal to the distance between the points representing these numbers in the plane of the complex variable (Fig. 163b)

$$|z_1 - z_2| = \sqrt{(a_1 - a_2)^2 + (b_1 - b_2)^2}$$

3. Multiplication of complex numbers. The *product* of two complex numbers $z_1 = a_1 + ib_1$ and $z_2 = a_2 + ib_2$ is a complex number obtained when these two numbers are multiplied as binomials by the rules of algebra, provided that

$$i^2 = -1, \quad i^3 = -i, \quad i^4 = (-i) \cdot i = -i^2 = 1, \quad i^5 = i, \text{ etc.}$$

and, generally, for any integral k,

$$i^{4k} = 1, \quad i^{4k+1} = i, \quad i^{4k+2} = -1, \quad i^{4k+3} = -i$$

From this rule we get

$$z_1 z_2 = (a_1 + i b_1)(a_2 + i b_2) = a_1 a_2 + i b_1 a_2 + i a_1 b_2 + i^2 b_1 b_2$$

or

$$z_1 z_2 = (a_1 a_2 - b_1 b_2) + i (b_1 a_2 + a_1 b_2) \tag{3}$$

Let the complex numbers be written in trigonometric form

$$z_1 = r_1 (\cos \varphi_1 + i \sin \varphi_1), \quad z_2 = r_2 (\cos \varphi_2 + i \sin \varphi_2)$$

then

$$\begin{aligned}
z_1 z_2 &= r_1 (\cos \varphi_1 + i \sin \varphi_1) \, r_2 (\cos \varphi_2 + i \sin \varphi_2) \\
&= r_1 r_2 \, [\cos \varphi_1 \cos \varphi_2 + i \sin \varphi_1 \cos \varphi_2 + i \cos \varphi_1 \sin \varphi_2 \\
&\quad + i^2 \sin \varphi_1 \sin \varphi_2] = r_1 r_2 \, [(\cos \varphi_1 \cos \varphi_2 - \sin \varphi_1 \sin \varphi_2) \\
&\quad + i (\sin \varphi_1 \cos \varphi_2 + \cos \varphi_1 \sin \varphi_2)] \\
&= r_1 r_2 \, [\cos (\varphi_1 + \varphi_2) + i \sin (\varphi_1 + \varphi_2)]
\end{aligned}$$

Thus,

$$z_1 z_2 = r_1 r_2 \, [\cos (\varphi_1 + \varphi_2) + i \sin (\varphi_1 + \varphi_2)] \tag{3'}$$

i. e., *the product of two complex numbers is a complex number, the modulus of which is equal to the product of the moduli of the factors, and the amplitude is equal to the sum of the amplitudes of the factors.*

Note 1. The product of two conjugate complex numbers $z = a + ib$ and $\bar{z} = a - ib$ is, by virtue of (3), expressed as follows:

$$z\bar{z} = a^2 + b^2$$

or

$$z\bar{z} = |z|^2 = |\bar{z}|^2$$

The product of two conjugate complex numbers is equal to the square of the modulus of each number.

4. Division of complex numbers. The *division* of complex numbers is defined as the inverse operation of multiplication.

Suppose we have $z_1 = a_1 + ib_1$, $z_2 = a_2 + ib_2$, $|z_2| = \sqrt{a_2^2 + b_2^2} \neq 0$. Then $\frac{z_1}{z_2} = z$ is a complex number such that $z_1 = z_2 z$. If

$$\frac{a_1 + ib_1}{a_2 + ib_2} = x + iy$$

then
$$a_1 + ib_1 = (a_2 + ib_2)(x + iy)$$
or
$$a_1 + ib_1 = (a_2 x - b_2 y) + i(a_2 y + b_2 x)$$

x and y are found from the system of equations
$$a_1 = a_2 x - b_2 y, \quad b_1 = b_2 x + a_2 y$$

Solving this system we get
$$x = \frac{a_1 a_2 + b_1 b_2}{a_2^2 + b_2^2}, \qquad y = \frac{a_2 b_1 - a_1 b_2}{a_2^2 + b_2^2}$$

and finally we have
$$z = \frac{a_1 a_2 + b_1 b_2}{a_2^2 + b_2^2} + i \, \frac{a_2 b_1 - a_1 b_2}{a_2^2 + b_2^2} \tag{4}$$

Actually, complex numbers are divided as follows: to divide $z_1 = a_1 + ib_1$ by $z_2 = a_2 + ib_2$, multiply the dividend and divisor by a complex number conjugate to the divisor (that is, by $a_2 - ib_2$). Then the divisor will be a real number; dividing the real and imaginary parts of the dividend by it, we get the quotient

$$\frac{a_1 + ib_1}{a_2 + ib_2} = \frac{(a_1 + ib_1)(a_2 - ib_2)}{(a_2 + ib_2)(a_2 - ib_2)} =$$
$$= \frac{(a_1 a_2 + b_1 b_2) + i(a_2 b_1 - a_1 b_2)}{a_2^2 + b_2^2} = \frac{a_1 a_2 + b_1 b_2}{a_2^2 + b_2^2} + i \, \frac{a_2 b_1 - a_1 b_2}{a_2^2 + b_2^2}$$

If the complex numbers are given in the trigonometric form
$$z_1 = r_1(\cos \varphi_1 + i \sin \varphi_1), \quad z_2 = r_2(\cos \varphi_2 + i \sin \varphi_2)$$

then
$$\frac{z_1}{z_2} = \frac{r_1(\cos \varphi_1 + i \sin \varphi_1)}{r_2(\cos \varphi_2 + i \sin \varphi_2)} = \frac{r_1}{r_2}[\cos(\varphi_1 - \varphi_2) + i \sin(\varphi_1 - \varphi_2)] \tag{5}$$

To verify this equation, multiply the divisor by the quotient:

$$r_2(\cos \varphi_2 + i \sin \varphi_2) \frac{r_1}{r_2}[\cos(\varphi_1 - \varphi_2) + i \sin(\varphi_1 - \varphi_2)]$$
$$= r_2 \frac{r_1}{r_2}[\cos(\varphi_2 + \varphi_1 - \varphi_2) + i \sin(\varphi_2 + \varphi_1 - \varphi_2)] = r_1(\cos \varphi_1 + i \sin \varphi_1)$$

Thus, *the modulus of the quotient of two complex numbers is equal to the quotient of the moduli of the dividend and the divisor; the amplitude of the quotient is equal to the difference between the amplitudes of the dividend and divisor.*

Note 2. From the rules of operations involving complex numbers it follows that the operations of addition, subtraction, multiplication and division of complex numbers yield a complex number.

If the rules of operations on complex numbers are applied to real numbers, these being regarded as a special case of complex numbers, they will coincide with the ordinary rules of arithmetic.

Note 3. Returning to the definitions of a sum, difference, product and quotient of complex numbers, it is easy to show that if each complex number in these expressions is replaced by its conjugate, then the results of the aforementioned operations will yield conjugate numbers, whence, as a particular case, we have the following theorem.

Theorem. *If in a polynomial with real coefficients*

$$A_0 x^n + A_1 x^{n-1} + \ldots + A_n$$

we put, in place of x, *the number* $a + ib$ *and then the conjugate number* $a - ib$ *the results of these substitutions will be mutually conjugate.*

7.3 POWERS AND ROOTS OF COMPLEX NUMBERS

1. Powers. From formula (3') of the preceding section it follows that if n is a positive integer, then

$$[r(\cos\varphi + i\sin\varphi)]^n = r^n(\cos n\varphi + i\sin n\varphi) \qquad (1)$$

This formula is called *De Moivre's formula.* It shows that *when a complex number is raised to a positive integral power the modulus is raised to this power, and the amplitude is multiplied by the exponent.*

Now consider another application of De Moivre's formula.

Setting $r = 1$ in this formula, we get

$$(\cos\varphi + i\sin\varphi)^n = \cos n\varphi + i\sin n\varphi$$

Expanding the left-hand side by the binomial theorem and equating the real and imaginary parts, we can express $\sin n\varphi$ and $\cos n\varphi$ in terms of powers of $\sin\varphi$ and $\cos\varphi$. For instance, if $n = 3$ we have

$$\cos^3\varphi + i\,3\cos^2\varphi\sin\varphi - 3\cos\varphi\sin^2\varphi - i\sin^3\varphi = \cos 3\varphi + i\sin 3\varphi$$

Making use of the condition of equality of two complex numbers, we get

$$\cos 3\varphi = \cos^3\varphi - 3\cos\varphi\sin^2\varphi$$
$$\sin 3\varphi = -\sin^3\varphi + 3\cos^2\varphi\sin\varphi$$

2. Roots. The nth root of a complex number is another complex number whose nth power is equal to the radicand, or

$$\sqrt[n]{r(\cos\varphi + i\sin\varphi)} = \rho(\cos\psi + i\sin\psi)$$

if

$$\rho^n(\cos n\psi + i\sin n\psi) = r(\cos\varphi + i\sin\varphi)$$

Since the moduli of equal complex numbers must be equal, while their amplitudes may differ by a multiple of 2π, we have

$$\rho^n = r, \quad n\psi = \varphi + 2k\pi$$

Whence we find

$$\rho = \sqrt[n]{r}, \quad \psi = \frac{\varphi + 2k\pi}{n}$$

where k is any integer, $\sqrt[n]{r}$ is the principal (positive real) root of the positive number r. Therefore,

$$\sqrt[n]{r(\cos \varphi + i \sin \varphi)} = \sqrt[n]{r}\left(\cos \frac{\varphi + 2k\pi}{n} + i \sin \frac{\varphi + 2k\pi}{n}\right) \quad (2)$$

Giving k the values 0, 1, 2, ..., $n-1$, we get n different values of the root. For the other values of k, the amplitudes will differ from those obtained by a multiple of 2π, and, for this reason, root values will be obtained that coincide with those considered.

Thus, the nth root of a complex number has n different values.

The nth root of a real nonzero number A also has n values, since a real number is a special case of a complex number and may be represented in trigonometric form:

if $A > 0$, then $A = |A|(\cos 0 + i \sin 0)$

if $A < 0$, then $A = |A|(\cos \pi + i \sin \pi)$

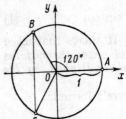

Fig. 164

Example 1. Find all the values of the cube root of unity.

Solution. We represent unity in trigonometric form:

$$1 = \cos 0 + i \sin 0$$

By formula (2) we have

$$\sqrt[3]{1} = \sqrt[3]{\cos 0 + i \sin 0} = \cos \frac{0 + 2k\pi}{3} + i \sin \frac{0 + 2k\pi}{3}$$

Setting k equal to 0, 1, 2, we find three values of the root:

$$x_1 = \cos 0 + i \sin 0 = 1, \quad x_2 = \cos \frac{2\pi}{3} + i \sin \frac{2\pi}{3},$$

$$x_3 = \cos \frac{4\pi}{3} + i \sin \frac{4\pi}{3}$$

Noting that

$$\cos \frac{2\pi}{3} = -\frac{1}{2}, \quad \sin \frac{2\pi}{3} = \frac{\sqrt{3}}{2}, \quad \cos \frac{4\pi}{3} = -\frac{1}{2}, \quad \sin \frac{4\pi}{3} = -\frac{\sqrt{3}}{2}$$

we get

$$x_1 = 1, \quad x_2 = -\frac{1}{2} + i \frac{\sqrt{3}}{2}, \quad x_3 = -\frac{1}{2} - i \frac{\sqrt{3}}{2}$$

In Fig. 164, the points A, B, C are geometric representations of the roots obtained.

3. Solution of a binomial equation. An equation of the form

$$x^n = A$$

is called a *binomial equation*. Let us find its roots.

If A is a real positive number, then

$$x = \sqrt[n]{A}\left(\cos\frac{2k\pi}{n} + i\sin\frac{2k\pi}{n}\right)\ (k = 0, 1, 2, \ldots, n-1)$$

The expression in the brackets gives all the values of the nth root of 1.

If A is a real negative number, then

$$x = \sqrt[n]{|A|}\left(\cos\frac{\pi+2k\pi}{n} + i\sin\frac{\pi+2k\pi}{n}\right)$$

The expression in the brackets gives all the values of the nth root of -1.

If A is a complex number, then the values of x are found from formula (2).

Example 2. Solve the equation

$$x^4 = 1$$

Solution.

$$x = \sqrt[4]{\cos 2k\pi + i\sin 2k\pi} = \cos\frac{2k\pi}{4} + i\sin\frac{2k\pi}{4}$$

Setting k equal to 0, 1, 2, 3, we get

$$x_1 = \cos 0 + i\sin 0 = 1$$

$$x_2 = \cos\frac{2\pi}{4} + i\sin\frac{2\pi}{4} = i$$

$$x_3 = \cos\frac{4\pi}{4} + i\sin\frac{4\pi}{4} = -1$$

$$x_4 = \cos\frac{6\pi}{4} + i\sin\frac{6\pi}{4} = -i$$

7.4 EXPONENTIAL FUNCTION WITH COMPLEX EXPONENT AND ITS PROPERTIES

Let $z = x + iy$. If x and y are real variables, then z is called a complex variable. To each value of the complex variable z in the xy-plane (**the complex plane**) there corresponds a definite point (see Fig. 162).

Definition. If to every value of the complex variable z of a certain range of complex values there corresponds a definite value of another complex quantity w, then w is a *function of the complex variable z*. Functions of a complex variable are denoted by $w = f(z)$ or $w = w(z)$.

Here, we consider the exponential function of a complex variable:

$$w = e^z$$

or

$$w = e^{x+iy}$$

The complex values of the function w are defined as follows*:

$$e^{x+iy} = e^x (\cos y + i \sin y) \tag{1}$$

that is

$$w(z) = e^x (\cos y + i \sin y) \tag{2}$$

Examples:

1. $z = 1 + \dfrac{\pi}{4} i$, $e^{1+\frac{\pi}{4}i} = e\left(\cos\dfrac{\pi}{4} + i\sin\dfrac{\pi}{4}\right) = e\left(\dfrac{\sqrt{2}}{2} + i\dfrac{\sqrt{2}}{2}\right).$

2. $z = 0 + \dfrac{\pi}{2} i$, $e^{0+\frac{\pi}{2}i} = e^0\left(\cos\dfrac{\pi}{2} + i\sin\dfrac{\pi}{2}\right) = i.$

3. $z = 1 + i$, $e^{1+i} = e^1(\cos 1 + i\sin 1) \approx 0.54 + i\cdot0.83.$

4. $z = x$ is a real number, $e^{x+0i} = e^x(\cos 0 + i\sin 0) = e^x$ is an ordinary exponential function.

Properties of an exponential function.

1. If z_1 and z_2 are two complex numbers, then

$$e^{z_1+z_2} = e^{z_1}e^{z_2} \tag{3}$$

Proof. Let

$$z_1 = x_1 + iy_1, \quad z_2 = x_2 + iy_2$$

then

$$e^{z_1+z_2} = e^{(x_1+iy_1)+(x_2+iy_2)} = e^{(x_1+x_2)+i(y_1+y_2)}$$
$$= e^{x_1}e^{x_2}[\cos(y_1+y_2) + i\sin(y_1+y_2)] \tag{4}$$

On the other hand, by the theorem of the product of two complex numbers in trigonometric form we will have

$$e^{z_1}e^{z_2} = e^{x_1+iy_1}e^{x_2+iy_2} = e^{x_1}(\cos y_1 + i\sin y_1)e^{x_2}(\cos y_2 + i\sin y_2)$$
$$= e^{x_1}e^{x_2}[\cos(y_1+y_2) + i\sin(y_1+y_2)] \tag{5}$$

In (4) and (5) the right sides are equal, hence the left sides are equal too:

$$e^{z_1+z_2} = e^{z_1}e^{z_2}$$

2. The following formula is similarly proved:

$$e^{z_1-z_2} = \frac{e^{z_1}}{e^{z_2}} \tag{6}$$

---

* The advisability of this definition of the exponential function of a complex variable will also be shown later on (see Sec. 13.21 and Sec. 16.18 of Vol. II).

3. If m is an integer, then

$$(e^z)^m = e^{mz} \qquad (7)$$

For $m > 0$, this formula is readily obtained from (3); if $m < 0$, then it is obtained from formulas (3) and (6).

4. The identity

$$e^{z+2\pi i} = e^z \qquad (8)$$

holds.

Indeed, from (3) and (1) we get

$$e^{z+2\pi i} = e^z e^{2\pi i} = e^z \left(\cos 2\pi + i \sin 2\pi \right) = e^z$$

From identity (8) it follows that the exponential function e^z is a periodic function with a *period* of $2\pi i$.

5. Let us now consider the complex quantity

$$w = u(x) + iv(x)$$

where $u(x)$ and $v(x)$ are real functions of a real variable x. This is a *complex function of a real variable.*

(a) Let there exist the limits

$$\lim_{x \to x_0} u(x) = u(x_0), \quad \lim_{x \to x_0} v(x) = v(x_0)$$

Then $u(x_0) + iv(x_0) = w_0$ is called the *limit* of the complex variable w.

(b) If the derivatives $u'(x)$ and $v'(x)$ exist, then we shall call the expression

$$w'_x = u'(x) + iv'(x) \qquad (9)$$

the *derivative* of a complex function of a real variable with respect to a real argument.

Let us now consider the following exponential function:

$$w = e^{\alpha x + i\beta x} = e^{(\alpha + i\beta) x}$$

where α and β are real constants and x is a real variable. This is a complex function of a real variable, which function may be rewritten, according to (1), as follows:

$$w = e^{\alpha x} \left[\cos \beta x + i \sin \beta x \right]$$

or

$$w = e^{\alpha x} \cos \beta x + i e^{\alpha x} \sin \beta x$$

Let us find the derivative w'_x. From (9) we have

$$\begin{aligned}
w'_x &= (e^{\alpha x} \cos \beta x)' + i (e^{\alpha x} \sin \beta x)' \\
&= e^{\alpha x} (\alpha \cos \beta x - \beta \sin \beta x) + i e^{\alpha x} (\alpha \sin \beta x + \beta \cos \beta x) \\
&= \alpha \left[e^{\alpha x} (\cos \beta x + i \sin \beta x) \right] + i\beta \left[e^{\alpha x} (\cos \beta x + i \sin \beta x) \right] \\
&= (\alpha + i\beta) \left[e^{\alpha x} (\cos \beta x + i \sin \beta x) \right] = (\alpha + i\beta) e^{(\alpha + i\beta) x}
\end{aligned}$$

To summarize then, if $w = e^{(\alpha + i\beta) x}$, then $w' = (\alpha + i\beta) e^{(\alpha + i\beta) x}$ or

$$[e^{(\alpha + i\beta) x}]' = (\alpha + i\beta) e^{(\alpha + i\beta) x} \qquad (10)$$

Thus, if k is a complex number (or, in the special case, a real number) and x is a real number, then

$$(e^{kx})' = ke^{kx} \qquad (9')$$

We have thus obtained the ordinary formula for differentiating an exponential function. Further,

$$(e^{kx})'' = [(e^{kx})']' = k (e^{kx})' = k^2 e^{kx}$$

and for arbitrary n

$$(e^{kx})^{(n)} = k^n e^{kx}$$

We shall need these formulas later on.

7.5 EULER'S FORMULA.
THE EXPONENTIAL FORM OF A COMPLEX NUMBER

Putting $x = 0$ in formula (1) of the preceding section, we get

$$e^{iy} = \cos y + i \sin y \qquad (1)$$

This is *Euler's formula*, which expresses an exponential function with an imaginary exponent in terms of trigonometric functions.

Replacing y by $-y$ in (1) we get

$$e^{-iy} = \cos y - i \sin y \qquad (2)$$

From (1) and (2) we find $\cos y$ and $\sin y$:

$$\left. \begin{array}{l} \cos y = \dfrac{e^{iy} + e^{-iy}}{2} \\[2mm] \sin y = \dfrac{e^{iy} - e^{-iy}}{2i} \end{array} \right\} \qquad (3)$$

These formulas are used in particular to express powers of $\cos \varphi$ and $\sin \varphi$ and their products in terms of the sine and cosine of multiple arcs.

Example 1. $\cos^2 y = \left(\dfrac{e^{iy} + e^{-iy}}{2} \right)^2 = \dfrac{1}{4} (e^{i2y} + 2 + e^{-i2y})$

$\qquad\qquad = \dfrac{1}{4} [(\cos 2y + i \sin 2y) + 2 + (\cos 2y - i \sin 2y)]$

$\qquad\qquad = \dfrac{1}{4} (2 \cos 2y + 2) = \dfrac{1}{2} (1 + \cos 2y)$

Example 2. $\cos^2 \varphi \sin^2 \varphi = \left(\dfrac{e^{i\varphi} + e^{-i\varphi}}{2} \right)^2 \left(\dfrac{e^{i\varphi} - e^{-i\varphi}}{2i} \right)^2$

$\qquad\qquad = \dfrac{(e^{i2\varphi} - e^{-i2\varphi})^2}{4 \cdot 4i^2} = -\dfrac{1}{8} \cos 4\varphi + \dfrac{1}{8}$

The exponential form of a complex number. Let us represent a complex number in trigonometric form:

$$z = r(\cos\varphi + i\sin\varphi)$$

where r is the modulus of the complex number and φ is the argument (amplitude) of the complex number. By Euler's formula,

$$\cos\varphi + i\sin\varphi = e^{i\varphi} \tag{4}$$

Thus, any complex number may be represented in the so-called **exponential** form:

$$z = re^{i\varphi}$$

Example 3. Represent the numbers 1, i, -2, $-i$ in exponential form.
Solution. $1 = \cos 2k\pi + i\sin 2k\pi = e^{2k\pi i}$

$$i = \cos\frac{\pi}{2} + i\sin\frac{\pi}{2} = e^{\frac{\pi}{2}i}$$

$$-2 = 2(\cos\pi + i\sin\pi) = 2e^{\pi i}$$

$$-i = \cos\left(-\frac{\pi}{2}\right) + i\sin\left(-\frac{\pi}{2}\right) = e^{-\frac{\pi}{2}i}$$

By Properties (3), (6), (7), Sec. 7.4, of an exponential function, it is easy to operate on complex numbers in exponential form. Suppose we have

$$z_1 = r_1 e^{i\varphi_1}, \quad z_2 = r_2 e^{i\varphi_2}$$

then

$$z_1 \cdot z_2 = r_1 e^{i\varphi_1} \cdot r_2 e^{i\varphi_2} = r_1 r_2 e^{i(\varphi_1 + \varphi_2)} \tag{5}$$

$$\frac{z_1}{z_2} = \frac{r_1 e^{i\varphi_1}}{r_2 e^{i\varphi_2}} = \frac{r_1}{r_2} e^{i(\varphi_1 - \varphi_2)} \tag{6}$$

$$z^n = (re^{i\varphi})^n = r^n e^{in\varphi} \tag{7}$$

$$\sqrt[n]{re^{i\varphi}} = \sqrt[n]{r}\, e^{i\frac{\varphi + 2k\pi}{n}} \quad (k = 0, 1, 2, \ldots, n-1) \tag{8}$$

Formula (5) coincides with (3′) of Sec. 7.2; (6), with (5) of Sec. 7.2; (7), with (1) of Sec. 7.3; (8) with (2) of Sec. 7.3.

7.6 FACTORING A POLYNOMIAL

The function

$$f(x) = A_0 x^n + A_1 x^{n-1} + \ldots + A_n$$

where n is an integer, is known as a *polynomial* or a *rational integral function* of x; the number n is called the *degree of the polynomial*. Here, the coefficients A_0, A_1, $\ldots$, A_n are real or complex numbers; the independent variable x can also take on both real and complex values. The *root* of a polynomial is that value of the variable x at which the polynomial becomes zero.

Theorem 1 (Remainder Theorem). *Division of a polynomial $f(x)$ by $x-a$ yields a remainder equal to $f(a)$.*

Proof. The quotient obtained by the division of $f(x)$ by $x-a$ is a polynomial $f_1(x)$ of degree one less than that of $f(x)$, and the remainder is a constant R. We can thus write

$$f(x) = (x-a) f_1(x) + R \qquad (1)$$

This equation holds for all values of x different from a (division by $x-a$ when $x=a$ is meaningless).

Now let x approach a. Then the limit of the left side of (1) will equal $f(a)$, and the limit of the right side will equal R. Since the functions $f(x)$ and $(x-a)f_1(x) + R$ are equal for all $x \neq a$, their limits are likewise equal as $x \to a$, that is, $f(a) = R$.

Corollary. *If a is a root of the polynomial, that is, if $f(a) = 0$, then $x-a$ divides $f(x)$ without remainder and, hence, $f(x)$ is represented in the form of a product*

$$f(x) = (x-a) f_1(x)$$

where $f_1(x)$ is a polynomial.

Example 1. The polynomial $f(x) = x^3 - 6x^2 + 11x - 6$ becomes zero for $x=1$; thus, $f(1) = 0$, and so $x-1$ divides this polynomial without remainder:

$$x^3 - 6x^2 + 11x - 6 = (x-1)(x^2 - 5x + 6)$$

Let us now consider equations in one unknown, x.

Any number (real or complex) which, when substituted into the equation in place of x, converts the equation into an identity is called a *root* of the equation.

Example 2. The numbers $x_1 = \dfrac{\pi}{4}$, $x_2 = \dfrac{5\pi}{4}$, $x_3 = \dfrac{9\pi}{4}$, ... are the roots of the equation $\cos x = \sin x$.

If the equation is of the form $P(x) = 0$, where $P(x)$ is a polynomial of degree n, it is called an *algebraic* equation of degree n. From the definition it follows that the roots of an algebraic equation $P(x) = 0$ are the same as are the roots of the polynomial $P(x)$.

Quite naturally the question arises: Does every equation have roots?

In the case of nonalgebraic equations, the answer is no: there are nonalgebraic equations which do not have a single root, either real or complex; for example, the equation $e^x = 0$. *

---

* Indeed, if the number $x_1 = a + ib$ were the root of this equation, we would have the identity $e^{a+ib} = 0$ or (by Euler's formula) $e^a (\cos b + i \sin b) = 0$. But e^a cannot equal zero for any real value of a; neither is $\cos b + i \sin b$ equal to zero (because the modulus of this number is $\sqrt{\cos^2 b + \sin^2 b} = 1$ for any b). Hence, the product $e^a (\cos b + i \sin b) \neq 0$, i.e., $e^{a+ib} \neq 0$; but this means that the equation $e^x = 0$ has no roots.

But in the case of an algebraic equation the answer is yes. This is given by the fundamental theorem of algebra.

Theorem 2 (Fundamental Theorem of Algebra). *Every rational integral function $f(x)$ has at least one root, real or complex.*

The proof of this theorem is given in higher algebra. Here we accept it without proof.

With the aid of the fundamental theorem of algebra it is easy to prove the following theorem.

Theorem 3. *Every polynomial of degree n may be factored into n linear factors of the form $x - a$ and a factor equal to the coefficient of x^n.*

Proof. Let $f(x)$ be a polynomial of degree n:

$$f(x) = A_0 x^n + A_1 x^{n-1} + \ldots + A_n$$

By virtue of the fundamental theorem, this polynomial has at least one root; we denote it by a_1. Then, by a corollary of the remainder theorem, we can write

$$f(x) = (x - a_1) f_1(x)$$

where $f_1(x)$ is a polynomial of degree $n - 1$; $f_1(x)$ also has a root. We designate it by a_2. Then

$$f_1(x) = (x - a_2) f_2(x)$$

where $f_2(x)$ is a polynomial of degree $n - 2$. Similarly,

$$f_2(x) = (x - a_3) f_3(x)$$

Continuing this process of factoring out linear factors, we arrive at the relation

$$f_{n-1}(x) = (x - a_n) f_n$$

where f_n is a polynomial of degree zero, i.e., some specified number. This number is obviously equal to the coefficient of x^n; that is, $f_n = A_0$.

On the basis of the equations obtained we can write

$$f(x) = A_0 (x - a_1)(x - a_2) \ldots (x - a_n) \tag{2}$$

From the expansion (2) it follows that the numbers $a_1, a_2, \ldots, a_n$ are roots of the polynomial $f(x)$, since upon the substitution $x = a_1$, $x = a_2, \ldots, x = a_n$ the right side, and hence, the left, becomes zero.

Example 3. The polynomial $f(x) = x^3 - 6x^2 + 11x - 6$ becomes zero when

$$x = 1, \; x = 2, \; x = 3$$

Therefore,

$$x^3 - 6x^2 + 11x - 6 = (x - 1)(x - 2)(x - 3)$$

No value $x = a$ that is different from $a_1, a_2, \ldots, a_n$ can be a root of the polynomial $f(x)$, since no factor on the right side of (2) vanishes when $x = a$. Whence the following proposition.

A polynomial of degree n cannot have more than n distinct roots. But then the following theorem obtains.

Theorem 4. *If the values of two polynomials of degree n, $\varphi_1(x)$ and $\varphi_2(x)$, coincide for $n + 1$ distinct values $a_0, a_1, a_2, \ldots, a_n$ of the argument x, then these polynomials are identical.*

Proof. Denote the difference of the polynomials by $f(x)$:

$$f(x) = \varphi_1(x) - \varphi_2(x)$$

It is given that $f(x)$ is a polynomial of degree not higher than n that becomes zero at the points $a_1, \ldots, a_n$. It can therefore be represented in the form

$$f(x) = A_0(x - a_1)(x - a_2) \ldots (x - a_n)$$

But it is given that $f(x)$ also vanishes at the point a_0. Then $f(a_0) = 0$ and not a single one of the linear factors equals zero. For this reason, $A_0 = 0$ and then from (2) it follows that the polynomial $f(x)$ is identically equal to zero. Consequently, $\varphi_1(x) - \varphi_2(x) \equiv 0$ or $\varphi_1(x) \equiv \varphi_2(x)$.

Theorem 5. *If a polynomial*

$$P(x) = A_0 x^n + A_1 x^{n-1} + \ldots + A_{n-1}x + A_n$$

is identically equal to zero, all its coefficients equal zero.

Proof. Let us write its factorization using formula (2):

$$P(x) = A_0 x^n + A_1 x^{n-1} + \ldots + A_{n-1}x + A_n = A_0(x - a_1) \ldots (x - a_n) \quad (1')$$

If this polynomial is identically equal to zero, it is also equal to zero for some value of x different from $a_1, \ldots, a_n$. But then none of the bracketed values $x - a_1, \ldots, x - a_n$ is equal to zero, and, hence, $A_0 = 0$.

Similarly it is proved that $A_1 = 0$, $A_2 = 0$, and so forth.

Theorem 6. *If two polynomials are identically equal, the coefficients of one polynomial are equal to the corresponding coefficients of the other.*

This follows from the fact that the difference between the polynomials is a polynomial identically equal to zero. Therefore, from the preceding theorem all its coefficients are zeros.

Example 4. If the polynomial $ax^3 + bx^2 + cx + d$ is identically equal to the polynomial $x^2 - 5x$, then $a = 0$, $b = 1$, $c = -5$, and $d = 0$.

7.7 THE MULTIPLE ROOTS OF A POLYNOMIAL

If, in the factorization of a polynomial of degree n into linear factors

$$f(x) = A_0(x - a_1)(x - a_2) \ldots (x - a_n) \tag{1}$$

certain linear factors turn out the same, they may be combined, and then factorization of the polynomial will yield

$$f(x) = A_0 (x-a_1)^{k_1} (x-a_2)^{k_2} \ldots (x-a_m)^{k_m} \qquad (1')$$

Here

$$k_1 + k_2 + \ldots + k_m = n$$

In this case, the root a_1 is called a *root of multiplicity* k_1, or a k_1-tuple root, a_2, a root of multiplicity k_2, etc.

Example. The polynomial $f(x) = x^3 - 5x^2 + 8x - 4$ may be factored into the following linear factors:

$$f(x) = (x-2)(x-2)(x-1)$$

This factorization may be written as follows:

$$f(x) = (x-2)^2 (x-1)$$

The root $a_1 = 2$ is a double root, $a_2 = 1$ is a simple root.

If a polynomial has a root a of multiplicity k, then we will consider that the polynomial has k coincident roots. Then from the theorem of factorization of a polynomial into linear factors we get the following theorem.

Every polynomial of degree n has exactly n roots (real or complex).

Note. All that has been said of the roots of the polynomial

$$f(x) = A_0 x^n + A_1 x^{n-1} + \ldots + A_n$$

may obviously be formulated in terms of the roots of the algebraic equation

$$A_0 x^n + A_1 x^{n-1} + \ldots + A_n = 0$$

Let us now prove the following theorem.

Theorem. *If, for the polynomial* $f(x)$, a_1 *is a root of multiplicity* $k_1 > 1$, *then for the derivative* $f'(x)$ *this number is a root of multiplicity* $k_1 - 1$.

Proof. If a_1 is a root of multiplicity $k_1 > 1$, then it follows from formula $(1')$ that

$$f(x) = (x-a_1)^{k_1} \varphi(x)$$

where $\varphi(x) = (x-a_2)^{k_2} \ldots (x-a_m)^{k_m}$ does not become zero at $x = a_1$; that is, $\varphi(a_1) \neq 0$. Differentiating, we get

$$f'(x) = k_1 (x-a_1)^{k_1-1} \varphi(x) + (x-a_1)^{k_1} \varphi'(x)$$
$$= (x-a_1)^{k_1-1} [k_1 \varphi(x) + (x-a_1) \varphi'(x)]$$

Put

$$\psi(x) = k_1 \varphi(x) + (x-a_1) \varphi'(x)$$

Then

$$f'(x) = (x-a_1)^{k_1-1} \psi(x)$$

and here

$$\psi(a_1) = k_1 \varphi(a_1) + (a_1-a_1) \varphi'(a_1) = k_1 \varphi(a_1) \neq 0$$

In other words, $x = a_1$ is a root of multiplicity $k_1 - 1$ of the polynomial $f'(x)$. From the foregoing proof it follows that if $k_1 = 1$, then a_1 is not a root of the derivative $f'(x)$.

From the proved theorem it follows that a_1 is a root of multiplicity $k_1 - 2$ for the derivative $f''(x)$, a root of multiplicity $k_1 - 3$ for the derivative $f'''(x) \ldots$, and a root of multiplicity one (simple root) for the derivative $f^{(k_1-1)}(x)$ and is not a root for the derivative $f^{(k_1)}(x)$, or

$$f(a_1) = 0, \ f'(a_1) = 0, \ f''(a_1) = 0, \ \ldots, \ f^{(k_1-1)}(a_1) = 0$$

but

$$f^{(k)}(a_1) \neq 0$$

7.8 FACTORING A POLYNOMIAL IN THE CASE OF COMPLEX ROOTS

In formula (1), Sec. 7.7, the roots $a_1, a_2, \ldots, a_n$ may be either real or complex. We have the following theorem.

Theorem. *If a polynomial $f(x)$ with real coefficients has a complex root $a + ib$, it also has a conjugate root $a - ib$.*

Proof. Substitute, in the polynomial $f(x)$, $a + ib$ in place of x, raise to a power and collect separately terms containing i and those not containing i; we then get

$$f(a + ib) = M + iN,$$

where M and N are expressions that do not contain i.

Since $a + ib$ is a root of the polynomial, we have

$$f(a + ib) = M + iN = 0$$

whence

$$M = 0, \ N = 0$$

Now substitute the expression $a - ib$ for x in the polynomial. Then (on the basis of Note 3 at the end of Sec. 7.2) we get the conjugate of the number $M + iN$, or

$$f(a - ib) = M - iN$$

Since $M = 0$ and $N = 0$, we have $f(a - ib) = 0$; $a - ib$ is a root of the polynomial.

Thus, in the factorization

$$f(x) = A_0 (x - a_1)(x - a_2) \ldots (x - a_n)$$

the complex roots enter as **conjugate pairs**.

Multiplying together the linear factors that correspond to a pair of complex conjugate roots, we get a trinomial of degree two with real coefficients:

$$[x-(a+ib)]\,[x-(a-ib)]$$
$$= [(x-a)-ib]\,[(x-a)+ib]$$
$$= (x-a)^2+b^2 = x^2-2ax+a^2+b^2 = x^2+px+q$$

where $p=-2a$, $q=a^2+b^2$ are real numbers.

If the number $a+ib$ is a root of multiplicity k, the conjugate number $a-ib$ must be a root of the same multiplicity k, so that factorization of the polynomial will yield the same number of linear factors $x-(a+ib)$ as those of the form $x-(a-ib)$.

Thus, *a polynomial with real coefficients may be factored into factors with real coefficients of the first and second degree of corresponding multiplicity;* that is,

$$f(x) = A_0\,(x-a_1)^{k_1}\,(x-a_2)^{k_2}$$
$$\ldots (x-a_r)^{k_r}\,(x^2+p_1x+q_1)^{l_1}\ldots (x^2+p_sx+q_s)^{l_s}$$

where

$$k_1+k_2+\ldots+k_r+2l_1+\ldots+2l_s = n$$

7.9 INTERPOLATION.
LAGRANGE'S INTERPOLATION FORMULA

Let it be established, in the study of some phenomenon, that there is a functional relationship between the quantities y and x which describes the quantitative aspect of the phenomenon; the function $y=\varphi(x)$ is unknown, but experiment has established the values of this function $y_0, y_1, y_2, \ldots, y_n$ for certain values of the argument $x_0, x_1, x_2, \ldots, x_n$, in the interval $[a, b]$.

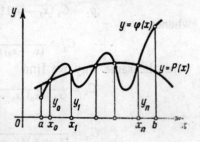

Fig. 165

The problem is to find a function (as simple as possible from the computational standpoint; for example, a polynomial) which will represent the unknown function $y=\varphi(x)$ on the interval $[a, b]$ either exactly or approximately. In more abstract fashion the problem may be formulated as follows: given on the interval $[a, b]$ the values of an unknown function $y=\varphi(x)$ at $n+1$ distinct points $x_0, x_1, \ldots, x_n$:

$$y_0 = \varphi(x_0),\ y_1 = \varphi(x_1),\ \ldots,\ y_n = \varphi(x_n)$$

It is required to find a **polynomial** $P(x)$ of degree $\leqslant n$ that approximately expresses the function $\varphi(x)$.

It is natural to take a polynomial whose values at the points $x_0, x_1, x_2, \ldots, x_n$ coincide with the corresponding values $y_0, y_1,$

$y_2, \ldots, y_n$ of the function $\varphi(x)$ (Fig. 165). Then the problem, which is called the "problem of *interpolating* a function", is formulated thus: for a given function $\varphi(x)$ find a polynomial $P(x)$ of degree $\leqslant n$, which, for the given values of $x_0, x_1, \ldots, x_n$, will take on the values

$$y_0 = \varphi(x_0), \; y_1 = \varphi(x_1), \; \ldots, \; y_n = \varphi(x_n)$$

For the desired polynomial, take a polynomial of degree n of the form

$$
\begin{aligned}
P(x) = & C_0 (x-x_1)(x-x_2) \ldots (x-x_n) \\
& + C_1 (x-x_0)(x-x_2) \ldots (x-x_n) \\
& + C_2 (x-x_0)(x-x_1)(x-x_3) \ldots (x-x_n) \\
& + \ldots + C_n (x-x_0)(x-x_1) \ldots (x-x_{n-1})
\end{aligned} \tag{1}
$$

and define the coefficients $C_0, C_1, \ldots, C_n$ so that the following conditions are fulfilled:

$$P(x_0) = y_0, \; P(x_1) = y_1, \; \ldots, \; P(x_n) = y_n \tag{2}$$

In (1) put $x = x_0$; then, taking into account (2), we get

$$y_0 = C_0 (x_0 - x_1)(x_0 - x_2) \ldots (x_0 - x_n)$$

whence

$$C_0 = \frac{y_0}{(x_0-x_1)(x_0-x_2) \ldots (x_0-x_n)}$$

Then, setting $x = x_1$, we get

$$y_1 = C_1 (x_1 - x_0)(x_1 - x_2) \ldots (x_1 - x_n)$$

whence

$$C_1 = \frac{y_1}{(x_1-x_0)(x_1-x_2) \ldots (x_1-x_n)}$$

In the same way we find

$$C_2 = \frac{y_2}{(x_2-x_0)(x_2-x_1)(x_2-x_3) \ldots (x_2-x_n)}$$

$$\cdots\cdots\cdots\cdots\cdots\cdots\cdots\cdots$$

$$C_n = \frac{y_n}{(x_n-x_0)(x_n-x_1)(x_n-x_2) \ldots (x_n-x_{n-1})}$$

Substituting these values of the coefficients into (1), we get

$$
\begin{aligned}
P(x) = & \frac{(x-x_1)(x-x_2) \ldots (x-x_n)}{(x_0-x_1)(x_0-x_2) \ldots (x_0-x_n)} y_0 \\
& + \frac{(x-x_0)(x-x_2) \ldots (x-x_n)}{(x_1-x_0)(x_1-x_2) \ldots (x_1-x_n)} y_1 \\
& + \frac{(x-x_0)(x-x_1)(x-x_3) \ldots (x-x_n)}{(x_2-x_0)(x_2-x_1)(x_2-x_3) \ldots (x_2-x_n)} y_2 + \\
& \cdots + \frac{(x-x_0)(x-x_1) \ldots (x-x_{n-1})}{(x_n-x_0)(x_n-x_1) \ldots (x_n-x_{n-1})} y_n
\end{aligned} \tag{3}
$$

This formula is called *Lagrange's interpolation formula.*

Let it be noted, without proof, that if $\varphi(x)$ has a derivative of the $(n+1)$th order on the interval $[a, b]$, the error resulting from replacing the function $\varphi(x)$ by the polynomial $P(x)$, i. e., the quantity $\cdot R(x) = \varphi(x) - P(x)$, satisfies the inequality

$$|R(x)| < |(x-x_0)(x-x_1)\ldots(x-x_n)| \frac{1}{(n+1)!} \max|\varphi^{(n+1)}(x)|$$

Note. From Theorem 4, Sec. 7.6, it follows that the polynomial $P(x)$ which we found is the only one that satisfies the given conditions.

There are other interpolation formulas, one of which (Newton's) is considered in Sec. 7.10.

Example. From experiment we get the values of the function $y = \varphi(x)$; $y_0 = 3$ for $x_0 = 1$, $y_1 = -5$ for $x_1 = 2$, $y_2 = 4$ for $x_2 = -4$. It is required to represent the function $y = \varphi(x)$ approximately by a polynomial of degree two.
Solution. From (3) we have (for $n = 2$):

$$P(x) = \frac{(x-2)(x+4)}{(1-2)(1+4)} 3 + \frac{(x-1)(x+4)}{(2-1)(2+4)} (-5)$$
$$+ \frac{(x-1)(x-2)}{(-4-1)(-4-2)} 4$$

or

$$P(x) = -\frac{39}{30} x^2 - \frac{123}{30} x + \frac{252}{30}$$

7.10 NEWTON'S INTERPOLATION FORMULA

Suppose we know $(n+1)$ values of a function $\varphi(x)$, namely $y_0, y_1, \ldots, y_n$ for $(n+1)$ values of the argument $x_0, x_1, \ldots, x_n$. The values of the argument are equally spaced. We denote the constant difference of the arguments by h. This yields a table of values of the unknown function $y = \varphi(x)$ for respective values of the argument.

x	x_0	$x_1 = x_0 + h$	$x_2 = x_0 + 2h$	$\ldots$	$x_n = x_0 + nh$
y	y_0	y_1	y_2	$\ldots$	y_n

Let us set up a polynomial of degree not greater than n that takes on appropriate values for the corresponding values of x. This polynomial will represent the function $\varphi(x)$ in approximate fashion.

'6*

We introduce the following notation:

$$\Delta y_0 = y_1 - y_0, \quad \Delta y_1 = y_2 - y_1, \quad \Delta y_2 = y_3 - y_2, \ldots$$

$$\Delta^2 y_0 = y_2 - 2y_1 + y_0 = \Delta y_1 - \Delta y_0, \quad \Delta^2 y_1 = \Delta y_2 - \Delta y_1, \ldots$$

$$\Delta^3 y_0 = y_3 - 3y_2 + 3y_1 - y_0 = \Delta^2 y_1 - \Delta^2 y_0, \ldots$$

$$\cdot\ \cdot\ \cdot\ \cdot\ \cdot\ \cdot\ \cdot\ \cdot\ \cdot\ \cdot\ \cdot\ \cdot\ \cdot$$

$$\Delta^n y_0 = \Delta^{n-1} y_1 - \Delta^{n-1} y_0$$

These are the so-called first, second, ..., nth differences.

We write down a polynomial that takes on the values y_0, y_1 for x_0 and x_1, respectively. This is a polynomial of the first degree,

$$P_1(x) = y_0 + \Delta y_0 \frac{x - x_0}{h} \tag{1}$$

Indeed

$$P_1(x)\big|_{x=x_0} = y_0, \quad P_1\big|_{x=x_1} = y_0 + \Delta y_0 \frac{h}{h} = y_0 + (y_1 - y_0) = y_1$$

Now write down the polynomial that takes on the values y_0, y_1, y_2 for x_0, x_1, x_2, respectively. This is a polynomial of degree 2:

$$P_2(x) = y_0 + \Delta y_0 \frac{x - x_0}{h} + \frac{\Delta^2 y_0}{2!} \frac{x - x_0}{h}\left(\frac{x - x_0}{h} - 1\right) \tag{2}$$

Indeed,

$$P_2\big|_{x=x_0} = y_0, \quad P_2\big|_{x=x_1} = y_1,$$

$$P_2\big|_{x=x_2} = y_0 + \Delta y_0 \cdot 2 + \frac{\Delta^2 y_0}{2!} \frac{2h}{h}\left(\frac{2h}{1} - 1\right) = y_2$$

A polynomial of degree three will look like this:

$$P_3(x) = y_0 + \Delta y_0 \frac{x - x_0}{h} + \frac{\Delta^2 y_0}{2!} \frac{x - x_0}{h}\left(\frac{x - x_0}{h} - 1\right)$$

$$+ \frac{\Delta^3 y_0}{3!} \frac{x - x_0}{h}\left(\frac{x - x_0}{h} - 1\right)\left(\frac{x - x_0}{h} - 2\right) \tag{3}$$

Finally, a polynomial of degree n taking on the values y_0, y_1, y_2, ..., y_n for the respective values x_0, x_1, x_2, ..., x_n will be of the form

$$P_n(x) = y_0 + \Delta y_0 \frac{x - x_0}{h} + \frac{\Delta^2 y_0}{2!} \frac{x - x_0}{h}\left(\frac{x - x_0}{h} - 1\right) + \ldots$$

$$+ \frac{\Delta^n y_0}{n!} \frac{x - x_0}{h}\left(\frac{x - x_0}{h} - 1\right) \ldots \left[\frac{x - x_0}{h} - (n - 1)\right] \tag{4}$$

This can be seen at once by direct substitution. This is the *Newton interpolation formula* (or the *Newton interpolation polynomial*).

Actually, the Lagrange polynomial and the Newton polynomial are identical for the given table of values but are written differently, since a polynomial of degree not exceeding n and assuming $(n+1)$ values for $(n+1)$ given values of x is found in unique fashion.

In many cases, Newton's interpolation polynomial is more convenient than Lagrange's interpolation polynomial. The peculiarity of this polynomial lies in the fact that when passing from a polynomial of degree k to one of degree $k+1$ the first $(k+1)$ terms remain unchanged, and we add one new term, which for all preceding values of the argument is zero.

Note. The Lagrange interpolation formula [see formula (3), Sec. 7.9] and the Newton interpolation formula [see formula (4), Sec. 7.10] are used to determine values of a function on the interval $x_0 < x < x_n$. If these formulas are used to find values of the function for $x < x_0$ (this can be done for small $|x-x_0|$), then we say that the *table is extrapolated backward*. If the value of the function is sought for $x > x_n$, then we say that the *table is extrapolated forward*.

7.11 NUMERICAL DIFFERENTIATION

Suppose the values of some unknown function $\varphi(x)$ are given in tabular form, say, by the table of Sec. 7.10. It is required to approximate the derivative of the function. The problem is solved by constructing the Lagrange (or Newton) interpolation polynomial and then taking the derivative of that polynomial.

Since equally spaced tables of the argument are ordinarily employed, we will make use of the Newton interpolation formula. Suppose we have three values of the function, y_0, y_1, y_2, for the values x_0, x_1, x_2 of the argument. Then write down polynomial (2) of Sec. 7.10 and differentiate it to get the approximate value of the derivative function on the interval $x_0 \leqslant x \leqslant x_2$,

$$\varphi'(x) \approx P'_2(x) = \frac{\Delta y_0}{h} + \frac{\Delta^2 y_0}{2h}\left(2\frac{x-x_0}{h}-1\right) \tag{1}$$

For $x = x_0$ we have

$$\varphi'(x_0) \approx P'_2(x_0) = \frac{\Delta y_0}{h} - \frac{\Delta^2 y_0}{2h} \tag{2}$$

If we consider a third-degree polynomial [see (3), Sec. 7.10], then differentiation yields the following expression for the derivative:

$$\varphi'(x) \approx P'_3(x) = \frac{\Delta y_0}{h} + \frac{\Delta^2 y_0}{2h}\left(2\frac{x-x_0}{h}-1\right)$$
$$+ \frac{\Delta^3 y_0}{2 \cdot 3h}\left[3\left(\frac{x-x_0}{h}\right)^2 - 6\left(\frac{x-x_0}{h}\right)+2\right] \tag{3}$$

In particular, for $x = x_0$, we get

$$\varphi'(x_0) \approx P_3'(x) = \frac{\Delta y_0}{h} - \frac{\Delta^2 y_0}{2h} + \frac{\Delta^3 y_0}{3h} \qquad (4)$$

Using formula (4), Sec. 7.10, we approximate the derivative for $x = x_0$ as

$$\varphi'(x_0) \approx P_n'(x) = \frac{\Delta y_0}{h} - \frac{\Delta^2 y_0}{2h} + \frac{\Delta^3 y_0}{3h} - \frac{\Delta^4 y_0}{4h} + \dots \qquad (5)$$

Note that for a function having derivatives, the difference Δy_0 is an infinitesimal of the first order, $\Delta^2 y_0$ is an infinitesimal of the second order, $\Delta^3 y_0$ is an infinitesimal of the third order, etc., relative to h.

7.12 ON THE BEST APPROXIMATION OF FUNCTIONS BY POLYNOMIALS. CHEBYSHEV'S THEORY

A natural question arises from what was discussed in Secs. 7.9 and 7.10. If a continuous function $\varphi(x)$ is given on a closed interval $[a, b]$, can this function be represented approximately in the form of a polynomial $P(x)$ **to any preassigned degree of accuracy?** In other words, is it possible to choose a polynomial $P(x)$ such that the absolute difference between $\varphi(x)$ and $P(x)$ at all points of the interval $[a, b]$ is less than any preassigned positive number ε? The following theorem, which we give without proof, answers this question in the affirmative.*

Weierstrass' Approximation Theorem. *If a function $\varphi(x)$ is continuous on a closed interval $[a, b]$, then for every $\varepsilon > 0$ there exists a polynomial $P(x)$ such that $|\varphi(x) - P(x)| < \varepsilon$ at all points of the interval.*

The Soviet mathematician Academician S. N. Bernstein gave the following method for the direct construction of such polynomials that are approximately equal to the continuous function $\varphi(x)$ on the given interval.

Let $\varphi(x)$ be continuous on the interval $[0, 1]$. We write the expression

$$B_n(x) = \sum_{m=0}^{n} \varphi\left(\frac{m}{n}\right) C_n^m x^m (1-x)^{n-m}$$

Here, C_n^m are binomial coefficients, $\varphi\left(\dfrac{m}{n}\right)$ is the value of the given function at the point $x = \dfrac{m}{n}$. The expression $B_n(x)$ is an nth degree polynomial called the *Bernstein polynomial*.

---

* It will be noted that the Lagrange interpolation formula [see (3) Sec. 7.9] cannot yet answer this question. Its values are equal to those of the function at the points $x_0, x_1, x_2, \dots, x_n$, but they may be very far from the values of the function at other points of the interval $[a, b]$.

If an arbitrary $\varepsilon > 0$ is given, one can choose a Bernstein polynomial (that is, select its degree n) such that for all values of x on the interval $[0, 1]$, the following inequality will hold:

$$| B_n(x) - \varphi(x) | < \varepsilon$$

It should be noted that consideration of the interval $[0, 1]$, and not an arbitrary interval $[a, b]$, is not an essential restriction of generality, since by changing the variable $x = a + t (b-a)$ it is possible to convert any interval $[a, b]$ into $[0, 1]$. In this case, an nth degree polynomial will be transformed into a polynomial of the same degree.

The creator of the theory of best approximation of functions by polynomials is the Russian mathematician P. L. Chebyshev (1821-1894). In this field, he obtained the most profound results, which exerted a great influence on the work of later mathematicians. Studies involving the theory of articulated mechanisms, which are widely used in machines, served as the starting point of Chebyshev's theory. While studying these mechanisms he arrived at the problem of finding, among all polynomials of a given degree with leading coefficient unity, a polynomial of least deviation from zero on the given interval. He found these polynomials, which subsequently became known as *Chebyshev polynomials*. They possess many remarkable properties and at present are a powerful tool of investigation in many problems of mathematics and engineering.

Exercises on Chapter 7

1. Find $(3+5i)(4-i)$. *Ans.* $17+17i$. **2.** Find $(6+11i)(7+3i)$. *Ans.* $9+95i$.
3. Find $\dfrac{3-i}{4+5i}$. *Ans.* $\dfrac{7}{41} - \dfrac{19}{41}i$. **4.** Find $(4-7i)^3$. *Ans.* $-524+7i$. **5.** Find $\sqrt{i}$.
Ans. $\pm \dfrac{1+i}{\sqrt{2}}$. **6.** Find $\sqrt{-5-12i}$. *Ans.* $\pm (2-3i)$. **7.** Reduce the following
expressions to trigonometric form: (a) $1+i$. *Ans.* $\sqrt{2}\left(\cos \dfrac{\pi}{4} + i \sin \dfrac{\pi}{4} \right)$, (b)
$1-i$. *Ans.* $\sqrt{2}\left(\cos \dfrac{7\pi}{4} + i \sin \dfrac{7\pi}{4} \right)$. **8.** Find $\sqrt[3]{i}$. *Ans.* $\dfrac{i+\sqrt{3}}{2}$, $-i$,
$\dfrac{i-\sqrt{3}}{2}$. **9.** Express the following expressions in terms of powers of $\sin x$ and
$\cos x$: $\sin 2x$, $\cos 2x$, $\sin 4x$, $\cos 4x$, $\sin 5x$, $\cos 5x$. **10.** Express the following in terms of the sine and cosine of multiple arcs: $\cos^2 x$, $\cos^3 x$, $\cos^4 x$, $\cos^5 x$, $\cos^6 x$; $\sin^2 x$, $\sin^3 x$, $\sin^4 x$, $\sin^5 x$. **11.** Divide $f(x) = x^3 - 4x^2 + 8x - 1$ by $x+4$. *Ans.* $f(x) = (x+4)(x^2-8x+40) - 161$, that is, the quotient is equal to $x^2 - 8x + 40$; and the remainder is $f(-4) = -161$. **12.** Divide $f(x) = x^4 + 12x^3 + 54x^2 + 108x + 81$ by $x+3$. *Ans.* $f(x) = (x+3)(x^3 + 9x^2 + 27x + 27)$. **13.** Divide $f(x) = x^7 - 1$ by $x-1$. *Ans.* $f(x) = (x-1)(x^6 + x^5 + x^4 + x^3 + x^2 + x + 1)$.
Factor the following polynomials into factors with real coefficients:
14. $f(x) = x^4 - 1$. *Ans.* $f(x) = (x-1)(x+1)(x^2+1)$. **15.** $f(x) = x^2 - x - 2$. *Ans.* $f(x) = (x-2)(x+1)$. **16.** $f(x) = x^3 + 1$. *Ans.* $f(x) = (x+1)(x^2 - x + 1)$.

17. Experiment yielded the following values of y as a function of x:

$$y_1 = 4 \quad \text{for} \quad x_1 = 0$$
$$y_2 = 6 \quad \text{for} \quad x_2 = 1$$
$$y_3 = 10 \quad \text{for} \quad x_3 = 2$$

Approximate the function by a second-degree polynomial. *Ans.* $x^2 + x + 4$.

18. Find a polynomial of degree four that takes on the values 2, 1, -1, 5, 0 for $x = 1$, 2, 3, 4, 5, respectively. *Ans.* $-\dfrac{7}{6} x^4 + \dfrac{79}{6} x^3 - \dfrac{151}{3} x^2 + \dfrac{226}{3} x - 35$.

19. Find a polynomial of the lowest possible degree that takes on the values 3, 7, 9, 19 for $x = 2$, 4, 5, 10, respectively. *Ans.* $2x - 1$.

20. Find Bernstein polynomials of degree 1, 2, 3 and 4 for the function $y = \sin \pi x$ on the interval $[0, 1]$. *Ans.* $B_1(x) = 0$, $B_2(x) = 2x(1-x)$, $B_3(x) = \dfrac{3\sqrt{3}}{2} x(1-x)$, $B_4(x) = 2x(1-x)\left[(2\sqrt{2}-3)x^2 - (2\sqrt{2}-3)x + \sqrt{2}\right]$.

CHAPTER 8

FUNCTIONS OF SEVERAL VARIABLES

8.1 DEFINITION OF A FUNCTION OF SEVERAL VARIABLES

When considering a function of one variable we pointed out that in the study of many phenomena one encounters functions of two or more independent variables. Some examples follow.

Example 1. The area S of a rectangle with sides of length x and y is expressed by the formula

$$S = xy.$$

To each pair of values of x and y there corresponds a definite value of the area S. S is a function of two variables.

Example 2. The volume V of a rectangular parallelepiped with edges of length x, y, z is expressed by the formula

$$V = xyz$$

Here, V is a function of three variables, x, y, z.

Example 3. The range R of a shell fired with initial velocity v_0 from a gun, whose barrel is inclined to the horizon at an angle φ, is expressed by the formula

$$R = \frac{v_0^2 \sin 2\varphi}{g}$$

(air resistance is disregarded). Here, g is the acceleration of gravity.

For every pair of values of v_0 and φ this formula yields a definite value of R; in other words, R is a function of two variables, v_0 and φ.

Example 4.

$$u = \frac{x^2 + y^2 + z^2 + t^2}{\sqrt{1+x^2}}.$$

Here, u is a function of four variables x, y, z, t.

Definition 1. If to each pair (x, y) of values of two independent variable quantities x and y (from some range D) there corresponds a definite value of the quantity z, we say that z is a *function of the two independent variables x and y* defined in D.

A function of two variables is symbolically given as

$$z = f(x, y), \quad z = F(x, y) \text{ and so forth}$$

A function of two variables may be represented, for example, by means of a table or analytically (by a formula) as in the four examples given above. The formula may be used to construct a table of values of the function for certain number pairs of the independent variables. From Example 1 we can build the following table:

$$S = xy$$

$\diagdown$ x y	0	1	1.5	2	3
1	0	1	1.5	2	3
2	0	2	3	4	6
3	0	3	4.5	6	9
4	0	4	6	8	12

In this table, the intersections of the lines and columns, which correspond to definite values of x and y, yield the corresponding values of the function S.

If the functional relation $z = f(x, y)$ is obtained as a result of changes in the quantity z in some experimental study of a phenomenon, we straightway get a table defining z as a function of two variables. In this case, the function is specified by the table alone.

As in the case of a single independent variable, a function of two variables does not, generally speaking, exist for all values of x and y.

Definition 2. The collection of pairs (x, y) of values of x and y, for which the function

$$z = f(x, y)$$

is defined, is called the *domain of definition* of the function.

The domain of a function is apparent when illustrated geometrically. If each number pair x and y is given as a point $M(x, y)$ in the xy-plane, then the domain of definition of the function will be represented as a certain collection of points in the plane. We shall also call this collection of points the domain of definition of the function. In particular, the entire plane may be the domain. In future we shall mainly have to do with such domains as are **parts of the plane bounded by lines.** The line bounding the given domain will be the *boundary* of the domain. The points of the domain not lying on the boundary are called *interior* points of the domain. A domain consisting solely of interior points is called an *open* domain; that which includes the points of the boundary is called a *closed* domain. A domain is *bounded* if there exists a constant C such that the distance from any point M of the domain to the origin O is less than C, i.e., $|OM| < C$.

Example 5. Determine the natural domain of definition of the function

$$z = 2x - y$$

The analytic expression $2x - y$ is meaningful for all values of x and y. Therefore, the entire xy-plane is the natural domain of the function.

Example 6. $z = \sqrt{1 - x^2 - y^2}$.

For z to have a real value it is necessary that the radicand be a nonnegative number; in other words, x and y must satisfy the inequality

$$1 - x^2 - y^2 \geq 0, \quad \text{or} \quad x^2 + y^2 \leqslant 1$$

All the points $M(x, y)$ whose coordinates satisfy the given inequality lie in a circle of radius 1 with centre at the origin and on the boundary of the circle.

Example 7. $z = \ln(x + y)$.

Since logarithms are defined only for positive numbers, the following inequality must be satisfied:

$$x + y > 0 \quad \text{or} \quad y > -x$$

This means that the natural domain of definition of the function z is the half-plane above the straight line $y = -x$, the line itself not included (Fig. 166).

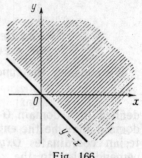

Fig. 166

Example 8. The area S of a triangle is a function of the base x and the altitude y:

$$S = \frac{xy}{2}$$

The domain of this function is $x > 0$, $y > 0$ (since the base of a triangle and its altitude cannot be negative or zero). We notice that the domain of this function does not coincide with the natural domain of definition of the analytic expression used to define the function, because the natural domain of the expression $\frac{xy}{2}$ is obviously the entire xy-plane.

It is easy to generalize the definition of a function of two variables to the case of three or more variables.

Definition 3. If to every collection of values of the variables $x, y, z, \ldots, u, t$ there corresponds a definite value of the variable w, we shall then call w the *function of the independent variables* $x, y, z, \ldots, u, t$ and write $w = F(x, y, z, \ldots, u, t)$ or $w = f(x, y, z, \ldots, u, t)$, and so on.

Just as in the case of a function of two variables, we can speak of the domain of definition of a function of three, four or more variables.

To take an example, for a function of three variables, the domain of definition is a certain collection of number triples (x, y, z). Let it be noted that each number triple is associated with some point $M(x, y, z)$ in xyz-space. Consequently, the domain of definition of a function of three variables is some collection of points in space.

Similarly, one can speak of the domain of a function of four variables $u = f(x, y, z, t)$ as of a certain collection of number quadruples (x, y, z, t). However, the domain of a function of four or a larger number of variables no longer permits of a simple geometric interpretation.

Example 2 gives a function of three variables defined for all values of x, y, z.

In Example 4 we have a function of four variables.

Example 9. $w = \sqrt{1 - x^2 - y^2 - z^2 - u^2}$.

Here w is a function of the four variables x, y, z, u defined for values of the variables that satisfy the relation

$$1 - x^2 - y^2 - z^2 - u^2 \geqslant 0$$

8.2 GEOMETRIC REPRESENTATION OF A FUNCTION OF TWO VARIABLES

We consider the function

$$z = f(x, y) \qquad (1)$$

defined in a domain G in the xy-plane (as a particular case, this domain may be the entire plane), and a system of rectangular Cartesian coordinates $Oxyz$ (Fig. 167). At each point (x, y) erect a perpendicular to the xy-plane and on it lay off a segment equal to $f(x, y)$.

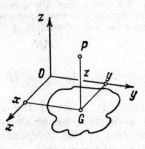

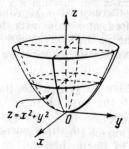

Fig. 167   Fig. 168

This gives us a point P in space with coordinates

$$x, \ y, \ z = f(x, y)$$

The locus of points P whose coordinates satisfy equation (1) is the graph of a function of two variables. From the course of analytic geometry we know that equation (1) defines a surface in space. Thus, the graph of a function of two variables is a surface projected onto the xy-plane in the domain of definition of the function. Each perpendicular to the xy-plane intersects the surface $z = f(x, y)$ at not more than one point.

Example. As we know from analytic geometry, the graph of the function $z = x^2 + y^2$ is a paraboloid of revolution (Fig. 168).

Note. It is impossible to depict a function of three or more variables by means of a graph in space.

8.3 PARTIAL AND TOTAL INCREMENT OF A FUNCTION

Consider the line of intersection PS of the surface

$$z = f(x, y)$$

with a plane $y = \text{const}$ parallel to the xz-plane (Fig. 169).

Since in this plane y remains constant, z will vary along the curve PS depending only on the changes in x. Increase the inde-
pendent variable x by Δx; then z will be increased; this increase is called the *partial increment of z with respect to x* and it is denoted by $\Delta_x z$ (the segment SS' in the figure), so that

$$\Delta_x z = f(x + \Delta x, y) - f(x, y) \quad (1)$$

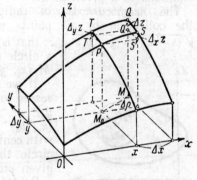

Similarly, if x is held constant and y is increased by Δy, then z is increased, and this increase is called the *partial increment of z with respect to y* (symbolized by $\Delta_y z$, the segment TT' in the figure):

Fig. 169

$$\Delta_y z = f(x, y + \Delta y) - f(x, y) \quad (2)$$

The function receives the increment $\Delta_y z$ "along the line" of intersection of the surface $z = f(x, y)$ with the plane $x = \text{const}$ parallel to the yz-plane.

Finally, increasing the argument x by Δx, and the argument y by the increment Δy, we get for z a new increment Δz, which is called the *total increment* of the function z and is defined by the formula

$$\Delta z = f(x + \Delta x, y + \Delta y) - f(x, y) \quad (3)$$

In Fig. 169 Δz is shown as the segment QQ'.

It must be noted that, generally speaking, the total increment is not equal to the sum of the partial increments, $\Delta z \neq \Delta_x z + \Delta_y z$.

Example. $z = xy$.

$$\Delta_x z = (x + \Delta x) y - xy = y \Delta x$$
$$\Delta_y z = x(y + \Delta y) - xy = x \Delta y$$
$$\Delta z = (x + \Delta x)(y + \Delta y) - xy = y \Delta x + x \Delta y + \Delta x \, \Delta y$$

For $x = 1$, $y = 2$, $\Delta x = 0.2$, $\Delta y = 0.3$ we have $\Delta_x z = 0.4$, $\Delta_y z = 0.3$, $\Delta z = 0.76$.

Similarly we define the partial and total increments of a function of any number of variables. Thus, for a function of three variables $u = f(x, y, t)$ we have

$$\Delta_x u = f(x + \Delta x, y, t) - f(x, y, t)$$
$$\Delta_y u = f(x, y + \Delta y, t) - f(x, y, t)$$
$$\Delta_t u = f(x, y, t + \Delta t) - f(x, y, t)$$
$$\Delta u = f(x + \Delta x, y + \Delta y, t + \Delta t) - f(x, y, t)$$

8.4 CONTINUITY OF A FUNCTION OF SEVERAL VARIABLES

We introduce an important auxiliary concept, that of the neighbourhood of a given point.

The *neighbourhood*, of radius r, of a point $M_0(x_0, y_0)$ is the collection of all points (x, y) that satisfy the inequality $\sqrt{(x - x_0)^2 + (y - y_0)^2} < r$; that is, the set of all points that lie inside a circle of radius r with centre in the point $M_0(x_0, y_0)$.

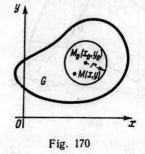

If we say that a function $f(x, y)$ possesses some property "near the point (x_0, y_0)" or "in the neighbourhood of the point (x_0, y_0)" we mean that there is a circle with centre at (x_0, y_0), at all points of which circle the given function possesses the given property.

Before considering the concept of continuity of a function of several variables, let us examine the notion of the limit of a function of several variables. *

Fig. 170

Let there be a function

$$z = f(x, y)$$

defined in some domain G of an xy-plane. Let us consider some definite point $M_0(x_0, y_0)$ in G or on its boundary (Fig. 170).

Definition 1. The number A is called the *limit* of the function $f(x, y)$ as $M(x, y)$ approaches $M_0(x_0, y_0)$ if for every $\varepsilon > 0$ there is an $r > 0$ such that for all points $M(x, y)$ for which the inequality $\overline{MM_0} < r$ is fulfilled we have the inequality

$$|f(x, y) - A| < \varepsilon$$

---

* We shall mainly consider functions of two variables, since three and more variables do not introduce any fundamental changes, but do introduce additional technical difficulties.

If A is the limit of $f(x, y)$ as $M(x, y) \longrightarrow M_0(x_0, y_0)$ then we write

$$\lim_{\substack{x \to x_0 \\ y \to y_0}} f(x, y) = A$$

Definition 2. Let the point $M_0(x_0, y_0)$ belong to the domain of the function $f(x, y)$. The function $z = f(x, y)$ is called *continuous at the point* $M_0(x_0, y_0)$ if we have

$$\lim_{\substack{x \to x_0 \\ y \to y_0}} f(x, y) = f(x_0, y_0) \tag{1}$$

and $M(x, y)$ approaches $M_0(x_0, y_0)$ in arbitrary fashion all the while remaining in the domain of the function.

Designate $x = x_0 + \Delta x$, $y = y_0 + \Delta y$, then (1) may be rewritten as follows:

$$\lim_{\substack{\Delta x \to 0 \\ \Delta y \to 0}} f(x_0 + \Delta x, y_0 + \Delta y) = f(x_0, y_0) \tag{1'}$$

or

$$\lim_{\substack{\Delta x \to 0 \\ \Delta y \to 0}} [f(x_0 + \Delta x, y_0 + \Delta y) - f(x_0, y_0)] = 0 \tag{1''}$$

We set $\Delta \rho = \sqrt{(\Delta x)^2 + (\Delta y)^2}$ (see Fig. 169). As $\Delta x \to 0$ and $\Delta y \to 0$, $\Delta \rho \to 0$; and conversely, if $\Delta \rho \to 0$, then $\Delta x \to 0$ and $\Delta y \to 0$.

Noting further that the expression in the square brackets in (1'') is the total increment Δz of the function, (1'') may be rewritten in the form

$$\lim_{\Delta \rho \to 0} \Delta z = 0 \tag{1'''}$$

A function continuous at each point of some domain is *continuous in the domain*.

If at some point $N(x_0, y_0)$ condition (1) is not fulfilled, then the point $N(x_0, y_0)$ is called a *point of discontinuity* of the function $z = f(x, y)$. For example, condition (1') may not be fulfilled in the following cases:

(1) $z = f(x, y)$ is defined at all points of a certain neighbourhood of the point $N(x_0, y_0)$ with the exception of the point $N(x_0, y_0)$ itself;

(2) the function $z = f(x, y)$ is defined at all points of a neighbourhood of the point $N(x_0, y_0)$ but there is no limit $\lim\limits_{\substack{x \to x_0 \\ y \to y_0}} f(x, y)$;

(3) the function is defined at all points of the neighbourhood of $N(x_0, y_0)$ and $\lim\limits_{\substack{x \to x_0 \\ y \to y_0}} f(x, y)$ exists, but

$$\lim_{\substack{x \to x_0 \\ y \to y_0}} f(x, y) \neq f(x_0, y_0)$$

Example 1. The function

$$z = x^2 + y^2$$

is continuous for all values of x and y; that is, it is continuous at every point in the xy-plane.

Indeed, no matter what the numbers x and y, Δx and Δy, we have

$$\Delta z = [(x + \Delta x)^2 + (y + \Delta y)^2] - (x^2 + y^2) = 2x\Delta x + 2y\Delta y + \Delta x^2 + \Delta y^2$$

Consequently,

$$\lim_{\substack{\Delta x \to 0 \\ \Delta y \to 0}} \Delta z = 0.$$

The following is an example of a discontinuous function.

Example 2. The function

$$z = \frac{2xy}{x^2 + y^2}$$

is defined everywhere except at the point $x = 0$, $y = 0$ (Figs. 171, 172).

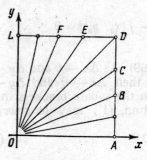
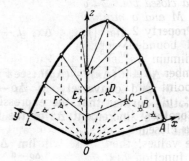

Fig. 171   Fig. 172

Let us examine the values of z along the straight line $y = kx$ ($k = $ const). Obviously, along this line

$$z = \frac{2kx^2}{x^2 + k^2 x^2} = \frac{2k}{1 + k^2} = \text{const}$$

This means that a function z along any straight line passing through the origin retains a constant value that depends upon the slope k of the line. Thus, approaching the origin along different paths we will obtain different limiting values, and this means that the function $f(x, y)$ has no limit when the point (x, y) in the xy-plane approaches the origin. Thus, the function is discontinuous at this point. It is impossible to redefine this function at the coordinate origin so that it should become continuous. On the other hand, it is readily seen that the function is continuous at all other points.

We give without proof some important properties of a function of many variables continuous in a closed and bounded domain. These properties are similar to the properties of a function of one variable continuous on an interval (see Sec. 2.10).

Property 1. If a function $f(x, y, \ldots)$ is defined and continuous in a closed and bounded domain D, then there will be at least one point $N(x_0, y_0, \ldots)$ in D such that for all other points of the domain the relation

$$f(x_0, y_0, \ldots) \geqslant f(x, y, \ldots)$$

holds true, and at least one point $\overline{N}(\overline{x}_0, \overline{y}_0, \ldots)$ such that for all other points of the domain the relation

$$f(\overline{x}_0, \overline{y}_0, \ldots) \leqslant f(x, y, \ldots)$$

holds true.

We call the value of the function $f(x_0, y_0, \ldots) = M$ the *maximum value* of the function $f(x, y, \ldots)$ in the domain D, and the value $f(\overline{x}_0, \overline{y}_0, \ldots) = m$ the *minimum value*.

This property is also stated as follows. *A function continuous in a closed bounded domain D at least once reaches a maximum value M and a minimum value m.*

Property 2. If a function $f(x, y, \ldots)$ is continuous in a closed and bounded domain D and if M and m are the maximum and minimum values of the function in that domain, then for any number μ that satisfies the condition $m < \mu < M$, there will be a point $N^*(x_0^*, y_0^*, \ldots)$ in the domain such that the equation $f(x_0^*, y_0^*, \ldots) = \mu$ holds true.

Corollary to Property 2. If a function $f(x, y, \ldots)$ is continuous in a closed bounded domain and assumes both positive and negative values, then there will be points inside the domain at which the function $f(x, y, \ldots)$ vanishes.

8.5 PARTIAL DERIVATIVES OF A FUNCTION OF SEVERAL VARIABLES

Definition. *The partial derivative, with respect to x, of a function $z = f(x, y)$ is the limit of the ratio of the partial increment $\Delta_x z$, with respect to x, to the increment Δx as Δx approaches zero.*

The partial derivative, with respect to x, of the function $z = f(x, y)$ is denoted by one of the following symbols:

$$z'_x, \; f'_x(x, y); \; \frac{\partial z}{\partial x}, \; \frac{\partial f}{\partial x}$$

Thus, by definition,

$$\frac{\partial z}{\partial x} = \lim_{\Delta x \to 0} \frac{\Delta_x z}{\Delta x} = \lim_{\Delta x \to 0} \frac{f(x + \Delta x, y) - f(x, y)}{\Delta x}$$

Similarly, the *partial derivative, with respect to y,* of a function $z = f(x, y)$ is defined as the limit of the ratio of the partial increment $\Delta_y z$ with respect to y to the increment Δy as Δy approaches zero. The partial derivative with respect to y is denoted by one of the following symbols:

$$z'_y, \quad f'_y, \quad \frac{\partial z}{\partial y}, \quad \frac{\partial f}{\partial y}$$

Thus,

$$\frac{\partial z}{\partial y} = \lim_{\Delta y \to 0} \frac{\Delta_y z}{\Delta y} = \lim_{\Delta y \to 0} \frac{f(x, y+\Delta y) - f(x, y)}{\Delta y}$$

Noting that $\Delta_x z$ is calculated with y held constant, and $\Delta_y z$ with x held constant, we can formulate the definitions of partial derivatives as follows: the *partial derivative of the function* $z = = f(x, y)$ *with respect to* x is the derivative with respect to x calculated on the assumption that y is constant. The *partial derivative of the function* $z = f(x, y)$ *with respect to* y is the derivative with respect to y calculated on the assumption that x is constant.

It is clear from this definition that the rules for computing partial derivatives coincide with the rules given for functions of one variable, and the only thing to remember is with respect to which variable the derivative is sought.

Example 1. Given the function $z = x^2 \sin y$; find the partial derivatives $\frac{\partial z}{\partial x}$ and $\frac{\partial z}{\partial y}$.

Solution.

$$\frac{\partial z}{\partial x} = 2x \sin y, \quad \frac{\partial z}{\partial y} = x^2 \cos y.$$

Example 2. $z = x^y$.
Here

$$\frac{\partial z}{\partial x} = yx^{y-1}$$

$$\frac{\partial z}{\partial y} = x^y \ln x.$$

The partial derivatives of a function of any number of variables are determined similarly. Thus, if we have a function u of four variables x, y, z, t:

$$u = f(x, y, z, t)$$

Thus

$$\frac{\partial u}{\partial x} = \lim_{\Delta x \to 0} \frac{f(x+\Delta x, y, z, t) - f(x, y, z, t)}{\Delta x},$$

$$\frac{\partial u}{\partial y} = \lim_{\Delta y \to 0} \frac{f(x, y+\Delta y, z, t) - f(x, y, z, t)}{\Delta y}, \text{ and so forth.}$$

Example 3. $u = x^2 + y^2 + xtz^3$.

$$\frac{\partial u}{\partial x} = 2x + tz^3, \quad \frac{\partial u}{\partial y} = 2y, \quad \frac{\partial u}{\partial z} = 3xtz^2, \quad \frac{\partial u}{\partial t} = xz^3$$

8.6 THE GEOMETRIC INTERPRETATION OF THE PARTIAL DERIVATIVES OF A FUNCTION OF TWO VARIABLES

Let the equation

$$z = f(x, y)$$

be the equation of a surface shown in Fig. 173.

Draw the plane $x = $ const. The intersection of this plane with the surface yields the line PT. For a given x, let us consider a certain point $M(x, y)$ in the xy-plane. To the point M there corresponds a point $P(x, y, z)$ on the surface $z = f(x, y)$. Holding x constant, let us increase the variable y by $\Delta y = MN = PT'$. Then the function z will be increased by $\Delta_y z = TT'$ [to the point $N(x, y + \Delta y)$ there corresponds a point $T(x, y + \Delta y, z + \Delta_y z)$ on the surface $z = f(x, y)$].

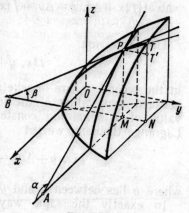

Fig. 173

The ratio $\dfrac{\Delta_y z}{\Delta y}$ is equal to the tangent of the angle formed by the *secant line PT* with the positive y-axis:

$$\frac{\Delta_y z}{\Delta y} = \tan \angle TPT'$$

Consequently, the limit

$$\lim_{\Delta y \to 0} \frac{\Delta_y z}{\Delta y} = \frac{\partial z}{\partial y}$$

is equal to the tangent of the angle β formed by the tangent line PB to the curve PT at the point P with the positive y-axis:

$$\frac{\partial z}{\partial y} = \tan \beta$$

Thus, the partial derivative $\dfrac{\partial z}{\partial y}$ is numerically equal to the tangent of the angle of inclination of the tangent line to the curve resulting from the surface $z = f(x, y)$ being cut by the plane $x = $ const.

Similarly, the partial derivative $\dfrac{\partial z}{\partial x}$ is numerically equal to the tangent of the angle of inclination α of the tangent line to the section of the surface $z = f(x, y)$ cut by the plane $y = $ const.

17*

8.7 TOTAL INCREMENT AND TOTAL DIFFERENTIAL

By the definition of the total increment of a function $z = f(x, y)$ we have (see Sec. 8.3)

$$\Delta z = f(x + \Delta x, \ y + \Delta y) - f(x, \ y) \qquad (1)$$

Let us suppose that $f(x, y)$ has continuous partial derivatives at the point (x, y) under consideration.

Express Δz in terms of partial derivatives. To do this, add to and subtract from the right side of (1) $f(x, \ y + \Delta y)$:

$$\Delta z = [f(x + \Delta x, \ y + \Delta y) - f(x, \ y + \Delta y)] + [f(x, \ y + \Delta y) - f(x, \ y)] \qquad (2)$$

The expression

$$f(x, \ y + \Delta y) - f(x, \ y)$$

in the second square brackets may be regarded as the difference between two values of the function of the variable y alone (the value of x remaining constant). Applying to this difference the Lagrange theorem, we get

$$f(x, \ y + \Delta y) - f(x, \ y) = \Delta y \frac{\partial f(x, \ \bar{y})}{\partial y} \qquad (3)$$

where $\bar{y}$ lies between y and $y + \Delta y$.

In exactly the same way the expression in the first square brackets of (2) may be regarded as the difference between two values of the function of the variable x alone (the second argument retains the same value $y + \Delta y$). Applying the Lagrange theorem to this difference, we have

$$f(x + \Delta x, \ y + \Delta y) - f(x, \ y + \Delta y) = \Delta x \frac{\partial f(\bar{x}, \ y + \Delta y)}{\partial x} \qquad (4)$$

where $\bar{x}$ lies between x and $x + \Delta x$.

Introducing expressions (3) and (4) into (2), we get

$$\Delta z = \Delta x \frac{\partial f(\bar{x}, \ y + \Delta y)}{\partial x} + \Delta y \frac{\partial f(x, \ \bar{y})}{\partial y} \qquad (5)$$

Since it is assumed that the partial derivatives are continuous,

$$\left.\begin{aligned} \lim_{\substack{\Delta x \to 0 \\ \Delta y \to 0}} \frac{\partial f(\bar{x}, \ y + \Delta y)}{\partial x} &= \frac{\partial f(x, \ y)}{\partial x} \\ \lim_{\substack{\Delta x \to 0 \\ \Delta y \to 0}} \frac{\partial f(x, \ \bar{y})}{\partial y} &= \frac{\partial f(x, \ y)}{\partial y} \end{aligned}\right\} \qquad (6)$$

(because $\bar{x}$ and $\bar{y}$ respectively lie between x and $x + \Delta x$, and y and $y + \Delta y$, $\bar{x}$ and $\bar{y}$ approach x and y, respectively, as $\Delta x \to 0$ and $\Delta y \to 0$). Equations (6) may be rewritten in the form

$$\left. \begin{array}{l} \dfrac{\partial f(\bar{x}, y + \Delta y)}{\partial x} = \dfrac{\partial f(x, y)}{\partial x} + \gamma_1 \\[3mm] \dfrac{\partial f(x, \bar{y})}{\partial y} = \dfrac{\partial f(x, y)}{\partial y} + \gamma_2 \end{array} \right\} \qquad (6')$$

where the quantities γ_1 and γ_2 approach zero as Δx and Δy approach zero (that is, as $\Delta \rho = \sqrt{\Delta x^2 + \Delta y^2} \to 0$).

By virtue of (6'), relation (5) becomes

$$\Delta z = \frac{\partial f(x, y)}{\partial x} \Delta x + \frac{\partial f(x, y)}{\partial y} \Delta y + \gamma_1 \Delta x + \gamma_2 \Delta y \qquad (5')$$

The sum of the latter two terms of the right side is an infinitesimal of higher order relative to $\Delta \rho = \sqrt{\Delta x^2 + \Delta y^2}$. Indeed, the ratio $\frac{\gamma_1 \Delta x}{\Delta \rho} \to 0$ as $\Delta \rho \to 0$ since γ_1 is an infinitesimal and $\frac{\Delta x}{\Delta \rho}$ is bounded $\left(\left| \frac{\Delta x}{\Delta \rho} \right| \leqslant 1 \right)$. In similar fashion it is verified that $\frac{\gamma_2 \Delta y}{\Delta \rho} \to 0$.

The sum of the first two terms is a linear expression in Δx and Δy. For $f'_x(x, y) \neq 0$ and $f'_y(x, y) \neq 0$, this expression is the **principal** part of the increment, differing from Δz by an infinitesimal of higher order relative to $\Delta \rho = \sqrt{\Delta x^2 + \Delta y^2}$.

Definition. The function $z = f(x, y)$ [the total increment (Δz) of which at the given point (x, y) may be represented as a sum of two terms: a linear expression in Δx and Δy, and an infinitesimal of higher order relative to $\Delta \rho$] is called *differentiable at the given point*, while the linear part of the increment is known as the *total differential* and is denoted by dz or df.

From (5') it follows that if the function $f(x, y)$ has continuous partial derivatives at a given point, it is differentiable at that point and has a total differential:

$$dz = f'_x(x, y) \Delta x + f'_y(x, y) \Delta y$$

Equation (5') may be rewritten in the form

$$\Delta z = dz + \gamma_1 \Delta x + \gamma_2 \Delta y$$

and, to within infinitesimals of higher order relative to $\Delta \rho$, we may write the following **approximate** equation:

$$\Delta z \approx dz$$

We shall call the increments of the independent variables Δx and Δy *differentials* of the independent variables x and y and we shall denote them by dx and dy, respectively. Then the expression of the total differential will assume the form

$$dz = \frac{\partial f}{\partial x} dx + \frac{\partial f}{\partial y} dy$$

Thus, if the function $z = f(x, y)$ has continuous partial derivatives, it is differentiable at the point (x, y), and its total differential is equal to the sum of the products of the partial derivatives by the differentials of the corresponding independent variables.

Example 1. Find the total differential and the total increment of the function $z = xy$ at the point (2, 3) for $\Delta x = 0.1$, $\Delta y = 0.2$.

Solution.

$$\Delta z = (x + \Delta x)(y + \Delta y) - xy = y\,\Delta x + x\,\Delta y + \Delta x\,\Delta y$$
$$dz = \frac{\partial z}{\partial x} dx + \frac{\partial z}{\partial y} dy = y\,dx + x\,dy = y\,\Delta x + x\,\Delta y$$

Consequently,

$$\Delta z = 3 \cdot 0.1 + 2 \cdot 0.2 + 0.1 \cdot 0.2 = 0.72$$
$$dz = 3 \cdot 0.1 + 2 \cdot 0.2 = 0.7$$

Fig. 174 is an illustration of this example.

The foregoing reasoning and definitions are appropriately generalized to functions of any number of arguments.

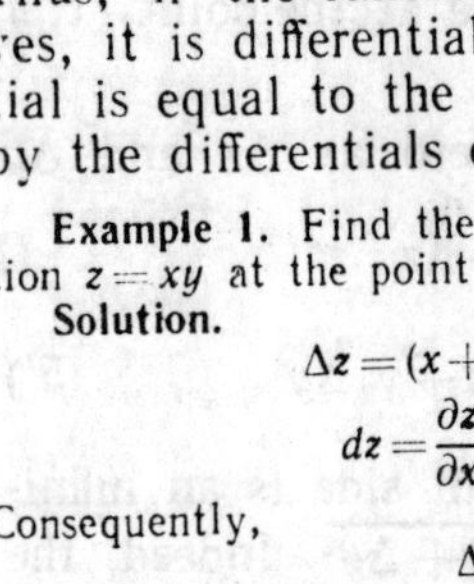

If we have a function of any number of variables

Fig. 174

$$w = f(x, y, z, u, \ldots, t)$$

and all partial derivatives $\frac{\partial f}{\partial x}$, $\frac{\partial f}{\partial y}$, $\ldots$, $\frac{\partial f}{\partial t}$ are continuous at the point $(x, y, z, u, \ldots, t)$, the expression

$$dw = \frac{\partial f}{\partial x} dx + \frac{\partial f}{\partial y} dy + \frac{\partial f}{\partial z} dz + \ldots + \frac{\partial f}{\partial t} dt$$

is the principal part of the total increment of the function and is called the *total differential*. Proof of the fact that the difference $\Delta w - dw$ is an infinitesimal of higher order than $\sqrt{(\Delta x)^2 + (\Delta y)^2 + \ldots + (\Delta t)^2}$ is conducted in exactly the same way as for a function of two variables.

Example 2. Find the total differential of the function $u = e^{x^2 + y^2} \sin^2 z$ of three variables x, y, z.

Solution. Noting that the partial derivatives

$$\frac{\partial u}{\partial x} = e^{x^2 + y^2} 2x \sin^2 z$$
$$\frac{\partial u}{\partial y} = e^{x^2 + y^2} 2y \sin^2 z$$
$$\frac{\partial u}{\partial z} = e^{x^2 + y^2} 2 \sin z \cos z = e^{x^2 + y^2} \sin 2z$$

are continuous for all values of x, y, z, we find that

$$du = \frac{\partial u}{\partial x} dx + \frac{\partial u}{\partial y} dy + \frac{\partial u}{\partial z} dz = e^{x^2+y^2} (2x \sin^2 z \, dx + 2y \sin^2 z \, dy + \sin 2z \, dz)$$

8.8 APPROXIMATION BY TOTAL DIFFERENTIALS

Let the function $z = f(x, y)$ be differentiable at the point (x, y). Find the total increment of this function:

$$\Delta z = f(x + \Delta x, \ y + \Delta y) - f(x, y)$$

whence

$$f(x + \Delta x, \ y + \Delta y) = f(x, y) + \Delta z \qquad (1)$$

We had the approximate formula

$$\Delta z \approx dz \qquad (2)$$

where

$$dz = \frac{\partial f}{\partial x} \Delta x + \frac{\partial f}{\partial y} \Delta y \qquad (3)$$

Substituting into formula (1) the expanded expression for dz in place of Δz, we get the approximate formula

$$f(x + \Delta x, \ y + \Delta y) \approx f(x, y) + \frac{\partial f(x, y)}{\partial x} \Delta x + \frac{\partial f(x, y)}{\partial y} \Delta y \qquad (4)$$

to within infinitesimals of higher order relative to Δx and Δy.

We shall now show how formulas (2) and (4) are used for approximate calculations.

Problem. Calculate the volume of material needed to make a cylindrical glass of the following dimensions (Fig. 175): radius of interior cylinder R, altitude of interior cylinder H, thickness of walls and bottom of glass k.

Solution. We give two solutions of this problem: exact and approximate.

(a) **Exact solution.** The desired volume v is equal to the difference between the volumes of the exterior cylinder and interior cylinder. Since the radius of the exterior cylinder is equal to $R + k$, and the altitude is $H + k$,

$$v = \pi (R + k)^2 (H + k) - \pi R^2 H$$

or

$$v = \pi (2RHk + R^2 k + Hk^2 + 2Rk^2 + k^3) \qquad (5)$$

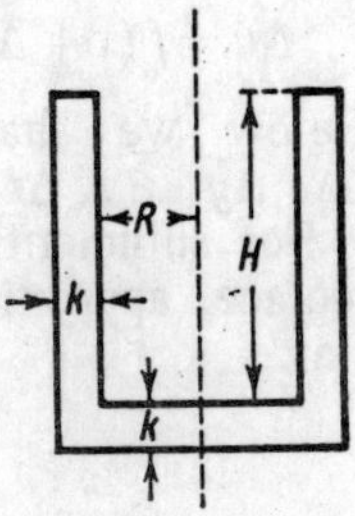

(b) **Approximate solution.** Let us denote by f the volume of the interior cylinder, then $f = \pi R^2 H$. This is a function of two variables R and H. If we increase R and H by k, then the function f will increase by Δf; but this will be the sought-for volume v, $v = \Delta f$.

On the basis of relation (1) we have the approximate equation

$$v \approx df$$

or

$$v \approx \frac{\partial f}{\partial R} \Delta R + \frac{\partial f}{\partial H} \Delta H$$

Fig. 175

But since

$$\frac{\partial f}{\partial R} = 2\pi RH, \quad \frac{\partial f}{\partial H} = \pi R^2, \quad \Delta R = \Delta H = k$$

we get

$$v \approx \pi \left(2RHk + R^2 k\right) \tag{6}$$

Comparing the results of (5) and (6), we see that they differ by the quantity $\pi (Hk^2 + 2Rk^2 + k^3)$, which consists of terms of second and third order of smallness relative to k.

Let us apply these formulas to numerical examples.

Let $R = 4$ cm, $H = 20$ cm, $k = 0.1$ cm.

Applying (5), we get, exactly,

$$v = \pi \left(2 \cdot 4 \cdot 20 \cdot 0.1 + 4^2 \cdot 0.1 + 20 \cdot 0.1^2 + 2 \cdot 4 \cdot 0.1^2 + 0.1^3\right) = 17.881\pi$$

Applying formula (6), we have, approximately,

$$v \approx \pi \left(2 \cdot 4 \cdot 20 \cdot 0.1 + 4^2 \cdot 0.1\right) = 17.6\pi$$

Hence, the approximate formula (6) gives an answer with an error less than 0.3π, which is $100 \cdot \dfrac{0.3\pi}{17.881\pi}$ %, i. e., it is less than 2% of the measured quantity.

8.9 USE OF A DIFFERENTIAL TO ESTIMATE ERRORS IN CALCULATIONS

Let some quantity u be a function of the quantities $x, y, z, \ldots, t$

$$u = f (x, y, z, \ldots, t)$$

and let there be errors $\Delta x, \Delta y, \ldots, \Delta t$ made in determining the values of $x, y, z, \ldots, t$. Then the value of u computed from the inexact values of the arguments will be obtained with an error

$$\Delta u = f (x + \Delta x, \ y + \Delta y, \ \ldots, \ z + \Delta z, \ t + \Delta t) - f (x, y, z, \ldots, t)$$

Below we shall estimate the error Δu, provided the errors $\Delta x, \Delta y, \ldots, \Delta t$ are known.

For sufficiently small absolute values of $\Delta x, \Delta y, \ldots, \Delta t$ we can replace, approximately, the total increment by the total differential:

$$\Delta u \approx \frac{\partial f}{\partial x} \Delta x + \frac{\partial f}{\partial y} \Delta y + \ldots + \frac{\partial f}{\partial t} \Delta t$$

Here, the values of the partial derivatives and the errors of the arguments may be either positive or negative. Replacing them by the absolute values, we get the inequality

$$|\Delta u| \leqslant \left|\frac{\partial f}{\partial x}\right| |\Delta x| + \left|\frac{\partial f}{\partial y}\right| |\Delta y| + \ldots + \left|\frac{\partial f}{\partial t}\right| |\Delta t| \tag{1}$$

If in terms of $|\Delta^* x|, |\Delta^* y|, \ldots, |\Delta^* u|$ we denote the *maximum absolute* errors of the corresponding quantities (the boundaries for the absolute values of the errors), it is obviously possible to take

$$|\Delta^*u| = \left|\frac{\partial f}{\partial x}\right||\Delta^*x| + \left|\frac{\partial f}{\partial y}\right||\Delta^*y| + \cdots + \left|\frac{\partial f}{\partial t}\right||\Delta^*t| \qquad (2)$$

Examples.

1. Let $u = x + y + z$, then $|\Delta^*u| = |\Delta^*x| + |\Delta^*y| + |\Delta^*z|$.
2. Let $u = x - y$, then $|\Delta^*u| = |\Delta^*x| + |\Delta^*y|$.
3. Let $u = xy$, then $|\Delta^*u| = |x||\Delta^*y| + |y||\Delta^*x|$.
4. Let $u = \dfrac{x}{y}$, then $|\Delta^*u| = \left|\dfrac{1}{y}\right||\Delta^*x| + \left|\dfrac{x}{y^2}\right||\Delta^*y| = \dfrac{|y||\Delta^*x| + |x||\Delta^*y|}{y^2}$.

5. The hypotenuse c and the leg a of a right triangle ABC, determined with maximum absolute errors $|\Delta^*c| = 0.2$, $|\Delta^*a| = 0.1$, are, respectively, $c = 75$, $a = 32$. Determine the angle A from the formula $\sin A = \dfrac{a}{c}$; and determine the maximum absolute error $|\overline{\Delta A}|$ in the calculation of angle A.

Solution. $\sin A = \dfrac{a}{c}$, $A = \arcsin\dfrac{a}{c}$, hence,

$$\frac{\partial A}{\partial a} = \frac{1}{\sqrt{c^2-a^2}}, \qquad \frac{\partial A}{\partial c} = -\frac{a}{c\sqrt{c^2-a^2}}$$

From formula (2) we get

$$|\overline{\Delta A}| = \frac{1}{\sqrt{(75)^2-(32)^2}}\cdot 0.1 + \frac{32}{75\sqrt{(75)^2-(32)^2}}\cdot 0.2 = 0.00273 \text{ radian} = 9'24''$$

Thus,

$$A = \arcsin\frac{32}{75} \pm 9'24''$$

6. In the right triangle ABC, let the leg $b = 121.56$ metres and the angle $A = 25°21'40''$, and the maximum absolute error in determining the leg b is $|\Delta^*b| = 0.05$ metre, the maximum absolute error in determining the angle A is $|\Delta^*A| = 12''$.

Determine the maximum absolute error in calculating the leg a from the formula $a = b\tan A$.

Solution. From formula (2) we find

$$|\Delta^*a| = |\tan A||\Delta^*b| + \frac{|b|}{\cos^2 A}|\Delta^*A|$$

Substituting the appropriate values (and remembering that $|\Delta^*A|$ must be expressed in radians), we get

$$|\Delta^*a| = \tan 25°21'40''\cdot 0.05 + \frac{121.56}{\cos^2 25°21'40''}\frac{12}{206\,265} =$$
$$= 0.0237 + 0.0087 = 0.0324 \text{ metre}$$

The ratio of the error Δx of some quantity to the approximate value of x of this quantity is called the *relative error* of the quantity. Let us designate it δx,

$$\delta x = \frac{\Delta x}{x}$$

The *maximum relative error* of a quantity x is the ratio of the maximum absolute error to the absolute value of x and is denoted by $|\delta^*x|$,

$$|\delta^*x| = \frac{|\Delta^*x|}{|x|} \qquad (3)$$

To estimate the maximum relative error of a function u, divide all numbers of (2) by $|u| = |f(x, y, z, \ldots, t)|$:

$$\frac{|\Delta^*u|}{|u|} = \left|\frac{\partial f}{\partial x}\right| |\Delta^*x| + \left|\frac{\partial f}{\partial y}\right| |\Delta^*y| + \ldots + \left|\frac{\partial f}{\partial t}\right| |\Delta^*t| \qquad (4)$$

but

$$\frac{\frac{\partial f}{\partial x}}{f} = \frac{\partial}{\partial x}\ln|f|, \qquad \frac{\frac{\partial f}{\partial y}}{f} = \frac{\partial}{\partial y}\ln|f|, \ldots, \qquad \frac{\frac{\partial f}{\partial t}}{f} = \frac{\partial}{\partial t}\ln|f|$$

For this reason, (3) may be rewritten as follows:

$$|\delta^*u| =$$
$$= \left|\frac{\partial}{\partial x}\ln|f|\right| |\Delta^*x| + \left|\frac{\partial}{\partial y}\ln|f|\right| |\Delta^*y| + \ldots + \left|\frac{\partial}{\partial t}\ln|f|\right| |\Delta^*t| \ldots, \qquad (5)$$

or briefly,

$$|\delta^*u| = |\Delta^* \ln|f|| \qquad (6)$$

From both (3) and (5) it follows that the maximum relative error of the function is equal to the maximum absolute error of the logarithm of the function.

From (6) follow the rules used in approximate calculations.

1. Let $u = xy$. Using the results of Example 3, we get

$$|\delta^*u| = \frac{|y||\Delta^*x|}{|xy|} + \frac{|x||\Delta^*y|}{|xy|} = \frac{|\Delta^*x|}{|x|} + \frac{|\Delta^*y|}{|y|} = |\delta^*x| + |\delta^*y|$$

that is, the maximum relative error of a product is equal to the sum of the maximum relative errors of the factors.

2. If $u = \frac{x}{y}$, then, using the results of Example 4, we have

$$|\delta^*u| = |\delta^*x| + |\delta^*y|$$

Note. From Example 2 it follows that if $u = x - y$, then

$$|\delta^*u| = \frac{|\Delta^*x| + |\Delta^*y|}{|x-y|}$$

If x and y are close, it may happen that $|\delta^*u|$ will be very great compared with the quantity $x-y$ being determined. This should be taken into account when performing the calculations.

Example 7. The oscillation period of a pendulum is

$$T = 2\pi \sqrt{\frac{l}{g}}$$

where l is the length of the pendulum and g is the acceleration of gravity.

What relative error will be made in determining T when using this formula if we take $\pi \approx 3.14$ (accurate to 0.005), $l = 1$ m (accurate to 0.01 m), $g = 9.8$ m/sec^2 (accurate to 0.02) m/sec^2.

Solution. From (6) the maximum relative error is

$$|\delta^* T| = |\Delta^* \ln T|$$

But

$$\ln T = \ln 2 + \ln \pi + \frac{1}{2} \ln l - \frac{1}{2} \ln g$$

Calculate $|\Delta^* \ln T|$. Taking into account that $\pi \approx 3.14$, $\Delta^* \pi = 0.005$, $l = 1$ m, $\Delta^* l = 0.01$ m, $g = 9.8$ m/sec^2, $\Delta^* g = 0.02$ m/sec^2, we get

$$\Delta^* \ln T = \frac{\Delta^* \pi}{\pi} + \frac{\Delta^* l}{2l} + \frac{\Delta^* g}{2g} = \frac{0.005}{3.14} + \frac{0.01}{2} + \frac{0.02}{2 \cdot 9.8} = 0.0076$$

Thus, the maximum relative error is

$$\delta^* T = 0.0076 = 0.76\%$$

8.10 THE DERIVATIVE OF A COMPOSITE FUNCTION.
THE TOTAL DERIVATIVE.
THE TOTAL DIFFERENTIAL OF A COMPOSITE FUNCTION

Let us assume that in the equation

$$z = F(u, v) \tag{1}$$

u and v are functions of the independent variables x and y:

$$u = \varphi(x, y), \quad v = \psi(x, y) \tag{2}$$

In this case, z is a composite function of the arguments x and y.

Of course, z can be expressed directly in terms of x, y; namely,

$$z = F[\varphi(x, y) \quad \psi(x, y)] \tag{3}$$

Example 1. Let

$$z = u^3 v^3 + u + 1, \quad u = x^2 + y^2, \quad v = e^{x+y} + 1$$

then

$$z = (x^2 + y^2)^3 (e^{x+y} + 1)^3 + (x^2 + y^2) + 1$$

Now suppose that the functions $F(u, v)$, $\varphi(x, y)$, $\psi(x, y)$ have continuous partial derivatives with respect to all their arguments. We pose the problem: evaluate $\dfrac{\partial z}{\partial x}$ and $\dfrac{\partial z}{\partial y}$ on the basis of equations (1) and (2) without having recourse to equation (3).

Increase the argument x by Δx, holding the value of y constant. Then, by virtue of equation (2), u and v will increase by $\Delta_x u$ and $\Delta_x v$.

But if u and v receive increments $\Delta_x u$ and $\Delta_x v$, then the function $z = F(u, v)$ will receive an increment Δz defined by formula (5'), Sec. 8.7:

$$\Delta z = \frac{\partial F}{\partial u}\,\Delta_x u + \frac{\partial F}{\partial v}\,\Delta_x v + \gamma_1 \Delta_x u + \gamma_2 \Delta_x v$$

Divide all terms of this equation by Δx:

$$\frac{\Delta z}{\Delta x} = \frac{\partial F}{\partial u}\frac{\Delta_x u}{\Delta x} + \frac{\partial F}{\partial v}\frac{\Delta_x v}{\Delta x} + \gamma_1 \frac{\Delta_x u}{\Delta x} + \gamma_2 \frac{\Delta_x v}{\Delta x}$$

If $\Delta x \to 0$, then $\Delta_x u \to 0$ and $\Delta_x v \to 0$ (by virtue of the continuity of the functions u and v). But then γ_1 and γ_2 also approach zero. Passing to the limit as $\Delta x \to 0$, we get

$$\lim_{\Delta x \to 0}\frac{\Delta z}{\Delta x} = \frac{\partial z}{\partial x}, \quad \lim_{\Delta x \to 0}\frac{\Delta_x u}{\Delta x} = \frac{\partial u}{\partial x}, \quad \lim_{\Delta x \to 0}\frac{\Delta_x v}{\Delta x} = \frac{\partial v}{\partial x}$$

$$\lim_{\Delta x \to 0}\gamma_1 = 0, \quad \lim_{\Delta x \to 0}\gamma_2 = 0$$

and, consequently,

$$\frac{\partial z}{\partial x} = \frac{\partial F}{\partial u}\frac{\partial u}{\partial x} + \frac{\partial F}{\partial v}\frac{\partial v}{\partial x} \tag{4}$$

If we increased the variable y by Δy and held x constant, then by similar reasoning we would find that

$$\frac{\partial z}{\partial y} = \frac{\partial F}{\partial u}\frac{\partial u}{\partial y} + \frac{\partial F}{\partial v}\frac{\partial v}{\partial y} \tag{4'}$$

Example 2.

$$z = \ln(u^2 + v), \quad u = e^{x+y^2}, \quad v = x^2 + y$$
$$\frac{\partial z}{\partial u} = \frac{2u}{u^2 + v}, \quad \frac{\partial z}{\partial v} = \frac{1}{u^2 + v}.$$
$$\frac{\partial u}{\partial x} = e^{x+y^2}, \quad \frac{\partial u}{\partial y} = 2ye^{x+y^2}, \quad \frac{\partial v}{\partial x} = 2x, \quad \frac{\partial v}{\partial y} = 1$$

Using formulas (4) and (4') we find

$$\frac{\partial z}{\partial x} = \frac{2u}{u^2 + v}\,e^{x+y^2} + \frac{1}{u^2 + v}\,2x = \frac{2}{u^2 + v}\,(ue^{x+y^2} + x)$$
$$\frac{\partial z}{\partial y} = \frac{2u}{u^2 + v}\,2ye^{x+y^2} + \frac{1}{u^2 + v} = \frac{1}{u^2 + v}\,(4uye^{x+y^2} + 1)$$

In these expressions, we have to substitute e^{x+y^2} and $x^2 + y$ for u and v respectively.

Formulas (4) and (4') are readily generalized to the case of a larger number of variables.

For example, if $w = F(z, u, v, s)$ is a function of four arguments z, u, v, s, and each of them depends on x and y, then formulas (4) and (4') assume the form

$$\left.\begin{array}{l} \dfrac{\partial w}{\partial x} = \dfrac{\partial w}{\partial z}\dfrac{\partial z}{\partial x} + \dfrac{\partial w}{\partial \bar u}\dfrac{\partial u}{\partial x} + \dfrac{\partial w}{\partial v}\dfrac{\partial v}{\partial x} + \dfrac{\partial w}{\partial s}\dfrac{\partial s}{\partial x} \\[3mm] \dfrac{\partial w}{\partial y} = \dfrac{\partial w}{\partial z}\dfrac{\partial z}{\partial y} + \dfrac{\partial w}{\partial u}\dfrac{\partial u}{\partial y} + \dfrac{\partial w}{\partial v}\dfrac{\partial v}{\partial y} + \dfrac{\partial w}{\partial s}\dfrac{\partial s}{\partial y} \end{array}\right\} \tag{5}$$

If a function is given $z = F(x, y, u, v)$, where y, u, v in turn depend on a single independent variable (argument) x:

$$y = f(x), \quad u = \varphi(x), \quad v = \psi(x)$$

then z is actually a function only of the **one** variable x, and we may pose the question of finding the derivative $\dfrac{dz}{dx}$.

This derivative is calculated from the first of the formulas in (5):

$$\frac{dz}{dx} = \frac{\partial z}{\partial x}\frac{\partial x}{\partial x} + \frac{\partial z}{\partial y}\frac{\partial y}{\partial x} + \frac{\partial z}{\partial u}\frac{\partial u}{\partial x} + \frac{\partial z}{\partial v}\frac{\partial v}{\partial x}$$

But since y, u, v are functions of x **alone**, the partial derivatives become ordinary derivatives; besides $\dfrac{\partial x}{\partial x} = 1$. For this reason,

$$\frac{dz}{dx} = \frac{\partial z}{\partial x} + \frac{\partial z}{\partial y}\frac{dy}{dx} + \frac{\partial z}{\partial u}\frac{du}{dx} + \frac{\partial z}{\partial v}\frac{dv}{dx}$$

This formula is known as the formula for calculating the *total derivative* $\dfrac{dz}{dx}$ $\left(\text{in contrast to the } \textbf{partial} \text{ derivative } \dfrac{\partial z}{\partial x}\right)$.

Example 3.

$$z = x^2 + \sqrt{y}, \quad y = \sin x$$
$$\frac{\partial z}{\partial x} = 2x, \quad \frac{\partial z}{\partial y} = \frac{1}{2\sqrt{y}}, \quad \frac{dy}{dx} = \cos x$$

Formula (6), here, yields the following result:

$$\frac{dz}{dx} = \frac{\partial z}{\partial x} + \frac{\partial z}{\partial y}\frac{dy}{dx} = 2x + \frac{1}{2\sqrt{y}}\cos x = 2x + \frac{1}{2\sqrt{\sin x}}\cos x$$

Now let us find the total differential of the composite function defined by equations (1) and (2).

Substituting the expressions $\dfrac{\partial z}{\partial x}$ and $\dfrac{\partial z}{\partial y}$, defined by (4) and (4'), into the formula for the total differential

$$dz = \frac{\partial z}{\partial x}dx + \frac{\partial z}{\partial y}dy \tag{6}$$

we get

$$dz = \left(\frac{\partial F}{\partial u}\frac{\partial u}{\partial x} + \frac{\partial F}{\partial v}\frac{\partial v}{\partial x}\right)dx + \left(\frac{\partial F}{\partial u}\frac{\partial u}{\partial y} + \frac{\partial F}{\partial v}\frac{\partial v}{\partial y}\right)dy$$

Transforming the right-hand side we get

$$dz = \frac{\partial F}{\partial u}\left(\frac{\partial u}{\partial x}dx + \frac{\partial u}{\partial y}dy\right) + \frac{\partial F}{\partial v}\left(\frac{\partial v}{\partial x}dx + \frac{\partial v}{\partial y}dy\right) \qquad (7)$$

But

$$\left.\begin{array}{l} \dfrac{\partial u}{\partial x}dx + \dfrac{\partial u}{\partial y}dy = du \\[2mm] \dfrac{\partial v}{\partial x}dx + \dfrac{\partial v}{\partial y}dy = dv \end{array}\right\} \qquad (8)$$

Taking into account (8), equation (7) may be rewritten thus:

$$dz = \frac{\partial F}{\partial u}du + \frac{\partial F}{\partial v}dv \qquad (9)$$

or

$$dz = \frac{\partial z}{\partial u}du + \frac{\partial z}{\partial v}dv \qquad (9')$$

Comparing (6) and (9') we can say that the expression of the total differential of a function of several variables (the first differential) is of the same form (that is, the form of the differential is preserved) whether u and v are independent variables or functions of independent variables.

Example 4. Find the total differential of the composite function

$$z = u^2 v^3, \quad u = x^2 \sin y, \quad v = x^3 e^y$$

Solution. By formula (9') we have

$$dz = 2uv^3\, du + 3u^2 v^2\, dv = 2uv^3\,(2x \sin y\, dx + x^2 \cos y\, dy) + 3u^2 v^2\,(3x^2 e^y\, dx + x^3 e^y\, dy)$$

This can be rewritten as

$$dz = (2uv^3 \cdot 2x \sin y + 3u^2 v^2 \cdot 3x^2 e^y)\, dx + (2uv^3 x^2 \cos y + 3u^2 v^2 x^3 e^y)\, dy = \frac{\partial z}{\partial x}dx + \frac{\partial z}{\partial y}dy$$

8.11 THE DERIVATIVE OF A FUNCTION DEFINED IMPLICITLY

Let us begin this discussion with an implicit function of one variable. * Let some function y of x be defined by the equation

$$F(x,\, y) = 0$$

We shall prove the following theorem.

Theorem. *Let a continuous function y of x be defined implicitly by the equation*

$$F(x,\, y) = 0 \qquad (1)$$

---

* In Sec. 3.11, we solved the problem of differentiating an implicit function of one variable. We considered individual cases and did not find a general formula that would yield the derivative of an implicit function; likewise we failed to clarify the conditions for the existence of this derivative.

where $F(x, y)$, $F'_x(x, y)$, $F'_y(x, y)$ are continuous functions in some domain D containing the point (x, y) whose coordinates satisfy equation (1); also, at this point $F'_y(x, y) \neq 0$. Then the function y of x has the derivative

$$y'_x = -\frac{F'_x(x, y)}{F'_y(x, y)} \qquad (2)$$

Proof. Let the value of the function y correspond to some value of x. Here,

$$F(x, y) = 0$$

Increase the independent variable x by Δx. Then the function y will receive an increment Δy; that is, to the value of the argument $x + \Delta x$ there corresponds the value of the function $y + \Delta y$. By virtue of equation $F(x, y) = 0$ we shall have

$$F(x + \Delta x, y + \Delta y) = 0$$

Hence

$$F(x + \Delta x, y + \Delta y) - F(x, y) = 0$$

The left member of this equation, which is the total increment of the function of two variables by formula (5'), Sec. 8.7, may be rewritten as follows:

$$F(x + \Delta x, y + \Delta y) - F(x, y) = \frac{\partial F}{\partial x} \Delta x + \frac{\partial F}{\partial y} \Delta y + \gamma_1 \Delta x + \gamma_2 \Delta y$$

where γ_1 and γ_2 approach zero as Δx and Δy approach zero. Since the left side of this expression is equal to zero, we can write:

$$\frac{\partial F}{\partial x} \Delta x + \frac{\partial F}{\partial y} \Delta y + \gamma_1 \Delta x + \gamma_2 \Delta y = 0$$

Divide by Δx and calculate $\frac{\Delta y}{\Delta x}$:

$$\frac{\Delta y}{\Delta x} = -\frac{\frac{\partial F}{\partial x} + \gamma_1}{\frac{\partial F}{\partial y} + \gamma_2}$$

Let Δx approach zero. Then, taking into account that γ_1 and γ_2 also approach zero and that $\frac{\partial F}{\partial y} \neq 0$, we have, in the limit

$$y'_x = -\frac{\frac{\partial F}{\partial x}}{\frac{\partial F}{\partial y}} \qquad (2')$$

We have proved the existence of the derivative y'_x of a function defined implicitly, and we have found the formula for calculating it.

Example 1. The equation
$$x^2 + y^2 - 1 = 0$$
defines y as an implicit function of x. Here,
$$F(x, y) = x^2 + y^2 - 1, \quad \frac{\partial F}{\partial x} = 2x, \quad \frac{\partial F}{\partial y} = 2y$$
Consequently, from (1),
$$\frac{dy}{dx} = -\frac{2x}{2y} = -\frac{x}{y}$$

It will be noted that the given equation defines two different functions [since to every value of x in the interval $(-1, 1)$ there correspond two values of y]; however, the value that we found of y'_x holds for both functions.

Example 2. An equation is given that connects x and y;
$$e^y - e^x + xy = 0$$
Here, $F(x, y) = e^y - e^x + xy$,
$$\frac{\partial F}{\partial x} = -e^x + y, \quad \frac{\partial F}{\partial y} = e^y + x$$
Consequently, from formula (1) we get
$$\frac{dy}{dx} = -\frac{-e^x + y}{e^y + x} = \frac{e^x - y}{e^y + x}$$

Let us now consider an equation of the form
$$F(x, y, z) = 0 \tag{3}$$

If to each number pair x and y in some domain there correspond one or several values of z that satisfy equation (3), then this equation implicitly defines one or several single-valued functions z of x and y.

For instance, the equation
$$x^2 + y^2 + z^2 - R^2 = 0$$
implicitly defines two continuous functions z of x and y, which functions may be expressed explicitly by solving the equation for z; in this case we have
$$z = \sqrt{R^2 - x^2 - y^2} \quad \text{and} \quad z = -\sqrt{R^2 - x^2 - y^2}$$

Let us find the partial derivatives $\frac{\partial z}{\partial x}$ and $\frac{\partial z}{\partial y}$ of the implicit function z of x and y defined by equation (3).

When we seek $\frac{\partial z}{\partial x}$, we consider y fixed. And so formula (2') is applicable, provided x is considered the independent variable and z the function. Thus,
$$z'_x = -\frac{\dfrac{\partial F}{\partial x}}{\dfrac{\partial F}{\partial z}}$$

In the same way we find

$$z'_y = -\frac{\dfrac{\partial F}{\partial y}}{\dfrac{\partial F}{\partial z}}$$

It is assumed that $\dfrac{\partial F}{\partial z} \neq 0$.

Similarly, we determine the implicit functions of any **number** of variables and find their partial derivatives.

Example 3. $x^2 + y^2 + z^2 - R^2 = 0$.

$$\frac{\partial z}{\partial x} = -\frac{2x}{2z} = -\frac{x}{z}, \quad \frac{\partial z}{\partial y} = -\frac{y}{z}$$

Differentiating this function as an explicit function (after solving the **equation** for z), we would obtain the very same result.

Example 4. $e^z + x^2y + z + 5 = 0$.

Here,

$$F(x,\ y,\ z) = e^z + x^2y + z + 5$$

$$\frac{\partial F}{\partial x} = 2xy, \quad \frac{\partial F}{\partial y} = x^2, \quad \frac{\partial F}{\partial z} = e^z + 1$$

$$\frac{\partial z}{\partial x} = -\frac{2xy}{e^z + 1}, \quad \frac{\partial z}{\partial y} = -\frac{x^2}{e^z + 1}$$

Note. Throughout this section we have assumed that the **equa**tion $F(x,\ y) = 0$ defines a certain function of one variable $y = \varphi(x)$ and the equation $F(x,\ y,\ z) = 0$ defines a certain function of two variables $z = f(x,\ y)$. We now state, without proof, the **condition** that must be satisfied by the function $F(x,\ y)$ so that the **equa**tion $F(x,\ y) = 0$ defines a single-valued function $y = \varphi(x)$.

Theorem. *Let a function $F(x,\ y)$ be continuous in the neighbourhood of a point $(x_0,\ y_0)$ and have continuous partial derivatives there, and let $F'_y(x,\ y) \neq 0$ and $F(x_0,\ y_0) = 0$. Then there exists a neighbourhood containing the point $(x_0,\ y_0)$ at which the equation $F(x,\ y) = 0$ defines a single-valued function $y = \varphi(x)$.*

An analogous theorem is also valid for the conditions of existence of an implicit function defined by the equation $F(x,\ y,\ z) = 0$.

Note. When deriving the rules for differentiating implicit **func**tions, we made use of conditions that determine the existence of implicit functions.

8.12 PARTIAL DERIVATIVES OF HIGHER ORDERS

Suppose we have a function of two variables:

$$z = f(x,\ y)$$

The partial derivatives $\dfrac{\partial z}{\partial x} = f'_x(x,\ y)$ and $\dfrac{\partial z}{\partial y} = f'_y(x,\ y)$ are, generally speaking, functions of the variables x and y. And so from them we can again find partial derivatives. Thus, there are **four** partial derivatives of the second order of a function of two variables, since each of the functions $\frac{\partial z}{\partial x}$ and $\frac{\partial z}{\partial y}$ may be differentiated both with respect to x and with respect to y.

The second partial derivatives are denoted as follows:

$\frac{\partial^2 z}{\partial x^2} = f''_{xx}(x, y)$, here f is differentiated twice successively with respect to x;

$\frac{\partial^2 z}{\partial x \partial y} = f''_{xy}(x, y)$, here f is differentiated first with respect to x and then the result is differentiated with respect to y;

$\frac{\partial^2 z}{\partial y \partial x} = f''_{yx}(x, y)$, here f is differentiated first with respect to y and then the result is differentiated with respect to x;

$\frac{\partial^2 z}{\partial y^2} = f''_{yy}(x, y)$, here the function f is differentiated twice successively with respect to y.

Derivatives of the second order may again be differentiated both with respect to x and y. We then get partial derivatives of the third order. Obviously, there will be eight of them:

$$\frac{\partial^3 z}{\partial x^3}, \quad \frac{\partial^3 z}{\partial x^2 \partial y}, \quad \frac{\partial^3 z}{\partial x \partial y \partial x}, \quad \frac{\partial^3 z}{\partial x \partial y^2}, \quad \frac{\partial^3 z}{\partial y \partial x^2}, \quad \frac{\partial^3 z}{\partial y \partial x \partial y}, \quad \frac{\partial^3 z}{\partial y^2 \partial x}, \quad \frac{\partial^3 z}{\partial y^3}$$

Generally speaking, a *partial derivative of the nth order* is the first derivative of the derivative of the $(n-1)$th order. For example, $\frac{\partial^n z}{\partial x^p \partial y^{n-p}}$ is a derivative of the nth order; here the function z was first differentiated p times with respect to x, and then $n - p$ times with respect to y.

For a function of any number of variables, the higher partial derivatives are determined in similar fashion.

Example 1. Compute the second partial derivatives of the function

$$f(x, y) = x^2 y + y^3$$

Solution. We find successively

$$\frac{\partial f}{\partial x} = 2xy, \quad \frac{\partial f}{\partial y} = x^2 + 3y^2,$$

$$\frac{\partial^2 f}{\partial x^2} = 2y, \quad \frac{\partial^2 f}{\partial x \partial y} = \frac{\partial(2xy)}{\partial y} = 2x, \quad \frac{\partial^2 f}{\partial y \partial x} = \frac{\partial(x^2 + 3y^2)}{\partial x} = 2x, \quad \frac{\partial^2 f}{\partial y^2} = 6y$$

Example 2. Compute $\frac{\partial^3 z}{\partial x^2 \partial y}$ and $\frac{\partial^3 z}{\partial y \partial x^2}$ if $z = y^2 e^x + x^2 y^3 + 1$.

Solution. We successively find

$$\frac{\partial z}{\partial x}=y^2e^x+2xy^3, \qquad \frac{\partial^2 z}{\partial x^2}=y^2e^x+2y^3, \qquad \frac{\partial^3 z}{\partial x^2\,\partial y}=2ye^x+6y^2$$

$$\frac{\partial z}{\partial y}=2ye^x+3x^2y^2, \qquad \frac{\partial^2 z}{\partial y\,\partial x}=2ye^x+6xy^2, \qquad \frac{\partial^3 z}{\partial y\,\partial x^2}=2ye^x+6y^2$$

Example 3. Compute $\dfrac{\partial^4 u}{\partial x^2\,\partial y\,\partial z}$ if $u=z^2e^{x+y^2}$.

Solution.

$$\frac{\partial u}{\partial x}=z^2e^{x+y^2}, \quad \frac{\partial^2 u}{\partial x^2}=z^2e^{x+y^2}, \quad \frac{\partial^3 u}{\partial x^2\,\partial y}=2yz^2e^{x+y^2}, \quad \frac{\partial^4 u}{\partial x^2\,\partial y\,\partial z}=4yze^{x+y^2}$$

The natural question that arises is whether the result of differentiating a function of several variables depends on the order of differentiation with respect to the different variables; in other words, will, for instance, the following derivatives be identically equal:

$$\frac{\partial^2 f}{\partial x\,\partial y} \quad \text{and} \quad \frac{\partial^2 f}{\partial y\,\partial x}$$

or

$$\frac{\partial^3 f(x,\,y,\,t)}{\partial x\,\partial y\,\partial t} \quad \text{and} \quad \frac{\partial^3 f(x,\,y,\,t)}{\partial t\,\partial x\,\partial y}$$

and so forth. It turns out that the following theorem is true.

Theorem. *If a function* $z=f(x,\,y)$ *and its partial derivatives* f'_x, f'_y, f''_{xy} *and* f''_{yx} *are defined and continuous at a point* $M(x,\,y)$ *and in some neighbourhood of it, then at this point*

$$\frac{\partial^2 f}{\partial x\,\partial y}=\frac{\partial^2 f}{\partial y\,\partial x} \qquad (f''_{xy}=f''_{yx})$$

Proof. Consider the expression

$$A=[f(x+\Delta x,\,y+\Delta y)-f(x+\Delta x,\,y)]-[f(x,\,y+\Delta y)-f(x,\,y)]$$

If we introduce an auxiliary function $\varphi(x)$ defined by

$$\varphi(x)=f(x,\,y+\Delta y)-f(x,\,y)$$

then A may be written in the form

$$A=\varphi(x+\Delta x)-\varphi(x)$$

Since it is assumed that f'_x is defined in the neighbourhood of the point $(x,\,y)$, it follows that $\varphi(x)$ is differentiable on the interval $[x,\,x+\Delta x]$; but then, applying the Lagrange theorem, we get

$$A=\Delta x\varphi'(\bar{x})$$

where $\bar{x}$ lies between x and $x+\Delta x$. But

$$\varphi'(\bar{x})=f'_x(\bar{x},\,y+\Delta y)-f'_x(\bar{x},\,y)$$

Since f''_{xy} is defined in the neighbourhood of the point (x, y), f'_x is differentiable on the interval $[y, y + \Delta y]$; and so by applying once again the Lagrange theorem (with respect to the variable y) to the difference obtained, we have

$$f'_x (\overline{x}, \; y + \Delta y) - f'_x (\overline{x}, \; y) = \Delta y f''_{xy} (\overline{x}, \; \overline{y})$$

where $\overline{y}$ lies between y and $y + \Delta y$.

Consequently, the original expression of A is

$$A = \Delta x \Delta y f''_{xy} (\overline{x}, \; \overline{y}) \tag{1}$$

Changing the places of the middle terms in the original expression for A, we get

$$A = [f (x + \Delta x, \; y + \Delta y) - f (x, \; y + \Delta y)] - [f (x + \Delta x, \; y) - f (x, \; y)]$$

Introducing the auxiliary function

$$\psi (y) = f (x + \Delta x, \; y) - f (x, \; y)$$

we have

$$A = \psi (y + \Delta y) - \psi (y)$$

Again applying the Lagrange theorem we get

$$A = \Delta y \psi' (\overline{\overline{y}})$$

where $\overline{\overline{y}}$ lies between y and $y + \Delta y$. But

$$\psi' (\overline{\overline{y}}) = f'_y (x + \Delta x, \; \overline{\overline{y}}) - f'_y (x, \; \overline{\overline{y}})$$

Again applying the Lagrange theorem, we get

$$f'_y (x + \Delta x, \; \overline{\overline{y}}) - f'_y (x, \; \overline{\overline{y}}) = \Delta x f''_{yx} (\overline{\overline{x}}, \; \overline{\overline{y}})$$

where $\overline{\overline{x}}$ lies between x and $x + \Delta x$.

Thus, the original expression of A may be written in the form

$$A = \Delta y \, \Delta x f''_{yx} (\overline{\overline{x}}, \; \overline{\overline{y}}) \tag{2}$$

The left members of (1) and (2) are equal to A, therefore the right ones are equal too; that is,

$$\Delta x \, \Delta y f''_{xy} (\overline{x}, \; \overline{y}) = \Delta y \, \Delta x f''_{yx} (\overline{\overline{x}}, \; \overline{\overline{y}})$$

whence

$$f''_{xy} (\overline{x}, \; \overline{y}) = f''_{yx} (\overline{\overline{x}}, \; \overline{\overline{y}})$$

Passing to the limit in this equality as $\Delta x \to 0$ and $\Delta y \to 0$, we get

$$\lim_{\substack{\Delta x \to 0 \\ \Delta y \to 0}} f''_{xy} (\overline{x}, \; \overline{y}) = \lim_{\substack{\Delta x \to 0 \\ \Delta y \to 0}} f''_{yx} (\overline{\overline{x}}, \; \overline{\overline{y}})$$

Since the derivatives f''_{xy} and f''_{yx} are continuous at the point (x, y), we have $\lim\limits_{\substack{\Delta x \to 0 \\ \Delta y \to 0}} f''_{xy}(\bar{x}, \bar{y}) = f''_{xy}(x, y)$ and $\lim\limits_{\substack{\Delta x \to 0 \\ \Delta y \to 0}} f''_{yx}(\bar{\bar{x}}, \bar{y}) = f''_{yx}(x, y)$. And finally we get

$$f''_{xy}(x, y) = f''_{yx}(x, y)$$

as required.

A corollary of this theorem is that if the partial derivatives $\dfrac{\partial^n f}{\partial x^k \partial y^{n-k}}$ and $\dfrac{\partial^n f}{\partial y^{n-k} \partial x^k}$ are continuous, then

$$\frac{\partial^n f}{\partial x^k \partial y^{n-k}} = \frac{\partial^n f}{\partial y^{n-k} \partial x^k}$$

A similar theorem holds also for a function of any number of variables.

Example 4. Find $\dfrac{\partial^3 u}{\partial x \partial y \partial z}$ and $\dfrac{\partial^3 u}{\partial y \partial z \partial x}$ if $u = e^{xy} \sin z$.

Solution.

$$\frac{\partial u}{\partial x} = y e^{xy} \sin z, \quad \frac{\partial^2 u}{\partial x \partial y} = e^{xy} \sin z + x y e^{xy} \sin z = e^{xy}(1 + xy) \sin z$$

$$\frac{\partial^3 u}{\partial x \partial y \partial z} = e^{xy}(1 + xy) \cos z, \quad \frac{\partial u}{\partial y} = x e^{xy} \sin z, \quad \frac{\partial^2 u}{\partial x \partial z} = x e^{xy} \cos z$$

$$\frac{\partial^3 u}{\partial y \partial z \partial x} = e^{xy} \cos z + x y e^{xy} \cos z = e^{xy}(1 + xy) \cos z$$

Hence,

$$\frac{\partial^3 u}{\partial x \partial y \partial z} = \frac{\partial^3 u}{\partial y \partial z \partial x}$$

(also see Examples 1 and 2 of this section).

8.13 LEVEL SURFACES

In a space (x, y, z) let there be a region D in which the function

$$u = u(x, y, z) \tag{1}$$

is defined. In this case we say that a *scalar field* is defined in the region D. If, for example, $u(x, y, z)$ denotes the temperature at the point $M(x, y, z)$, then we say that a scalar field of temperatures is defined; if D is filled with a liquid or gas and $u(x, y, z)$ denotes pressure, we have a scalar field of pressures, etc.

Consider the points of a region D in which the function $u(x, y, z)$ has a fixed value c:

$$u(x, y, z) = c \tag{2}$$

The totality of these points forms a certain surface. If a different value of c is taken, we obtain a different surface. These surfaces are called *level surfaces*.

Example 1. Let there be given a scalar field

$$u(x,\ y,\ z) = \frac{x^2}{4} + \frac{y^2}{9} + \frac{z^2}{16}$$

Here, the level surfaces are

$$\frac{x^2}{4} + \frac{y^2}{9} + \frac{z^2}{16} = c$$

or ellipsoids with semi-axes $2\sqrt{c}$, $3\sqrt{c}$, $4\sqrt{c}$.

If the function u is a function of two variables x and y,

$$u = u(x,\ y)$$

then instead of level surfaces we have lines on the xy-plane:

$$u(x,\ y) = c \qquad\qquad (2')$$

which are called *level lines*.

If we plot values of u on the z-axis:

$$z = u(x,\ y)$$

the level lines in the xy-plane will be projections of lines obtained at the intersection of the surface $z = u(x,\ y)$ with the planes $z = c$ (Fig. 176). Knowing the level lines, it is easy to study the character of the surface $z = u(x,\ y)$.

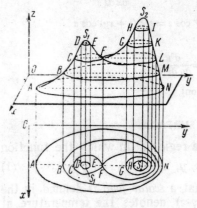

Fig. 176

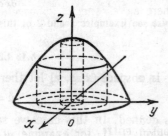

Fig. 177

Example 2. Determine the level lines of the function $z = 1 - x^2 - y^2$. They are lines with equations $1 - x^2 - y^2 = c$, which are (Fig. 177) circles with radius $\sqrt{1-c}$. In particular, when $c = 0$ we get the circle $x^2 + y^2 = 1$.

8.14 DIRECTIONAL DERIVATIVE

In a region D, consider the function $u = u(x,\ y,\ z)$ and the point $M(x,\ y,\ z)$. Draw from M a vector S whose direction cosines are $\cos\alpha$, $\cos\beta$, $\cos\gamma$ (Fig. 178). On the vector S, at a distance Δs

from its origin, let us consider a point $M_1 (x + \Delta x,\ y + \Delta y,\ z + \Delta z)$. Thus,

$$\Delta s = \sqrt{\Delta x^2 + \Delta y^2 + \Delta z^2}$$

We shall assume that the function $u(x,\ y,\ z)$ is continuous and has continuous derivatives with respect to their arguments in the region D.

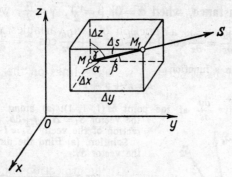

Fig. 178

As in Sec. 8.7, we will represent the total increment of the function as follows:

$$\Delta u = \frac{\partial u}{\partial x}\, \Delta x + \frac{\partial u}{\partial y}\, \Delta y + \frac{\partial u}{\partial z}\, \Delta z + \varepsilon_1 \Delta x + \varepsilon_2 \Delta y + \varepsilon_3 \Delta z \qquad (1)$$

where ε_1, ε_2 and ε_3 approach zero as $\Delta s \to 0$. Divide all terms of (1) by Δs:

$$\frac{\Delta u}{\Delta s} = \frac{\partial u}{\partial x}\frac{\Delta x}{\Delta s} + \frac{\partial u}{\partial y}\frac{\Delta y}{\Delta s} + \frac{\partial u}{\partial z}\frac{\Delta z}{\Delta s} + \varepsilon_1 \frac{\Delta x}{\Delta s} + \varepsilon_2 \frac{\Delta y}{\Delta s} + \varepsilon_3 \frac{\Delta z}{\Delta s} \qquad (2)$$

It is obvious that

$$\frac{\Delta x}{\Delta s} = \cos \alpha, \qquad \frac{\Delta y}{\Delta s} = \cos \beta, \qquad \frac{\Delta z}{\Delta s} = \cos \gamma$$

Consequently, equation (2) may be rewritten as

$$\frac{\Delta u}{\Delta s} = \frac{\partial u}{\partial x} \cos \alpha + \frac{\partial u}{\partial y} \cos \beta + \frac{\partial u}{\partial z} \cos \gamma + \varepsilon_1 \cos \alpha + \varepsilon_2 \cos \beta + \varepsilon_3 \cos \gamma \qquad (3)$$

The limit of the ratio $\frac{\Delta u}{\Delta s}$ as $\Delta s \to 0$ is called the *derivative of the function* $u = u(x,\ y,\ z)$ *at the point* $(x,\ y,\ z)$ *along the direction of the vector* **S** and is denoted by $\frac{\partial u}{\partial s}$; i.e.,

$$\lim_{\Delta s \to 0} \frac{\Delta u}{\Delta s} = \frac{\partial u}{\partial s} \qquad (4)$$

Thus, passing to the limit in (3), we get

$$\frac{\partial u}{\partial s} = \frac{\partial u}{\partial x}\cos\alpha + \frac{\partial u}{\partial y}\cos\beta + \frac{\partial u}{\partial z}\cos\gamma \tag{5}$$

From formula (5) it follows that if we know the partial derivatives it is easy to find the derivative along any direction S. The partial derivatives themselves are a particular case of a directional derivative. For instance, when $\alpha = 0$, $\beta = \frac{\pi}{2}$, $\gamma = \frac{\pi}{2}$, we get

$$\frac{\partial u}{\partial s} = \frac{\partial u}{\partial x}\cos 0 + \frac{\partial u}{\partial y}\cos\frac{\pi}{2} + \frac{\partial u}{\partial z}\cos\frac{\pi}{2} = \frac{\partial u}{\partial x}$$

Example. Given a function

$$u = x^2 + y^2 + z^2$$

Find the derivative $\frac{\partial u}{\partial s}$ at the point $M(1, 1, 1)$: (a) along the direction of the vector $S_1 = 2i + j + 3k$; (b) along the direction of the vector $S_2 = i + j + k$.

Solution. (a) Find the direction cosines of the vector S_1:

$$\cos\alpha = \frac{2}{\sqrt{4+1+9}} = \frac{2}{\sqrt{14}}$$

$$\cos\beta = \frac{1}{\sqrt{14}}, \quad \cos\gamma = \frac{3}{\sqrt{14}}$$

Hence,

$$\frac{\partial u}{\partial s_1} = \frac{\partial u}{\partial x}\frac{2}{\sqrt{14}} + \frac{\partial u}{\partial y}\frac{1}{\sqrt{14}} + \frac{\partial u}{\partial z}\frac{3}{\sqrt{14}}$$

The partial derivatives

$$\frac{\partial u}{\partial x} = 2x, \quad \frac{\partial u}{\partial y} = 2y, \quad \frac{\partial u}{\partial z} = 2z$$

at the point $M(1, 1, 1)$ are

$$\left(\frac{\partial u}{\partial x}\right)_M = 2, \quad \left(\frac{\partial u}{\partial y}\right)_M = 2, \quad \left(\frac{\partial u}{\partial z}\right)_M = 2$$

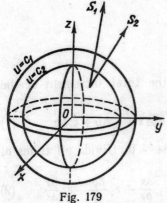

Fig. 179

Thus,

$$\frac{\partial u}{\partial s_1} = 2\cdot\frac{2}{\sqrt{14}} + 2\cdot\frac{1}{\sqrt{14}} + 2\cdot\frac{3}{\sqrt{14}} = \frac{12}{\sqrt{14}}$$

(b) Find the direction cosines of the vector S_2:

$$\cos\alpha = \frac{1}{\sqrt{3}}, \quad \cos\beta = \frac{1}{\sqrt{3}}, \quad \cos\gamma = \frac{1}{\sqrt{3}}$$

Hence,

$$\frac{\partial u}{\partial s_2} = 2\cdot\frac{1}{\sqrt{3}} + 2\cdot\frac{1}{\sqrt{3}} + 2\cdot\frac{1}{\sqrt{3}} = \frac{6}{\sqrt{3}} = 2\sqrt{3}$$

We note here (and it will be needed later on) that $2\sqrt{3} > \frac{12}{\sqrt{14}}$ (Fig. 179).

8.15 GRADIENT

At every point of the region D, in which the function $u = u(x, y, z)$ is given, we determine the vector whose projections on the coordinate axes are the values of the partial derivatives $\dfrac{\partial u}{\partial x}$, $\dfrac{\partial u}{\partial y}$, $\dfrac{\partial u}{\partial z}$ of this function at the appropriate point:

$$\operatorname{grad} u = \frac{\partial u}{\partial x} \boldsymbol{i} + \frac{\partial u}{\partial y} \boldsymbol{j} + \frac{\partial u}{\partial z} \boldsymbol{k} \tag{1}$$

This vector is called the *gradient* of the function $u(x, y, z)$. We say that a *vector field of gradients* is defined in D. Let us now prove the following theorem which establishes a relationship between the gradient and the directional derivative.

Theorem. *Given a scalar field* $u = u(x, y, z)$; *in this field, let there be defined a field of gradients*

$$\operatorname{grad} u = \frac{\partial u}{\partial x} \boldsymbol{i} + \frac{\partial u}{\partial y} \boldsymbol{j} + \frac{\partial u}{\partial z} \boldsymbol{k}$$

The derivative $\dfrac{\partial u}{\partial s}$ *along the direction of some vector* $\boldsymbol{S}$ *is equal to the projection of the vector* $\operatorname{grad} u$ *on the vector* $\boldsymbol{S}$.

Proof. Consider the unit vector $\boldsymbol{S}^0$, which corresponds to the vector $\boldsymbol{S}$:

$$\boldsymbol{S}^0 = \boldsymbol{i} \cos\alpha + \boldsymbol{j} \cos\beta + \boldsymbol{k} \cos\gamma$$

Find the scalar product of the vectors $\operatorname{grad} u$ and $\boldsymbol{S}^0$:

$$\operatorname{grad} u \cdot \boldsymbol{S}^0 = \frac{\partial u}{\partial x} \cos\alpha + \frac{\partial u}{\partial y} \cos\beta + \frac{\partial u}{\partial z} \cos\gamma \tag{2}$$

The expression on the right is the derivative of the function $u(x, y, z)$ along the vector $\boldsymbol{S}$. Hence, we can write

$$\operatorname{grad} u \cdot \boldsymbol{S}^0 = \frac{\partial u}{\partial s}$$

If we designate the angle between the vectors $\operatorname{grad} u$ and $\boldsymbol{S}^0$ by φ (Fig. 180), we can write

$$|\operatorname{grad} u| \cos\varphi = \frac{\partial u}{\partial s} \tag{3}$$

or

$$\text{projection } \boldsymbol{S}^0 \operatorname{grad} u = \frac{\partial u}{\partial s} \tag{4}$$

and the theorem is proved.

This theorem gives us a clear picture of the relationship between the gradient and the derivative, at a given point, along any direction. Referring to Fig. 181, construct the vector $\operatorname{grad} u$ at some point $M(x, y, z)$. Construct a sphere for which $\operatorname{grad} u$ is the diameter. Draw the vector S from M. Denote by P the point of intersection of S with the surface of the sphere. It is then obvious that $MP = |\operatorname{grad} u| \cos \varphi$, if φ is the angle between the directions of the gradient and the segment MP $\left(\text{here, } \varphi < \frac{\pi}{2}\right)$, or $MP = \frac{\partial u}{\partial s}$. Obviously, when the direction of the vector S is reversed, the derivative changes sign but its absolute value remains unchanged.

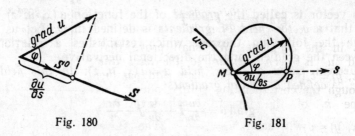

Fig. 180   Fig. 181

Let us establish certain properties of a gradient.

(1) *The derivative at a given point along the direction of the vector S has a maximum if the direction of S coincides with that of the gradient; this maximal value of the derivative is equal to* $|\operatorname{grad} u|$.

The truth of this assertion follows directly from (3): $\frac{\partial u}{\partial s}$ will be a maximum when $\varphi = 0$, and in this case

$$\frac{\partial u}{\partial s} = |\operatorname{grad} u|$$

(2) *The derivative along the direction of a vector that is perpendicular to the vector* $\operatorname{grad} u$ *is zero.*

This assertion follows from formula (3). Indeed, in this case,

$$\varphi = \frac{\pi}{2}, \quad \cos \varphi = 0 \text{ and } \frac{\partial u}{\partial s} = |\operatorname{grad} u| \cos \varphi = 0$$

Example 1. Given the function

$$u = x^2 + y^2 + z^2$$

(a) Determine the gradient at the point $M(1, 1, 1)$. The expression of the gradient of this function at an arbitrary point is

$$\operatorname{grad} u = 2x\boldsymbol{i} + 2y\boldsymbol{j} + 2z\boldsymbol{k}$$

Hence,

$$(\operatorname{grad} u)_M = 2\boldsymbol{i} + 2\boldsymbol{j} + 2\boldsymbol{k}, \; |\operatorname{grad} u|_M = 2\sqrt{3}$$

(b) Determine the derivative of the function u at the point $M(1, 1, 1)$ along the direction of the gradient. The direction cosines of the gradient are

$$\cos \alpha = \frac{2}{\sqrt{2^2 + 2^2 + 2^2}} = \frac{1}{\sqrt{3}}, \quad \cos \beta = \frac{1}{\sqrt{3}}, \quad \cos \gamma = \frac{1}{\sqrt{3}}.$$

And so

$$\frac{\partial u}{\partial s}=2\,\frac{1}{\sqrt{3}}+2\,\frac{1}{\sqrt{3}}+2\,\frac{1}{\sqrt{3}}=2\,\sqrt{3}$$

or

$$\frac{\partial u}{\partial s}=|\,\text{grad}\,u\,|$$

Note. If the function $u = u(x, y)$ is a function of two variables, then the vector

$$\text{grad}\,u = \frac{\partial u}{\partial x}\,i + \frac{\partial u}{\partial y}\,j$$

lies in the xy-plane. We shall prove that grad u is *perpendicular to the level line* $u(x, y) = c$ lying in the xy-plane and passing through the corresponding point. Indeed, the slope k_1 of the tangent to the level line $u(x, y) = c$ will equal $k_1 = -\frac{u'_x}{u'_y}$. The slope

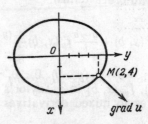

Fig. 182

k_2 of the gradient is $k_2 = \frac{u'_y}{u'_x}$. Obviously, $k_1 k_2 = -1$. This proves our assertion (Fig. 182). A similar property of the gradient of a function of three variables will be established in Sec. 9.6.

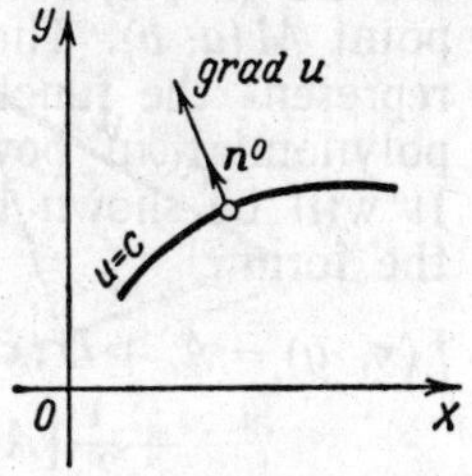

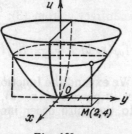

Fig. 183

Fig. 184

Example 2. Determine the gradient of the function $u = \frac{x^2}{2}+\frac{y^2}{3}$ (Fig. 183) at the point $M(2, 4)$.
Solution. Here

$$\frac{\partial u}{\partial x}=x\,\Big|_M=2,\ \ \frac{\partial u}{\partial y}=\frac{2}{3}\,y\,\Big|_M=\frac{8}{3}$$

Hence

$$\text{grad}\,u = 2i + \frac{8}{3}\,j$$

The equation of the level line (Fig. 184) passing through the given point is

$$\frac{x^2}{2}+\frac{y^2}{3}=\frac{22}{3}$$

8.16 TAYLOR'S FORMULA FOR A FUNCTION
OF TWO VARIABLES

Suppose we have a function of two variables

$$z = f(x, y)$$

which is continuous, together with all its partial derivatives up to the $(n+1)$th order inclusive, in some neighbourhood of the point $M(a, b)$. Then, like in the case of one variable (see Sec. 4.6) represent the function of two variables as a sum of an nth degree polynomial in powers of $(x-a)$ and $(y-b)$ and some remainder. It will be shown below that for the case of $n=2$ this formula has the form

$$f(x, y) = A_0 + D(x-a) + E(y-b)$$
$$+ \frac{1}{2!}[A(x-a)^2 + 2B(x-a)(y-b) + C(y-b)^2] + R_2 \quad (1)$$

where the coefficients A_0, D, E, A, B, C are independent of x and y, and R_2 is the remainder, the structure of which is similar to the structure of the remainder in the Taylor formula for a function of one variable.

Let us apply the Taylor formula for a function $f(x, y)$ of the variable y and assuming x to be constant (we shall confine ourselves to second-order terms):

$$f(x, y) =$$
$$= f(x, b) + \frac{y-b}{1} f'_y(x, b) + \frac{(y-b)^2}{1 \cdot 2} f''_{yy}(x, b) + \frac{(y-b)^3}{1 \cdot 2 \cdot 3} f'''_{yyy}(x, \eta_1) \quad (2)$$

where $\eta_1 = b + \theta_1(y-b)$, $0 < \theta_1 < 1$. We expand the functions $f(x, b)$, $f'_y(x, b)$, $f''_{yy}(x, b)$ in a Taylor's series in powers of $(x-a)$, confining ourselves to mixed derivatives up to the third order inclusive:

$$f(x, b)$$
$$= f(a, b) + \frac{x-a}{1} f'_x(a, b) + \frac{(x-a)^2}{1 \cdot 2} f''_{xx}(a, b) + \frac{(x-a)^3}{1 \cdot 2 \cdot 3} f'''_{xxx}(\xi_1, b) \quad (3)$$

where $\xi_1 = x + \theta_2(x-a)$, $0 < \theta_2 < 1$;

$$f'_y(x, b) = f'_y(a, b) + \frac{x-a}{1} f''_{yx}(a, b) + \frac{(x-a)^2}{1 \cdot 2} f'''_{yxx}(\xi_2, b). \quad (4)$$

where $\xi_2 = x + \theta_3(x-a)$, $0 < \theta_3 < 1$;

$$f''_{yy}(x, b) = f''_{yy}(a, b) + \frac{x-a}{1} f'''_{yyx}(\xi_3, b) \quad (5)$$

where $\xi_3 = x + \theta_4(x-a)$, $0 < \theta_4 < 1$.

Substituting expressions (3), (4) and (5) into formula (2), we get

$$f(x, y) = f(a, b) + \frac{x-a}{1} f'_x (a, b) + \frac{(x-a)^2}{1 \cdot 2} f''_{xx} (a, b)$$

$$+ \frac{(x-a)^3}{1 \cdot 2 \cdot 3} f'''_{xxx} (\xi_1, b) + \frac{y-b}{1} \left[f'_y (a, b) + \frac{x-a}{1} f''_{yx} (a, b) \right.$$

$$\left. + \frac{(x-a)^2}{1 \cdot 2} f'''_{yxx} (\xi_2, b) \right] + \frac{(y-b)^2}{1 \cdot 2} \left[f''_{yy} (a, b) + \frac{x-a}{1} f'''_{yyx} (\xi_3, b) \right]$$

$$+ \frac{(y-b)^3}{1 \cdot 2 \cdot 3} f'''_{yyy} (x, \eta_1)$$

Arranging the numbers as indicated in formula (1), we get

$$f(x, y) = f(a, b) + (x-a) f'_x (a, b) + (y-b) f'_y (a, b)$$

$$+ \frac{1}{2!} [(x-a)^2 f''_{xx} (a, b) + 2 (x-a) (y-b) f''_{xy} (a, b)$$

$$+ (y-b)^2 f''_{yy} (a, b)] + \frac{1}{3!} [(x-a)^3 f'''_{xxx} (\xi_1, b)$$

$$+ 3 (x-a)^2 (y-b) f'''_{xxy} (\xi_2, b) + 3 (x-a) (y-b)^2 f'''_{xyy} (\xi_3, b)$$

$$+ (y-b)^3 f'''_{yyy} (a, \eta_1)] \qquad (6)$$

This is *Taylor's formula for* $n = 2$. The expression

$$R_2 = \frac{1}{3!} [(x-a)^3 f'''_{xxx} (\xi_1, b) + 3 (x-a)^2 (y-b) f'''_{xxy} (\xi_2, b)$$

$$+ 3 (x-a) (y-b)^2 f'''_{xyy} (\xi_3, b) + (y-b)^3 f'''_{yyy} (a, \eta_1)]$$

is called the *remainder*. Further, let us denote $x - a = \Delta x, y - b = \Delta y$, $\Delta \rho = \sqrt{(\Delta x)^2 + (\Delta y)^2}$. Transform R_2:

$$R_2 = \frac{1}{3!} \left[\frac{\Delta x^3}{\Delta \rho^3} f'''_{xxx} (\xi_1, b) + 3 \frac{\Delta x^2 \Delta y}{\Delta \rho^3} f'''_{xxy} (\xi_2, b) \right.$$

$$\left. + 3 \frac{\Delta x \Delta y^2}{\Delta \rho^3} f'''_{xyy} (\xi_3, b) + \frac{\Delta y^3}{\Delta \rho^3} f'''_{yyy} (a, \eta_1) \right] \Delta \rho^3$$

Since $|\Delta x| < \Delta \rho$, $|\Delta y| < \Delta \rho$ and the third derivatives are bounded (this is given), the coefficient of $\Delta \rho^3$ is bounded in the domain under consideration; let us denote it by α_0.

Then we can write

$$R_2 = \alpha_0 \Delta \rho^3$$

In this notation, Taylor's formula (6) will, for the case $n = 2$, take the form

$$f(x, y) = f(a, b) + \Delta x f'_x (a, b) + \Delta y f'_y (a, b)$$

$$+ \frac{1}{2!} [\Delta x^2 f''_{xx} (a, b) + 2 \Delta x \Delta y f''_{xy} (a, b) + \Delta y^2 f''_{yy} (a, b)] + \alpha_0 \Delta \rho^3 \qquad (6')$$

Taylor's formula is of a similar form for arbitrary n.

8.17 MAXIMUM AND MINIMUM OF A FUNCTION OF SEVERAL VARIABLES

Definition 1. We say that a function $z = f(x, y)$ has a *maximum* at a point $M_0(x_0, y_0)$ (that is, when $x = x_0$ and $y = y_0$) if

$$f(x_0, y_0) > f(x, y)$$

for all points (x, y) sufficiently close to the point (x_0, y_0) and different from it.

Definition 2. Quite analogously we say that a function $z = f(x, y)$ has a *minimum* at a point $M_0(x_0, y_0)$ if

$$f(x_0, y_0) < f(x, y)$$

for all points (x, y) sufficiently close to the point (x_0, y_0) and different from it.

The maximum and minimum of a function are called *extrema* of the function; we say that a function has an extremum at a given point if it has a maximum or minimum at the given point.

Example 1. The function

$$z = (x-1)^2 + (y-2)^2 - 1$$

attains a minimum at $x = 1$, $y = 2$; i.e., at the point $(1, 2)$. Indeed, $f(1, 2) = -1$, and since $(x-1)^2$ and $(y-2)^2$ are always positive for $x \neq 1$, $y \neq 2$, it follows that

$$(x-1)^2 + (y-2)^2 - 1 > -1$$

that is,

$$f(x, y) > f(1, 2)$$

The geometric analogy of this case is shown in Fig. 185.

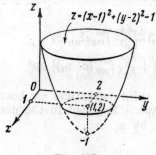

Fig. 185

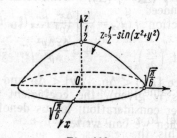

Fig. 186

Example 2. The function

$$z = \frac{1}{2} - \sin(x^2 + y^2)$$

for $x = 0$, $y = 0$ (coordinate origin) attains a maximum (Fig. 186).
Indeed,

$$f(0, 0) = \frac{1}{2}$$

Inside the circle $x^2 + y^2 = \dfrac{\pi}{6}$ take a point (x, y) different from the point $(0, 0)$. Then for $0 < x^2 + y^2 < \dfrac{\pi}{6}$,

$$\sin (x^2 + y^2) > 0$$

and therefore

$$f(x, y) = \frac{1}{2} - \sin (x^2 + y^2) < \frac{1}{2}$$

or

$$f(x, y) < f(0, 0)$$

The definition, given above, of the maximum and minimum of a function may be rephrased as follows.

Let $x = x_0 + \Delta x$, $y = y_0 + \Delta y$, then

$$f(x, y) - f(x_0, y_0) = f(x_0 + \Delta x, y_0 + \Delta y) - f(x_0, y_0) = \Delta f$$

(1) If $\Delta f < 0$ for all sufficiently small increments in the independent variables, then the function $f(x, y)$ reaches a *maximum* at the point $M(x_0, y_0)$.

(2) If $\Delta f > 0$ for all sufficiently small increments in the independent variables, then the function $f(x, y)$ reaches a *minimum* at the point $M(x_0, y_0)$.

These formulations may be extended, without any change, to functions of any number of variables.

Theorem 1. (Necessary Conditions for an Extremum). *If a function $z = f(x, y)$ attains an extremum at $x = x_0$, $y = y_0$ then each first partial derivative with respect to z either vanishes for these values of the arguments or does not exist.*

Indeed, give the variable y a definite value $y = y_0$. Then the function $f(x, y_0)$ will be a function of one variable, x. Since at $x = x_0$ it has an extremum (maximum or minimum), it follows that $\left(\dfrac{\partial z}{\partial x}\right)_{\substack{x = x_0 \\ y = y_0}}$ is either equal to zero or does not exist. In exactly the same fashion it is possible to prove that $\left(\dfrac{\partial z}{\partial y}\right)_{\substack{x = x_0 \\ y = y_0}}$ is either equal to zero or does not exist.

This theorem is not sufficient for investigating the extremal values of a function, but permits finding these values for cases in which we are sure of the existence of a maximum or minimum. Otherwise, more investigation is required.

For instance, the function $z = x^2 - y^2$ has derivatives $\dfrac{\partial z}{\partial x} = + 2x$, $\dfrac{\partial z}{\partial y} = -2y$, which vanish at $x = 0$ and $y = 0$. But for the given values, this function has neither maximum nor minimum. It is equal to zero at the origin and takes on both positive and negative values at points arbitrarily close to the origin. Hence, the value zero is neither a maximum nor a minimum (Fig. 187).

Points at which $\dfrac{\partial z}{\partial x} = 0$ (or does not exist) and $\dfrac{\partial z}{\partial y} = 0$ (or does not exist) are called *critical* points of the function $z = f(x, y)$. If a function reaches an extremum at some point, then (by virtue of Theorem 1) this can occur only at a critical point.

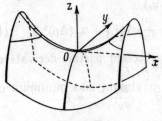

For investigation of a function at critical points, let us establish sufficient conditions for the extremum of a function of two variables.

Theorem 2. *Let a function $f(x, y)$ have continuous partial derivatives up to order three inclusive in a certain domain containing the point $M_0(x_0, y_0)$;*

Fig. 187

in addition, let the point $M_0(x_0, y_0)$ be a critical point of the function $f(x, y)$; that is,

$$\frac{\partial f(x_0, y_0)}{\partial x} = 0, \qquad \frac{\partial f(x_0, y_0)}{\partial y} = 0$$

Then for $x = x_0$, $y = y_0$:
(1) $f(x, y)$ has a maximum if

$$\frac{\partial^2 f(x_0, y_0)}{\partial x^2} \cdot \frac{\partial^2 f(x_0, y_0)}{\partial y^2} - \left(\frac{\partial^2 f(x_0, y_0)}{\partial x \, \partial y}\right)^2 > 0 \text{ and } \frac{\partial^2 f(x_0, y_0)}{\partial x^2} < 0$$

(2) $f(x, y)$ has a minimum if

$$\frac{\partial^2 f(x_0, y_0)}{\partial x^2} \cdot \frac{\partial^2 f(x_0, y_0)}{\partial y^2} - \left(\frac{\partial^2 f(x_0, y_0)}{\partial x \, \partial y}\right)^2 > 0 \text{ and } \frac{\partial^2 f(x_0, y_0)}{\partial x^2} > 0$$

(3) $f(x, y)$ has neither maximum nor minimum if

$$\frac{\partial^2 f(x_0, y_0)}{\partial x^2} \cdot \frac{\partial^2 f(x_0, y_0)}{\partial y^2} - \left(\frac{\partial^2 f(x_0, y_0)}{\partial x \, \partial y}\right)^2 < 0$$

(4) if $\dfrac{\partial^2 f(x_0, y_0)}{\partial x^2} \cdot \dfrac{\partial^2 f(x_0, y_0)}{\partial y^2} - \left(\dfrac{\partial^2 f(x_0, y_0)}{\partial x \, \partial y}\right)^2 = 0$, then there may

or may not be an extremum (in this case, an additional investigation is required).

Proof. Let us write the second-order Taylor formula for the function $f(x, y)$ [Formula (6), Sec. 8.16]. Assuming

$$a = x_0, \ b = y_0, \ x = x_0 + \Delta x, \ y = y_0 + \Delta y,$$

we will have

$$f(x_0 + \Delta x, \ y_0 + \Delta y) = f(x_0, y_0) + \frac{\partial f(x_0, y_0)}{\partial x} \Delta x + \frac{\partial f(x_0, y_0)}{\partial y} \Delta y +$$

$$+ \frac{1}{2} \left[\frac{\partial^2 f(x_0, y_0)}{\partial x^2} \Delta x^2 + 2 \frac{\partial^2 f(x_0, y_0)}{\partial x \, \partial y} \Delta x \, \Delta y + \frac{\partial^2 f(x_0, y_0)}{\partial y^2} \Delta y^2 \right] + \alpha_0 (\Delta \rho)^3$$

where $\Delta \rho = \sqrt{\Delta x^2 + \Delta y^2}$ and α_0 approaches zero as $\Delta \rho \to 0$.

It is given that

$$\frac{\partial f (x_0, y_0)}{\partial x} = 0, \quad \frac{\partial f (x_0, y_0)}{\partial y} = 0$$

Hence

$$\Delta f = f (x_0 + \Delta x, y_0 + \Delta y) - f (x_0, y_0)$$

$$= \frac{1}{2!} \left[\frac{\partial^2 f}{\partial x^2} \Delta x^2 + 2 \frac{\partial^2 f}{\partial x \partial y} \Delta x \Delta y + \frac{\partial^2 f}{\partial y^2} \Delta y^2 \right] + \alpha_0 (\Delta \rho)^3 \quad (1)$$

Let us now denote the values of the second partial derivatives at the point $M_0 (x_0, y_0)$ in terms of A, B, C:

$$\left(\frac{\partial^2 f}{\partial x^2} \right)_{M_0} = A, \quad \left(\frac{\partial^2 f}{\partial x \partial y} \right)_{M_0} = B, \quad \left(\frac{\partial^2 f}{\partial y^2} \right)_{M_0} = C$$

Denote by φ the angle between the direction of the segment $M_0 M$, where M is the point $M (x_0 + \Delta x, y_0 + \Delta y)$, and the x-axis; then

$$\Delta x = \Delta \rho \cos \varphi, \quad \Delta y = \Delta \rho \sin \varphi$$

Substituting these expressions into the formula for Δf, we find

$$\Delta f = \frac{1}{2} (\Delta \rho)^2 [A \cos^2 \varphi + 2B \cos \varphi \sin \varphi + C \sin^2 \varphi + 2\alpha_0 \Delta \rho] \quad (2)$$

Suppose that $A \neq 0$.

Dividing and multiplying by A the expression in the brackets, we have

$$\Delta f = \frac{1}{2} (\Delta \rho)^2 \left[\frac{(A \cos \varphi + B \sin \varphi)^2 + (AC - B^2) \sin^2 \varphi}{A} + 2\alpha_0 \Delta \rho \right] \quad (3)$$

Let us now consider four possible cases.

(1) Let $AC - B^2 > 0$, $A < 0$. Then in the numerator of the fraction we have a sum of two nonnegative quantities. They do not vanish simultaneously because the first term vanishes for $\tan \varphi = -\frac{A}{B}$, while the second vanishes for $\sin \varphi = 0$.

If $A < 0$, then the fraction is a negative quantity that does not vanish. Denote it by $-m^2$; then

$$\Delta f = \frac{1}{2} (\Delta \rho)^2 [-m^2 + 2\alpha_0 \Delta \rho]$$

where m is independent of $\Delta \rho$, $\alpha_0 \Delta \rho \rightarrow 0$ as $\Delta \rho \rightarrow 0$. Hence, for sufficiently small $\Delta \rho$ we have

$$\Delta f < 0$$

or

$$f (x_0 + \Delta x, y_0 + \Delta y) - f (x_0, y_0) < 0$$

But then for all points $(x_0 + \Delta x, y_0 + \Delta y)$ sufficiently close to the point (x_0, y_0) we have the inequality

$$f (x_0 + \Delta x, y_0 + \Delta y) < f (x_0, y_0)$$

which means that at the point (x_0, y_0) the function attains a **maximum**.

(2) Let $AC - B^2 > 0$, $A > 0$. Then, reasoning in the same way, we get

$$\Delta f = \frac{1}{2} (\Delta\rho)^2 [m^2 + 2\alpha_0 \Delta\rho]$$

or

$$f(x_0 + \Delta x, \; y_0 + \Delta y) > f(x_0, \; y_0)$$

that is, $f(x, y)$ has a **minimum** at the point (x_0, y_0).

(3′) Let $AC - B^2 < 0$, $A > 0$. In this case the function **has neither a maximum nor a minimum**. The function increases when we move from the point (x_0, y_0) in certain directions and decreases when we move in other directions. Indeed, when moving along the ray $\varphi = 0$, we have

$$\Delta f = \frac{1}{2} (\Delta\rho)^2 [A + 2\alpha_0 \Delta\rho] > 0$$

When moving along this ray the function increases. But if we move along a ray $\varphi = \varphi_0$ such that $\tan \varphi_0 = -\dfrac{A}{B}$, then for $A > 0$ we have

$$\Delta f = \frac{1}{2} (\Delta\rho)^2 \left[\frac{AC - B^2}{A} \sin^2 \varphi_0 + 2\alpha_0 \Delta\rho \right] < 0$$

When moving along this ray the function decreases.

(3″) Let $AC - B^2 < 0$, $A < 0$. Here the function again **has neither a maximum nor a minimum**. The investigation is conducted in the same way as for 3′.

(3‴) Let $AC - B^2 < 0$, $A = 0$. Then $B \neq 0$, and (2) may be rewritten as follows:

$$\Delta f = \frac{1}{2} (\Delta\rho)^2 [\sin \varphi (2B \cos \varphi + C \sin \varphi) + 2\alpha_0 \Delta\rho]$$

For sufficiently small values of φ the expression in the parentheses retains its sign, since it is close to $2B$, while the factor $\sin \varphi$ changes sign depending on whether φ is greater or less than zero (after the choice of $\varphi > 0$ and $\varphi < 0$ we can take ρ so small that $2\alpha_0$ will not change the sign of the whole square bracket). Consequently, in this case, too, Δf changes sign for different φ, that is, for different Δx and Δy; hence, in this case too there is neither a maximum nor a minimum.

Thus, no matter what the sign of A we always have the following situation:

If $AC - B^2 < 0$ at the point (x_0, y_0), then the function has neither a maximum nor a minimum at this point. In this case, the surface, which serves as a graph of the function, can, near this point, have, say, the shape of a saddle (see Fig. 187). The function at this point is said to have a *minimax*.

(4) Let $AC - B^2 = 0$. In this case, by formulas (2) and (3), it is impossible to decide about the sign of Δf. For instance, when $A \neq 0$ we will have

$$\Delta f = \frac{1}{2}(\Delta\rho)^2 \left[\frac{(A\cos\varphi + B\sin\varphi)^2}{A} + 2\alpha_0\Delta\rho\right]$$

When $\varphi = \arctan\left(-\dfrac{A}{B}\right)$, the sign of Δf is determined by the sign of $2\alpha_0$; here, a **special additional investigation is required** (for example, with the aid of a higher-order Taylor formula or in some other way). Thus, Theorem 2 is fully proved.

Example 3. Test the following function for maximum and minimum:

$$z = x^2 - xy + y^2 + 3x - 2y + 1$$

Solution. (1) Find the critical points

$$\frac{\partial z}{\partial x} = 2x - y + 3, \quad \frac{\partial z}{\partial y} = -x + 2y - 2$$

Solving the system of equations

$$\left.\begin{array}{r} 2x - y + 3 = 0 \\ -x + 2y - 2 = 0 \end{array}\right\}$$

we get

$$x = -\frac{4}{3}, \quad y = \frac{1}{3}$$

(2) Find the second-order derivatives at the critical point $\left(-\dfrac{4}{3}, \dfrac{1}{3}\right)$ and determine the character of the critical point:

$$A = \frac{\partial^2 z}{\partial x^2} = 2, \quad B = \frac{\partial^2 z}{\partial x\,\partial y} = -1, \quad C = \frac{\partial^2 z}{\partial y^2} = 2$$

$$AC - B^2 = 2 \cdot 2 - (-1)^2 = 3 > 0$$

Thus, at the point $\left(-\dfrac{4}{3}, \dfrac{1}{3}\right)$ the given function has a minimum, namely

$$z_{\min} = -\frac{4}{3}$$

Example 4. Test for maximum and minimum the function $z = x^3 + y^3 - 3xy$.

Solution. (1) Find the critical points using the necessary conditions of an extremum:

$$\left.\begin{array}{l} \dfrac{\partial z}{\partial x} = 3x^2 - 3y = 0 \\[2mm] \dfrac{\partial z}{\partial y} = 3y^2 - 3x = 0 \end{array}\right\}$$

Whence we get two critical points:

$$x_1 = 1, \; y_1 = 1 \text{ and } x_2 = 0, \; y_2 = 0$$

(2) Find the second-order derivatives:

$$\frac{\partial^2 z}{\partial x^2} = 6x, \quad \frac{\partial^2 z}{\partial x\, \partial y} = -3, \quad \frac{\partial^2 z}{\partial y^2} = 6y$$

(3) Investigate the character of the first critical point:

$$A = \left(\frac{\partial^2 z}{\partial x^2}\right)_{\substack{x=1 \\ y=1}} = 6, \quad B = \left(\frac{\partial^2 z}{\partial x\, \partial y}\right)_{\substack{x=1 \\ y=1}} = -3, \quad C = \left(\frac{\partial^2 z}{\partial y^2}\right)_{\substack{x=1 \\ y=1}} = 6$$

$$AC - B^2 = 36 - 9 = 27 > 0, \quad A > 0$$

Hence, at the point (1, 1) the given function has a minimum, namely:

$$z_{min} = -1$$

(4) Investigate the character of the second critical point M_2 (0, 0):

$$A = 0, \quad B = -3, \quad C = 0, \quad AC - B^2 = -9 < 0$$

Hence, at the second critical point the function has neither a maximum nor a minimum (mirimax).

Example 5. Decompose a given positive number a into three positive terms so that their product is a maximum.

Solution. Denote the first term by x, the second by y; then the third will be $a - x - y$. The product of these terms is

$$u = x \cdot y \, (a - x - y)$$

It is given that $x > 0$, $y > 0$, $a - x - y > 0$, that is, $x + y < a$, $u > 0$. Hence, x and y can assume values in the domain bounded by the straight lines $x = 0$, $y = 0$, $x + y = a$.

Find the partial derivatives of the function u:

$$\frac{\partial u}{\partial x} = y \, (a - 2x - y)$$

$$\frac{\partial u}{\partial y} = x \, (a - 2y - x)$$

Equating the derivatives to zero, we get a system of equations:

$$y \, (a - 2x - y) = 0, \quad x \, (a - 2y - x) = 0$$

Solving this system, we get the critical points:

$$x_1 = 0, \quad y_1 = 0, \quad M_1\,(0,\,0)$$
$$x_2 = 0, \quad y_2 = a, \quad M_2\,(0,\,a)$$
$$x_3 = a, \quad y_3 = 0, \quad M_3\,(a,\,0)$$
$$x_4 = \frac{a}{3}, \quad y_4 = \frac{a}{3}, \quad M_4\left(\frac{a}{3},\,\frac{a}{3}\right)$$

The first three points lie on the boundary of the region, the last one, inside. On the boundary of the region, the function u is equal to zero, while inside it is positive; consequently, at the point $\left(\frac{a}{3},\, \frac{a}{3}\right)$, the function u has a maximum (since it is the only extremal point inside the triangle). The maximum value of the product

$$u_{max} = \frac{a}{3}\,\frac{a}{3}\left(a - \frac{a}{3} - \frac{a}{3}\right) = \frac{a^3}{27}$$

Investigate the character of the critical points using the sufficiency conditions. Find the second partial derivatives of the function u:

$$\frac{\partial^2 u}{\partial x^2} = -2y, \quad \frac{\partial^2 u}{\partial x\,\partial y} = a - 2x - 2y, \quad \frac{\partial^2 u}{\partial y^2} = -2x$$

At the point $M_1(0,0)$ we have $A = \frac{\partial^2 u}{\partial x^2} = 0$, $B = \frac{\partial^2 u}{\partial x\,\partial y} = a$, $C = \frac{\partial^2 u}{\partial y^2} = 0$, $AC - B^2 = -a^2 < 0$. Hence, at the point M_1 there is neither a maximum nor a minimum. At the point $M_2(0, a)$ we have $A = \frac{\partial^2 u}{\partial x^2} = -2a$, $B = \frac{\partial^2 u}{\partial x\,\partial y} = -a$, $C = \frac{\partial^2 u}{\partial y^2} = 0$, $AC - B^2 = -a^2 < 0$. Which means that at the point M_2 there is neither a maximum nor a minimum. At the point $M_3(a, 0)$ we have $A = 0$, $B = -a$, $C = -2a$, $AC - B^2 = -a^2 < 0$. At M_3 too there is neither a maximum nor a minimum. At the point $M_4\left(\frac{a}{3}, \frac{a}{3}\right)$ we have $A = -\frac{2a}{3}$, $B = -\frac{a}{3}$, $C = -\frac{2a}{3}$, $AC - B^2 = \frac{4a^2}{9} - \frac{a^2}{9} > 0$, $A < 0$. Hence, at M_4 we have a maximum.

Note. The theory of maxima and minima of a function of several variables serves as the basis for a method of obtaining formulas for representing functional relationships on the basis of experimental findings. This problem is examined in Sec. 8.19.

8.18 MAXIMUM AND MINIMUM OF A FUNCTION OF SEVERAL VARIABLES RELATED BY GIVEN EQUATIONS (CONDITIONAL MAXIMA AND MINIMA)

In many problems on maxima and minima, one has to find the extrema of a function of several variables that are not independent, but are related to one another by side conditions (for example, they must satisfy given equations).

By way of illustration let us consider the following problem. Using a piece of tin $2a$ in area it is required to build a closed box in the form of a parallelepiped of maximum volume.

Denote the length, width and height of the box by x, y, and z. The problem reduces to finding the maximum of the function

$$v = xyz$$

provided that $2xy + 2xz + 2yz = 2a$. The problem here deals with a *conditional extremum*: the variables x, y, z are **restricted by the condition** that $2xy + 2xz + 2yz = 2a$. In this section we shall consider methods of solving such problems.

Let us first consider the question of the conditional extremum of a function of two variables if these variables are restricted by a **single** condition.

Let it be required to find the maxima and minima of the function

$$u = f(x, y) \tag{1}$$

with the proviso that x and y are connected by the equation

$$\varphi(x, y) = 0 \tag{2}$$

Given condition (2), of the two variables x and y there will be only **one** which **is independent** (for instance, x) since y is defined from (2) as a function of x. If we solved equation (2) for y and put into (1) the expression found in place of y, we would obtain a function of **one** variable, x, and would reduce the problem to one that would involve testing for maximum and minimum a function of one independent variable, x.

But the problem may be solved without solving equation (2) for x or y. For those values of x at which the function u can have a maximum or minimum, the derivative of u with respect to x should vanish.

From (1) we find $\frac{du}{dx}$, remembering that y is a function of x:

$$\frac{du}{dx} = \frac{\partial f}{\partial x} + \frac{\partial f}{\partial y}\frac{dy}{dx}$$

Hence, at the points of the extremum

$$\frac{\partial f}{\partial x} + \frac{\partial f}{\partial y}\frac{dy}{dx} = 0 \tag{3}$$

From equation (2) we find

$$\frac{\partial \varphi}{\partial x} + \frac{\partial \varphi}{\partial y}\frac{dy}{dx} = 0 \tag{4}$$

This equation is satisfied for all x and y that satisfy equation (2) (see Sec. 8.11).

Multiplying the terms of (4) by an (as yet) undetermined coefficient λ and adding them to the corresponding terms of (3), we have

$$\left(\frac{\partial f}{\partial x} + \frac{\partial f}{\partial y}\frac{\partial y}{\partial x}\right) + \lambda\left(\frac{\partial \varphi}{\partial x} + \frac{\partial \varphi}{\partial y}\frac{\partial y}{\partial x}\right) = 0$$

or

$$\left(\frac{\partial f}{\partial x} + \lambda\frac{\partial \varphi}{\partial x}\right) + \left(\frac{\partial f}{\partial y} + \lambda\frac{\partial \varphi}{\partial y}\right)\frac{dy}{dx} = 0 \tag{5}$$

The latter equation is fulfilled at all extremum points. Choose λ such that for the values of x and y which correspond to the extremum of the function u, the second parentheses in (5) should vanish: *

$$\frac{\partial f}{\partial y} + \lambda \frac{\partial \varphi}{\partial y} = 0$$

But then, for these values of x and y, from (5) we have

$$\frac{\partial f}{\partial x} + \lambda \frac{\partial \varphi}{\partial x} = 0$$

It thus turns out that at the extremum points three equations (in three unknowns x, y, λ) are satisfied:

$$\left. \begin{array}{c} \dfrac{\partial f}{\partial x} + \lambda \dfrac{\partial \varphi}{\partial x} = 0 \\[2mm] \dfrac{\partial f}{\partial y} + \lambda \dfrac{\partial \varphi}{\partial y} = 0 \\[2mm] \varphi(x, y) = 0 \end{array} \right\} \qquad (6)$$

From these equations determine x, y, and λ; the latter only played an auxiliary role and will not be needed any more.

From this conclusion it follows that equations (6) are *necessary conditions of a conditional extremum;* or equations (6) are satisfied at the extremum points. But there will not be a conditional extremum for every x and y (and λ) that satisfy equations (6). A supplementary investigation of the nature of the critical point is required. In the solution of concrete problems it is sometimes possible to establish the character of the critical point from the statement of the problem. It will be noted that the left-hand sides of equations (6) are partial derivatives of the function

$$F(x, y, \lambda) = f(x, y) + \lambda \varphi(x, y) \qquad (7)$$

with respect to the variables x, y and λ.

Thus, in order to find the values of x and y which satisfy condition (2), for which the function $u = f(x, y)$ can have a conditional maximum or a conditional minimum, one has to construct an auxiliary function, (7), equate to zero its derivatives with respect to x, y, and λ, and from the three equations (6) thus obtained determine the sought-for x, y (and the auxiliary factor λ). The foregoing method can be extended to a study of the conditional extremum of a function of any number of variables.

Let it be required to find the maxima and minima of a function of n variables, $u = f(x_1, x_2, \ldots, x_n)$, provided that the variables

---

* For the sake of definiteness, we shall assume that at the critical points

$$\frac{\partial \varphi}{\partial y} \neq 0$$

x_1, x_2, ..., x_n are connected by $m\,(m < n)$ equations:

$$\left.\begin{array}{l} \varphi_1\,(x_1,\ x_2,\ \ldots,\ x_n) = 0 \\ \varphi_2\,(x_1,\ x_2,\ \ldots,\ x_n) = 0 \\ \cdots\cdots\cdots\cdots\cdots \\ \varphi_m\,(x_1,\ x_2,\ \ldots,\ x_n) = 0 \end{array}\right\} \tag{8}$$

In order to find the values of x_1, x_2, ..., x_n, for which there may be conditional maxima and minima, one has to form the function

$$F\,(x_1,\ x_2,\ \ldots,\ x_n,\ \lambda_1,\ \ldots,\ \lambda_m) = f\,(x_1,\ \ldots,\ x_n) + \lambda_1\varphi_1\,(x_1,\ \ldots,\ x_n)$$
$$+ \lambda_2\varphi_2\,(x_1,\ \ldots,\ x_n) + \ldots + \lambda_m\varphi_m\,(x_1,\ \ldots,\ x_n)$$

equate to zero its partial derivatives with respect to $x_1, x_2, \ldots, x_n$:

$$\left.\begin{array}{l} \dfrac{\partial f}{\partial x_1} + \lambda_1\,\dfrac{\partial \varphi_1}{\partial x_1} + \ldots + \lambda_m\,\dfrac{\partial \varphi_m}{\partial x_1} = 0 \\[2mm] \dfrac{\partial f}{\partial x_2} + \lambda_1\,\dfrac{\partial \varphi_1}{\partial x_2} + \ldots + \lambda_m\,\dfrac{\partial \varphi_m}{\partial x_2} = 0 \\[2mm] \cdots\cdots\cdots\cdots\cdots\cdots\cdots \\[1mm] \dfrac{\partial f}{\partial x_n} + \lambda_1\,\dfrac{\partial \varphi_1}{\partial x_n} + \ldots + \lambda_m\,\dfrac{\partial \varphi_m}{\partial x_n} = 0 \end{array}\right\} \tag{9}$$

and from the $m + n$ equations (8) and (9) determine x_1, x_2, ..., x_n and the auxiliary unknowns λ_1, ..., λ_m. Just as in the case of a function of two variables, we shall, in the general case, leave undecided the question of whether the function, for the values found, has a maximum or a minimum or has neither. We will decide this matter on the basis of additional reasoning.

Example 1. Let us return to the problem formulated at the beginning of this section: to find the maximum of the function

$$v = xyz$$

provided that

$$xy + xz + yz - a = 0 \quad (x > 0,\ y > 0,\ z > 0) \tag{10}$$

We form the auxiliary function

$$F\,(x,\ y,\ \lambda) = xyz + \lambda\,(xy + xz + yz - a)$$

We find its partial derivatives and equate them to zero:

$$\left.\begin{array}{l} yz + \lambda\,(y + z) = 0 \\ xz + \lambda\,(x + z) = 0 \\ xy + \lambda\,(x + y) = 0 \end{array}\right\} \tag{11}$$

The problem reduces to solving a system of four equations (10) and (11) in four unknowns (x, y, z and λ). To solve this system, multiply the first of equations (11) by x, the second by y, the third by z, and add; taking (10) into account, we find that $\lambda = -\dfrac{3xyz}{2a}$. Putting this value of λ into equations

(11) we get

$$yz\left[1-\frac{3x}{2a}(y+z)\right]=0$$

$$xz\left[1-\frac{3y}{2a}(x+z)\right]=0$$

$$xy\left[1-\frac{3z}{2a}(x+y)\right]=0$$

Since it is evident from the statement of the problem that x, y, z are different from zero, we get from the latter equations

$$\frac{3x}{2a}(y+z)=1, \quad \frac{3y}{2a}(x+z)=1, \quad \frac{3z}{2a}(x+y)=1$$

From the first two equations we find $x=y$, from the second and third equations, $y=z$. But then from equation (10) we get $x=y=z=\sqrt{\dfrac{a}{3}}$. This is the only system of values of x, y and z, for which there can be a maximum or a minimum.

It can be proved that the solution obtained yields a maximum. Incidentally, this is also evident from geometrical reasoning (the statement of the problem indicates that the volume of the box cannot be big without bound; it is therefore natural to expect that for some definite values of the sides the volume will be a maximum).

Thus, for the volume of the box to be a maximum, the box must be a cube, an edge of which is equal to $\sqrt{\dfrac{a}{3}}$.

Example 2. Determine the maximum value of the nth root of a product of numbers x_1, x_2, ..., x_n provided that their sum is equal to a given number a. Thus, the problem is stated as follows: it is required to find the maximum of the function $u=\sqrt[n]{x_1 \ldots x_n}$ on the condition that

$$x_1+x_2+\ldots+x_n-a=0 \quad (x_1>0, \; x_2>0, \; \ldots, \; x_n>0) \qquad (12)$$

Form an auxiliary function:

$$F(x_1, \ldots, x_n, \lambda)=\sqrt[n]{x_1 \ldots x_n}+\lambda(x_1+x_2+\ldots+x_n-a)$$

Find its partial derivatives:

$$F'_{x_1}=\frac{1}{n}\frac{x_2 x_3 \ldots x_n}{(x_1 \ldots x_n)^{\frac{n-1}{n}}}+\lambda=\frac{1}{n}\frac{u}{x_1}+\lambda=0 \quad \text{or} \quad u=-n\lambda x_1$$

$$F'_{x_2}=\frac{1}{n}\frac{u}{x_2}+\lambda=0 \qquad\qquad\qquad \text{or} \quad u=-n\lambda x_2$$

$$\cdots\cdots\cdots\cdots\cdots\cdots\cdots\cdots\cdots\cdots\cdots$$

$$F'_{x_n}=\frac{1}{n}\frac{u}{x_n}+\lambda=0 \qquad\qquad\qquad \text{or} \quad u=-n\lambda x_n$$

From the foregoing equations we find

$$x_1=x_2=\ldots=x_n$$

and from equation (12) we have

$$x_1=x_2=\ldots=x_n=\frac{a}{n}$$

By the meaning of the problem these values yield a maximum of the function $\sqrt[n]{x_1 \ldots x_n}$ equal to $\dfrac{a}{n}$.

Thus, for any positive numbers x_1, x_2, ..., x_n connected by the relationship $x_1 + x_2 + \ldots + x_n = a$, the inequality

$$\sqrt[n]{x_1 \ldots x_n} \leqslant \frac{a}{n} \tag{13}$$

is fulfilled (since it has already been proved that $\dfrac{a}{n}$ is the maximum of this function). Now substituting into (13) the value of a obtained from (12), we get

$$\sqrt[n]{x_1 x_2 \ldots x_n} \leqslant \frac{x_1 + \ldots + x_n}{n} \tag{14}$$

This inequality holds for all positive numbers x_1, x_2, ..., x_n. The expression on the left-hand side of (14) is called the *geometric mean* of these numbers. Thus, the geometric mean of several positive numbers is not greater than their arithmetic mean.

8.19 OBTAINING A FUNCTION ON THE BASIS OF EXPERIMENTAL DATA BY THE METHOD OF LEAST SQUARES

Suppose that in an experiment it is required to establish a functional relationship between y and x:

$$y = \varphi(x) \tag{1}$$

The experiment, let us say, has yielded n values of the function y for corresponding values of the argument. The results are tabulated as follows:

x	x_1	x_2	...	x_n
y	y_1	y_2	...	y_n

The form of the function $x = \varphi(x)$ is obtained either from theoretical reasoning or on the basis of how the points corresponding to the experimentally found values (we will call them experimental points) are located on a coordinate plane. Let us suppose that the experimental points are located as shown in Fig. 188. Since experimental errors are almost inevitable, it is natural to suppose that the desired function $y = \varphi(x)$ may be sought in the form of a linear function $y = ax + b$.

If the experimental points are located as in Fig. 189, it is natural to seek the function $y = \varphi(x)$ in the form $y = ax^b$, and so forth.

For the chosen form of function $y = \varphi(x, a, b, c, \ldots)$ it remains to select the parameters $a, b, c, \ldots$ so that the function describes the process at hand in the best possible fashion.

A widely used method for solving this problem is the *method of least squares*. It consists in the following. We consider the sum

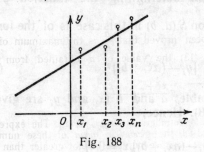

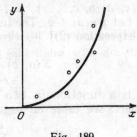

Fig. 188   Fig. 189

of the squares of the differences between the experimentally obtained values y_i and the function $\varphi(x, a, b, c, \ldots)$ at the appropriate points:

$$S(a, b, c, \ldots) = \sum_{i=1}^{n} [y_i - \varphi(x_i, a, b, c, \ldots)]^2 \qquad (2)$$

We choose the parameters $a, b, c, \ldots$ so that this sum is a minimum:

$$S(a, b, c, \ldots) = \sum_{i=1}^{n} [y_i - \varphi(x_i, a, b, c, \ldots)]^2 = \min \qquad (3)$$

The problem thus reduces to finding the values of the parameters $a, b, c, \ldots$ for which the function $S(a, b, c, \ldots)$ is a minimum.

From Theorem 1, Sec. 8.17, it follows that these values $a, b, c, \ldots$ satisfy the system of equations

$$\frac{\partial S}{\partial a} = 0, \quad \frac{\partial S}{\partial b} = 0, \quad \frac{\partial S}{\partial c} = 0, \ldots \qquad (4)$$

or, expanded,

$$\left. \begin{aligned}
\sum_{i=1}^{n} [y_i - \varphi(x_i, a, b, c, \ldots)] \frac{\partial \varphi(x_i, a, b, c, \ldots)}{\partial a} &= 0 \\
\sum_{i=1}^{n} [y_i - \varphi(x_i, a, b, c, \ldots)] \frac{\partial \varphi(x_i, a, b, c, \ldots)}{\partial b} &= 0 \\
\sum_{i=1}^{n} [y_i - \varphi(x_i, a, b, c, \ldots)] \frac{\partial \varphi(x_i, a, b, c, \ldots)}{\partial c} &= 0 \\
\ldots \ldots \ldots \ldots \ldots \ldots \ldots \ldots \ldots \ldots
\end{aligned} \right\} \qquad (5)$$

Here, the number of equations equals the number of unknowns. In each instance, an investigation is made of the existence of a solution to the system of equations (5) and of the existence of a minimum of the function $S(a, b, c, \ldots)$.

We consider some cases in determining the function $y = \varphi(x, a, b, c, \ldots)$.

I. Let $y = ax + b$. The function $S(a, b)$ in this case is of the form [see expression (2)]

$$S(a, b) = \sum_{i=1}^{n} [y_i - (ax_i + b)]^2 \tag{6}$$

This is a function in two variables a and b (x_i and y_i are given numbers; see table on page 298). Hence,

$$\left.\begin{array}{l} \dfrac{\partial S}{\partial a} = -2 \sum\limits_{i=1}^{n} [y_i - (ax_i + b)]\, x_i = 0 \\[2mm] \dfrac{\partial S}{\partial b} = -2 \sum\limits_{i=1}^{n} [y_i - (ax_i + b)] = 0 \end{array}\right\}$$

The system of equations (5) then becomes

$$\left.\begin{array}{l} \sum\limits_{i=1}^{n} y_i x_i - a \sum\limits_{i=1}^{n} x_i^2 - b \sum\limits_{i=1}^{n} x_i = 0 \\[2mm] \sum\limits_{i=1}^{n} y_i - a \sum\limits_{i=1}^{n} x_i - bn = 0 \end{array}\right\} \tag{7}$$

We have a system of two linear equations in two unknowns a and b. It is obvious that the system has a definite solution and that for the values a and b thus found the function $S(a, b)$ has a minimum.*

II. For the approximating function we take the quadratic trinomial

$$y = ax^2 + bx + c$$

---

* This is also readily established on the basis of sufficient conditions (see Theorem 2, Sec. 8.17). Indeed, here

$$\frac{\partial^2 S}{\partial a^2} = 2 \sum_{i=1}^{n} x_i^2, \quad \frac{\partial^2 S}{\partial a \partial b} = 2 \sum_{i=1}^{n} x_i, \quad \frac{\partial^2 S}{\partial b^2} = 2n$$

and so

$$\frac{\partial^2 S}{\partial a^2} \frac{\partial^2 S}{\partial b^2} - \left(\frac{\partial^2 S}{\partial a \partial b}\right)^2 = 4n \sum_{i=1}^{n} x_i^2 - \left(2 \sum_{i=1}^{n} x_i\right)^2 = 4 \sum_{\substack{i,\, j \\ i < j}} (x_i - x_j)^2 > 0, \quad \frac{\partial^2 S}{\partial a^2} > 0$$

Then expression (2) has the form

$$S(a, b, c) = \sum_{i=1}^{n} [y_i - (ax_i^2 + bx_i + c)]^2 \qquad (8)$$

This is a function of three variables a, b, c. The system of equations (5) assumes the form

$$\left. \begin{array}{l} \sum\limits_{i=1}^{n} [y_i - (ax_i^2 + bx_i + c)]x_i^2 = 0 \\[2mm] \sum\limits_{i=1}^{n} [y_i - (ax_i^2 + bx_i + c)]\, x_i = 0 \\[2mm] \sum\limits_{i=1}^{n} [y_i - (ax_i^2 + bx_i + c)] = 0 \end{array} \right\}$$

or, expanded,

$$\left. \begin{array}{l} \sum\limits_{i=1}^{n} y_i x_i^2 - a \sum\limits_{i=1}^{n} x_i^4 - b \sum\limits_{i=1}^{n} x_i^3 - c \sum\limits_{i=1}^{n} x_i^2 = 0 \\[2mm] \sum\limits_{i=1}^{n} y_i x_i - a \sum\limits_{i=1}^{n} x_i^3 - b \sum\limits_{i=1}^{n} x_i^2 - c \sum\limits_{i=1}^{n} x_i = 0 \\[2mm] \sum\limits_{i=1}^{n} y_i - a \sum\limits_{i=1}^{n} x_i^2 - b \sum\limits_{i=1}^{n} x_i - cn = 0 \end{array} \right\} \qquad (9)$$

We obtain a system of linear equations for determining the unknowns a, b, c. From the nature of the problem it follows that the system has a definite solution and that for the values a, b, c obtained, the function $S(a, b, c)$ is a **minimum**.

Example. Suppose an experiment yields four values of the desired function $y = \varphi(x)$ for four values of the argument ($n = 4$), which are tabulated as follows:

x	1	2	3	5
y	3	4	2.5	0.5

We seek the function φ in the form of a linear function $y = ax + b$, and set up the expression for $S(a, b)$:

$$S(a, b) = \sum_{i=1}^{4} [y_i - (ax_i + b)]^2$$

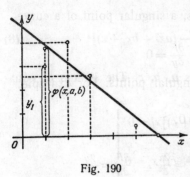

To set up system (7) in order to determine the coefficients a and b we first compute

$$\sum_{i=1}^{4} y_i x_i = 21, \qquad \sum_{i=1}^{4} x_i^2 = 39$$

$$\sum_{i=1}^{4} x_i = 11, \qquad \sum_{i=1}^{4} y_i = 10$$

System (2) has the form

$$\left.\begin{array}{c} 21 - 39a - 11b = 0 \\ 10 - 11a - 4b = 0 \end{array}\right\}$$

Fig. 190

Solving this system, we get a and b: $a = -26/35$, $b = 159/35$. The desired straight line (Fig. 190) is

$$y = -\frac{26}{35}x + \frac{159}{35}$$

8.20 SINGULAR POINTS OF A CURVE

The concept of a partial derivative is used in investigating curves.

Let a curve be given by the equation

$$F(x, y) = 0$$

The slope of the tangent to the curve is determined from the formula

$$\frac{dy}{dx} = -\frac{\dfrac{\partial F}{\partial x}}{\dfrac{\partial F}{\partial y}}$$

(see Sec. 8.11).

If at a given point $M(x, y)$ of the curve under consideration, at least one of the partial derivatives $\frac{\partial F}{\partial x}$ and $\frac{\partial F}{\partial y}$ does not vanish, then at this point either $\frac{\partial y}{\partial x}$ or $\frac{\partial x}{\partial y}$ is completely determined. The curve $F(x, y) = 0$ has a very definite tangent line at this point. In this case, the point $M(x, y)$ is called an *ordinary* point.

But if at some point $M_0(x_0, y_0)$ we have

$$\left(\frac{\partial F}{\partial x}\right)_{\substack{x=x_0 \\ y=y_0}} = 0 \quad \text{and} \quad \left(\frac{\partial F}{\partial y}\right)_{\substack{x=x_0 \\ y=y_0}} = 0$$

then the slope of the tangent becomes indeterminate.

Definition. If at the point $M_0(x_0, y_0)$ of the curve $F(x, y) = 0$, both partial derivatives $\frac{\partial F}{\partial x}$ and $\frac{\partial F}{\partial y}$ vanish, then such a point is called a *singular point* of the curve. Thus, a singular point of a curve is defined by the system of equations

$$F = 0, \quad \frac{\partial F}{\partial x} = 0, \quad \frac{\partial F}{\partial y} = 0$$

Naturally, not every curve has singular points. For example, for the ellipse

$$\frac{x^2}{a^2} + \frac{y^2}{b^2} - 1 = 0,$$

obviously,

$$F(x, \ y) = \frac{x^2}{a^2} + \frac{y^2}{b^2} - 1, \quad \frac{\partial F}{\partial x} = \frac{2x}{a^2}, \quad \frac{\partial F}{\partial y} = \frac{2y}{b^2}$$

the derivatives $\frac{\partial F}{\partial x}$ and $\frac{\partial F}{\partial y}$ vanish only when $x = 0$, $y = 0$, but these values of x and y do not satisfy the equation of the ellipse. Consequently, the ellipse does not have any singular points.

Without undertaking a detailed investigation of the behaviour of a curve near a singular point, let us examine some examples of curves that have singular points.

Example 1. Investigate the singular points of the curve

$$y^2 - x(x-a)^2 = 0 \ (a > 0)$$

Solution. Here, $F(x, \ y) = y^2 - x(x-a)^2$ and therefore

$$\frac{\partial F}{\partial x} = (x-a)(a-3x), \quad \frac{\partial F}{\partial y} = 2y$$

Solving the three equations simultaneously,

$$F(x, \ y) = 0, \quad \frac{\partial F}{\partial x} = 0, \quad \frac{\partial F}{\partial y} = 0$$

we find the only system of values of x and y that satisfies them:

$$x_0 = a, \quad y_0 = 0$$

Consequently, the point $M_0(a, 0)$ is a singular point of the curve.

Let us investigate the behaviour of the curve near the singular point and then construct the curve.

Rewrite the equation in the form

$$y = \pm(x-a)\sqrt{x}$$

From this formula it follows that the curve: (1) is defined only for $x \geqslant 0$; (2) is symmetrical about the x-axis; (3) cuts the x-axis at the points $(0, 0)$ and $(a, 0)$. The latter point is singular, as we have pointed out.

Let us first examine that part of the curve which corresponds to the plus sign:

$$y = (x-a)\sqrt{x}$$

Find the first and second derivatives of y with respect to x:

$$y' = \frac{3x-a}{2\sqrt{x}}, \quad y'' = \frac{3x+a}{4x\sqrt{x}}$$

For $x = 0$ we have $y' = \infty$. Thus, the curve touches the y-axis at the origin. For $x = \dfrac{a}{3}$ we have $y' = 0$, $y'' > 0$, which means that for $x = \dfrac{a}{3}$ the function y has a minimum:

$$y = -\frac{2a}{3} \sqrt{\frac{a}{3}}$$

On the interval $0 < x < a$ we have $y < 0$; for $x > \dfrac{a}{3}$ $y' > 0$; as $x \to \infty$ $y \to \infty$.

For $x = a$ we have $y' = \sqrt{a}$, which means that at the singular point $M_0 (a, 0)$ the branch of the curve $y = + (x - a) \sqrt{x}$ has a tangent

$$y = \sqrt{a}\,(x - a)$$

Since the second branch of the curve $y = - (x - a) \sqrt{x}$ is symmetrical with the first about the x-axis, the curve has also a second tangent (to the second branch) at the singular point

$$y = - \sqrt{a}\,(x - a)$$

The curve passes through the singular point twice. Such a point is called a *nodal point*.

The foregoing curve is shown in Fig. 191.

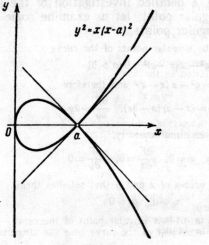

Fig. 191   Fig. 192

Example 2. Test for singular points the curve (semicubical parabola)

$$y^2 - x^3 = 0$$

Solution. The coordinates of the singular points are determined from the following set of equations:

$$y^2 - x^3 = 0, \quad 3x^2 = 0, \quad 2y = 0$$

Consequently, $M_0 (0, 0)$ is a singular point.

Let us rewrite the given equation as

$$y = \pm \sqrt{x^3}$$

To construct the curve let us first investigate the branch to which the plus sign in the equation corresponds, since the branch of the curve corresponding to the minus sign is symmetric with the first about the x-axis.

The function y is defined only for $x \geqslant 0$, it is nonnegative and increases as x increases.

Let us find the first and second derivatives of the function $y = \sqrt{x^3}$:

$$y' = \frac{3}{2} \sqrt{x}, \quad y'' = \frac{3}{4} \frac{1}{\sqrt{x}}$$

For $x = 0$ we have $y = 0$, $y' = 0$. And so the given branch of the curve has a tangent $y = 0$ at the origin. The second branch of the curve $y = -\sqrt{x^3}$ also passes through the origin and has the same tangent $y = 0$. Thus, two different branches of the curve meet at the origin, have the same tangent, and are situated on different sides of the tangent. This kind of singular point is called a *cusp of the first kind* (Fig. 192).

Note. The curve $y^2 - x^3 = 0$ may be regarded as a limiting case of the curve $y^2 = x(x-a)^2 = 0$ (considered in Example 1) as $a \to 0$; that is, when the loop of the curve is contracted into a point.

Example 3. Investigate the curve $(y - x^2)^2 - x^5 = 0$.

Solution. The coordinates of the singular points are defined by the following set of equations:

$$-4x(y - x^2) - 5x^4 = 0, \quad 2(y - x^2) = 0$$

which has only one solution: $x = 0$, $y = 0$. Hence, the origin is a singular point.

Rewrite the given equation in the form

$$y = x^2 \pm \sqrt{x^5}$$

From this equation it follows that x can take on values from 0 to $+\infty$.

Let us determine the first and second derivatives:

$$y' = 2x \pm \frac{5}{2} \sqrt{x^3}, \quad y'' = 2 \pm \frac{15}{4} \sqrt{x}$$

Investigate, separately, the branches of the curve corresponding to plus and minus. In both cases, when $x = 0$ we have $y = 0$, $y' = 0$, which means that for both branches the x-axis is a tangent.

Let us first consider the branch

$$y = x^2 + \sqrt{x^5}$$

As x increases from 0 to ∞, y increases from 0 to ∞.

The second branch

$$y = x^2 - \sqrt{x^5}$$

cuts the x-axis at the points $(0, 0)$ and $(1, 0)$.

For $x = \frac{16}{25}$ the function $y = x^2 - \sqrt{x^5}$ has a maximum. If $x \to +\infty$, then $y \to -\infty$.

Thus, in this case the two branches of the curve meet at the origin; both branches have the same tangent and are situated on the same side of the tangent near the point of tangency. This kind of singular point is called a *cusp of the second kind*. The graph of this function is shown in Fig. 193.

Example 4. Investigate the curve $y^2 - x^4 + x^6 = 0$.

Solution. The origin is a singular point. To investigate the curve near this point rewrite the equation of the curve in the form

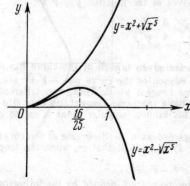

$$y = \pm x^2 \sqrt{1 - x^2}$$

Since the equation of the curve contains only even powers of the variables,

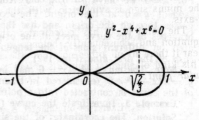

Fig. 193   Fig. 194

the curve is symmetric about the coordinate axes and, consequently, it is sufficient to investigate that part of the curve which corresponds to the positive values of x and y. From the latter equation it follows that x can vary over the interval from 0 to 1, that is, $0 \leqslant x \leqslant 1$.

Let us compute the first derivative for that branch of the curve which is a graph of the function $y = + x^2 \sqrt{1 - x^2}$:

$$y' = \frac{x(2 - 3x^2)}{\sqrt{1 - x^2}}$$

For $x = 0$ we have $y = 0$, $y' = 0$. Thus, the curve touches the x-axis at the origin.

For $x = 1$ we have $y = 0$, $y' = \infty$; consequently, at the point (1, 0) the tangent is parallel to the y-axis. For $x = \sqrt{\frac{2}{3}}$ the function has a maximum (Fig. 194).

At the origin (at the singular point) the two branches of the curve corresponding to plus and minus in front of the radical sign are mutually tangent. A singular point of this kind is called a *point of osculation* (also known as tacnode or double cusp).

Example 5. Investigate the curve

$$y^2 - x^2(x - 1) = 0$$

Solution. Let us write the system of equations defining the singular points:

$$y^2 - x^2(x - 1) = 0$$
$$-3x^2 + 2x = 0, \quad 2y = 0$$

This system has the solution $x = 0$, $y = 0$. Therefore, the point (0, 0) is a singular point of the curve. Let us rewrite the given equation in the form $y = \pm x \sqrt{x - 1}$. It is obvious that x can vary from 1 to $+\infty$ and also take the value 0 (in which case $y = 0$).

Let us investigate the branch of the curve corresponding to the plus sign in front of the radical. As x increases from 1 to ∞, y increases from 0 to ∞. The derivative

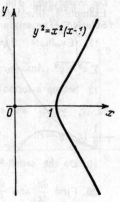

$$y' = \frac{3x-2}{2\sqrt{x-1}}$$

When $x=1$ we have $y'=\infty$; hence, at the point $(1, 0)$ the tangent is parallel to the y-axis.

The second branch of the curve corresponding to the minus sign is symmetric with the first about the x-axis.

The point $(0, 0)$ has coordinates that satisfy the equation and, consequently, belongs to the curve, but near it there are no other points of the curve (Fig. 195). This kind of singular point is called an *isolated singular point*.

Fig. 195

Exercises on Chapter 8

Find the partial derivatives of the following functions:

1. $z = x^2 \sin^2 y$. *Ans.* $\dfrac{\partial z}{\partial x} = 2x \sin^2 y$, $\dfrac{\partial z}{\partial y} = x^2 \sin 2y$.   **2.** $z = x^{y^2}$. *Ans.*

$\dfrac{\partial z}{\partial x} = y^2 x^{y^2-1}$, $\dfrac{\partial z}{\partial y} = x^{y^2} \cdot 2y \ln x$.   **3.** $u = e^{x^2+y^2+z^2}$. *Ans.* $\dfrac{\partial u}{\partial x} = 2xe^{x^2+y^2+z^2}$,

$\dfrac{\partial u}{\partial y} = 2ye^{x^2+y^2+z^2}$, $\dfrac{\partial u}{\partial z} = 2ze^{x^2+y^2+z^2}$.   **4.** $u = \sqrt{x^2+y^2+z^2}$. *Ans.* $\dfrac{\partial u}{\partial x} =$

$= \dfrac{x}{\sqrt{x^2+y^2+z^2}}$.   **5.** $z = \arctan(xy)$. *Ans.* $\dfrac{\partial z}{\partial x} = \dfrac{y}{1+x^2y^2}$, $\dfrac{\partial z}{\partial y} = \dfrac{x}{1+x^2y^2}$.

6. $z = \arctan \dfrac{y}{x}$. *Ans.* $\dfrac{\partial z}{\partial x} = \dfrac{-y}{x^2+y^2}$, $\dfrac{\partial z}{\partial y} = \dfrac{x}{x^2+y^2}$.   **7.** $z = \ln \dfrac{\sqrt{x^2+y^2}-x}{\sqrt{x^2+y^2}+x}$.

Ans. $\dfrac{\partial z}{\partial x} = -\dfrac{2}{\sqrt{x^2+y^2}}$, $\dfrac{\partial z}{\partial y} = \dfrac{2x}{y\sqrt{x^2+y^2}}$.   **8.** $u = e^{\frac{x}{y}} + e^{\frac{z}{y}}$. *Ans.* $\dfrac{\partial u}{\partial x} = \dfrac{1}{y} e^{\frac{x}{y}}$,

$\dfrac{\partial u}{\partial y} = -\dfrac{x}{y^2} e^{\frac{x}{y}} - \dfrac{z}{y^2} e^{\frac{z}{y}}$, $\dfrac{\partial u}{\partial z} = \dfrac{1}{y} e^{\frac{z}{y}}$.   **9.** $z = \arcsin(x+y)$. *Ans.* $\dfrac{\partial z}{\partial x} =$

$= \dfrac{1}{\sqrt{1-(x+y)^2}} = \dfrac{\partial z}{\partial y}$.   **10.** $z = \arctan \sqrt{\dfrac{x^2-y^2}{x^2+y^2}}$. *Ans.* $\dfrac{\partial z}{\partial x} = \dfrac{y^3}{x\sqrt{x^4-y^4}}$,

$\dfrac{\partial z}{\partial y} = \dfrac{-y}{\sqrt{x^4-y^4}}$.

Find the total differentials of the following functions:

11. $z = x^2 + xy^2 + \sin y$. *Ans.* $dz = (2x+y^2)\,dx + (2xy + \cos y)\,dy$.   **12.** $z = \ln(xy)$. *Ans.* $dz = \dfrac{dx}{x} + \dfrac{dy}{y}$.   **13.** $z = e^{x^2+y^2}$. *Ans.* $dz = 2e^{x^2+y^2}(x\,dx + y\,dy)$.   **14.** $u =$

$= \tan(3x-y) + 6^{y+z}$. *Ans.* $du = \dfrac{3\,dx}{\cos^2(3x-y)} + \left(-\dfrac{1}{\cos^2(3x-y)} + 6^{y+z}\ln 6\right) \times$

$\times dy + 6^{y+z}\ln 6\, dz$.   **15.** $w = \arcsin \dfrac{x}{y}$. *Ans.* $dw = \dfrac{y\,dx - x\,dy}{|y|\sqrt{y^2-x^2}}$.

16. Evaluate $f'_x(2, 3)$ and $f'_y(2, 3)$ if $f(x, y) = x^2 + y^3$. Ans. $f'_x(2, 3) = 4$, $f'_y(2, 3) = 27$.

17. Evaluate $df(x, y)$ for $x = 1$, $y = 0$, $dx = \dfrac{1}{2}$, $dy = \dfrac{1}{4}$ if $f(x, y) =$
$= \sqrt{x^2 + y^2}$. Ans. $\dfrac{1}{2}$.

18. Set up a formula which, for small absolute values of the quantities x, y and z, yields an approximate expression for $\sqrt{\dfrac{1+x}{(1+y)(1+z)}}$. Ans. $1 +$
$+ \dfrac{1}{2}(x - y - z)$.

19. Do the same for $\sqrt{\dfrac{1+x}{1+y+z}}$. Ans. $1 + \dfrac{1}{2}(x - y - z)$.

20. Find $\dfrac{\partial z}{\partial x}$ and $\dfrac{\partial z}{\partial y}$, if $z = u + v^2$, $u = x^2 + \sin y$, $v = \ln(x+y)$. Ans.
$\dfrac{\partial z}{\partial x} = 2x + 2\dfrac{\ln(x+y)}{x+y}$, $\dfrac{\partial z}{\partial y} = \cos y + 2\dfrac{\ln(x+y)}{x+y}$.

21. Find $\dfrac{\partial z}{\partial x}$ if $z = \sqrt{\dfrac{1+u}{1+v}}$, $u = -\cos x$, $v = \cos x$. Ans. $\dfrac{\partial z}{\partial x} = \dfrac{1}{2\cos^2 \dfrac{x}{2}}$.

22. Find $\dfrac{\partial z}{\partial x}$ and $\dfrac{\partial z}{\partial y}$ if $z = e^{u-2v}$, $u = \sin x$, $v = x^3 + y^2$. Ans. $\dfrac{\partial z}{\partial x} = e^{u-2v} \times$
$\times (\cos x - 6x^2)$, $\dfrac{\partial z}{\partial y} = e^{u-2v}(0 - 2\cdot 2y) = -4ye^{u-2v}$, where $\sin x$ and $x^3 + y^2$ have to be substituted for u and v.

23. Find the total derivatives of the given functions: $z = \arcsin(u+v)$, $u = \sin x \cos \alpha$, $v = \cos x \sin \alpha$. Ans. $\dfrac{\partial z}{\partial x} = 1$ if $2k\pi - \dfrac{\pi}{2} < x + \alpha < 2k\pi + \dfrac{\pi}{2}$, $\dfrac{\partial z}{\partial x} =$
$= -1$ if $2k\pi + \dfrac{\pi}{2} < x + \alpha < (2k+1)\pi + \dfrac{\pi}{2}$. **24.** $u = \dfrac{e^{ax}(y-z)}{a^2+1}$, $y = a\sin x$,
$z = \cos x$. Ans. $\dfrac{\partial u}{\partial x} = e^{ax} \sin x$. **25.** $z = \ln(1 - x^4)$, $x = \sqrt{\sin \theta}$. Ans. $\dfrac{\partial z}{\partial \theta} =$
$= -2 \tan \theta$.

Find the derivatives of implicit functions of x given by the following equations:

26. $\dfrac{x^2}{a^2} + \dfrac{y^2}{b^2} - 1 = 0$. Ans. $\dfrac{dy}{dx} = -\dfrac{b^2}{a^2}\dfrac{x}{y}$. **27.** $\dfrac{x^2}{a^2} - \dfrac{y^2}{b^2} = 1$. Ans. $\dfrac{dy}{dx} = \dfrac{b^2}{a^2}\dfrac{x}{y}$.

28. $y^x = x^y$. Ans. $\dfrac{dy}{dx} = \dfrac{yx^{y-1} - y^x \ln y}{xy^{x-1} - x^y \ln x}$. **29.** $\sin(xy) - e^{xy} - x^2y = 0$. Ans. $\dfrac{dy}{dx} =$
$= \dfrac{y[\cos(xy) - e^{xy} - 2x]}{x[x + e^{xy} - \cos(xy)]}$. **30.** $\dfrac{x^2}{a^2} + \dfrac{y^2}{b^2} + \dfrac{z^2}{c^2} = 1$, find $\dfrac{\partial z}{\partial x}$ and $\dfrac{\partial z}{\partial y}$. Ans. $\dfrac{\partial z}{\partial x} =$
$= -\dfrac{c^2x}{a^2z}$, $\dfrac{\partial z}{\partial y} = -\dfrac{c^2y}{b^2z}$. **31.** $u - v\tan aw = 0$, find $\dfrac{\partial w}{\partial u}$ and $\dfrac{\partial w}{\partial v}$. Ans. $\dfrac{\partial w}{\partial u} = \dfrac{\cos^2 aw}{av}$,
$\dfrac{\partial w}{\partial v} = -\dfrac{\sin 2aw}{2av}$. **32.** $z^2 + \dfrac{2}{x} = \sqrt{y^2 - z^2}$, show that $x^2\dfrac{\partial z}{\partial x} + \dfrac{1}{y}\dfrac{\partial z}{\partial y} = \dfrac{1}{z}$. **33.** $\dfrac{z}{x} =$
$= F\left(\dfrac{y}{x}\right)$, show that $x\dfrac{\partial z}{\partial x} + y\dfrac{\partial z}{\partial y} = z$, no matter what the differentiable function F.

Compute the second partial derivatives:

34. $z = x^3 - 4x^2y + 5y^2$. Ans. $\dfrac{\partial^2 z}{\partial x^2} = 6x - 8y$, $\dfrac{\partial^2 z}{\partial y\,\partial x} = -8x$, $\dfrac{\partial^2 z}{\partial y^2} = 10$.

35. $z = e^x \ln y + \sin y \ln x$. Ans. $\dfrac{\partial^2 z}{\partial x^2} = e^x \ln y - \dfrac{\sin y}{x^2}$, $\dfrac{\partial^2 z}{\partial x\,\partial y} = \dfrac{e^x}{y} + \dfrac{\cos y}{x}$,

$\dfrac{\partial^2 z}{\partial y^2} = -\dfrac{e^x}{y^2} - \sin y \ln x$.

36. Prove that if $u = \dfrac{1}{\sqrt{x^2 + y^2 + z^2}}$, then $\dfrac{\partial^2 u}{\partial x^2} + \dfrac{\partial^2 u}{\partial y^2} + \dfrac{\partial^2 u}{\partial z^2} = 0$.

37. Prove that if $z = \dfrac{x^2 y^2}{x + y}$, then $x \dfrac{\partial^2 z}{\partial x^2} + y \dfrac{\partial^2 z}{\partial x\,\partial y} = 2 \dfrac{\partial z}{\partial x}$.

38. Prove that if $z = \ln(x^2 + y^2)$, then $\dfrac{\partial^2 z}{\partial x^2} + \dfrac{\partial^2 z}{\partial y^2} = 0$.

39. Prove that if $z = \varphi(y + ax) + \psi(y - ax)$, then $a^2 \dfrac{\partial^2 z}{\partial y^2} - \dfrac{\partial^2 z}{\partial x^2} = 0$ for any twice differentiable φ and ψ.

40. Find the derivative of the function $z = 3x^4 - xy + y^3$ at the point $M(1, 2)$ in the direction that makes an angle of $60°$ with the x-axis. Ans. $5 + \dfrac{11\sqrt{3}}{2}$.

41. Find the derivative of the function $z = 5x^2 - 3x - y - 1$ at the point $M(2, 1)$ in the direction from this point to the point $N(5, 5)$. Ans. $\dfrac{47}{5} = 9.4$.

42. Find the derivative of the function $f(x, y)$ in the direction of: (1) the bisector of the quadrantal angle Oxy. Ans. $\dfrac{1}{\sqrt{2}}\left(\dfrac{\partial f}{\partial x} + \dfrac{\partial f}{\partial y}\right)$; (2) the negative x-axis. Ans. $-\dfrac{\partial f}{\partial x}$.

43. $f(x, y) = x^3 + 3x^2 + 4xy + y^2$. Show that at the point $M\left(\dfrac{2}{3}, -\dfrac{4}{3}\right)$ the derivative in any direction is equal to zero (the "function is stationary").

44. Of all triangles with the same perimeter $2p$, determine the triangle with greatest area. Ans. Equilateral triangle.

45. Find a rectangular parallelepiped of greatest volume for a given total surface S. Ans. A cube with edge $\sqrt{\dfrac{S}{6}}$.

46. Find the distance between two straight lines in space whose equations are $\dfrac{x-1}{1} = \dfrac{y}{2} = \dfrac{z}{1}$, $\dfrac{x}{1} = \dfrac{y}{1} = \dfrac{z}{1}$. Ans. $\dfrac{\sqrt{2}}{2}$.

Test for maximum and minimum the functions:

47. $z = x^3 y^2(a - x - y)$. Ans. Maximum z at $x = \dfrac{a}{2}$, $y = \dfrac{a}{3}$.

48. $z = x^2 + xy + y^2 + \dfrac{1}{x} + \dfrac{1}{y}$. Ans. Minimum z at $x = y = \dfrac{1}{\sqrt[3]{3}}$.

49. $z = \sin x + \sin y + \sin(x + y)$ $\left(0 < x < \dfrac{\pi}{2}, 0 < y < \dfrac{\pi}{2}\right)$. Ans. Maximum z at $x = y = \dfrac{\pi}{3}$.

50. $z = \sin x \sin y \sin (x+y)$ $(0 \leqslant x \leqslant \pi,\ 0 \leqslant y \leqslant \pi)$. *Ans.* Maximum z at $x = y = \dfrac{\pi}{3}$.

Find the singular points of the following curves, investigate their character and form equations of the tangents at these points:

51. $x^3 + y^3 - 3axy = 0$. *Ans.* $M_0\,(0,\ 0)$ is a node, $x = 0$, $y = 0$ are the equations of the tangents.

52. $a^4 y^2 = x^4\,(a^2 - x^2)$. *Ans.* A double cusp at the origin, the double tangent $y^2 = 0$.

53. $y^2 = \dfrac{x^3}{2a-x}$. *Ans.* $M_0\,(0,\ 0)$ is a cusp of the first kind, $y^2 = 0$ is a tangent.

54. $y^2 = x^2\,(9 - x^2)$. *Ans.* $M_0\,(0,\ 0)$ is a node, $y = \pm\,3x$ are the equations of the tangents.

55. $x^4 - 2ax^2 y - axy^2 + a^2 x^2 = 0$. *Ans.* $M_0\,(0,\ 0)$ is a cusp of the second kind, $y^2 = 0$ is a double tangent.

56. $y^2\,(a^2 + x^2) = x^2\,(a^2 - x^2)$. *Ans.* $M_0\,(0,\ 0)$ is a node, $y = \pm\,x$ are the equations of the tangents.

57. $b^2 x^2 + a^2 y^2 = x^2 y^2$. *Ans.* $M_0\,(0,\ 0)$ is an isolated point.

58. Show that the curve $y = x \ln x$ has an end point at the coordinate origin and a tangent which is the y-axis.

59. Show that the curve $y = \dfrac{x}{1 + e^{\frac{1}{x}}}$ has a nodal point at the origin and that the tangents at this point are: on the right $y = 0$, on the left $y = x$.

CHAPTER 9

APPLICATIONS OF DIFFERENTIAL CALCULUS TO SOLID GEOMETRY

9.1 THE EQUATIONS OF A CURVE IN SPACE

Let us consider the vector $\overline{OA} = r$ whose origin is coincident with the coordinate origin and whose terminus is a certain point $A(x, y, z)$ (Fig. 196). A vector of this kind is called a *radius vector*.

Let us express this vector in terms of the projections on the coordinate axes:

$$r = x\boldsymbol{i} + y\boldsymbol{j} + z\boldsymbol{k} \tag{1}$$

Let the projections of the vector r be functions of some parameter t:

$$\left. \begin{array}{l} x = \varphi(t) \\ y = \psi(t) \\ z = \chi(t) \end{array} \right\} \tag{2}$$

Then formula (1) may be rewritten as follows:

$$r = \varphi(t)\boldsymbol{i} + \psi(t)\boldsymbol{j} + \chi(t)\boldsymbol{k} \tag{1'}$$

or, in abbreviated form,

$$r = r(t) \tag{1''}$$

As t varies, x, y, and z vary; and the point A (the terminus of the vector r) will trace out a line in space that is called the *hodograph* of the vector $r = r(t)$. Equation (1') or (1'') is called the *vector equation* of the line in space. Equations (2) are known as the *parametric equations* of the line in space. With the aid of these equations, the coordinates x, y, z of the corresponding point of the curve are determined for each value of t.

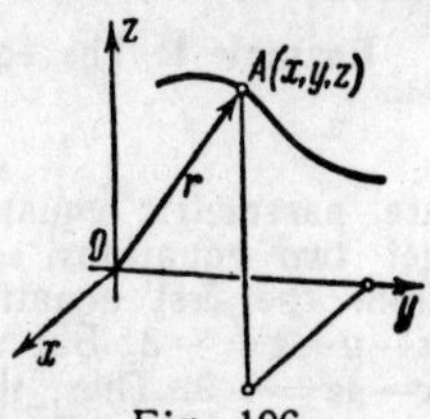

Fig. 196

Note. A curve in space can also be defined as the locus of points of the intersection of two surfaces. It can therefore be given by two equations of two surfaces:

$$\left. \begin{array}{l} \Phi_1(x, y, z) = 0 \\ \Phi_2(x, y, z) = 0 \end{array} \right\} \tag{3}$$

Thus, for example, the equations

$$x^2 + y^2 + z^2 = 4, \quad z = 1$$

are the equations of a circle obtained at the intersection of a sphere and a plane (Fig. 197).

Thus, a curve in space may be represented either by parametric equations (2) or by two surface equations (3).

If we eliminate the parameter t from equations (2) and get two equations connecting x, y, z, we will thus make the transition

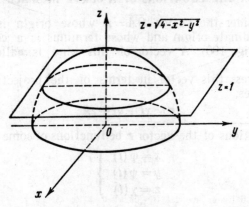

Fig. 197

from parametric representation of a line to the surface representation. And conversely, if we put $x = \varphi(t)$, where $\varphi(t)$ is an arbitrary function, and find y and z as functions of t from equations

$$\Phi_1\,[\varphi(t), \; y, \; z] = 0, \quad \Phi_2\,[\varphi(t), \; y, \; z] = 0$$

we will then make the transition from representation of a line by means of surfaces to its parametric representation.

Example 1. The equations

$$x = 4t - 1, \quad y = 3t, \quad z = t + 2$$

are parametric equations of a straight line. Eliminating the parameter t, we get two equations, each of which is an equation of a plane. For instance, if from the first equation we subtract, termwise, the second and third, we get $x - y - z = -3$. But subtracting (from the first) four times the third we get $x - 4z = -9$. Thus, the given straight line is the line of intersection of the planes $x - y - z + 3 = 0$ and $x - 4z + 9 = 0$.

Example 2. Let us consider a right circular cylinder of radius a, whose axis coincides with the z-axis (Fig. 198). Onto this cylinder we wind a right triangle C_1AC so that the vertex A of the triangle lies at the point of intersection of the generator of the cylinder with the x-axis, while the leg AC_1 is wound onto the circular section of the cylinder lying in the xy-plane. Then the hypotenuse will generate on the cylinder a line that is called a *helix*.

Let us write the equation of the helix, denoting by x, y, and z the coordinates of its variable point M and by t the angle $\widehat{AOP}$ (see Fig. 198). Then

$$x = a \cos t, \quad y = a \sin t, \quad z = PM = \widehat{AP} \tan \theta$$

where θ denotes the acute angle of the triangle $C_1 AC$. Noting that $\widehat{AP} = at$, since $\widehat{AP}$ is an arc of a circle of radius a corresponding to the central angle t,

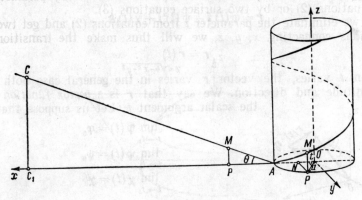

Fig. 198

and denoting $\tan \theta$ by m, we get the parametric equations of the helix in the form

$$x = a \cos t, \quad y = a \sin t, \quad z = amt$$

(here t is the parameter), or in the vector form:

$$\boldsymbol{r} = \boldsymbol{i} a \cos t + \boldsymbol{j} a \sin t + \boldsymbol{k} amt$$

It is not difficult to eliminate the parameter t from the parametric equations of the helix: square the first two equations and add. We find $x^2 + y^2 = a^2$. This is the equation of the cylinder on which the helix lies. Then, dividing termwise the second equation by the first and substituting into the obtained equation the value of t found from the third equation, we find the equation of another surface on which the helix lies:

$$\frac{y}{x} = \tan \frac{z}{am}$$

This is the so-called *helicoid*. It is generated as the trace of a half-line parallel to the xy-plane if the end point of this half-line lies on the z-axis and if the half-line itself rotates about the z-axis at a constant angular velocity, and rises with constant velocity so that its extremity is translated along the z-axis. The helix is the line of intersection of these two surfaces and so can be represented by two equations:

$$x^2 + y^2 = a^2, \quad \frac{y}{x} = \tan \frac{z}{am}$$

9.2 THE LIMIT AND DERIVATIVE
OF THE VECTOR FUNCTION OF A SCALAR ARGUMENT.
THE EQUATION OF A TANGENT TO A CURVE.
THE EQUATION OF A NORMAL PLANE

Reverting to the formulas $(1')$ and $(1'')$ of the preceding section, we have

$$r = \varphi(t)\,i + \psi(t)\,j + \chi(t)\,k$$

or

$$r = r(t)$$

When t varies, the vector r varies in the general case both in magnitude and direction. We say that r is a *vector function* of the scalar argument t. Let us suppose that

$$\lim_{t \to t_0} \varphi(t) = \varphi_0$$
$$\lim_{t \to t_0} \psi(t) = \psi_0$$
$$\lim_{t \to t_0} \chi(t) = \chi_0$$

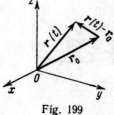

Fig. 199

Then we say that the vector $r_0 = \varphi_0 i + \psi_0 j + \chi_0 k$ is the *limit of the vector* $r = r(t)$ and we write (Fig. 199)

$$\lim_{t \to t_0} r(t) = r_0$$

From the latter equation follow the obvious equations

$$\lim_{t \to t_0} |r(t) - r_0| = \lim_{t \to t_0} \sqrt{[\varphi(t) - \varphi_0]^2 + [\psi(t) - \psi_0]^2 + [\chi(t) - \chi_0]^2} = 0$$

and

$$\lim_{t \to t_0} |r(t)| = |r_0|$$

Let us now take up the question of the derivative of the vector function of a scalar argument,

$$r(t) = \varphi(t)\,i + \psi(t)\,j + \chi(t)\,k \tag{1}$$

assuming that the origin of the vector $r(t)$ lies at the coordinate origin. We know that the latter equation is the equation of some space curve.

Let us take some fixed value t corresponding to a definite point M on the curve, and let us change t by the increment Δt; we then get the vector

$$r\,t + \Delta t) = \varphi(t + \Delta t)\,i + \psi(t + \Delta t)\,j + \chi(t + \Delta t)\,k$$

which defines a certain point M_1 on the curve (Fig. 200). Let us find the increment of the vector

$$\Delta r = r(t + \Delta t) - r(t)$$
$$= [\varphi(t + \Delta t) - \varphi(t)] \, i$$
$$+ [\psi(t + \Delta t) - \psi(t)] \, j$$
$$+ [\chi(t + \Delta t) - \chi(t)] \, k$$

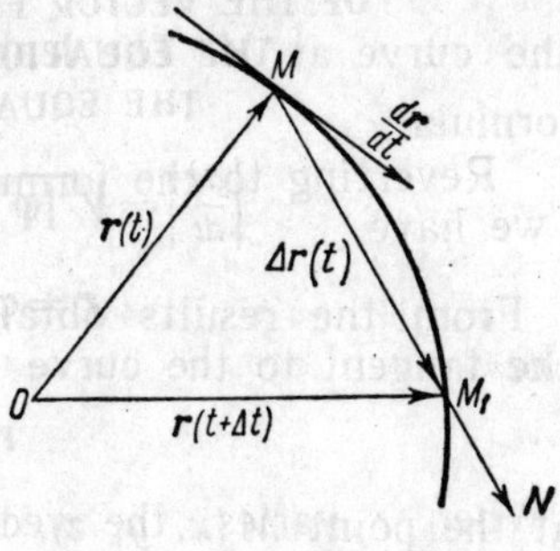

In Fig. 200, where $\overline{OM} = r(t)$, $\overline{OM_1} = r(t + \Delta t)$, this increment is shown by the vector $\overline{MM_1} = \Delta r(t)$.

Fig. 200

Let us consider the ratio $\dfrac{\Delta r(t)}{\Delta t}$ of the increment in the vector function to the increment in the scalar argument; this is obviously a vector collinear with the vector $\Delta r(t)$, since it is obtained from the latter by multiplication by the scalar factor $\dfrac{1}{\Delta t}$. We can write this vector as follows:

$$\frac{\Delta r(t)}{\Delta t} = \frac{\varphi(t + \Delta t) - \varphi(t)}{\Delta t} i + \frac{\psi(t + \Delta t) - \psi(t)}{\Delta t} j + \frac{\chi(t + \Delta t) - \chi(t)}{\Delta t} k$$

If the functions $\varphi(t)$, $\psi(t)$, $\chi(t)$ have derivatives for the chosen value of t, the factors of i, j, k will in the limit become the derivatives $\varphi'(t)$, $\psi'(t)$, $\chi'(t)$ as $\Delta t \rightarrow 0$. Therefore, in this case the limit of $\dfrac{\Delta r}{\Delta t}$ as $\Delta t \rightarrow 0$ exists and is equal to the vector $\varphi'(t) \, i + \psi'(t) \, j + \chi'(t) \, k$:

$$\lim_{\Delta t \rightarrow 0} \frac{\Delta r}{\Delta t} = \varphi'(t) \, i + \psi'(t) \, j + \chi'(t) \, k$$

The vector defined by this equation is called the *derivative* of the vector $r(t)$ with respect to the scalar argument t. The derivative is denoted by the symbol $\dfrac{dr}{dt}$ or r'.

Thus,

$$\frac{dr}{dt} = r' = \varphi'(t) \, i + \psi'(t) \, j + \chi'(t) \, k \qquad (2)$$

or

$$\frac{dr}{dt} = \frac{dx}{dt} i + \frac{dy}{dt} j + \frac{dz}{dt} k \qquad (2')$$

Let us determine the direction of the vector $\dfrac{dr}{dt}$.

Since as $\Delta t \rightarrow 0$ the point M_1 approaches M, the direction of the secant MM_1 yields, in the limit, the direction of the tangent.

Hence, the vector of the derivative $\frac{dr}{dt}$ lies along the tangent to the curve at M. The length of the vector $\frac{dr}{dt}$ is defined by the formula*

$$\left|\frac{dr}{dt}\right| = V\overline{[\varphi'(t)]^2 + [\psi'(t)]^2 + [\chi'(t)]^2} \tag{3}$$

From the results obtained it is easy to write the equation of the tangent to the curve

$$r = x\mathbf{i} + y\mathbf{j} + z\mathbf{k}$$

at the point $M(x, y, z)$, bearing in mind that in the equation of the curve $x = \varphi(t)$, $y = \psi(t)$, $z = \chi(t)$.

The equation of the straight line passing through the point $M(x, y, z)$ is of the form

$$\frac{X-x}{m} = \frac{Y-y}{n} = \frac{Z-z}{p}$$

where X, Y, Z are the coordinates of the variable point of the straight line, while m, n, and p are quantities proportional to the direction cosines of this straight line (that is to say, to the projections of the directional vector of the straight line).

On the other hand, we have established that the vector

$$\frac{dr}{dt} = \frac{dx}{dt}\mathbf{i} + \frac{dy}{dt}\mathbf{j} + \frac{dz}{dt}\mathbf{k}$$

is directed along the tangent. For this reason, the projections of this vector are numbers that are proportional to the direction cosines of the tangent, hence also to the numbers m, n, p. Thus, the *equation of the tangent* will be of the form

$$\frac{X-x}{\frac{dx}{dt}} = \frac{Y-y}{\frac{dy}{dt}} = \frac{Z-z}{\frac{dz}{dt}} \tag{4}$$

Example 1. Write the equation of a tangent of the helix

$$x = a \cos t, \ y = a \sin t, \ z = amt$$

for an arbitrary value of t and for $t = \frac{\pi}{4}$.

Solution.

$$\frac{dx}{dt} = -a \sin t, \ \frac{dy}{dt} = a \cos t, \ \frac{dz}{dt} = am$$

---

* We shall assume that at the points under consideration $\left|\frac{dr}{dt}\right| \neq 0$.

From formula (4) we have

$$\frac{X-a\cos t}{-a\sin t}=\frac{Y-a\sin t}{a\cos t}=\frac{Z-amt}{am}$$

In particular, for $t=\frac{\pi}{4}$ we get

$$\frac{X-\frac{a\sqrt{2}}{2}}{-\frac{a\sqrt{2}}{2}}=\frac{Y-\frac{a\sqrt{2}}{2}}{\frac{a\sqrt{2}}{2}}=\frac{Z-am\frac{\pi}{4}}{am}$$

or

$$\frac{X-\frac{a\sqrt{2}}{2}}{-1}=\frac{Y-\frac{a\sqrt{2}}{2}}{1}=\frac{Z-\frac{\pi\,am}{4}}{m\sqrt{2}}$$

Just as in the case of a plane curve, a straight line perpendicular to a tangent and passing through the point of tangency is called a *normal* to the space curve at the given point. Obviously, one can draw an infinitude of normals to a given space curve at a given point. They all lie in the plane perpendicular to the tangent line. This plane is the *normal plane*.

From the condition of perpendicularity of a normal plane to the tangent (4), we get the equation of the normal plane:

$$\frac{dx}{dt}(X-x)+\frac{dy}{dt}(Y-y)+\frac{dz}{dt}(Z-z)=0 \tag{5}$$

Example 2. Write the equation of the normal plane to a helix at a point for which $t=\frac{\pi}{4}$.

Solution. From Example 1 and formula (5) we get

$$-\left(X-\frac{a\sqrt{2}}{2}\right)+\left(Y-\frac{a\sqrt{2}}{2}\right)+m\sqrt{2}\left(Z-am\frac{\pi}{4}\right)=0$$

or

$$-X+Y+m\sqrt{2}\,Z=am^2\frac{\pi}{4}\sqrt{2}$$

Let us now derive the equation of the tangent line and the normal plane of a space curve for the case when this curve is given by the equations

$$\Phi_1(x,\,y,\,z)=0,\quad \Phi_2(x,\,y,\,z)=0 \tag{6}$$

We express the coordinates $x,\,y,\,z$ of this curve as functions of some parameter t:

$$x=\varphi(t),\quad y=\psi(t),\quad z=\chi(t) \tag{7}$$

We shall assume that $\varphi(t)$, $\psi(t)$, $\chi(t)$ are differentiable functions of t.

Substituting into equations (6), in place of x, y, z, their values for the points of the curve expressed in terms of t, we get two identities in t:

$$\Phi_1\,[\varphi(t),\ \psi(t),\ \chi(t)] = 0 \tag{8a}$$
$$\Phi_2\,[\varphi(t),\ \psi(t),\ \chi(t)] = 0 \tag{8b}$$

Differentiating the identities (8a) and (8b) with respect to t, we get

$$\left.\begin{aligned}
\frac{\partial\Phi_1}{\partial x}\frac{dx}{dt} + \frac{\partial\Phi_1}{\partial y}\frac{dy}{dt} + \frac{\partial\Phi_1}{\partial z}\frac{dz}{dt} = 0 \\[2mm]
\frac{\partial\Phi_2}{\partial x}\frac{dx}{dt} + \frac{\partial\Phi_2}{\partial y}\frac{dy}{dt} + \frac{\partial\Phi_2}{\partial z}\frac{dz}{dt} = 0
\end{aligned}\right\} \tag{9}$$

From these equations it follows that

$$\frac{\dfrac{dx}{dt}}{\dfrac{dz}{dt}} = \frac{\dfrac{\partial\Phi_1}{\partial y}\dfrac{\partial\Phi_2}{\partial z} - \dfrac{\partial\Phi_1}{\partial z}\dfrac{\partial\Phi_2}{\partial y}}{\dfrac{\partial\Phi_1}{\partial x}\dfrac{\partial\Phi_2}{\partial y} - \dfrac{\partial\Phi_1}{\partial y}\dfrac{\partial\Phi_2}{\partial x}}, \quad \frac{\dfrac{dy}{dt}}{\dfrac{dz}{dt}} = \frac{\dfrac{\partial\Phi_1}{\partial z}\dfrac{\partial\Phi_2}{\partial x} - \dfrac{\partial\Phi_1}{\partial x}\dfrac{\partial\Phi_2}{\partial z}}{\dfrac{\partial\Phi_1}{\partial x}\dfrac{\partial\Phi_2}{\partial y} - \dfrac{\partial\Phi_1}{\partial y}\dfrac{\partial\Phi_2}{\partial x}} \tag{10}$$

Here, we naturally assume that the expression $\dfrac{\partial\Phi_1}{\partial x}\dfrac{\partial\Phi_2}{\partial y} - \dfrac{\partial\Phi_1}{\partial y}\dfrac{\partial\Phi_2}{\partial x} \neq$ $\neq 0$; however, it may be proved that the final formulas (11) and (12) (see below) hold also for the case when this expression is equal to zero, provided that at least one of the determinants in the final formulas differs from zero.

From equations (10) we have

$$\frac{\dfrac{dx}{dt}}{\dfrac{\partial\Phi_1}{\partial y}\dfrac{\partial\Phi_2}{\partial z} - \dfrac{\partial\Phi_1}{\partial z}\dfrac{\partial\Phi_2}{\partial y}} = \frac{\dfrac{dy}{dt}}{\dfrac{\partial\Phi_1}{\partial z}\dfrac{\partial\Phi_2}{\partial x} - \dfrac{\partial\Phi_1}{\partial x}\dfrac{\partial\Phi_2}{\partial z}} = \frac{\dfrac{dz}{dt}}{\dfrac{\partial\Phi_1}{\partial x}\dfrac{\partial\Phi_2}{\partial y} - \dfrac{\partial\Phi_1}{\partial y}\dfrac{\partial\Phi_2}{\partial x}}$$

Consequently, from formula (4) the equation of the tangent line will have the form

$$\frac{X-x}{\dfrac{\partial\Phi_1}{\partial y}\dfrac{\partial\Phi_2}{\partial z} - \dfrac{\partial\Phi_1}{\partial z}\dfrac{\partial\Phi_2}{\partial y}} = \frac{Y-y}{\dfrac{\partial\Phi_1}{\partial z}\dfrac{\partial\Phi_2}{\partial x} - \dfrac{\partial\Phi_1}{\partial x}\dfrac{\partial\Phi_2}{\partial z}} = \frac{Z-z}{\dfrac{\partial\Phi_1}{\partial x}\dfrac{\partial\Phi_2}{\partial y} - \dfrac{\partial\Phi_1}{\partial y}\dfrac{\partial\Phi_2}{\partial x}}$$

or, using determinants,

$$\frac{X-x}{\begin{vmatrix} \dfrac{\partial\Phi_1}{\partial y} & \dfrac{\partial\Phi_1}{\partial z} \\[2mm] \dfrac{\partial\Phi_2}{\partial y} & \dfrac{\partial\Phi_2}{\partial z} \end{vmatrix}} = \frac{Y-y}{\begin{vmatrix} \dfrac{\partial\Phi_1}{\partial z} & \dfrac{\partial\Phi_1}{\partial x} \\[2mm] \dfrac{\partial\Phi_2}{\partial z} & \dfrac{\partial\Phi_2}{\partial x} \end{vmatrix}} = \frac{Z-z}{\begin{vmatrix} \dfrac{\partial\Phi_1}{\partial x} & \dfrac{\partial\Phi_1}{\partial y} \\[2mm] \dfrac{\partial\Phi_2}{\partial x} & \dfrac{\partial\Phi_2}{\partial y} \end{vmatrix}} \tag{11}$$

The normal plane is represented by the equation

$$(X-x)\begin{vmatrix} \dfrac{\partial \Phi_1}{\partial y} & \dfrac{\partial \Phi_1}{\partial z} \\ \dfrac{\partial \Phi_2}{\partial y} & \dfrac{\partial \Phi_2}{\partial z} \end{vmatrix} + (Y-y)\begin{vmatrix} \dfrac{\partial \Phi_1}{\partial z} & \dfrac{\partial \Phi_1}{\partial x} \\ \dfrac{\partial \Phi_2}{\partial z} & \dfrac{\partial \Phi_2}{\partial x} \end{vmatrix} + (Z-z)\begin{vmatrix} \dfrac{\partial \Phi_1}{\partial x} & \dfrac{\partial \Phi_1}{\partial y} \\ \dfrac{\partial \Phi_2}{\partial x} & \dfrac{\partial \Phi_2}{\partial y} \end{vmatrix} = 0 \quad (12)$$

These formulas are meaningful only when at least one of the determinants involved is different from zero. But if at some point of the curve all three determinants

$$\begin{vmatrix} \dfrac{\partial \Phi_1}{\partial y} & \dfrac{\partial \Phi_1}{\partial z} \\ \dfrac{\partial \Phi_2}{\partial y} & \dfrac{\partial \Phi_2}{\partial z} \end{vmatrix}, \quad \begin{vmatrix} \dfrac{\partial \Phi_1}{\partial z} & \dfrac{\partial \Phi_1}{\partial x} \\ \dfrac{\partial \Phi_2}{\partial z} & \dfrac{\partial \Phi_2}{\partial x} \end{vmatrix}, \quad \begin{vmatrix} \dfrac{\partial \Phi_1}{\partial x} & \dfrac{\partial \Phi_1}{\partial y} \\ \dfrac{\partial \Phi_2}{\partial x} & \dfrac{\partial \Phi_2}{\partial y} \end{vmatrix}$$

vanish, this point is called a *singular point* of the space curve. At this point the curve may not have a tangent at all. as was the case with singular points in plane curves (see Sec. 8.20).

Example 3. Find the equations of the tangent line and the normal plane to the line of intersection of the sphere $x^2+y^2+z^2=4r^2$ and the cylinder $x^2+y^2=2ry$ at the point $M(r,\ r,\ r\sqrt{2})$ (Fig. 201).

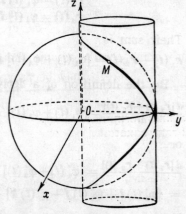

Fig. 201

Solution.

$$\Phi_1(x,\ y,\ z)=x^2+y^2+z^2-4r^2$$
$$\Phi_2(x,\ y,\ z)=x^2+y^2-2ry$$

$$\frac{\partial \Phi_1}{\partial x}=2x, \quad \frac{\partial \Phi_1}{\partial y}=2y, \quad \frac{\partial \Phi_1}{\partial z}=2z$$

$$\frac{\partial \Phi_2}{\partial x}=2x, \quad \frac{\partial \Phi_2}{\partial y}=2y-2r, \quad \frac{\partial \Phi_2}{\partial z}=0$$

The values of the derivatives at the given point M will be

$$\frac{\partial \Phi_1}{\partial x}=2r, \quad \frac{\partial \Phi_1}{\partial y}=2r, \quad \frac{\partial \Phi_1}{\partial z}=2r\sqrt{2}$$

$$\frac{\partial \Phi_2}{\partial x}=2r, \quad \frac{\partial \Phi_2}{\partial y}=0, \quad \frac{\partial \Phi_2}{\partial z}=0$$

For this reason the equation of the tangent line has the form

$$\frac{X-r}{0}=\frac{Y-r}{\sqrt{2}}=\frac{Z-r\sqrt{2}}{-1}$$

The equation of the normal plane is

$$\sqrt{2}(Y-r)-(Z-r\sqrt{2})=0 \text{ or } \sqrt{2}\,Y-Z=0$$

9.3 RULES FOR DIFFERENTIATING VECTORS
(VECTOR FUNCTIONS)

As we have seen, the derivative of a vector

$$r(t) = \varphi(t)\,i + \psi(t)\,j + \chi(t)\,k \tag{1}$$

is, by definition, equal to

$$r'(t) = \varphi'(t)\,i + \psi'(t)\,j + \chi'(t)\,k \tag{2}$$

From this it follows directly that the basic rules for differentiating functions hold for vectors as well. Here, we shall derive the formulas for differentiating a sum and a scalar product of vectors; the other formulas we shall write down and leave their derivation for the student.

I. *The derivative of a sum of vectors is equal to the sum of the derivatives of the vectors.*

Indeed, let there be two vectors:

$$\left.\begin{array}{l} r_1(t) = \varphi_1(t)\,i + \psi_1(t)\,j + \chi_1(t)\,k \\ r_2(t) = \varphi_2(t)\,i + \psi_2(t)\,j + \chi_2(t)\,k \end{array}\right\} \tag{3}$$

Their sum is

$$r_1(t) + r_2(t) = [\varphi_1(t) + \varphi_2(t)]\,i + [\psi_1(t) + \psi_2(t)]\,j + [\chi_1(t) + \chi_2(t)]\,k$$

By the definition of a derivative of a variable vector, we have

$$\frac{d\,[r_1(t) + r_2(t)]}{dt} = [\varphi_1(t) + \varphi_2(t)]'\,i + [\psi_1(t) + \psi_2(t)]'\,j + [\chi_1(t) + \chi_2(t)]'\,k$$

or

$$\frac{d\,[r_1(t) + r_2(t)]}{dt} = [\varphi_1'(t) + \varphi_2'(t)]\,i + [\psi_1'(t) + \psi_2'(t)]\,j + [\chi_1'(t) + \chi_2'(t)]\,k$$

$$= [\varphi_1'(t)\,i + \psi_1'(t)\,j + \chi_1'(t)\,k] + [\varphi_2'(t)\,i + \psi_2'(t)\,j + \chi_2'(t)\,k] = r_1' + r_2'$$

Hence,

$$\frac{d\,[r_1(t) + r_2(t)]}{dt} = \frac{dr_1}{dt} + \frac{dr_2}{dt} \tag{I}$$

II. *The derivative of a scalar product of vectors is expressed by the formula*

$$\frac{d\,(r_1 r_2)}{dt} = \frac{dr_1}{dt}\,r_2 + r_1\,\frac{dr_2}{dt} \tag{II}$$

Indeed, if $r_1(t)$, $r_2(t)$ are defined by formulas (3), then, as we know, the scalar product of these vectors is equal to

$$r_1(t)\,r_2(t) = \varphi_1\varphi_2 + \psi_1\psi_2 + \chi_1\chi_2$$

For this reason

$$\frac{d(r_1 r_2)}{dt} = \varphi_1' \varphi_2 + \varphi_1 \varphi_2' + \psi_1' \psi_2 + \psi_1 \psi_2' + \chi_1' \chi_2 + \chi_1 \chi_2'$$

$$= (\varphi_1' \varphi_2 + \psi_1' \psi_2 + \chi_1' \chi_2) + (\varphi_1 \varphi_2' + \psi_1 \psi_2' + \chi_1 \chi_2')$$

$$= (\varphi_1' i + \psi_1' j + \chi_1' k)(\varphi_2 i + \psi_2 j + \chi_2 k) + (\varphi_1 i + \psi_1 j + \chi_1 k)(\varphi_2' i + \psi_2' j + \chi_2' k)$$

$$= \frac{dr_1}{dt} r_2 + r_1 \frac{dr_2}{dt}$$

The theorem is proved.

From formula (II) we have the following important corollary.

Corollary. *If the vector e is a unit vector, that is, $|e| = 1$, then its derivative is a vector perpendicular to it.*

Proof. If e is a unit vector, then

$$ee = 1$$

Let us take the derivative, with respect to t, of both sides of the equation:

$$e \frac{de}{dt} + \frac{de}{dt} e = 0$$

or

$$2e \frac{de}{dt} = 0$$

that is, the scalar product

$$e \frac{de}{dt} = 0$$

But this means that the vector $\frac{de}{dt}$ is perpendicular to the vector e.

III. *If $f(t)$ is a scalar function and $r(t)$ is a vector function, then the derivative of the product $f(t) r(t)$ is given by the formula*

$$\frac{d(fr)}{dt} = \frac{df}{dt} r + f \frac{dr}{dt} \qquad (III)$$

Proof. If the vector $r(t)$ is defined by formula (1), then

$$f(t) r(t) = f(t) \varphi(t) i + f(t) \psi(t) j + f(t) \chi(t) k$$

By formula (2) we get

$$\frac{d(f(t) r(t))}{dt} = \left(\frac{df}{dt} \varphi + f \frac{d\varphi}{dt} \right) i + \left(\frac{df}{dt} \psi + f \frac{d\psi}{dt} \right) j + \left(\frac{df}{dt} \chi + f \frac{d\chi}{df} \right) k$$

$$= \frac{df}{dt} (\varphi i + \psi j + \chi k) + f \left(\frac{d\varphi}{dt} i + \frac{d\psi}{dt} j + \frac{d\chi}{dt} k \right) = \frac{df}{dt} r + f \frac{dr}{dt}$$

IV. *A constant numerical factor can be taken outside the sign of the derivative:*

$$\frac{d(a \cdot r(t))}{dt} = a \frac{dr}{dt} = ar'(t) \qquad (IV)$$

This follows from III if $f(t) = a = $ const. Hence, $\frac{df}{dt} = 0$.

V. *The derivative of a vector product of vectors* $r_1(t)$ *and* $r_2(t)$ *is determined by the formula*

$$\frac{d(r_1 \times r_2)}{dt} = \frac{dr_1}{dt} \times r_2 + r_1 \times \frac{dr_2}{dt} \tag{V}$$

The proof is similar to that of formula II.

9.4 THE FIRST AND SECOND DERIVATIVES OF A VECTOR WITH RESPECT TO ARC LENGTH. THE CURVATURE OF A CURVE. THE PRINCIPAL NORMAL. THE VELOCITY AND ACCELERATION OF A POINT IN CURVILINEAR MOTION

The arc length * of a space curve $\widehat{M_0A} = s$ (Fig. 202) is determined just as in the case of curves in a plane. When a variable point $A(x, y, z)$ moves along a curve, the arc length s varies; conversely, when s varies, the coordinates x, y, z of the variable point A lying on the curve also vary. Therefore, the coordinates x, y, z of the variable point A of the curve may be regarded as functions of the arc length s:

$$x = \varphi(s)$$
$$y = \psi(s)$$
$$z = \chi(s)$$

In these parametric equations of the curve, the arc length s is the parameter. The vector $\overline{OA} = r$ is, accordingly, expressed as

$$r = \varphi(s)\,i + \psi(s)\,j + \chi(s)\,k$$

or

$$r = r(s) \tag{1}$$

Thus the vector r is a function of the arc length s.

Let us find out the geometrical meaning of the derivative $\frac{dr}{ds}$. As is evident from Fig. 202, we have the following equations:

$$\widehat{M_0A} = s, \quad \widehat{AB} = \Delta s, \quad \widehat{M_0B} = s + \Delta s$$
$$\overline{OA} = r(s), \quad \overline{OB} = r(s + \Delta s)$$
$$\overline{AB} = \Delta r = r(s + \Delta s) - r(s)$$
$$\frac{\Delta r}{\Delta s} = \frac{\overline{AB}}{\widehat{AB}}$$

---

* The *arc length* of a space curve is defined in exactly the same way as the arc length of a plane curve (see Sec. 6.1 and Sec. 12.3).

We have already seen in Sec. 9.2 that the vector $\frac{d\boldsymbol{r}}{ds} = \lim\limits_{\Delta s \to 0} \frac{\Delta \boldsymbol{r}}{\Delta s}$ is in the direction of the tangent to the curve at the point A towards increasing s. On the other hand, we have the equation $\lim \left| \dfrac{\overline{AB}}{\overbrace{AB}} \right| = 1$

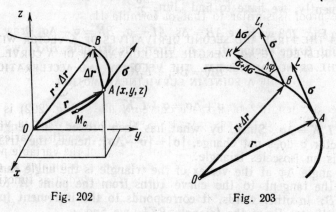

Fig. 202   Fig. 203

[the limit of the ratio of the chord length to the arc length *].

Hence, $\frac{d\boldsymbol{r}}{ds}$ is a **unit** vector in the direction of the tangent; let us denote it by σ:

$$\frac{d\boldsymbol{r}}{ds} = \sigma \qquad (2)$$

If the vector $\boldsymbol{r}$ is represented by the projections

$$\boldsymbol{r} = x\boldsymbol{i} + y\boldsymbol{j} + z\boldsymbol{k}$$

then

$$\sigma = \frac{dx}{ds}\boldsymbol{i} + \frac{dy}{ds}\boldsymbol{j} + \frac{dz}{ds}\boldsymbol{k} \qquad (3)$$

and

$$\sqrt{\left(\frac{dx}{ds}\right)^2 + \left(\frac{dy}{ds}\right)^2 + \left(\frac{dz}{ds}\right)^2} = 1$$

Let us now examine the **second** derivative of the vector function, $\frac{d^2\boldsymbol{r}}{ds^2}$, that is, the derivative with respect to $\frac{d\boldsymbol{r}}{ds}$, and determine its

---

* In Sec. 6.1, we mentioned this relation for a plane curve. It also holds for a space curve: $\boldsymbol{r}(t) = \varphi(t)\boldsymbol{i} + \psi(t)\boldsymbol{j} + \chi(t)\boldsymbol{k}$ if the functions $\varphi(t)$, $\psi(t)$ and $\chi(t)$ have continuous derivatives that do not vanish simultaneously.

geometric meaning. From formula (2) it follows that

$$\frac{d^2r}{ds^2} = \frac{d}{ds}\left[\frac{dr}{ds}\right] = \frac{d\sigma}{ds}$$

Consequently, we have to find $\lim\limits_{\Delta s \to 0} \dfrac{\Delta\sigma}{ds}$.

From Fig. 203 we have $AB = \Delta s$, $\overline{AL} = \sigma$, $\overline{BK} = \sigma + \Delta\sigma$. Draw from the point B the vector $\overline{BL_1} = \sigma$. From the triangle BKL_1 we find

$$\overline{BK} = \overline{BL_1} + \overline{L_1K}$$

or

$$\sigma + \Delta\sigma = \sigma + \overline{L_1K}$$

Thus, $L_1K = \Delta\sigma$. Since, by what has been proved, the length of the vector σ does not change, $|\sigma| = |\sigma + \Delta\sigma|$; hence, the triangle BKL_1 is an isosceles triangle.

The angle $\Delta\varphi$ at the vertex of the triangle is the angle through which the tangent to the curve turns from the point A to the point B; in other words, it corresponds to the increment in the arc length Δs. From the triangle BKL_1 we find

$$L_1K = |\Delta\sigma| = 2|\sigma|\left|\sin\frac{\Delta\varphi}{2}\right| = 2\left|\sin\frac{\Delta\varphi}{2}\right|$$

(since $|\sigma| = 1$).

Divide both sides of this equation by Δs:

$$\left|\frac{\Delta\sigma}{\Delta s}\right| = 2\left|\frac{\sin\frac{\Delta\varphi}{2}}{\Delta s}\right| = \left|\frac{\sin\frac{\Delta\varphi}{2}}{\frac{\Delta\varphi}{2}}\right|\left|\frac{\Delta\varphi}{\Delta s}\right|$$

We now pass to the limit on both sides of this equation as $\Delta s \to 0$. On the left side we have

$$\lim_{\Delta s \to 0}\left|\frac{\Delta\sigma}{\Delta s}\right| = \left|\frac{d\sigma}{ds}\right|$$

Then

$$\lim_{\Delta s \to 0}\left|\frac{\sin\frac{\Delta\varphi}{2}}{\frac{\Delta\varphi}{2}}\right| = 1$$

since in this case we consider curves such that there exists a limit $\lim\limits_{\Delta s \to 0}\dfrac{\Delta\varphi}{\Delta s}$ and, consequently, $\Delta\varphi \to 0$ as $\Delta s \to 0$. Thus, after passing to the limit we have

$$\left|\frac{d\sigma}{ds}\right| = \lim_{\Delta s \to 0}\left|\frac{\Delta\varphi}{\Delta s}\right| \qquad (4)$$

The ratio in absolute value of the angle of turn $\Delta\varphi$ of the tangent, when the point A goes to the point B, to the length Δs of the arc AB is called (just as it is in the case of a plane curve) the *average curvature* of the given curve on the section AB:

$$\text{average curvature} = \left| \frac{\Delta\varphi}{\Delta s} \right|$$

The limit of the average curvature as $\Delta s \to 0$ is called the *curvature* of the curve at the point A and is denoted by K:

$$K = \lim_{\Delta s \to 0} \left| \frac{\Delta\varphi}{\Delta s} \right|$$

But then from (4) it follows that $\left| \frac{d\sigma}{ds} \right| = K$, which means that the length of the derivative of a unit vector * of a tangent with respect to the arc length is equal to the curvature of the line at the given point. Since the vector σ is a unit vector, its derivative $\frac{d\sigma}{ds}$ is perpendicular to it (see Sec. 9.3, Corollary).

Thus, the vector $\frac{d\sigma}{ds}$ is equal, in length, to the curvature of the curve, and, in direction, is perpendicular to the vector of the tangent.

Definition. The straight line that has the same direction as the vector $\frac{d\sigma}{ds}$ and passes through the corresponding point of the curve is called the *principal normal* of the curve at the given point. We denote by n the unit vector of this direction.

Since the length of the vector $\frac{d\sigma}{ds}$ is equal to K, which is the curvature of the curve, we have

$$\frac{d\sigma}{ds} = Kn$$

The reciprocal of the curvature is called the *radius of curvature* of the curve at the given point and is denoted by R, $\frac{1}{K} = R$.

So we can write

$$\frac{d^2 r}{ds^2} = \frac{d\sigma}{ds} = \frac{n}{R} \qquad (5)$$

From this formula it follows that

$$\frac{1}{R^2} = \left(\frac{d^2 r}{ds^2} \right)^2 \qquad (6)$$

---

* It should be remembered that the derivative of a vector is a vector and for this reason we can speak of the **length** of the derivative.

But

$$\frac{d^2r}{ds^2} = \frac{d^2x}{ds^2}\boldsymbol{i} + \frac{d^2y}{ds^2}\boldsymbol{j} + \frac{d^2z}{ds^2}\boldsymbol{k}$$

Hence,

$$\frac{1}{R} = \sqrt{\left(\frac{d^2x}{ds^2}\right)^2 + \left(\frac{d^2y}{ds^2}\right)^2 + \left(\frac{d^2z}{ds^2}\right)^2} \qquad (6')$$

This formula enables us to compute the curvature of a curve at any point provided that the curve is represented by parametric equations in which the parameter is the arc length s (i. e., provided the radius vector of the variable point of the given line is expressed as a function of the arc length).

Let us consider the case where the radius vector $\boldsymbol{r}$ is expressed as a function of an arbitrary parameter t:

$$\boldsymbol{r} = \boldsymbol{r}(t)$$

In this case the arc length s will be regarded as a function of the parameter t. Then the curvature is computed as follows:

$$\frac{d\boldsymbol{r}}{dt} = \frac{d\boldsymbol{r}}{ds}\frac{ds}{dt} \qquad (7)$$

Since

$$\left|\frac{d\boldsymbol{r}}{ds}\right| = 1 \;^*$$

we have

$$\left(\frac{d\boldsymbol{r}}{dt}\right)^2 = \left(\frac{ds}{dt}\right)^2 \qquad (8)$$

Differentiating the right and left sides of (8) and dividing by two, we get

$$\frac{d\boldsymbol{r}}{dt}\frac{d^2\boldsymbol{r}}{dt^2} = \frac{ds}{dt}\frac{d^2s}{dt^2} \qquad (9)$$

Further, from formula (7) it follows that

$$\frac{d\boldsymbol{r}}{ds} = \frac{d\boldsymbol{r}}{dt}\frac{1}{\frac{ds}{dt}}$$

Differentiate, with respect to s, both sides of this equation:

$$\frac{d^2\boldsymbol{r}}{ds^2} = \frac{d^2\boldsymbol{r}}{dt^2}\frac{1}{\left(\frac{ds}{dt}\right)^2} - \frac{d\boldsymbol{r}}{dt}\frac{\frac{d^2s}{dt^2}}{\left(\frac{ds}{dt}\right)^3}$$

---

* This equation follows from the fact that $\left|\dfrac{d\boldsymbol{r}}{ds}\right| = \lim\limits_{\Delta s \to 0}\left|\dfrac{\Delta\boldsymbol{r}}{\Delta s}\right|$. But $\Delta\boldsymbol{r}$ is a chord subtending an arc of length Δs. Therefore $\left|\dfrac{\Delta\boldsymbol{r}}{\Delta s}\right|$ approaches 1 as $\Delta s \to 0$.

Substituting into formula (6) the expression obtained for $\frac{d^2r}{ds^2}$, we get

$$\frac{1}{R^2}=\left[\frac{d^2r}{dt^2}\frac{1}{\left(\frac{ds}{dt}\right)^2}-\frac{dr}{dt}\frac{\frac{d^2s}{dt^2}}{\left(\frac{ds}{dt}\right)^3}\right]^2$$

$$=\frac{\left(\frac{d^2r}{dt^2}\right)^2\left(\frac{ds}{dt}\right)^2-2\frac{d^2r}{dt^2}\frac{dr}{dt}\frac{ds}{dt}\frac{d^2s}{dt^2}+\left(\frac{dr}{dt}\right)^2\left(\frac{d^2s}{dt^2}\right)^2}{\left(\frac{ds}{dt}\right)^6}$$

Expressing $\frac{ds}{dt}$ and $\frac{d^2s}{dt^2}$ by formulas (8) and (9) in terms of the derivatives of $r(t)$, we get *

$$\frac{1}{R^2}=\frac{\left(\frac{d^2r}{dt^2}\right)^2\left(\frac{dr}{dt}\right)^2-\left(\frac{d^2r}{dt^2}\frac{dr}{dt}\right)^2}{\left\{\left(\frac{dr}{dt}\right)^2\right\}^3} \tag{10}$$

Formula (10) may be rewritten as follows: **

$$K^2=\frac{1}{R^2}=\frac{\left[\frac{dr}{dt}\times\frac{d^2r}{dt^2}\right]^2}{\left\{\left(\frac{dr}{dt}\right)^2\right\}^3} \tag{11}$$

We have obtained a formula that enables us to calculate the curvature of a given curve at any point for an **arbitrary** parametric representation of the curve.

If in a particular case the curve is a plane curve and lies in the xy-plane, then its parametric equations have the form

$$x=\varphi(t)$$
$$y=\psi(t)$$
$$z=0$$

Putting these expressions of x, y, z into formula (11), we get the earlier derived (in Ch. 6) formula that yields the curvature of a

* We transform the denominator as follows: $\left(\frac{ds}{dt}\right)^6=\left\{\left(\frac{ds}{dt}\right)^2\right\}^3=\left\{\left(\frac{dr}{dt}\right)^2\right\}^3$. Here we cannot write $\left(\frac{dr}{dt}\right)^6$. By $\left(\frac{dr}{dt}\right)^2$ we mean the scalar square of the vector $\frac{dr}{dt}$; by $\left\{\left(\frac{dr}{dt}\right)^2\right\}^3$, the third power of $\left(\frac{dr}{dt}\right)^2$. The expression $\left(\frac{dr}{dt}\right)^6$ is meaningless.

** We utilized the identity $a^2b^2-(ab)^2=(a\times b)^2$ whose validity is readily recognizable if one rewrites the identity as follows: $a^2b^2-(ab\cos\varphi)^2=(ab\sin\varphi)^2$.

plane curve represented parametrically:

$$K = \frac{|\varphi'(t)\psi''(t) - \psi'(t)\varphi''(t)|}{\{[\varphi'(t)]^2 + [\psi'(t)]^2\}^{3/2}}$$

Example. Compute the curvature of the helix

$$r = i\,a\cos t + j\,a\sin t + k\,amt$$

at an arbitrary point.
Solution.

$$\frac{dr}{dt} = -i\,a\sin t + j\,a\cos t + k\,am$$

$$\frac{d^2r}{dt^2} = -i\,a\cos t - j\,a\sin t$$

$$\frac{dr}{dt} \times \frac{d^2r}{dt^2} = \begin{vmatrix} i & j & k \\ -a\sin t & a\cos t & am \\ -a\cos t & -a\sin t & 0 \end{vmatrix} = i\,a^2m\sin t - j\,a^2m\cos t + k\,a^2$$

$$\left(\frac{dr}{dt} \times \frac{d^2r}{dt^2}\right)^2 = a^4(m^2+1)$$

$$\left(\frac{dr}{dt}\right)^2 = a^2\sin^2 t + a^2\cos^2 t + a^2m^2 = a^2(1+m^2)$$

Consequently,

$$\frac{1}{R^2} = \frac{a^4(m^2+1)}{[a^2(1+m^2)]^3} = \frac{1}{a^2(1+m^2)^2}$$

whence

$$R = a(1+m^2) = \text{const}$$

Thus, the helix has a constant radius of curvature.

Note. If a curve lies in a plane, then without violating generality, we can assume that it lies in the *xy*-plane (this can always be achieved by transforming the coordinates). Now if the curve lies in the *xy*-plane, then $z = 0$; but then $\frac{d^2z}{ds^2} = 0$ also and, consequently, the vector n likewise lies in the *xy*-plane. We thus conclude that if a curve lies in a plane, then its principal normal lies in the same plane.

The velocity of a point in curvilinear motion. Let a moving point at time t be at point M defined by the radius vector $\overline{OM} = r(t)$ (see Fig. 200), and at time $t + \Delta t$ at point M_1 defined by the radius vector $\overline{OM_1} = r(t + \Delta t)$. Then the vector $\overline{MM_1}$ is called the *displacement vector of the point.* The ratio of the displacement vector $\overline{MM_1}$ to the associated time increment Δt is called the *average velocity of the point* during the time interval:

$$v_{av} = \frac{\overline{MM_1}}{\Delta t} = \frac{\Delta r}{\Delta t} = \overline{MN}$$

The vector of the average velocity is also directed along the chord MM_1 (see Fig. 200, page 315) in the direction of motion of the point (in rectilinear motion, its direction is that of the trajectory).

The velocity of the point at a given instant of time is defined thus:

$$v = \lim_{\Delta t \to 0} (v_{av}) = \lim_{\Delta t \to 0} \frac{\Delta r}{\Delta t} = \frac{dr}{dt}$$

that is,

$$v = \frac{dr}{dt} \tag{12}$$

We can therefore say that *the velocity of a point at a given time is equal to the first derivative of the radius vector of the point with respect to the time.*

By formula (2'), Sec. 9.2, it follows that the projections of the velocity on the coordinate axes are

$$v_x = \frac{dx}{dt}, \quad v_y = \frac{dy}{dt}, \quad v_z = \frac{dz}{dt}$$

The modulus of the velocity is found from formula (3), Sec. 9.2:

$$v = \sqrt{\left(\frac{dx}{dt}\right)^2 + \left(\frac{dy}{dt}\right)^2 + \left(\frac{dz}{dt}\right)^2} \tag{13}$$

If we introduce the arc length s, as was done at the beginning of this section, and consider s as a function of time t, then formula (12) may be written

$$v = \frac{dr}{dt} = \frac{dr}{ds}\frac{ds}{dt} = \sigma v \tag{14}$$

where $v = \frac{ds}{dt}$ is the absolute value of velocity and σ is the unit vector directed along the tangent line in the direction of motion.

Acceleration of a point in curvilinear motion. As was defined in Sec. 3.25, the *acceleration* of a point w in curvilinear motion is the derivative of the velocity vector with respect to time:

$$w = \frac{dv}{dt} \tag{15}$$

But $v = \frac{dr}{dt}$ and so

$$w = \frac{d^2r}{dt^2} \tag{16}$$

If we proceed from formula (14), then we get

$$w = \frac{dv}{dt} = \frac{d(v \cdot \sigma)}{dt}$$

Expanding this derivative, by formula (III), Sec. 9.3, we get

$$w = \frac{dv}{dt}\sigma + v\frac{d\sigma}{dt} \qquad (17)$$

Transform the derivative $\frac{d\sigma}{dt}$ using formulas (7) and (5):

$$\frac{d\sigma}{dt} = \frac{d\sigma}{ds}\frac{ds}{dt} = \frac{n}{R}v$$

Substituting into (17), we finally get

$$w = \frac{dv}{dt}\sigma + v^2\frac{n}{R} \qquad (18)$$

Here, σ is a unit vector directed along the tangent line in the direction of motion and n is a unit vector along the principal normal.

In words, formula (18) may be stated thus:

The projection of the acceleration of a point on the tangent line is equal to the first derivative of the absolute value of the velocity, and the projection of the acceleration on the principal normal is equal to the square of the velocity divided by the radius of curvature of the trajectory at the given point.

Since the vectors σ and n are mutually perpendicular, the modulus of acceleration is given by the formula

$$w = \sqrt{\left(\frac{uv}{dt}\right)^2 + \left(\frac{v^2}{R}\right)^2} \qquad (19)$$

9.5 OSCULATING PLANE. BINORMAL. TORSION

Definition 1. The plane passing through the tangent line and the principal normal to a given curve at a point A is called the *osculating plane* at the point A.

For a plane curve, the osculating plane coincides with the plane of the curve. But if the curve is not a plane curve, and if we take two points on it, P and P_1, we get two different osculating planes that form a dihedral angle μ. The bigger the angle μ, the more the curve differs in shape from a plane curve. To make this more precise, let us introduce another definition.

Definition 2. The normal (to a curve) perpendicular to the osculating plane is called a *binormal*.

On the binormal let us take a unit vector b and make its direction such that the vectors σ, n, b form a triple with the same orientation as the unit vectors i, j, k lying on the coordinate axes (Figs. 204, 205).

By virtue of the definition of a vector product and scalar product of vectors we have

$$b = \sigma \times n, \quad bb = 1 \tag{1}$$

We find the derivative of $\frac{db}{ds}$. By formula V, Sec. 9.3,

$$\frac{db}{ds} = \frac{d(\sigma \times n)}{ds} = \frac{d\sigma}{ds} \times n + \sigma \times \frac{dn}{ds} \tag{2}$$

But $\frac{d\sigma}{ds} = \frac{n}{R}$ (see Sec. 9.4), therefore

$$\frac{d\sigma}{ds} \times n = \frac{1}{R} n \times n = 0$$

and formula (2) takes the form

$$\frac{db}{ds} = \sigma \times \frac{dn}{ds} \tag{3}$$

From this it follows (by the definition of a vector product) that $\frac{db}{ds}$ is a vector perpendicular to the vector of the tangent line σ.

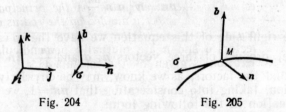

Fig. 204   Fig. 205

On the other hand, since b is a unit vector, $\frac{db}{ds}$ is perpendicular to b (see Sec. 9.3, Corollary).

This means that the vector $\frac{db}{ds}$ is perpendicular both to σ and to b; that is, it is collinear with the vector n.

Let us denote the length of the vector $\frac{db}{ds}$ by $\frac{1}{T}$:

$$\left| \frac{db}{ds} \right| = \frac{1}{T}$$

then

$$\frac{db}{ds} = \frac{1}{T} n \tag{4}$$

The quantity $\frac{1}{T}$ is the *torsion* of the given curve.

The dihedral angle μ between the osculating planes that correspond to two points of the curve is equal to the angle between the binormals. By analogy with formula (4), Sec. 9.4, one can write

$$\left|\frac{db}{ds}\right| = \lim_{\Delta s \to 0} \frac{\mu}{|\Delta s|}$$

To summarize, then, the torsion of a curve at a point A is equal, in absolute value, to the limit which is approached (as $\Delta s \to 0$) by the ratio of the angle μ between the osculating planes at the point A and the neighbouring point B to the length $|\Delta s|$ of the arc AB.

If the curve is **plane** then the osculating plane does not change its direction and, consequently, the torsion is equal to zero.

From the definition of torsion it is clear that it is a measure of the deviation of a space curve from a plane curve. The quantity T is called the *radius of torsion* of the curve.

Let us find a formula for computing torsion. From (3) and (4) it follows that

$$\frac{1}{T}\,n = \sigma \times \frac{dn}{ds}$$

Forming the scalar product of both sides by n, we get

$$\frac{1}{T}\,nn = n\left(\sigma \times \frac{dn}{ds}\right)$$

On the right side of this equation we have the so-called mixed (or triple) product of three vectors n, σ and $\frac{dn}{ds}$. In a product of this kind the factors, as we know, may be circularly permuted. In addition, taking into consideration that $nn = 1$, we rewrite the latter equation in the following form:

$$\frac{1}{T} = \sigma\left(\frac{dn}{ds} \times n\right)$$

or

$$\frac{1}{T} = -\sigma\left(n \times \frac{dn}{ds}\right) \tag{5}$$

But since $n = R\dfrac{d^2r}{ds^2}$, we have

$$\frac{dn}{ds} = R\frac{d^3r}{ds^3} + \frac{dR}{ds}\frac{d^2r}{ds^2}$$

and

$$\begin{aligned}
\left(n \times \frac{dn}{ds}\right) &= R\frac{d^2r}{ds^2} \times \left(R\frac{d^3r}{ds^3} + \frac{dR}{ds}\frac{d^2r}{ds^2}\right) \\
&= R^2\left(\frac{d^2r}{ds^2} \times \frac{d^3r}{ds^3}\right) + R\frac{dR}{ds}\left(\frac{d^2r}{ds^2} \times \frac{d^2r}{ds^2}\right)
\end{aligned}$$

But since the vector product of a vector into itself is equal to zero,

$$\frac{d^2r}{ds^2} \times \frac{d^2r}{ds^2} = 0$$

Thus,

$$n \times \frac{dn}{ds} = R^2 \left(\frac{d^2r}{ds^2} \times \frac{d^3r}{ds^3} \right)$$

Noting that $\sigma = \frac{dr}{ds}$ and reverting to (5), we get

$$\frac{1}{T} = -R^2 \frac{dr}{ds} \left(\frac{d^2r}{ds^2} \times \frac{d^3r}{ds^3} \right) \tag{6}$$

If the vector r is expressed as a function of an arbitrary parameter t, it may be shown,* much like was done in the preceding

---

* Indeed,

$$\frac{dr}{dt} = \frac{dr}{ds} \frac{ds}{dt}$$

Differentiating once again with respect to t, we get

$$\frac{d^2r}{dt^2} = \frac{d}{ds} \left(\frac{dr}{ds} \right) \frac{ds}{dt} \frac{ds}{dt} + \frac{dr}{ds} \frac{d^2s}{dt^2} = \frac{d^2r}{ds^2} \left(\frac{ds}{dt} \right)^2 + \frac{dr}{ds} \frac{d^2s}{dt^2}$$

Differentiate it once more with respect to t:

$$\frac{d^3r}{dt^3} = \frac{d}{ds} \left(\frac{d^2r}{ds^2} \right) \frac{ds}{dt} \left(\frac{ds}{dt} \right)^2 + \frac{d^2r}{ds^2} \cdot 2 \frac{ds}{dt} \frac{d^2s}{dt^2} + \frac{d}{ds} \left(\frac{dr}{ds} \right) \frac{ds}{dt} \frac{d^2s}{dt^2} + \frac{dr}{ds} \frac{d^3s}{dt^3}$$

$$= \frac{d^3r}{ds^3} \left(\frac{ds}{dt} \right)^3 + 3 \frac{d^2r}{ds^2} \frac{ds}{dt} \frac{d^2s}{dt^2} + \frac{dr}{ds} \frac{d^3s}{dt^3}$$

Let us now form a triple product:

$$\frac{dr}{dt} \left(\frac{d^2r}{dt^2} \times \frac{d^3r}{dt^3} \right)$$

$$= \frac{dr}{ds} \frac{ds}{dt} \left\{ \left[\frac{d^2r}{ds^2} \left(\frac{ds}{dt} \right)^2 + \frac{dr}{ds} \frac{d^2s}{dt^2} \right] \times \left[\frac{d^3r}{ds^3} \left(\frac{ds}{dt} \right)^3 + 3 \frac{d^2r}{ds^2} \frac{ds}{dt} \frac{d^2s}{dt^2} + \frac{dr}{ds} \frac{d^3s}{dt^3} \right] \right\}$$

Expanding this product by the rule for multiplying polynomials, and disregarding those terms that contain two identical vector factors (since the triple product of three factors where at least two are equal is zero), we get

$$\frac{dr}{dt} \left(\frac{d^2r}{dt^2} \times \frac{d^3r}{dt^3} \right) = \frac{dr}{ds} \left(\frac{d^2r}{ds^2} \times \frac{d^3r}{ds^3} \right) \left(\frac{ds}{dt} \right)^6$$

Finally, noting that

$$\left(\frac{ds}{dt} \right)^2 = \left(\frac{dr}{dt} \right)^2$$

or

$$\left(\frac{ds}{dt} \right)^6 = \left\{ \left(\frac{dr}{dt} \right)^2 \right\}^3$$

we obtain the required equation.

section, that

$$\frac{d\boldsymbol{r}}{ds}\left(\frac{d^2\boldsymbol{r}}{ds^2}\times\frac{d^3\boldsymbol{r}}{ds^3}\right)=\frac{\dfrac{d\boldsymbol{r}}{dt}\left(\dfrac{d^2\boldsymbol{r}}{dt^2}\times\dfrac{d^3\boldsymbol{r}}{dt^3}\right)}{\left\{\left(\dfrac{d\boldsymbol{r}}{dt}\right)^2\right\}^3}$$

Putting this expression into formula (6) and replacing R^2 by its expression from formula (11), Sec. 9.4, we finally get

$$\frac{1}{T}=-\frac{\dfrac{d\boldsymbol{r}}{dt}\left(\dfrac{d^2\boldsymbol{r}}{dt^2}\times\dfrac{d^3\boldsymbol{r}}{dt^3}\right)}{\left(\dfrac{d\boldsymbol{r}}{dt}\times\dfrac{d^2\boldsymbol{r}}{dt^2}\right)^2} \qquad (7)$$

This formula makes it possible to compute the torsion of the curve at any point if the curve is represented by parametric equations with an arbitrary parameter t.

Concluding this section, we note that the formulas which express the derivatives of the vectors σ, $\boldsymbol{b}$, $\boldsymbol{n}$ are called *Serret-Frenet formulas*:

$$\frac{d\boldsymbol{\sigma}}{ds}=\frac{\boldsymbol{n}}{R},\quad \frac{d\boldsymbol{b}}{ds}=\frac{\boldsymbol{n}}{T},\quad \frac{d\boldsymbol{n}}{ds}=-\frac{\boldsymbol{\sigma}}{R}-\frac{\boldsymbol{b}}{T}$$

The last one is obtained as follows:

$$\boldsymbol{n}=\boldsymbol{b}\times\boldsymbol{\sigma}$$

$$\frac{d\boldsymbol{n}}{ds}=\frac{d\,(\boldsymbol{b}\times\boldsymbol{\sigma})}{ds}=\frac{d\boldsymbol{b}}{ds}\times\boldsymbol{\sigma}+\boldsymbol{b}\times\frac{d\boldsymbol{\sigma}}{ds}=\frac{\boldsymbol{n}}{T}\times\boldsymbol{\sigma}+\boldsymbol{b}\times\frac{\boldsymbol{n}}{R}$$

$$=\frac{1}{T}\,\boldsymbol{n}\times\boldsymbol{\sigma}+\frac{1}{R}\,\boldsymbol{b}\times\boldsymbol{n}$$

but

$$\boldsymbol{n}\times\boldsymbol{\sigma}=-\boldsymbol{b},\quad \boldsymbol{b}\times\boldsymbol{n}=-\boldsymbol{\sigma}$$

therefore

$$\frac{d\boldsymbol{n}}{ds}=-\frac{\boldsymbol{b}}{T}-\frac{\boldsymbol{\sigma}}{R}$$

Example. Compute the torsion of the helix

$$\boldsymbol{r}=\boldsymbol{i}\,a\cos t+\boldsymbol{j}\,a\sin t+\boldsymbol{k}\,amt$$

Solution.

$$\frac{d\boldsymbol{r}}{dt}\left(\frac{d^2\boldsymbol{r}}{dt^2}\times\frac{d^3\boldsymbol{r}}{dt^3}\right)=\begin{vmatrix}-a\sin t & a\cos t & am\\ -a\cos t & -a\sin t & 0\\ a\sin t & -a\cos t & 0\end{vmatrix}=a^3m$$

$$\left(\frac{d\boldsymbol{r}}{dt}\times\frac{d^2\boldsymbol{r}}{dt^2}\right)^2=a^4\,(1+m^2) \text{ (see Example, Sec. 9.4).}$$

Consequently,

$$T=-\frac{a^4\,(1+m^2)}{a^3m}=-\frac{a\,(1+m^2)}{m}.$$

9.6 THE TANGENT PLANE
AND THE NORMAL TO A SURFACE

Let there be a surface given by an equation of the form

$$F(x, y, z) = 0 \qquad (1)$$

We introduce the following definition.

Definition 1. A straight line is a *tangent* to a surface at some point $P(x, y, z)$ if it is tangent to some curve lying on the surface and passing through P.

Since an infinitude of different curves lying on the surface pass through the point P, then, generally speaking, there will also be an infinitude of tangents to the surface passing through this point.

We introduce the concept of singular and ordinary points of a surface $F(x, y, z) = 0$.

If at the point $M(x, y, z)$ all three derivatives $\frac{\partial F}{\partial x}$, $\frac{\partial F}{\partial y}$, $\frac{\partial F}{\partial z}$ are equal to zero, or at least one of these derivatives does not exist, then M is called a *singular* point of the surface. If at $M(x, y, z)$ all three derivatives $\frac{\partial F}{\partial x}$, $\frac{\partial F}{\partial y}$, $\frac{\partial F}{\partial z}$ exist and are continuous, and at

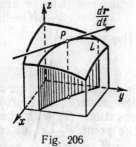

Fig. 206

least one of them differs from zero, then M is an *ordinary* point of the surface.

We can now formulate the following theorem.

Theorem. *All tangent lines to a given surface* (1) *at an ordinary point of it P lie in one plane.*

Proof. Let us consider, on a surface, a certain curve L (Fig. 206) passing through a given point P of the surface. Let this curve be represented by parametric equations:

$$x = \varphi(t), \ y = \psi(t), \ z = \chi(t) \qquad (2)$$

A tangent to the curve will be a tangent to the surface. The equations of this tangent have the form

$$\frac{X-x}{\frac{dx}{dt}} = \frac{Y-y}{\frac{dy}{dt}} = \frac{Z-z}{\frac{dz}{dt}}$$

If we put expressions (2) into equation (1), the latter will become an identity in t, since the curve (2) lies on the surface (1).

Differentiating it with respect to t, we get *

$$\frac{\partial F}{\partial x}\frac{dx}{dt} + \frac{\partial F}{\partial y}\frac{dy}{dt} + \frac{\partial F}{\partial z}\frac{dz}{dt} = 0 \qquad (3)$$

Let us further examine the vectors N and $\frac{dr}{dt}$ that pass through P:

$$N = \frac{\partial F}{\partial x}i + \frac{\partial F}{\partial y}j + \frac{\partial F}{\partial z}k \qquad (4)$$

The projections of this vector, $\frac{\partial F}{\partial x}$, $\frac{\partial F}{\partial y}$, $\frac{\partial F}{\partial z}$, depend on x, y, z, which are the coordinates of P; it will be noted that since P is an ordinary point, these projections do not simultaneously vanish at the point P and therefore

$$|N| = \sqrt{\left(\frac{\partial F}{\partial x}\right)^2 + \left(\frac{\partial F}{\partial y}\right)^2 + \left(\frac{\partial F}{\partial z}\right)^2} \neq 0$$

The vector

$$\frac{dr}{dt} = \frac{dx}{dt}i + \frac{dy}{dt}j + \frac{dz}{dt}k \qquad (5)$$

is tangent to the curve passing through the point P and lying on the surface. The projections of this vector are computed from equations (2) with the value of the parameter t corresponding to the point P. Let us compute the scalar product of the vectors N and $\frac{dr}{dt}$, which product is equal to the sum of the products of like projections:

$$N\frac{dr}{dt} = \frac{\partial F}{\partial x}\frac{dx}{dt} + \frac{\partial F}{\partial y}\frac{dy}{dt} + \frac{\partial F}{\partial z}\frac{dz}{dt}$$

On the basis of (3), the expression on the right is equal to zero; hence

$$N\frac{dr}{dt} = 0.$$

From this equation it follows that the vector N and the tangent vector $\frac{dr}{dt}$ to the curve (2) at the point P are perpendicular. The foregoing reasoning holds for any curve (2) passing through the point P and lying on the surface. Therefore, every tangent to the surface at the point P is perpendicular to one and the same vector N and for this reason all these tangents lie in a single plane that is perpendicular to the vector N. The theorem is proved.

---

* Here we apply the rule for differentiating a composite function of three variables. This rule is applicable here since all the partial derivatives $\frac{\partial F}{\partial x}$, $\frac{\partial F}{\partial y}$, $\frac{\partial F}{\partial z}$ are, as stated, continuous.

Definition 2. The plane in which lie all the tangent lines to the curves on the surface passing through the given point P is called the *tangent plane* to the surface at the point P (Fig. 207).

It should be noted that a tangent plane may not exist at the singular points of the surface. At such points, the tangent lines to the surface may not lie in one plane. For instance, the vertex of a conical surface is a singular point. The tangents to the conical surface at this point do not lie in one plane (they themselves form a conical surface).

Let us write the equation of the tangent plane to a surface (1) at an ordinary point. Since this plane is perpendicular to the vector (4), its equation has the form

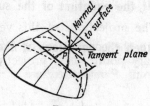

Fig. 207

$$\frac{\partial F}{\partial x}(X-x) + \frac{\partial F}{\partial y}(Y-y) + \frac{\partial F}{\partial z}(Z-z) = 0 \tag{6}$$

If the equation of the surface is given in the form

$$z = f(x, y) \quad \text{or} \quad z - f(x, y) = 0$$

then

$$\frac{\partial F}{\partial x} = -\frac{\partial f}{\partial x}, \quad \frac{\partial F}{\partial y} = -\frac{\partial f}{\partial y}, \quad \frac{\partial F}{\partial z} = 1$$

and the equation of the tangent plane is then of the form

$$Z - z = \frac{\partial f}{\partial x}(X-x) + \frac{\partial f}{\partial y}(Y-y) \tag{6'}$$

Note. If in formula (6') we put $X - x = \Delta x$, $Y - y = \Delta y$, then this formula will take the form

$$Z - z = \frac{\partial f}{\partial x}\Delta x + \frac{\partial f}{\partial y}\Delta y$$

Its right side is the total differential of the function $z = f(x, y)$. Therefore, $Z - z = dz$. Thus, the total differential of a function of two variables at the point $M(x, y)$, which differential corresponds to the increments Δx and Δy of the independent variables x and y, is equal to the corresponding increment in the z-coordinate of the tangent plane to the surface which is the graph of the given function.

Definition 3. The straight line drawn through the point $P(x, y, z)$ of surface (1) perpendicular to the tangent plane is called the *normal* to the surface (Fig. 207).

22—2081

Let us write the equations of the normal. Since its direction, coincides with that of the vector N, its equations will have the form

$$\frac{X-x}{\frac{\partial F}{\partial x}}=\frac{Y-y}{\frac{\partial F}{\partial y}}=\frac{Z-z}{\frac{\partial F}{\partial z}} \qquad (7)$$

If the equation of the surface is given in the form $z=f(x,\ y)$, or

$$z-f(x,\ y)=0$$

then the equations of the normal have the form

$$\frac{X-x}{-\frac{\partial f}{\partial x}}=\frac{Y-y}{-\frac{\partial f}{\partial y}}=\frac{Z-z}{1}$$

Note. Let the surface $F(x,\ y,\ z)=0$ be the level surface for some function of three variables $u=u(x,\ y,\ z)$; that is,

$$F(x,\ y,\ z)=u(x,\ y,\ z)-C=0$$

Obviously, the vector N, defined by formula (4) and in the direction of the normal to the level surface $F=u(x,\ y,\ z)-C=0$, will be

$$N=\frac{\partial u}{\partial x}i+\frac{\partial u}{\partial y}j+\frac{\partial u}{\partial z}k$$

that is,

$$N=\operatorname{grad} u$$

We have thus proved that the *gradient of the function $u(x,\ y,\ z)$ is in the direction of the normal to the level surface passing through the given point*.

Example. Write the equation of the tangent plane and the equations of the normal to the surface of the sphere $x^2+y^2+z^2=14$ at the point $P(1,\ 2,\ 3)$.
Solution.

$$F(x,\ y,\ z)=x^2+y^2+z^2-14=0,\quad \frac{\partial F}{\partial x}=2x,\quad \frac{\partial F}{\partial y}=2y,\quad \frac{\partial F}{\partial z}=2z$$

For $x=1,\ y=2,\ z=3$ we have

$$\frac{\partial F}{\partial x}=2,\quad \frac{\partial F}{\partial y}=4,\quad \frac{\partial F}{\partial z}=6$$

Therefore, the equation of the tangent plane will be

$$2(x-1)+4(y-2)+6(z-3)=0 \text{ or } x+2y+3z-14=0$$

The equations of the normal are

$$\frac{x-1}{2}=\frac{y-2}{4}=\frac{z-3}{6}$$

or

$$\frac{x-1}{1}=\frac{y-2}{2}=\frac{z-3}{3}$$

Exercises on Chapter 9

Find the derivatives of the following vectors:

1. $r = i \cot t + j \arctan t$. *Ans.* $r' = -\dfrac{1}{\sin^2 t} i + \dfrac{1}{1+t^2} j$. **2.** $r = i e^{-t} + j 2t +$
$+ k \ln t$. *Ans.* $r' = -i e^{-t} + 2j + \dfrac{k}{t}$. **3.** $r = t^2 i - \dfrac{j}{t} + \dfrac{k}{t^2}$. *Ans.* $r' = 2ti + \dfrac{j}{t^2} - \dfrac{2k}{t^3}$.

4. Find the vector of the tangent, the equations of the tangent and the equations of the normal plane to the curve $r = t i + t^2 j + t^3 k$ at the point $(3, 9, 27)$. *Ans.* $r' = i + 6j + 27k$; tangent: $\dfrac{x-3}{1} = \dfrac{y-9}{6} = \dfrac{z-27}{27}$; normal plane: $x + 6y + 27z = 786$.

5. Find the vector of the tangent, the equations of the tangent and the equation of the normal plane to the curve $r = i \cos^2 \dfrac{t}{2} + \dfrac{1}{2} j \sin t + k \sin \dfrac{t}{2}$.
Ans. $r' = -\dfrac{1}{2} i \sin t + \dfrac{1}{2} j \cos t + \dfrac{1}{2} k \cos \dfrac{t}{2}$; the equation of the tangent
$\dfrac{X - \cos^2 \dfrac{t}{2}}{-\sin t} = \dfrac{Y - \dfrac{1}{2}\sin t}{\cos t} = \dfrac{Z - \sin \dfrac{t}{2}}{\cos \dfrac{t}{2}}$; the equation of the normal plane:

$+ X \sin t - Y \cos t - Z \cos \dfrac{t}{2} = + x \sin t - y \cos t - z \cos \dfrac{t}{2}$, where x, y, z are the coordinates of that point of the curve at which the normal plane is drawn $\left(\text{that is, } x = \cos^2 \dfrac{t}{2}, \ y = \dfrac{1}{2} \sin t, \ z = \sin \dfrac{t}{2}\right)$.

6. Find the equations of the tangent to the curve $x = t - \sin t$, $y = 1 - \cos t$, $z = 4 \sin \dfrac{t}{2}$ and the cosines of the angles that it makes with the coordinate axes. *Ans.* $\dfrac{X - X_0}{\sin \dfrac{t_0}{2}} = \dfrac{Y - Y_0}{\cos \dfrac{t_0}{2}} = \dfrac{Z - Z_0}{\cot \dfrac{t_0}{2}}$, $\cos \alpha = \sin^2 \dfrac{t_0}{2}$, $\cos \beta = \dfrac{1}{2} \sin t_0$, $\cos \gamma = \cos \dfrac{t_0}{2}$.

7. Find the equation of the normal plane to the curve $z = x^2 - y^2$, $y = x$ at the origin. **Hint.** Write the equations of the curve in parametric form. *Ans.* $x + y = 0$.

8. Find σ, n, b at the point $t = \dfrac{\pi}{2}$ for the curve $r = i (\cos t + \sin^2 t) + j \sin t (1 - \cos t) - k \cos t$. *Ans.* $\sigma = \dfrac{1}{\sqrt{3}}(-i + j + k)$, $n = \dfrac{-5i - 4j - k}{\sqrt{42}}$, $b = \dfrac{i - 2j + 3k}{\sqrt{14}}$.

9. Find the equations of the principal normal and the binormal to the curve $x = \dfrac{t^4}{4}$, $y = \dfrac{t^3}{3}$, $z = \dfrac{t^2}{2}$ at the point (x_0, y_0, z_0). *Ans.* $\dfrac{x - x_0}{t_0^3 + 2t_0} = \dfrac{y - y_0}{1 - t_0^4} = \dfrac{z - z_0}{-2t_0^3 - t_0}$, $\dfrac{x - x_0}{1} = \dfrac{y - y_0}{-2t_0} = \dfrac{z - z_0}{t_0^2}$.

10. Find the equation of the osculating plane to the curve $y^2 = x$, $x^2 = z$ at the point M (1, 1, 1). *Ans.* $6x - 8y - z + 3 = 0$.

11. Find the radius of curvature for a curve represented by the equations $x^2 + y^2 + z^2 - 4 = 0$, $x + y - z = 0$. *Ans.* $R = 2$.

12. Find the radius of torsion of the curve $r = i \cos t + j \sin t + k \operatorname{sh} t$. *Ans.* $T = -\operatorname{ch} t$.

13. Find the radius of curvature and the torsion of the curve $r = t^2 i + 2t^3 j$. *Ans.* $R = \dfrac{2}{3} t (1 + 9t^2)^{3/2}$, $T = \infty$.

14. Prove that the curve $r = (a_1 t^2 + b_1 t + c_1) i + (a_2 t^2 + b_2 t + c_2) j + (a_3 t^2 + b_3 t + c_3) k$ is plane. *Ans.* $r''' \equiv 0$, therefore the torsion is equal to zero.

15. Find the curvature and torsion of the curve $x = e^t$, $y = e^{-t}$, $z = t \sqrt{2}$. *Ans.* The curvature is $\dfrac{\sqrt{2}}{(x+y)^2}$, the torsion is $\dfrac{\sqrt{2}}{(x+y)^2}$.

16. Find the curvature and torsion of the curve $x = e^{-t} \sin t$, $y = e^{-t} \cos t$, $z = e^{-t}$. *Ans.* The curvature is $\dfrac{\sqrt{2}}{3} e^t$, the torsion is $-\dfrac{1}{3} e^t$.

17. Find the equation of the tangent plane to the hyperboloid $\dfrac{x^2}{a^2} - \dfrac{y^2}{b^2} - \dfrac{z^2}{c^2} = 1$ at the point (x_1, y_1, z_1). *Ans.* $\dfrac{x_1 x}{a^2} - \dfrac{y_1 y}{b^2} - \dfrac{z_1 z}{c^2} = 1$.

18. Find the equation of the normal to the surface $x^2 - 4y^2 + 2z^2 = 6$ at the point (2, 2, 3). *Ans.* $y + 4x = 10$, $3x - z = 3$.

19. Find the equation of the tangent plane to the surface $z = 2x^2 + 4y^2$ at the point M (2, 1, 12). *Ans.* $8x + 8y - z = 12$.

20. Draw to the surface $x^2 + 2y^2 + z^2 = 1$ a tangent plane parallel to the plane $x - y + 2z = 0$. *Ans.* $x - y + 2z = \pm \sqrt{\dfrac{11}{2}}$.

CHAPTER 10

THE INDEFINITE INTEGRAL

10.1 ANTIDERIVATIVE AND THE INDEFINITE INTEGRAL

In Chapter 3 we considered the following problem: given a function $F(x)$, find its derivative, that is, the function $f(x) = F'(x)$.

In this chapter we shall consider the reverse problem: given a function $f(x)$, it is required to find a function $F(x)$ such that its derivative is equal to $f(x)$, that is,

$$F'(x) = f(x)$$

Definition 1. A function $F(x)$ is called the *antiderivative* of the function $f(x)$ on the interval $[a, b]$ if at all points of the interval $F'(x) = f(x)$.

Example. Find the antiderivative of the function $f(x) = x^2$.
From the definition of an antiderivative it follows that the function $F(x) = \frac{x^3}{3}$ is an antiderivative, since $\left(\frac{x^3}{3}\right)' = x^2$.

It is easy to see that if for the given function $f(x)$ there exists an antiderivative, then this antiderivative is not the only one. In the foregoing example, we could take the following functions as antiderivatives: $F(x) = \frac{x^3}{3} + 1$, $F(x) = \frac{x^3}{3} - 7$ or, generally, $F(x) = \frac{x^3}{3} + C$ (where C is an arbitrary constant), since

$$\left(\frac{x^3}{3} + C\right)' = x^2$$

On the other hand, it may be proved that functions of the form $\frac{x^3}{3} + C$ exhaust all antiderivatives of the function x^2. This is a consequence of the following theorem.

Theorem. *If $F_1(x)$ and $F_2(x)$ are two antiderivatives of a function $f(x)$ on an interval $[a, b]$, then the difference between them is a constant.*

Proof. By virtue of the definition of an antiderivative we have

$$\left.\begin{array}{c} F_1'(x) = f(x) \\ F_2'(x) = f(x) \end{array}\right\} \tag{1}$$

for any value of x on the interval $[a, b]$.

Let us put

$$F_1(x) - F_2(x) = \varphi(x) \qquad (2)$$

Then by (1) we have

$$F_1'(x) - F_2'(x) = f(x) - f(x) = 0$$

or

$$\varphi'(x) = [F_1(x) - F_2(x)]' \equiv 0$$

for any value of x on the interval $[a, b]$. But from $\varphi'(x) = 0$ it follows that $\varphi(x)$ is a constant.

Indeed, let us apply the Lagrange theorem (see Sec. 4.2) to the function $\varphi(x)$, which, obviously, is continuous and differentiable on the interval $[a, b]$. No matter what the point x on the interval $[a, b]$, we have, by virtue of the Lagrange theorem,

$$\varphi(x) - \varphi(a) = (x - a)\,\varphi'(\xi)$$

where $a < \xi < x$.

Since $\varphi'(\xi) = 0$,

$$\varphi(x) - \varphi(a) = 0$$

or

$$\varphi(x) = \varphi(a) \qquad (3)$$

Thus, the function $\varphi(x)$ at any point x of the interval $[a, b]$ retains the value $\varphi(a)$, and this means that the function $\varphi(x)$ is constant on $[a, b]$. Denoting the constant $\varphi(a)$ by C, we get, from (2) and (3),

$$F_1(x) - F_2(x) = C$$

From this theorem it follows that if for a given function $f(x)$ some one antiderivative $F(x)$ is found, then **any other** antiderivative of $f(x)$ has the form $F(x) + C$, where $C = \text{constant}$.

Definition 2. If the function $F(x)$ is an antiderivative of $f(x)$, then the expression $F(x) + C$ is the *indefinite integral* of the function $f(x)$ and is denoted by the symbol $\int f(x)\,dx$. Thus, by definition

$$\int f(x)\,dx = F(x) + C$$

if

$$F'(x) = f(x)$$

Here, the function $f(x)$ is called the *integrand*, $f(x)\,dx$ is the *element of integration* (the expression under the integral sign), and $\int$ is the *integral sign*.

Thus, an indefinite integral is **a family of functions** $y = F(x) + C$.

From the geometrical point of view, an indefinite integral is a collection (family) of curves, each of which is obtained by translating one of the curves parallel to itself upwards or downwards (that is, along the y-axis).

A natural question arises: do antiderivatives (and, hence, indefinite integrals) exist for every function $f(x)$? The answer is no. Let us note, however, without proof, that *if a function $f(x)$ is continuous on an interval* $[a, b]$, *then this function has an antiderivative* (and, hence, *there is also an indefinite integral*).

This chapter is devoted to working out methods by means of which we can find antiderivatives (and indefinite integrals) for certain classes of elementary functions.

The finding of an antiderivative of a given function $f(x)$ is called *integration* of the function $f(x)$.

Note the following: if the derivative of an elementary function is always an elementary function, then the antiderivative of the elementary function may not prove to be representable by a finite number of elementary functions. We shall return to this question at the end of the chapter.

From Definition 2 it follows that:

1. *The derivative of an indefinite integral is equal to the integrand, that is, if* $F'(x) = f(x)$, *then also*

$$\left(\int f(x)dx \right)' = (F(x) + C)' = f(x). \tag{4}$$

This equation should be understood in the sense that the derivative of any antiderivative is equal to the integrand.

2. *The differential of an indefinite integral is equal to the expression under the integral sign:*

$$d\left(\int f(x)\,dx \right) = f(x)\,dx \tag{5}$$

This results from formula (4).

3. *The indefinite integral of the differential of some function is equal to this function plus an arbitrary constant:*

$$\int dF(x) = F(x) + C$$

The truth of this equation may easily be checked by differentiation [the differentials of both sides are equal to $dF(x)$].

10.2 TABLE OF INTEGRALS

Before starting on methods of integration, we give the following table of integrals of the simplest functions.

The table of integrals follows directly from Definition 2, Sec. 10.1, and from the table of derivatives (given in Sec. 3.15). (The truth of the equations can easily be checked by differentiation: by establishing that the derivative of the right side is equal to the integrand.)

1. $\int x^{\alpha} dx = \frac{x^{\alpha+1}}{\alpha+1} + C$ ($\alpha \neq -1$). (Here and in the formulas that follow, C stands for an arbitrary constant.)

2. $\int \frac{dx}{x} = \ln |x| + C.$

3. $\int \sin x \, dx = -\cos x + C.$

4. $\int \cos x \, dx = \sin x + C.$

5. $\int \frac{dx}{\cos^2 x} = \tan x + C.$

6. $\int \frac{dx}{\sin^2 x} = -\cot x + C.$

7. $\int \tan x \, dx = -\ln |\cos x| + C.$

8. $\int \cot x \, dx = \ln |\sin x| + C.$

9. $\int e^x \, dx = e^x + C.$

10. $\int a^x \, dx = \frac{a^x}{\ln a} + C.$

11. $\int \frac{dx}{1+x^2} = \arctan x + C.$

11′. $\int \frac{dx}{a^2+x^2} = \frac{1}{a} \arctan \frac{x}{a} + C.$

12. $\int \frac{dx}{a^2-x^2} = \frac{1}{2a} \ln \left| \frac{a+x}{a-x} \right| + C.$

13. $\int \frac{dx}{\sqrt{1-x^2}} = \arcsin x + C.$

13′. $\int \frac{dx}{\sqrt{a^2-x^2}} = \arcsin \frac{x}{a} + C.$

14. $\int \frac{dx}{\sqrt{x^2 \pm a^2}} = \ln |x + \sqrt{x^2 \pm a^2}| + C.$

Note. The table of derivatives (Sec. 3.15) does not have formulas corresponding to formulas 7, 8, 11′, 12, 13′ and 14. However, differentiation will readily prove the truth of these as well.

In the case of Formula 7 we have

$$(-\ln |\cos x|)' = -\frac{-\sin x}{\cos x} = \tan x$$

consequently, $\int \tan x \, dx = -\ln |\cos x| + C.$

In the case of Formula 8

$$(\ln|\sin x|)' = \frac{\cos x}{\sin x} = \cot x$$

Consequently, $\int \cot x \, dx = \ln|\sin x| + C$.

In the case of Formula 12,

$$\left(\frac{1}{2a}\ln\left|\frac{a+x}{a-x}\right|\right)' = \frac{1}{2a}\left[\ln|a+x| - \ln|a-x|\right]'$$

$$= \frac{1}{2a}\left[\frac{1}{a+x} + \frac{1}{a-x}\right] = \frac{1}{a^2-x^2}$$

therefore,

$$\int \frac{dx}{a^2-x^2} = \frac{1}{2a}\ln\left|\frac{a+x}{a-x}\right| + C$$

It should be noted that the latter formula will also follow from the general results of Sec. 10.9.

In the case of Formula 14,

$$(\ln|x+\sqrt{x^2 \pm a^2}|)' = \frac{1}{x+\sqrt{x^2 \pm a^2}}\left(1 + \frac{x}{\sqrt{x^2 \pm a^2}}\right) = \frac{1}{\sqrt{x^2 \pm a^2}}$$

hence,

$$\int \frac{dx}{\sqrt{x^2 \pm a^2}} = \ln|x+\sqrt{x^2 \pm a^2}| + C$$

This formula likewise will follow from the general results of Sec. 10.10.

Formulas 11′ and 13′ may be verified in similar fashion. These formulas will later be derived from formulas 11 and 13 (see Sec. 10.4, Examples 3 and 4).

10.3 SOME PROPERTIES OF THE INDEFINITE INTEGRAL

Theorem 1. *The indefinite integral of an algebraic sum of two or more functions is equal to the algebraic sum of their integrals*

$$\int [f_1(x) + f_2(x)] \, dx = \int f_1(x) \, dx + \int f_2(x) \, dx \qquad (1)$$

To prove this, find the derivatives of the left and right sides of this equation. On the basis of (4) of the preceding section we have

$$\left(\int [f_1(x) + f_2(x)] \, dx\right)' = f_1(x) + f_2(x)$$

$$\left(\int f_1(x) \, dx + \int f_2(x) \, dx\right)'$$

$$= \left(\int f_1(x) \, dx\right)' + \left(\int f_2(x) \, dx\right)' = f_1(x) + f_2(x)$$

Thus, the derivatives of the left and right sides of (1) are equal; in other words, the derivative of any antiderivative on the left-hand side is equal to the derivative of any function on the right-hand side of the equation. Therefore, by the theorem of Sec. 10.1, any function on the left of (1) differs from any function on the right of (1) by a constant term. That is how we should understand equation (1).

Theorem 2. *A constant factor may be taken outside the integral sign; that is, if* $a = const$, *then*

$$\int af(x)\,dx = a \int f(x)\,dx \tag{2}$$

To prove (2), let us find the derivatives of the left and right sides:

$$\left(\int af(x)\,dx\right)' = af(x)$$

$$\left(a \int f(x)\,dx\right)' = a \left(\int f(x)\,dx\right)' = af(x)$$

The derivatives of the right and left sides are equal, therefore, as in (1), the difference of any two functions on the left and right is a constant. That is how we should understand equation (2).

When evaluating indefinite integrals it is useful to bear in mind the following rules.

I. If

$$\int f(x)\,dx = F(x) + C$$

then

$$\int f(ax)\,dx = \frac{1}{a} F(ax) + C \tag{3}$$

Indeed, differentiating the left and right sides of (3), we get

$$\left(\int f(ax)\,dx\right)' = f(ax)$$

$$\left(\frac{1}{a} F(ax)\right)' = \frac{1}{a}(F(ax))'_x = \frac{1}{a} F'(ax)\,a = F'(ax) = f(ax)$$

The derivatives of the right and left sides are equal, which is what we set out to prove.

II. If

$$\int f(x)\,dx = F(x) + C$$

then

$$\int f(x+b)\,dx = F(x+b) + C \tag{4}$$

III. If

$$\int f(x)\,dx = F(x) + C$$

then

$$\int f(ax+b)\,dx = \frac{1}{a}F(ax+b)+C \tag{5}$$

Equations (4) and (5) are proved by differentiation of the right and left sides.

Example 1.

$$\int (2x^3 - 3\sin x + 5\sqrt{x})\,dx = \int 2x^3\,dx - \int 3\sin x\,dx + \int 5\sqrt{x}\,dx$$

$$= 2\int x^3\,dx - 3\int \sin x\,dx + 5\int x^{\frac{1}{2}}\,dx$$

$$= 2\frac{x^{3+1}}{3+1} - 3(-\cos x) + 5\frac{x^{\frac{1}{2}+1}}{\frac{1}{2}+1} + C = \frac{1}{2}x^4 + 3\cos x + \frac{10}{3}x\sqrt{x} + C$$

Example 2.

$$\int \left(\frac{3}{\sqrt[3]{x}} + \frac{1}{2\sqrt{x}} + x\sqrt[4]{x}\right)dx = 3\int x^{-\frac{1}{3}}\,dx + \frac{1}{2}\int x^{-\frac{1}{2}}\,dx + \int x^{\frac{5}{4}}\,dx$$

$$= 3\frac{x^{-\frac{1}{3}+1}}{-\frac{1}{3}+1} + \frac{1}{2}\frac{x^{-\frac{1}{2}+1}}{-\frac{1}{2}+1} + \frac{x^{\frac{5}{4}+1}}{\frac{5}{4}+1} + C = \frac{9}{2}\sqrt[3]{x^2} + \sqrt{x} + \frac{4}{9}x^2\sqrt[4]{x} + C$$

Example 3.

$$\int \frac{dx}{x+3} = \ln|x+3| + C$$

Example 4.

$$\int \cos 7x\,dx = \frac{1}{7}\sin 7x + C$$

Example 5.

$$\int \sin(2x-6)\,dx = -\frac{1}{2}\cos(2x-6) + C$$

10.4 INTEGRATION BY SUBSTITUTION (CHANGE OF VARIABLE)

Let it be required to find the integral

$$\int f(x)\,dx;$$

we cannot directly select the antiderivative of $f(x)$ but we know that it exists.

Let us change the variable in the expression under the integral sign, putting

$$x = \varphi(t) \tag{1}$$

where $\varphi(t)$ is a continuous function (with continuous derivative) having an inverse function. Then $dx = \varphi'(t)\,dt$; we shall prove that in this case we have the following equation:

$$\int f(x)\,dx = \int f[\varphi(t)]\,\varphi'(t)\,dt \qquad (2)$$

Here it is assumed that after integration we substitute, on the right side, the expression of t in terms of x on the basis of (1).

To establish that the expressions to the right and left are the same in the sense indicated above, it is necessary to prove that their derivatives with respect to x are equal. Find the derivative of the left side:

$$\left(\int f(x)\,dx \right)_x' = f(x)$$

We differentiate the right side of (2) with respect to x as a composite function, where t is the intermediate argument. The dependence of t on x is expressed by (1); here, $\dfrac{dx}{dt} = \varphi'(t)$ and by the rule for differentiating an inverse function,

$$\frac{dt}{dx} = \frac{1}{\varphi'(t)}$$

We thus have

$$\left(\int f[\varphi(t)]\,\varphi'(t)\,dt \right)_x' = \left(\int f[\varphi(t)]\,\varphi'(t)\,dt \right)_t' \frac{dt}{dx}$$
$$= f[\varphi(t)]\,\varphi'(t)\,\frac{1}{\varphi'(t)} = f[\varphi(t)] = f(x)$$

Therefore, the derivatives, with respect to x, of the right and left sides of (2) are equal, as required.

The function $x = \varphi(t)$ should be chosen so that one can evaluate the indefinite integral on the right side of (2).

Note. When integrating, it is sometimes better to choose a change of the variable in the form of $t = \psi(x)$ and not $x = \varphi(t)$. By way of illustration, let it be required to calculate an integral of the form

$$\int \frac{\psi'(x)\,dx}{\psi(x)}$$

Here it is convenient to put

$$\psi(x) = t$$

then

$$\psi'(x)\,dx = dt$$

$$\int \frac{\psi'(x)\,dx}{\psi(x)} = \int \frac{dt}{t} = \ln|t| + C = \ln|\psi(x)| + C$$

The following are some instances of integration by substitution.

Example 1. $\int \sqrt{\sin x} \cos x\, dx = ?$ We make the substitution $t = \sin x$; then $dt = \cos x\, dx$ and, consequently, $\int \sqrt{\sin x} \cos x\, dx = \int \sqrt{t}\, dt = \int t^{\frac{1}{2}}\, dt = \frac{2t^{3/2}}{3} + C = \frac{2}{3} \sin^{3/2} x + C.$

Example 2. $\int \frac{x\, dx}{1+x^2} = ?$ We put $t = 1 + x^2$, then $dt = 2x\, dx$ and $\int \frac{x\, dx}{1+x^2} = \frac{1}{2} \int \frac{dt}{t} = \frac{1}{2} \ln t + C = \frac{1}{2} \ln(1+x^2) + C.$

Example 3. $\int \frac{dx}{a^2+x^2} = \frac{1}{a^2} \int \frac{dx}{1+\left(\frac{x}{a}\right)^2}.$ We put $t = \frac{x}{a}$; then $dx = a\, dt,$

$\int \frac{dx}{a^2+x^2} = \frac{1}{a^2} \int \frac{a\, dt}{1+t^2} = \frac{1}{a} \int \frac{dt}{1+t^2} = \frac{1}{a} \arctan t + C = \frac{1}{a} \arctan \frac{x}{a} + C.$

Example 4. $\int \frac{dx}{\sqrt{a^2-x^2}} = \frac{1}{a} \int \frac{dx}{\sqrt{1-\left(\frac{x}{a}\right)^2}}.$ We put $t = \frac{x}{a}$; then

$dx = a\, dt,$ $\int \frac{dx}{\sqrt{a^2-x^2}} = \frac{1}{a} \int \frac{a\, dt}{\sqrt{1-t^2}} = \int \frac{dt}{\sqrt{1-t^2}} = \arcsin t + C =$

$= \arcsin \frac{x}{a} + C$ (it is assumed that $a > 0$).

Examples 3 and 4 illustrate the derivation of formulas 11' and 13' given in the Table of Integrals (see above, Sec. 10.2).

Example 5. $\int (\ln x)^3 \frac{dx}{x} = ?$ Put $t = \ln x$; then $dt = \frac{dx}{x},$ $\int (\ln x)^3 \frac{dx}{x} = \int t^3\, dt = \frac{t^4}{4} + C = \frac{1}{4} (\ln x)^4 + C.$

Example 6. $\int \frac{x\, dx}{1+x^4} = ?$ Put $t = x^2$; then $dt = 2x\, dx$, $\int \frac{x\, dx}{1+x^4} = \frac{1}{2} \int \frac{dt}{1+t^2} = \frac{1}{2} \arctan t + C = \frac{1}{2} \arctan x^2 + C$

The method of substitution is one of the basic methods for calculating indefinite integrals. Even when we integrate by some other method, we often resort to substitution in the intermediate stages of calculation. The success of integration depends largely on how appropriate the substitution is for simplifying the given integral. Essentially, the study of methods of integration reduces to finding out what kind of substitution has to be performed for a given element of integration. Most of this chapter is devoted to this problem.

10.5 INTEGRALS OF SOME FUNCTIONS CONTAINING
A QUADRATIC TRINOMIAL

I. Let us consider the integral

$$I_1 = \int \frac{dx}{ax^2 + bx + c}$$

We first transform the trinomial in the denominator by representing it in the form of a sum or difference of squares:

$$ax^2 + bx + c = a\left[x^2 + \frac{b}{a}x + \frac{c}{a}\right]$$

$$= a\left[x^2 + 2\frac{b}{2a}x + \left(\frac{b}{2a}\right)^2 + \frac{c}{a} - \left(\frac{b}{2a}\right)^2\right]$$

$$= a\left[\left(x + \frac{b}{2a}\right)^2 + \left(\frac{c}{a} - \frac{b^2}{4a^2}\right)\right] = a\left[\left(x + \frac{b}{2a}\right)^2 \pm k^2\right]$$

where

$$\frac{c}{a} - \frac{b^2}{4a^2} = \pm k^2$$

The plus or minus sign is taken depending on whether the expression on the left is positive or negative, that is, on whether the roots of the trinomial $ax^2 + bx + c$ are complex or real.

Thus, the integral I_1 will take the form

$$I_1 = \int \frac{dx}{ax^2 + bx + c} = \frac{1}{a}\int \frac{dx}{\left[\left(x + \frac{b}{2a}\right)^2 \pm k^2\right]}$$

In this integral we make a change of variable:

$$x + \frac{b}{2a} = t, \quad dx = dt$$

We then get

$$I_1 = \frac{1}{a}\int \frac{dt}{t^2 \pm k^2}$$

These are tabular integrals (see Formulas 11′ and 12).

Example 1. Calculate the integral

$$\int \frac{dx}{2x^2 + 8x + 20}$$

Solution.

$$I = \int \frac{dx}{2x^2 + 8x + 20} = \frac{1}{2}\int \frac{dx}{x^2 + 4x + 10}$$

$$= \frac{1}{2}\int \frac{dx}{x^2 + 4x + 4 + 10 - 4} = \frac{1}{2}\int \frac{dx}{(x+2)^2 + 6}$$

Let us make the substitution $x + 2 = t$, $dx = dt$. Putting it into the integral, we get the tabular integral

$$I = \frac{1}{2} \int \frac{dt}{t^2 + 6} = \frac{1}{2} \frac{1}{\sqrt{6}} \arctan \frac{t}{\sqrt{6}} + C$$

Substituting in place of t its expression in terms of x, we finally get

$$I = \frac{1}{2\sqrt{6}} \arctan \frac{x+2}{\sqrt{6}} + C.$$

II. Let us consider an integral of a more general form:

$$I_2 = \int \frac{Ax + B}{ax^2 + bx + c} dx$$

Perform the identity transformation of the integrand:

$$I_2 = \int \frac{Ax + B}{ax^2 + bx + c} dx = \int \frac{\dfrac{A}{2a}(2ax + b) + \left(B - \dfrac{Ab}{2a}\right)}{ax^2 + bx + c} dx$$

Represent the latter integral in the form of a sum of two integrals. Taking the constant factors outside the integral sign, we get

$$I_2 = \frac{A}{2a} \int \frac{2ax + b}{ax^2 + bx + c} dx + \left(B - \frac{Ab}{2a}\right) \int \frac{dx}{ax^2 + bx + c}$$

The latter integral is the integral I_1, which we are able to evaluate. In the first integral make a change of variable:

$$ax^2 + bx + c = t, \quad (2ax + b)\,dx = dt$$

Thus,

$$\int \frac{(2ax + b)\,dx}{ax^2 + bx + c} = \int \frac{dt}{t} = \ln|t| + C = \ln|ax^2 + bx + c| + C$$

And we finally get

$$I_2 = \frac{A}{2a} \ln|ax^2 + bx + c| + \left(B - \frac{Ab}{2a}\right) I_1$$

Example 2. Evaluate the integral

$$I = \int \frac{x+3}{x^2 - 2x - 5} dx.$$

Applying the foregoing technique we have

$$I = \int \frac{x+3}{x^2 - 2x - 5} dx = \int \frac{\dfrac{1}{2}(2x - 2) + \left(3 + \dfrac{1}{2} 2\right)}{x^2 - 2x - 5} dx$$

$$= \frac{1}{2} \int \frac{(2x - 2)\,dx}{x^2 - 2x - 5} + 4 \int \frac{dx}{x^2 - 2x - 5}$$

$$= \frac{1}{2} \ln|x^2 - 2x - 5| + 4 \int \frac{dx}{(x-1)^2 - 6}$$

$$= \frac{1}{2} \ln|x^2 - 2x - 5| + 2\frac{1}{\sqrt{6}} \ln \left| \frac{\sqrt{6} - (x-1)}{\sqrt{6} + (x-1)} \right| + C$$

III. Let us consider the integral

$$\int \frac{dx}{\sqrt{ax^2+bx+c}}$$

By means of transformations considered in Item I, this integral reduces (depending on the sign of a) to tabular integrals of the form

$$\int \frac{dt}{\sqrt{t^2 \pm k^2}} \text{ for } a>0 \text{ or } \int \frac{dt}{\sqrt{k^2-t^2}} \text{ for } a<0$$

which have already been examined in the Table of Integrals (see formulas 13′ and 14).

IV. An integral of the form

$$\int \frac{Ax+B}{\sqrt{ax^2+bx+c}} dx$$

is evaluated by means of the following transformations, which are similar to those considered in Item II:

$$\int \frac{Ax+B}{\sqrt{ax^2+bx+c}} dx = \int \frac{\frac{A}{2a}(2ax+b)+\left(B-\frac{Ab}{2a}\right)}{\sqrt{ax^2+bx+c}} dx$$

$$= \frac{A}{2a} \int \frac{2ax+b}{\sqrt{ax^2+bx+c}} dx + \left(B-\frac{Ab}{2a}\right)\int \frac{dx}{\sqrt{ax^2+bx+c}}$$

Applying substitution to the first of the integrals obtained,

$$ax^2+bx+c=t, \quad (2ax+b)\,dx=dt$$

we get

$$\int \frac{(2ax+b)\,dx}{\sqrt{ax^2+bx+c}} = \int \frac{dt}{\sqrt{t}} = 2\sqrt{t}+C = 2\sqrt{ax^2+bx+c}+C$$

The second integral was considered in Item III of this section.

Example 3.

$$\int \frac{5x+3}{\sqrt{x^2+4x+10}} dx = \int \frac{\frac{5}{2}(2x+4)+(3-10)}{\sqrt{x^2+4x+10}} dx$$

$$= \frac{5}{2} \int \frac{2x+4}{\sqrt{x^2+4x+10}} dx - 7 \int \frac{dx}{\sqrt{(x+2)^2+6}}$$

$$= 5\sqrt{x^2+4x+10} - 7 \ln|x+2+\sqrt{(x+2)^2+6}| + C$$

$$= 5\sqrt{x^2+4x+10} - 7 \ln|x+2+\sqrt{x^2+4x+10}| + C$$

10.6 INTEGRATION BY PARTS

Let u and v be two differentiable functions of x. Then the differential of the product uv is found from the following formula:

$$d(uv) = u\,dv + v\,du$$

Whence, by integration, we have

$$uv = \int u\, dv + \int v\, du$$

or

$$\int u\, dv = uv - \int v\, du \tag{1}$$

This formula is called the *formula of integration by parts*. It is most frequently used in the integration of expressions that may be represented in the form of a product of two factors u and dv in such a way that the finding of the function v from its differential dv, and the evaluation of the integral $\int v\, du$ should, taken together, be a simpler problem than the direct evaluation of the integral $\int u\, dv$. To become skilled at breaking up a given element of integration into the factors u and dv, one has to solve problems; we shall show how this is done in a number of cases.

Example 1. $\int x \sin x\, dx =?$ We let

$$u = x, \quad dv = \sin x\, dx$$

then

$$du = dx, \quad v = -\cos x$$

Hence,

$$\int x \sin x\, dx = -x \cos x + \int \cos x\, dx = -x \cos x + \sin x + C$$

Note. When determining the function v from the differential dv we can take any arbitrary constant, since it does not enter into the final result [this can be seen by putting the expression $v + C$ into (1) in place of v]. It is therefore convenient to consider this constant equal to zero.

The rule for integration by parts is widely used. For example, integrals of the form

$$\int x^k \sin ax\, dx, \qquad \int x^k \cos ax\, dx$$
$$\int x^k e^{ax}\, dx, \qquad \int x^k \ln x\, dx$$

and certain integrals containing inverse trigonometric functions are evaluated by means of integration by parts.

Example 2. It is required to evaluate $\int \arctan x\, dx$. Letting $u = \arctan x$, $dv = dx$, we have $du = \dfrac{dx}{1 + x^2}$, $v = x$. Thus,

$$\int \arctan x\, dx = x \arctan x - \int \frac{x\, dx}{1 + x^2} = x \arctan x - \frac{1}{2} \ln |\, 1 + x^2\,| + C$$

Example 3. It is required to evaluate $\int x^2 e^x \, dx$. Let us put $u = x^2$, $dv = e^x \, dx$; then $du = 2x \, dx$, $v = e^x$,

$$\int x^2 e^x \, dx = x^2 e^x - 2 \int x e^x \, dx$$

We again integrate by parts the latter integral, letting

$$u_1 = x, \qquad du_1 = dx$$
$$dv_1 = e^x \, dx, \qquad v_1 = e^x$$

Then

$$\int x e^x \, dx = x e^x - \int e^x \, dx = x e^x - e^x + C$$

Finally we get

$$\int x^2 e^x \, dx = x^2 e^x - 2 \, (x e^x - e^x) + C = x^2 e^x - 2 x e^x + 2 e^x + C = e^x \, (x^2 - 2x + 2) + C$$

Example 4. It is required to evaluate $\int (x^2 + 7x - 5) \cos 2x \, dx$. We let $u = x^2 + 7x - 5$; $dv = \cos 2x \, dx$; then

$$du = (2x + 7) \, dx, \qquad v = \frac{\sin 2x}{2}$$

$$\int (x^2 + 7x - 5) \cos 2x \, dx = (x^2 + 7x - 5) \frac{\sin 2x}{2} - \int (2x + 7) \frac{\sin 2x}{2} \, dx$$

Apply integration by parts to the latter integral, letting $u_1 = \frac{2x + 7}{2}$, $dv_1 = \sin 2x \, dx$; then

$$du_1 = dx, \quad v_1 = -\frac{\cos 2x}{2}$$

$$\int \frac{2x + 7}{2} \sin 2x \, dx = \frac{2x + 7}{2} \left(-\frac{\cos 2x}{2} \right) - \int \left(-\frac{\cos 2x}{2} \right) dx$$
$$= -\frac{(2x + 7) \cos 2x}{4} + \frac{\sin 2x}{4} + C$$

Therefore, we finally get

$$\int (x^2 + 7x - 5) \cos 2x \, dx = (x^2 + 7x - 5) \frac{\sin 2x}{2} + (2x + 7) \frac{\cos 2x}{4} - \frac{\sin 2x}{4} + C$$
$$= (2x^2 + 14x - 11) \frac{\sin x}{4} + (2x + 7) \frac{\cos 2x}{4} + C$$

Example 5. $I = \int \sqrt{a^2 - x^2} \, dx = ?$

Perform identity transformations. Multiply and divide the integrand by $\sqrt{a^2 - x^2}$:

$$\int \sqrt{a^2 - x^2} \, dx = \int \frac{a^2 - x^2}{\sqrt{a^2 - x^2}} \, dx = a^2 \int \frac{dx}{\sqrt{a^2 - x^2}} - \int \frac{x^2 \, dx}{\sqrt{a^2 - x^2}}$$
$$= a^2 \arcsin \frac{x}{a} - \int x \frac{x \, dx}{\sqrt{a^2 - x^2}}$$

Integrate the last integral by parts, letting

$$u = x, \qquad du = dx$$
$$dv = \frac{x\,dx}{\sqrt{a^2 - x^2}}, \quad v = -\sqrt{a^2 - x^2}$$

Then

$$\int \frac{x^2\,dx}{\sqrt{a^2 - x^2}} = \int x \frac{x\,dx}{\sqrt{a^2 - x^2}} = -x\sqrt{a^2 - x^2} + \int \sqrt{a^2 - x^2}\,dx$$

Putting this result in the earlier obtained expression of the given integral, we have

$$\int \sqrt{a^2 - x^2}\,dx = a^2 \arcsin \frac{x}{a} + x\sqrt{a^2 - x^2} - \int \sqrt{a^2 - x^2}\,dx$$

Transposing the integral from right to left and performing elementary transformations, we finally get

$$\int \sqrt{a^2 - x^2}\,dx = \frac{a^2}{2} \arcsin \frac{x}{a} + \frac{x}{2}\sqrt{a^2 - x^2} + C$$

Example 6. Evaluate the integrals

$$I_1 = \int e^{ax} \cos bx\,dx \quad \text{and} \quad I_2 = \int e^{ax} \sin bx\,dx$$

Applying integration by parts to the first integral, we get

$$u = e^{ax}, \qquad du = ae^{ax}\,dx$$
$$dv = \cos bx\,dx, \quad v = \frac{1}{b} \sin bx$$

$$\int e^{ax} \cos bx\,dx = \frac{1}{b} e^{ax} \sin bx - \frac{a}{b} \int e^{ax} \sin bx\,dx$$

Again apply the method of integration by parts to the latter integral:

$$u = e^{ax}, \qquad du = ae^{ax}\,dx$$
$$dv = \sin bx\,dx, \quad v = -\frac{1}{b} \cos bx$$

$$\int e^{ax} \sin bx\,dx = -\frac{1}{b} e^{ax} \cos bx + \frac{a}{b} \int e^{ax} \cos bx\,dx$$

Putting the expression obtained into the preceding equation gives us

$$\int e^{ax} \cos bx\,dx = \frac{1}{b} e^{ax} \sin bx + \frac{a}{b^2} e^{ax} \cos bx - \frac{a^2}{b^2} \int e^{ax} \cos bx\,dx$$

From this equation let us find I_1

$$\left(1 + \frac{a^2}{b^2}\right) \int e^{ax} \cos bx\,dx = e^{ax} \left(\frac{1}{b} \sin bx + \frac{a}{b^2} \cos bx\right) + C\left(1 + \frac{a^2}{b^2}\right)$$

whence

$$I_1 = \int e^{ax} \cos bx\,dx = \frac{e^{ax}(b \sin bx + a \cos bx)}{a^2 + b^2} + C$$

Similarly we find

$$I_2 = \int e^{ax} \sin bx\,dx = \frac{e^{ax}(a \sin bx - b \cos bx)}{a^2 + b^2} + C$$

10.7 RATIONAL FRACTIONS.
PARTIAL RATIONAL FRACTIONS AND THEIR INTEGRATION

As we shall see below, not every elementary function by far has an integral expressed in elementary functions. For this reason, it is very important to separate out those classes of functions whose integrals are expressed in terms of elementary functions. The simplest of these classes is the class of rational functions.

Every rational function may be represented in the form of a rational fraction, that is to say, as a ratio of two polynomials:

$$\frac{Q(x)}{f(x)} = \frac{B_0 x^m + B_1 x^{m-1} + \ldots + B_m}{A_0 x^n + A_1 x^{n-1} + \ldots + A_n}$$

Without restricting the generality of our reasoning, we shall assume that these polynomials do not have common roots.

If the degree of the numerator is lower than that of the denominator, then the fraction is called *proper*, otherwise the fraction is called *improper*.

If the fraction is an improper one, then by dividing the numerator by the denominator (by the rule for division of polynomials), it is possible to represent the fraction as the sum of a polynomial and a proper fraction:

$$\frac{Q(x)}{f(x)} = M(x) + \frac{F(x)}{f(x)}$$

Here $M(x)$ is a polynomial, and $\frac{F(x)}{f(x)}$ is a proper fraction.

Example 1. Given an improper rational fraction

$$\frac{x^4 - 3}{x^2 + 2x + 1}$$

Dividing the numerator by the denominator (by the rule for division of polynomials), we get

$$\frac{x^4 - 3}{x^2 + 2x + 1} = x^2 - 2x + 3 - \frac{4x - 6}{x^2 + 2x + 1}$$

Since integration of polynomials does not present any difficulties, the basic barrier when integrating rational fractions is the integration of *proper* rational fractions.

Definition. Proper rational fractions of the form:

I. $\dfrac{A}{x - a}$,

II. $\dfrac{A}{(x - a)^k}$ (k a positive integer $\geqslant 2$),

III. $\dfrac{Ax + B}{x^2 + px + q}$ (the roots of the denominator are complex, that is, $\dfrac{p^2}{4} - q < 0$),

IV. $\dfrac{Ax+B}{(x^2+px+q)^k}$ (k a positive integer $\geqslant 2$; the roots of the denominator are complex) are called *partial fractions of types* I, II, III, *and* IV.

It will be proved below (see Sec. 10.8) that every rational fraction may be represented as a sum of partial fractions. We shall therefore first consider integrals of partial fractions.

The integration of partial fractions of types I, II and III does not present any particular difficulties so we shall perform their integration without any remarks:

I. $\displaystyle\int \frac{A}{x-a}\,dx = A\ln|x-a| + C.$

II. $\displaystyle\int \frac{A}{(x-a)^k}\,dx = A\int (x-a)^{-k}\,dx = A\frac{(x-a)^{-k+1}}{-k+1} + C$

$$= \frac{A}{(1-k)(x-a)^{k-1}} + C.$$

III. $\displaystyle\int \frac{Ax+B}{x^2+px+q}\,dx = \int \frac{\frac{A}{2}(2x+p)+\left(B-\frac{Ap}{2}\right)}{x^2+px+q}\,dx$

$$= \frac{A}{2}\int \frac{2x+p}{x^2+px+q}\,dx + \left(B-\frac{Ap}{2}\right)\int \frac{dx}{x^2+px+q}$$

$$= \frac{A}{2}\ln|x^2+px+q| + \left(B-\frac{Ap}{2}\right)\int \frac{dx}{\left(x+\frac{p}{2}\right)^2+\left(q-\frac{p^2}{4}\right)}$$

$$= \frac{A}{2}\ln|x^2+px+q| + \frac{2B-Ap}{\sqrt{4q-p^2}}\arctan\frac{2x+p}{\sqrt{4q-p^2}} + C \quad \text{(see}$$
Sec. 10.5).

The integration of partial fractions of type IV requires more involved computations. Suppose we have an integral of this type:

IV. $\displaystyle\int \frac{Ax+B}{(x^2+px+q)^k}\,dx.$

Perform the transformations:

$$\int \frac{Ax+B}{(x^2+px+q)^k}\,dx = \int \frac{\frac{A}{2}(2x+p)+\left(B-\frac{Ap}{2}\right)}{(x^2+px+q)^k}\,dx$$

$$= \frac{A}{2}\int \frac{2x+p}{(x^2+px+q)^k}\,dx + \left(B-\frac{Ap}{2}\right)\int \frac{dx}{(x^2+px+q)^k}$$

The first integral is taken via the substitution, $x^2+px+q=t$, $(2x+p)\,dx=dt$:

$$\int \frac{2x+p}{(x^2+px+q)^k}\,dx = \int \frac{dt}{t^k} = \int t^{-k}\,dt = \frac{t^{-k+1}}{1-k} + C$$

$$= \frac{1}{(1-k)(x^2+px+q)^{k-1}} + C$$

We write the second integral (let us denote it by I_k) in the form

$$I_k = \int \frac{dx}{(x^2 + px + q)^k} = \int \frac{dx}{\left[\left(x + \frac{p}{2}\right)^2 + \left(q - \frac{p^2}{4}\right)\right]^k} = \int \frac{dt}{(t^2 + m^2)^k}$$

setting

$$x + \frac{p}{2} = t, \quad dx = dt, \quad q - \frac{p^2}{4} = m^2$$

$\left(\text{it is assumed that the roots of the denominator are complex,}\right.$
and hence, $q - \frac{p^2}{4} > 0\Big)$. We then do as follows:

$$I_k = \int \frac{dt}{(t^2 + m^2)^k} = \frac{1}{m^2} \int \frac{(t^2 + m^2) - t^2}{(t^2 + m^2)^k} dt$$

$$= \frac{1}{m^2} \int \frac{dt}{(t^2 + m^2)^{k-1}} - \frac{1}{m^2} \int \frac{t^2}{(t^2 + m^2)^k} dt \qquad (1)$$

We transform the last integral:

$$\int \frac{t^2\, dt}{(t^2 + m^2)^k} = \int \frac{t \cdot t\, dt}{(t^2 + m^2)^k}$$

$$= \frac{1}{2} \int t \frac{d(t^2 + m^2)}{(t^2 + m^2)^k} = -\frac{1}{2(k-1)} \int t d\left(\frac{1}{(t^2 + m^2)^{k-1}}\right)$$

Integrating by parts we get

$$\int \frac{t^2\, dt}{(t^2 + m^2)^k} = -\frac{1}{2(k-1)} \left[t \frac{1}{(t^2 + m^2)^{k-1}} - \int \frac{dt}{(t^2 + m^2)^{k-1}} \right]$$

Putting this expression into (1), we have

$$I_k = \int \frac{dt}{(t^2 + m^2)^k} = \frac{1}{m^2} \int \frac{dt}{(t^2 + m^2)^{k-1}}$$

$$+ \frac{1}{m^2} \frac{1}{2(k-1)} \left[\frac{t}{(t^2 + m^2)^{k-1}} - \int \frac{dt}{(t^2 + m^2)^{k-1}} \right]$$

$$= \frac{t}{2m^2 (k-1)(t^2 + m^2)^{k-1}} - \frac{2k-3}{2m^2 (k-1)} \int \frac{dt}{(t^2 + m^2)^{k-1}}$$

On the right side is an integral of the same type as I_k, but the exponent of the denominator of the integrand is less by unity $(k-1)$; we have thus expressed I_k in terms of I_{k-1}.

Continuing in the same manner we will arrive at the familiar integral

$$I_1 = \int \frac{dt}{t^2 + m^2} = \frac{1}{m} \arctan \frac{t}{m} + C$$

Then substituting everywhere in place of t and m their values, we get the expression of integral IV in terms of x and the given numbers A, B, p, q.

Example 2.

$$\int \frac{x-1}{(x^2+2x+3)^2} dx = \int \frac{\frac{1}{2}(2x+2)+(-1-1)}{(x^2+2x+3)^2} dx$$

$$= \frac{1}{2} \int \frac{2x+2}{(x^2+2x+3)^2} dx - 2 \int \frac{dx}{(x^2+2x+3)^2}$$

$$= -\frac{1}{2} \frac{1}{(x^2+2x+3)} - 2 \int \frac{dx}{(x^2+2x+3)^2}$$

We apply the substitution $x+1=t$ to the last integral:

$$\int \frac{dx}{(x^2+2x+3)^2} = \int \frac{dx}{[(x+1)^2+2]^2} = \int \frac{dt}{(t^2+2)^2} = \frac{1}{2} \int \frac{(t^2+2)-t^2}{(t^2+2)^2} dt$$

$$= \frac{1}{2} \int \frac{dt}{t^2+2} - \frac{1}{2} \int \frac{t^2}{(t^2+2)^2} dt$$

$$= \frac{1}{2} \frac{1}{\sqrt{2}} \arctan \frac{t}{\sqrt{2}} - \frac{1}{2} \int \frac{t^2 \, dt}{(t^2+2)^2}$$

(handwritten margin notes:)
$t = \sqrt{2} \tan \theta$
$dt = \sqrt{2} \sec^2\theta \, d\theta$
$\int \frac{2\tan^2\theta \sec^2\theta}{(2\tan^2\theta+2)^2}$
$\int \frac{2\tan^2\theta \sec^2\theta}{4 \sec^2\theta \sec\theta}$
$\frac{1}{2} \int \sin^2\theta$

Let us consider the last integral:

$$\int \frac{t^2 \, dt}{(t^2+2)^2} = \frac{1}{2} \int \frac{t \, d(t^2+2)}{(t^2+2)^2} = -\frac{1}{2} \int t \, d\left(\frac{1}{t^2+2}\right)$$

$$= -\frac{1}{2} \frac{t}{t^2+2} + \frac{1}{2} \int \frac{dt}{t^2+2}$$

$$= -\frac{t}{2(t^2+2)} + \frac{1}{2} \frac{1}{\sqrt{2}} \arctan \frac{t}{\sqrt{2}}$$

(we do not yet write the arbitrary constant but will take it into account in the final result).

Consequently,

$$\int \frac{dx}{(x^2+2x+3)^2} = \frac{1}{2} \frac{1}{\sqrt{2}} \arctan \frac{x+1}{\sqrt{2}}$$

$$-\frac{1}{2}\left[-\frac{x+1}{2(x^2+2x+3)} + \frac{1}{2} \frac{1}{\sqrt{2}} \arctan \frac{x+1}{\sqrt{2}}\right]$$

Finally we get

$$\int \frac{x-1}{(x^2+2x+3)^2} dx = -\frac{x+2}{2(x^2+2x+3)} - \frac{\sqrt{2}}{4} \arctan \frac{x+1}{\sqrt{2}} + C$$

10.8 DECOMPOSITION OF A RATIONAL FRACTION INTO PARTIAL FRACTIONS

We shall now show that every proper rational fraction may be decomposed into a sum of partial fractions.

Suppose we have a proper rational fraction

$$\frac{F(x)}{f(x)}$$

We shall assume that the coefficients of the polynomials are real numbers and that the given fraction is in lowest terms (this means that the numerator and denominator do not have common roots).

Theorem 1. *Let $x = a$ be a root of multiplicity k of the denominator; that is $f(x) = (x-a)^k f_1(x)$, where $f_1(a) \neq 0$ (see Sec. 7.6). Then the given proper fraction $\dfrac{F(x)}{f(x)}$ may be represented in the form of a sum of two other proper fractions as follows:*

$$\frac{F(x)}{f(x)} = \frac{A}{(x-a)^k} + \frac{F_1(x)}{(x-a)^{k-1} f_1(x)} \tag{1}$$

where A is a nonzero constant, and $F_1(x)$ is a polynomial of degree less than the degree of the denominator $(x-a)^{k-1} f_1(x)$.

Proof. Let us write the identity

$$\frac{F(x)}{f(x)} = \frac{A}{(x-a)^k} + \frac{F(x) - A f_1(x)}{(x-a)^k f_1(x)} \tag{2}$$

(which is true for every A) and let us define the constant A so that the polynomial $F(x) - A f_1(x)$ can be divided by $x - a$. To do this, by the remainder theorem, it is necessary and sufficient that the following equation hold:

$$F(a) - A f_1(a) = 0$$

Since $f_1(a) \neq 0$, $F(a) \neq 0$, A is uniquely defined by

$$A = \frac{F(a)}{f_1(a)}$$

For such an A we shall have

$$F(x) - A f_1(x) = (x-a) F_1(x)$$

where $F_1(x)$ is a polynomial of degree less than that of the polynomial $(x-a)^{k-1} f_1(x)$. Cancelling $(x-a)$ from the fraction in formula (2), we get (1).

Corollary. Similar reasoning may be applied to the proper rational fraction

$$\frac{F_1(x)}{(x-a)^{k-1} f_1(x)}$$

in equation (1). Thus, if the denominator has a root $x = a$ of multiplicity k, we can write

$$\frac{F(x)}{f(x)} = \frac{A}{(x-a)^k} + \frac{A_1}{(x-a)^{k-1}} + \cdots + \frac{A_{k-1}}{x-a} + \frac{F_k(x)}{f_1(x)}$$

where $\dfrac{F_k(x)}{f_1(x)}$ is a proper fraction in lowest terms. To it we can apply the theorem that has just been proved, provided $f_1(x)$ has other real roots.

Let us now consider the case of complex roots of the denominator. Recall that the complex roots of a polynomial with real coefficients are always conjugate in pairs (see Sec. 7.8).

When factoring a polynomial into real factors, to each pair of complex roots of the polynomial there corresponds an expression of the form $x^2 + px + q$. But if the complex roots are of multiplicity μ, they correspond to the expression $(x^2 + px + q)^\mu$.

Theorem 2. *If* $f(x) = (x^2 + px + q)^\mu \varphi_1(x)$, *where the polynomial* $\varphi_1(x)$ *is not divisible by* $x^2 + px + q$, *then the proper rational fraction* $\dfrac{F(x)}{f(x)}$ *may be represented as a sum of two other proper fractions in the following manner:*

$$\frac{F(x)}{f(x)} = \frac{Mx+N}{(x^2+px+q)^\mu} + \frac{\Phi_1(x)}{(x^2+px+q)^{\mu-1}\varphi_1(x)} \tag{3}$$

where $\Phi_1(x)$ *is a polynomial of degree less than that of the polynomial* $(x^2 + px + q)^{\mu-1}\varphi_1(x)$.

Proof. Let us write the identity

$$\frac{F(x)}{f(x)} = \frac{F(x)}{(x^2+px+q)^\mu\varphi_1(x)} = \frac{Mx+N}{(x^2+px+q)^\mu} + \frac{F(x)-(Mx+N)\varphi_1(x)}{(x^2+px+q)^\mu\varphi_1(x)} \tag{4}$$

which is true for all M and N, and let us define M and N so that the polynomial $F(x) - (Mx+N)\varphi_1(x)$ is divisible by $x^2 + px + q$. To do this, it is necessary and sufficient that the equation

$$F(x) - (Mx+N)\varphi_1(x) = 0$$

have the same roots $\alpha \pm i\beta$ as the polynomial $x^2 + px + q$. Thus,

$$F(\alpha + i\beta) - [M(\alpha + i\beta) + N]\varphi_1(\alpha + i\beta) = 0$$

or

$$M(\alpha + i\beta) + N = \frac{F(\alpha + i\beta)}{\varphi_1(\alpha + i\beta)}$$

But $\dfrac{F(\alpha + i\beta)}{\varphi_1(\alpha + i\beta)}$ is a definite complex number which may be written in the form $K + iL$, where K and L are certain real numbers. Thus,

$$M(\alpha + i\beta) + N = K + iL$$

whence

$$M\alpha + N = K, \quad M\beta = L$$

or

$$M = \frac{L}{\beta}, \quad N = \frac{K\beta - L\alpha}{\beta}$$

With these values of the coefficients M and N the polynomial $F(x) - (Mx+N)\varphi_1(x)$ has the number $\alpha + i\beta$ for a root, and, hence, also the conjugate number $\alpha - i\beta$. But then the polynomial can be divided, without remainder, by the differences $x - (\alpha + i\beta)$ and $x - (\alpha - i\beta)$, and, therefore, by their product, which is $x^2 + px + q$. Denoting the quotient of this division by $\Phi_1(x)$, we get

$$F(x) - (Mx + N)\,\varphi_1(x) = (x^2 + px + q)\,\Phi_1(x)$$

Cancelling $x^2 + px + q$ from the last fraction in (4), we get (3), and it is clear that the degree of $\Phi_1(x)$ is less than that of the denominator, which is what we set out to prove.

Now applying to the proper fraction $\dfrac{F(x)}{f(x)}$ the results of Theorems 1 and 2, we can obtain, successively, all the partial fractions corresponding to all the roots of the denominator $f(x)$. Thus, from the foregoing the result follows that

If

$$f(x) = (x - a)^\alpha \ldots (x - b)^\beta\,(x^2 + px + q)^\mu \ldots (x^2 + lx + s)^\nu,$$

then the fraction $\dfrac{F(x)}{f(x)}$ *can be represented as follows:*

$$\left.\begin{aligned}
\frac{F(x)}{f(x)} &= \frac{A}{(x-a)^\alpha} + \frac{A_1}{(x-a)^{\alpha-1}} + \ldots + \frac{A_{\alpha-1}}{x-a} \\[1mm]
&\cdots\cdots\cdots\cdots\cdots\cdots\cdots\cdots\cdots\cdots \\[1mm]
&+ \frac{B}{(x-b)^\beta} + \frac{B_1}{(x-b)^{\beta-1}} + \ldots + \frac{B_{\beta-1}}{x-b} \\[1mm]
&+ \frac{Mx+N}{(x^2+px+q)^\mu} + \frac{M_1x+N_1}{(x^2+px+q)^{\mu-1}} + \ldots + \frac{M_{\mu-1}x+N_{\mu-1}}{x^2+px+q} \\[1mm]
&\cdots\cdots\cdots\cdots\cdots\cdots\cdots\cdots\cdots\cdots \\[1mm]
&+ \frac{Px+Q}{(x^2+lx+s)^\nu} + \frac{P_1x+Q_1}{(x^2+lx+s)^{\nu-1}} + \ldots + \frac{P_{\nu-1}x+Q_{\nu-1}}{x^2+lx+s}
\end{aligned}\right\} \quad (5)$$

The coefficients A, A_1, ..., B, B_1, ... may be determined by the following reasoning. This equality is an **identity**; and for this reason, by reducing the fractions to a common denominator we get identical polynomials in the numerators on the right and left. Equating the coefficients of the same degrees of x, we get a system of equations for determining the unknown coefficients A, A_1, ..., B, B_1, ... This method of finding coefficients is called the *method of undetermined coefficients.*

Besides, to determine the coefficients we can take advantage of the following: since the polynomials obtained on the right and left sides of the equation must be identically equal after reducing to a common denominator, their values are equal for all particular values of x. Assigning particular values to x, we get equations for determining the coefficients.

We thus see that every proper rational fraction may be represented in the form of a sum of partial rational fractions.

Example. Let it be required to decompose the fraction $\dfrac{x^2+2}{(x+1)^3(x-2)}$ into partial fractions. From (5) we have

$$\frac{x^2+2}{(x+1)^3(x-2)} = \frac{A}{(x+1)^3} + \frac{A_1}{(x+1)^2} + \frac{A_2}{x+1} + \frac{B}{x-2}$$

Reducing to a common denominator and equating the numerators, we have

$$x^2+2 = A(x-2) + A_1(x+1)(x-2) + A_2(x+1)^2(x-2) + B(x+1)^3 \quad (6)$$

or

$$x^2+2 = (A_2+B)x^3 + (A_1+3B)x^2$$
$$+ (A-A_1-3A_2+3B)x + (-2A-2A_1-2A_2+B)$$

Equating the coefficients of x^3, x^2, x^1, x^0 (absolute term), we get a system of equations for determining the coefficients:

$$0 = A_2+B$$
$$1 = A_1+3B$$
$$0 = A-A_1-3A_2+3B$$
$$2 = -2A-2A_1-2A_2+B$$

Solving this system we find

$$A=-1; \quad A_1=\frac{1}{3}; \quad A_2=-\frac{2}{9}; \quad B=\frac{2}{9}$$

It might also be possible to determine some of the coefficients of the equations that result for some particular values of x from (6), which is an identity in x.
Thus, setting $x=-1$ we have $3=-3A$ or $A=-1$; setting $x=2$, we have $6=27B$, $B=\dfrac{2}{9}$.

If to these two equations we add two equations that result from equating the coefficients of the same powers of x, we get four equations for determining the four unknown coefficients. As a result, we have the decomposition

$$\frac{x^2+2}{(x+1)^3(x-2)} = -\frac{1}{(x+1)^3} + \frac{1}{3(x+1)^2} - \frac{2}{9(x+1)} + \frac{2}{9(x-2)}$$

10.9 INTEGRATION OF RATIONAL FRACTIONS

Let it be required to evaluate the integral of a rational fraction $\dfrac{Q(x)}{f(x)}$; that is, the integral

$$\int \frac{Q(x)}{f(x)}\,dx$$

If the given fraction is **improper**, we represent it as the sum of a polynomial $M(x)$ and the **proper** rational fraction $\dfrac{F(x)}{f(x)}$ (see Sec. 10.7). This latter we represent, applying formula (5), Sec. 10.8, as a sum of **partial** fractions. Thus, the integration of a rational fraction reduces to the integration of a polynomial and several **partial** fractions.

From the results of Sec. 10.8 it follows that the form of partial fractions is determined by the roots of the denominator $f(x)$. The following cases are possible.

Case I. *The roots of the denominator are real and distinct, that is*

$$f(x) = (x-a)(x-b) \ldots (x-d)$$

Here, the fraction $\dfrac{F(x)}{f(x)}$ is decomposable into partial fractions of type I:

$$\frac{F(x)}{f(x)} = \frac{A}{x-a} + \frac{B}{x-b} + \ldots + \frac{D}{x-d}$$

and then

$$\int \frac{F(x)}{f(x)} dx = \int \frac{A}{x-a} dx + \int \frac{B}{x-b} dx + \ldots + \int \frac{D}{x-d} dx$$
$$= A \ln|x-a| + B \ln|x-b| + \ldots + D \ln|x-d| + C$$

Case II. *The roots of the denominator are real, and some of them are multiple:*

$$f(x) = (x-a)^\alpha (x-b)^\beta \ldots (x-d)^\delta$$

In this case the fraction $\dfrac{F(x)}{f(x)}$ is decomposable into partial fractions of types I and II.

Example 1 (see example in Sec. 10.8).

$$\int \frac{x^2+2}{(x+1)^3(x-2)} dx = -\int \frac{dx}{(x+1)^3} + \frac{1}{3} \int \frac{dx}{(x+1)^2} - \frac{2}{9} \int \frac{dx}{x+1}$$
$$+ \frac{2}{9} \int \frac{dx}{x-2} = \frac{1}{2} \frac{1}{(x+1)^2} - \frac{1}{3(x+1)} - \frac{2}{9} \ln|x+1| + \frac{2}{9} \ln|x-2| + C$$
$$= -\frac{2x-1}{6(x+1)^2} + \frac{2}{9} \ln \left| \frac{x-2}{x+1} \right| + C$$

Case III. *Among the roots of the denominator are complex non repeated (that is, distinct) roots:*

$$f(x) = (x^2 + px + q) \ldots (x^2 + lx + s)(x-a)^\alpha \ldots (x-d)^\delta$$

In this case the fraction $\dfrac{F(x)}{f(x)}$ is decomposable into partial fractions of types I, II, and III.

Example 2. Evaluate the integral

$$\int \frac{x\, dx}{(x^2+1)(x-1)}$$

Decompose the fraction under the integral sign into partial fractions [see (5), Sec. 10.8]

$$\frac{x}{(x^2+1)(x-1)} = \frac{Ax+B}{x^2+1} + \frac{C}{x-1}$$

Consequently,

$$x = (Ax+B)(x-1) + C(x^2+1)$$

Setting $x=1$, we get $1 = 2C$, $C = \frac{1}{2}$; setting $x=0$, we get $0 = -B+C$, $B = \frac{1}{2}$.

Equating the coefficients of x^2, we get $0 = A+C$, whence $A = -\frac{1}{2}$. Thus,

$$\int \frac{x\,dx}{(x^2+1)(x-1)} = -\frac{1}{2}\int \frac{x-1}{x^2+1}\,dx + \frac{1}{2}\int \frac{dx}{x-1}$$

$$= -\frac{1}{2}\int \frac{x\,dx}{x^2+1} + \frac{1}{2}\int \frac{dx}{x^2+1} + \frac{1}{2}\int \frac{dx}{x-1}$$

$$= -\frac{1}{4}\ln|x^2+1| + \frac{1}{2}\arctan x + \frac{1}{2}\ln|x-1| + C$$

Case IV. *The roots of the denominator include complex multiple roots*

$$f(x) = (x^2+px+q)^\mu \cdots (x^2+lx+s)^\nu (x-a)^\alpha \cdots (x-d)^\delta$$

In this case, decomposition of the fraction $\frac{F(x)}{f(x)}$ will also contain partial fractions of type IV.

Example 3. It is required to evaluate the integral

$$\int \frac{x^4+4x^3+11x^2+12x+8}{(x^2+2x+3)^2(x+1)}\,dx$$

Solution. Decompose the fraction into partial fractions:

$$\frac{x^4+4x^3+11x^2+12x+8}{(x^2+2x+3)^2(x+1)} = \frac{Ax+B}{(x^2+2x+3)^2} + \frac{Cx+D}{(x^2+2x+3)} + \frac{E}{x+1}$$

whence

$$x^4+4x^3+11x^2+12x+8$$
$$= (Ax+B)(x+1) + (Cx+D)(x^2+2x+3)(x+1) + E(x^2+2x+3)^2$$

Combining the above-indicated methods of determining coefficients, we find

$$A=1, \quad B=-1, \quad C=0, \quad D=0, \quad E=1$$

Thus, we get

$$\int \frac{x^4+4x^3+11x^2+12x+8}{(x^2+2x+3)^2(x+1)}\,dx = \int \frac{x-1}{(x^2+2x+3)^2}\,dx + \int \frac{dx}{x+1}$$

$$= -\frac{x+2}{2(x^2+2x+3)} - \frac{\sqrt{2}}{4}\arctan \frac{x+1}{\sqrt{2}} + \ln|x+1| + C$$

The first integral on the right was considered in Example 2, Sec. 10.7. The second integral is taken directly.

From the foregoing it follows that the integral of any rational function may be expressed in terms of elementary functions in closed form, namely, in terms of:

(1) logarithms in the case of partial fractions of type I;

(2) rational functions in the case of partial fractions of type II;

(3) logarithms and arc tangents in the case of partial fractions of type III;

(4) rational functions and arc tangents in the case of partial fractions of type IV.

10.10 INTEGRALS OF IRRATIONAL FUNCTIONS

It is impossible to express in terms of elementary functions the integral of every irrational function. In this and the following sections we shall consider irrational functions whose integrals are reduced (by means of substitution) to integrals of rational functions and, consequently, are integrated completely.

I. We consider the integral $\int R\left(x, x^{\frac{m}{n}}, \ldots, x^{\frac{r}{s}}\right) dx$ where R is a rational function of its arguments. *

Let k be a common denominator of the fractions $\frac{m}{n}, \ldots, \frac{r}{s}$. We make the substitution

$$x = t^k, \quad dx = kt^{k-1} dt$$

Then each **fractional** power of x will be expressed in terms of an **integral** power of t and the integrand will thus be transformed into a **rational function of** t.

Example 1. It is required to compute the integral

$$\int \frac{x^{\frac{1}{2}} dx}{x^{\frac{3}{4}} + 1}$$

---

* The notation $R\left(x, x^{\frac{m}{n}}, \ldots, x^{\frac{r}{s}}\right)$ indicates that only **rational** operations are performed on the quantities $x, x^{\frac{m}{n}}, \ldots, x^{\frac{r}{s}}$.

This is precisely the way that the following notations are henceforward to be understood: $R\left(x, \left(\frac{ax+b}{cx+d}\right)^{\frac{m}{n}}, \ldots\right)$, $R\left(x, \sqrt{ax^2+bx+c}\right)$, $R(\sin x, \cos x)$, etc. For instance, the notation $R(\sin x, \cos x)$ indicates that rational operations are to be performed on $\sin x$ and $\cos x$.

Solution. The common denominator of the fractions $\dfrac{1}{2}$, $\dfrac{3}{4}$ is 4; and so we substitute $x = t^4$, $dx = 4t^3\,dt$; then

$$\int \frac{x^{\frac{1}{2}}\,dx}{x^{\frac{3}{4}}+1} = 4 \int \frac{t^2}{t^3+1}\, t^3\,dt = 4 \int \frac{t^5}{t^3+1}\,dt = 4 \int \left(t^2 - \frac{t^2}{t^3+1}\right)dt$$

$$= 4 \int t^2\,dt - 4 \int \frac{t^2}{t^3+1}\,dt = 4\,\frac{t^3}{3} - \frac{4}{3}\ln|t^3+1| + C$$

$$= \frac{4}{3}\left[x^{\frac{3}{4}} - \ln\left|x^{\frac{3}{4}}+1\right|\right] + C$$

II. Now consider an integral of the form

$$\int R\left[x, \left(\frac{ax+b}{cx+d}\right)^{\frac{m}{n}}, \ldots, \left(\frac{ax+b}{cx+d}\right)^{\frac{r}{s}}\right]dx$$

This integral reduces to the integral of a rational function by means of the substitution

$$\frac{ax+b}{cx+d} = t^k$$

where k is the common denominator of the fractions $\dfrac{m}{n}, \ldots, \dfrac{r}{s}$.

Example 2. It is required to compute the integral

$$\int \frac{\sqrt{x+4}}{x}\,dx$$

Solution. We make the substitution $x+4 = t^2$, $x = t^2-4$, $dx = 2t\,dt$; then

$$\int \frac{\sqrt{x+4}}{x}\,dx = 2 \int \frac{t^2}{t^2-4}\,dt = 2 \int \left(1 + \frac{4}{t^2-4}\right)dt = 2\int dt + 8 \int \frac{dt}{t^2-4}$$

$$= 2t + 2\ln\left|\frac{t-2}{t+2}\right| + C = 2\sqrt{x+4} + 2\ln\left|\frac{\sqrt{x+4}-2}{\sqrt{x+4}+2}\right| + C$$

10.11 INTEGRALS OF THE FORM $\int R(x, \sqrt{ax^2+bx+c})\,dx$

Let us consider the integral

$$\int R(x, \sqrt{ax^2+bx+c})\,dx \quad (a \neq 0) \tag{1}$$

An integral of this kind reduces to the integral of a rational function of a new variable by means of the following Euler substitutions.

First Euler substitution. If $a > 0$, then we put

$$\sqrt{ax^2+bx+c} = \pm \sqrt{a}\,x + t$$

For the sake of definiteness we take the plus sign in front of $\sqrt{a}$. Then

$$ax^2 + bx + c = ax^2 + 2\sqrt{a}\,xt + t^2$$

whence x is determined as a rational function of t:

$$x = \frac{t^2 - c}{b - 2\sqrt{a}t}$$

(thus, dx will also be expressed rationally in terms of t). Therefore,

$$\sqrt{ax^2 + bx + c} = \sqrt{a}\,x + t = \sqrt{a}\,\frac{t^2 - c}{b - 2t\sqrt{a}} + t$$

Thus $\sqrt{ax^2 + bx + c}$ is a rational function of t.

Since $\sqrt{ax^2 + bx + c}$, x and dx are expressed rationally in terms of t, the given integral (1) is transformed into an integral of a rational function of t.

Example 1. It is required to compute the integral

$$\int \frac{dx}{\sqrt{x^2 + c}}$$

Solution. Since here $a = 1 > 0$, we put $\sqrt{x^2 + c} = -x + t$; then

$$x^2 + c = x^2 - 2xt + t^2$$

whence

$$x = \frac{t^2 - c}{2t}$$

Consequently,

$$dx = \frac{t^2 + c}{2t^2}\,dt$$

$$\sqrt{x^2 + c} = -x + t = -\frac{t^2 - c}{2t} + t = \frac{t^2 + c}{2t}$$

Returning to the original integral, we have

$$\int \frac{dx}{\sqrt{x^2 + c}} = \int \frac{\frac{t^2 + c}{2t^2}\,dt}{\frac{t^2 + c}{2t}} = \int \frac{dt}{t} = \ln|t| + C_1 = \ln|x + \sqrt{x^2 + c}| + C_1$$

(see formula 14 in the Table of Integrals).

Second Euler substitution. If $c > 0$, we put

$$\sqrt{ax^2 + bx + c} = xt \pm \sqrt{c}$$

then

$$ax^2 + bx + c = x^2t^2 + 2xt\sqrt{c} + c$$

(For the sake of definiteness we took the plus sign in front of the radical.) Then x is determined as a rational function of t:

$$x = \frac{2\sqrt{c}\, t - b}{a - t^2}$$

Since dx and $\sqrt{ax^2+bx+c}$ are also expressed rationally in terms of t, by substituting the values of x, $\sqrt{ax^2+bx+c}$ and dx into the integral $\int R(x, \sqrt{ax^2+bx+c})\, dx$, we reduce it to an integral of a rational function of t.

Example 2. It is required to compute the integral

$$\int \frac{(1 - \sqrt{1+x+x^2})^2}{x^2 \sqrt{1+x+x^2}}\, dx$$

Solution. We set $\sqrt{1+x+x^2} = xt + 1$, then

$$1+x+x^2 = x^2 t^2 + 2xt + 1, \quad x = \frac{2t-1}{1-t^2}, \quad dx = \frac{2t^2 - 2t + 2}{(1-t^2)^2}\, dt$$

$$\sqrt{1+x+x^2} = xt + 1 = \frac{t^2 - t + 1}{1 - t^2}$$

$$1 - \sqrt{1+x+x^2} = \frac{-2t^2 + t}{1 - t^2}$$

Putting the expressions obtained into the original integral, we find

$$\int \frac{(1 - \sqrt{1+x+x^2})^2}{x^2 \sqrt{1+x+x^2}}\, dx = \int \frac{(-2t^2 + t)^2 (1-t^2)^2 (1-t^2)(2t^2 - 2t + 2)}{(1-t^2)^2 (2t-1)^2 (t^2 - t + 1)(1-t^2)^2}\, dt$$

$$= +2 \int \frac{t^2}{1-t^2}\, dt = -2t + \ln\left| \frac{1+t}{1-t} \right| + C$$

$$= -\frac{2(\sqrt{1+x+x^2} - 1)}{x} + \ln\left| \frac{x + \sqrt{1+x+x^2} - 1}{x - \sqrt{1+x+x^2} + 1} \right| + C$$

$$= -\frac{2(\sqrt{1+x+x^2} - 1)}{x} + \ln\left| 2x + 2\sqrt{1+x+x^2} + 1 \right| + C$$

Third Euler substitution. Let α and β be the real roots of the trinomial $ax^2 + bx + c$. We put

$$\sqrt{ax^2 + bx + c} = (x - \alpha)\, t$$

Since $ax^2 + bx + c = a(x - \alpha)(x - \beta)$, we have

$$\sqrt{a(x - \alpha)(x - \beta)} = (x - \alpha)\, t$$

$$a(x - \alpha)(x - \beta) = (x - \alpha)^2\, t^2$$

$$a(x - \beta) = (x - \alpha)\, t^2$$

Whence we find x as a rational function of t:

$$x = \frac{a\beta - at^2}{a - t^2}$$

Since dx and $\sqrt{ax^2+bx+c}$ also rationally depend upon t, the given integral is transformed into an integral of a rational function of t.

Note 1. The third Euler substitution is applicable not only for $a < 0$, but also for $a > 0$, provided the polynomial ax^2+bx+c has two real roots.

Example 3. It is required to compute the integral

$$\int \frac{dx}{\sqrt{x^2+3x-4}}$$

Solution. Since $x^2+3x-4 = (x+4)(x-1)$, we put

$$\sqrt{(x+4)(x-1)} = (x+4)t$$

then

$$(x+4)(x-1) = (x+4)^2 t^2, \quad x-1 = (x+4)t^2$$

$$x = \frac{1+4t^2}{1-t^2}, \quad dx = \frac{10t}{(1-t^2)^2}dt$$

$$\sqrt{(x+4)(x-1)} = \left[\frac{1+4t^2}{1-t^2}+4\right]t = \frac{5t}{1-t^2}$$

Returning to the original integral, we have

$$\int \frac{dx}{\sqrt{x^2+3x-4}} = \int \frac{10t\,(1-t^2)}{(1-t^2)^2\,5t}dt = \int \frac{2}{1-t^2}dt = \ln\left|\frac{1+t}{1-t}\right|+C$$

$$= \ln\left|\frac{1+\sqrt{\dfrac{x-1}{x+4}}}{1-\sqrt{\dfrac{x-1}{x+4}}}\right|+C = \ln\left|\frac{\sqrt{x+4}+\sqrt{x-1}}{\sqrt{x+4}-\sqrt{x-1}}\right|+C$$

Note 2. It will be noted that to reduce integral (1) to an integral of a rational function, the first and third Euler substitutions are sufficient. Let us consider the trinomial ax^2+bx+c. If $b^2-4ac > 0$, then the roots of the trinomial are real, and, hence, the third Euler substitution is applicable. If $b^2-4ac \leqslant 0$, then in this case

$$ax^2+bx+c = \frac{1}{4a}[\,2ax+b)^2+(4ac-b^2)]$$

and therefore the trinomial has the same sign as that of a. For $\sqrt{ax^2+bx+c}$ to be real it is necessary that the trinomial be positive, and we must have $a > 0$. In this case, the first substitution is applicable.

10.12 INTEGRATION OF CERTAIN CLASSES
OF TRIGONOMETRIC FUNCTIONS

Up to now our sole concern has been a systematic study of the integrals of algebraic functions (rational and irrational). In this section we shall consider integrals of certain classes of nonalgebraic functions, primarily trigonometric. Let us consider an integral of the form

$$\int R(\sin x,\ \cos x)\,dx \qquad (1)$$

We shall show that this integral, by the substitution

$$\tan \frac{x}{2} = t \qquad (2)$$

always reduces to an integral of a rational function. Let us express $\sin x$ and $\cos x$ in terms of $\tan \frac{x}{2}$, and hence, in terms of t:

$$\sin x = \frac{2\sin \frac{x}{2}\cos \frac{x}{2}}{1} = \frac{2\sin \frac{x}{2}\cos \frac{x}{2}}{\sin^2 \frac{x}{2}+\cos^2 \frac{x}{2}} = \frac{2\tan \frac{x}{2}}{1+\tan^2 \frac{x}{2}} = \frac{2t}{1+t^2}.$$

$$\cos x = \frac{\cos^2 \frac{x}{2}-\sin^2 \frac{x}{2}}{1} = \frac{\cos^2 \frac{x}{2}-\sin^2 \frac{x}{2}}{\cos^2 \frac{x}{2}+\sin^2 \frac{x}{2}} = \frac{1-\tan^2 \frac{x}{2}}{1+\tan^2 \frac{x}{2}} = \frac{1-t^2}{1+t^2}$$

Furthermore,

$$x = 2\arctan t,\ \ dx = \frac{2dt}{1+t^2}$$

In this way, $\sin x$, $\cos x$ and dx are expressed rationally in terms of t. Since a rational function of rational functions is a rational function, by substituting the expressions obtained into the integral (1) we get an integral of a rational function:

$$\int R(\sin x,\ \cos x)\,dx = \int R\left(\frac{2t}{1+t^2},\ \frac{1-t^2}{1+t^2}\right)\frac{2dt}{1+t^2}$$

Example 1. Consider the integral

$$\int \frac{dx}{\sin x}$$

On the basis of the foregoing formulas we have

$$\int \frac{dx}{\sin x} = \int \frac{\frac{2dt}{1+t^2}}{\frac{2t}{1+t^2}} = \int \frac{dt}{t} = \ln|t| + C = \ln\left|\tan \frac{x}{2}\right| + C$$

This substitution enables us to integrate any function of the form $R(\cos x,\ \sin x)$. For this reason it is sometimes called a "universal trigonometric substitution". However, in practice it frequently leads to extremely complex rational functions. It is therefore convenient to know some other substitutions (in addition to the "universal" one) that sometimes lead more quickly to the desired end.

(1) If an integral is of the form $\int R(\sin x)\cos x\,dx$, the substitution $\sin x = t$, $\cos x\,dx = dt$ reduces this integral to the form $\int R(t)\,dt$.

(2) If the integral has the form $\int R(\cos x)\sin x\,dx$, it is reduced to an integral of a rational function by the substitution $\cos x = t$, $\sin x\,dx = -dt$.

(3) If the integrand is dependent only on $\tan x$, then the substitution $\tan x = t$, $x = \arctan t$, $dx = \dfrac{dt}{1+t^2}$ reduces this integral to an integral of a rational function:

$$\int R(\tan x)\,dx = \int R(t)\,\frac{dt}{1+t^2}$$

(4) If the integrand has the form $R(\sin x,\ \cos x)$, but $\sin x$ and $\cos x$ are involved only in **even** powers, then the same substitution is applied:

$$\tan x = t \qquad (2')$$

because $\sin^2 x$ and $\cos^2 x$ can be expressed rationally in terms of $\tan x$:

$$\cos^2 x = \frac{1}{1+\tan^2 x} = \frac{1}{1+t^2}$$

$$\sin^2 x = \frac{\tan^2 x}{1+\tan^2 x} = \frac{t^2}{1+t^2}$$

$$dx = \frac{dt}{1+t^2}$$

After the substitution we obtain an integral of a rational function.

Example 2. Compute the integral $\int \dfrac{\sin^3 x}{2+\cos x}\,dx$.

Solution. This integral is readily reduced to the form $\int R(\cos x)\sin x\,dx$. Indeed,

$$\int \frac{\sin^3 x}{2+\cos x}\,dx = \int \frac{\sin^2 x \sin x\,dx}{2+\cos x} = \int \frac{1-\cos^2 x}{2+\cos x}\sin x\,dx$$

We make the substitution $\cos x = z$. Then $\sin x\,dx = -dz$:

$$\int \frac{\sin^3 x}{2+\cos x}\,dx = \int \frac{1-z^2}{2+z}\,(-dz) = \int \frac{z^2-1}{z+2}\,dz = \int \left(z-2+\frac{3}{z+2}\right)dz$$

$$= \frac{z^2}{2} - 2z + 3\ln(z+2) + C = \frac{\cos^2 x}{2} - 2\cos x + 3\ln(\cos x + 2) + C$$

Example 3. Compute $\int \dfrac{dx}{2-\sin^2 x}$.

Make the substitution $\tan x = t$:

$$\int \frac{dx}{2 - \sin^2 x} = \int \frac{dt}{\left(2 - \frac{t^2}{1+t^2}\right)(1+t^2)} = \int \frac{dt}{2+t^2} = \frac{1}{\sqrt{2}} \arctan \frac{t}{\sqrt{2}} + C$$

$$= \frac{1}{\sqrt{2}} \arctan \left(\frac{\tan x}{\sqrt{2}}\right) + C$$

(5) Now let us consider one more integral of the form $\int R(\sin x, \cos x)\, dx$, namely an integral with integrand $\sin^m x \cos^n x\, dx$ (where m and n are integers). Here we consider three cases.

(a) $\int \sin^m x \cos^n x\, dx$, where m and n are such that at least one of them is **odd**. For definiteness let us assume that n is odd. Put $n = 2p + 1$ and transform the integral:

$$\int \sin^m x \cos^{2p+1} x\, dx = \int \sin^m x \cos^{2p} x \cos x\, dx$$

$$= \int \sin^m x (1 - \sin^2 x)^p \cos x\, dx$$

Change the variable:

$$\sin x = t, \quad \cos x\, dx = dt$$

Putting the new variable into the given integral, we get

$$\int \sin^m x \cos^n x\, dx = \int t^m (1 - t^2)^p\, dt$$

which is an integral of a rational function of t.

Example 4.

$$\int \frac{\cos^3 x}{\sin^4 x}\, dx = \int \frac{\cos^2 x \cos x\, dx}{\sin^4 x} = \int \frac{(1 - \sin^2 x) \cos x\, dx}{\sin^4 x}$$

Denoting $\sin x = t$, $\cos x\, dx = dt$, we get

$$\int \frac{\cos^3 x}{\sin^4 x}\, dx = \int \frac{(1 - t^2)\, dt}{t^4} = \int \frac{dt}{t^4} - \int \frac{dt}{t^2} = -\frac{1}{3t^3} + \frac{1}{t} + C$$

$$= -\frac{1}{3 \sin^3 x} + \frac{1}{\sin x} + C$$

(b) $\int \sin^m x \cos^n x\, dx$, where m and n are nonnegative and even numbers.

Put $m = 2p$, $n = 2q$. Write the familiar trigonometric formulas:

$$\sin^2 x = \frac{1}{2} - \frac{1}{2} \cos 2x, \quad \cos^2 x = \frac{1}{2} + \frac{1}{2} \cos 2x \qquad (3)$$

Putting them into the integral we get

$$\int \sin^{2p} x \cos^{2q} x\, dx = \int \left(\frac{1}{2} - \frac{1}{2} \cos 2x\right)^p \left(\frac{1}{2} + \frac{1}{2} \cos 2x\right)^q dx$$

Powering and opening brackets, we get terms containing $\cos 2x$ to odd and even powers. The terms with odd powers are integrated as indicated in Case (a). We again reduce the even exponents by formulas (3). Continuing in this manner we arrive at terms of the form $\int \cos kx\, dx$, which can easily be integrated.

Example 5.

$$\int \sin^4 x\, dx = \frac{1}{2^2} \int (1 - \cos 2x)^2\, dx = \frac{1}{4} \int (1 - 2\cos 2x + \cos^2 2x)\, dx$$

$$= \frac{1}{4} \left[x - \sin 2x + \frac{1}{2} \int (1 + \cos 4x)\, dx \right] = \frac{1}{4} \left[\frac{3}{2} x - \sin 2x + \frac{\sin 4x}{8} \right] + C$$

(c) If both exponents are even, and at least one of them is negative, then the preceding technique does not give the desired result. Here, one should make the substitution $\tan x = t$ (or $\cot x = t$).

Example 6.

$$\int \frac{\sin^2 x\, dx}{\cos^6 x} = \int \frac{\sin^2 x\, (\sin^2 x + \cos^2 x)^2}{\cos^6 x}\, dx = \int \tan^2 x\, (1 + \tan^2 x)^2\, dx$$

Put $\tan x = t$; then $x = \arctan t$, $dx = \dfrac{dt}{1 + t^2}$ and we get

$$\int \frac{\sin^2 x}{\cos^6 x}\, dx = \int t^2 (1 + t^2)^2 \frac{dt}{1 + t^2} = \int t^2 (1 + t^2)\, dt = \frac{t^3}{3} + \frac{t^5}{5} + C$$

$$= \frac{\tan^3 x}{3} + \frac{\tan^5 x}{5} + C$$

(6) In conclusion let us consider integrals of the form

$$\int \cos mx \cos nx\, dx, \qquad \int \sin mx \cos nx\, dx, \qquad \int \sin mx \sin nx\, dx$$

They are taken by means of the following   formulas* $(m \neq n)$:

$$\cos mx \cos nx = \frac{1}{2} \left[\cos (m + n)\, x + \cos (m - n)\, x \right]$$

$$\sin mx \cos nx = \frac{1}{2} \left[\sin (m + n)\, x + \sin (m - n)\, x \right]$$

$$\sin mx \sin nx = \frac{1}{2} \left[-\cos (m + n)\, x + \cos (m - n)\, x \right]$$

---

* These formulas are easily derived as follows:

$$\cos (m + n)\, x = \cos mx \cos nx - \sin mx \sin nx$$
$$\cos (m - n)\, x = \cos mx \cos nx + \sin mx \sin nx$$

Combining these equations termwise and dividing them in half, we get the first of the three formulas. Subtracting termwise and dividing in half, we get the third formula. The second formula is similarly derived if we write analogous equations for $\sin (m + n)\, x$ and $\sin (m - n)\, x$ and then combine them termwise.

Substituting and integrating, we get

$$\int \cos mx \cos nx \, dx = \frac{1}{2} \int [\cos (m+n) \, x + \cos (m-n) \, x] \, dx$$

$$= \frac{\sin (m+n) \, x}{2 \, (m+n)} + \frac{\sin (m-n) \, x}{2 \, (m-n)} + C$$

The other two integrals are evaluated similarly.

Example 7.

$$\int \sin 5x \sin 3x \, dx = \frac{1}{2} \int [-\cos 8x + \cos 2x] \, dx = -\frac{\sin 8x}{16} + \frac{\sin 2x}{4} + C$$

10.13 INTEGRATION OF CERTAIN IRRATIONAL FUNCTIONS BY MEANS OF TRIGONOMETRIC SUBSTITUTIONS

Let us return to the integral considered in Sec. 10.11:

$$\int R \left(x, \sqrt{ax^2 + bx + c}\right) dx \tag{1}$$

where $a \neq 0$ and $c - \frac{b^2}{4a} \neq 0$ (in the case $a = 0$ the integral has form II, Sec. 10.10; for $c - \frac{b^2}{4a} = 0$, the expression $ax^2 + bx + c = a\left(x + \frac{b}{2a}\right)^2$, and we have to do with a rational function, if $a > 0$; for $a < 0$ the function $\sqrt{ax^2 + bx + c}$ is not defined for any value of x). Here we shall give a method of transforming this integral into one of the form

$$\int \overline{R} \, (\sin z, \, \cos z) \, dz \tag{2}$$

which was considered in the preceding section.

Transform the trinomial under the radical sign:

$$ax^2 + bx + c = a\left(x + \frac{b}{2a}\right)^2 + \left(c - \frac{b^2}{4a}\right)$$

Change the variable, putting

$$x + \frac{b}{2a} = t, \quad dx = dt$$

Then

$$\sqrt{ax^2 + bx + c} = \sqrt{at^2 + \left(c - \frac{b^2}{4a}\right)}$$

Let us consider all possible cases.

1. Let $a > 0$, $c - \frac{b^2}{4a} > 0$. We introduce the designations: $a = m^2$, $c - \frac{b^2}{4a} = n^2$. In this case we have

$$\sqrt{ax^2 + bx + c} = \sqrt{m^2 t^2 + n^2}$$

2. Let $a > 0$, $c - \dfrac{b^2}{4a} < 0$. Then

$$a = m^2, \quad c - \frac{b^2}{4a} = -n^2$$

Thus,

$$\sqrt{ax^2 + bx + c} = \sqrt{m^2 t^2 - n^2}$$

3. Let $a < 0$, $c - \dfrac{b^2}{4a} > 0$. Then

$$a = -m^2, \quad c - \frac{b^2}{4a} = n^2$$

Hence,

$$\sqrt{ax^2 + bx + c} = \sqrt{n^2 - m^2 t^2}$$

4. Let $a < 0$, $c - \dfrac{b^2}{4a} < 0$. In this case $\sqrt{ax^2 + bx + c}$ is a complex number for every value of x.

In this way, integral (1) is reduced to one of the following types of integrals:

$$\text{I.} \quad \int R(t, \sqrt{m^2 t^2 + n^2})\, dt \tag{3a}$$

$$\text{II.} \quad \int R(t, \sqrt{m^2 t^2 - n^2})\, dt \tag{3b}$$

$$\text{III.} \quad \int R(t, \sqrt{n^2 - m^2 t^2})\, dt \tag{3c}$$

Obviously, integral (3a) is reduced to an integral of the form (2) by the substitution

$$t = \frac{n}{m} \tan z$$

Integral (3b) is reduced to the form (2) by the substitution

$$t = \frac{n}{m} \sec z$$

Integral (3c) is reduced to (2) by the substitution

$$t = \frac{n}{m} \sin t$$

Example. Compute the integral

$$\int \frac{dx}{\sqrt{(a^2 - x^2)^3}}$$

Solution. This is an integral of type III. Make the substitution $x = a \sin z$, then

$$dx = a \cos z \, dz$$

$$\int \frac{dx}{\sqrt{(a^2-x^2)^3}} = \int \frac{a \cos z \, dz}{\sqrt{(a^2 - a^2 \sin^2 z)^3}} = \int \frac{a \cos z \, dz}{a^3 \cos^3 z} \,^*$$

$$= \frac{1}{a^2} \int \frac{dz}{\cos^2 z} = \frac{1}{a^2} \tan z + C = \frac{1}{a^2} \frac{\sin z}{\cos z} + C = \frac{1}{a^2} \frac{\sin z}{\sqrt{1-\sin^2 z}} + C$$

$$= \frac{1}{a^2} \frac{x}{\sqrt{a^2-x^2}} + C$$

10.14 ON FUNCTIONS WHOSE INTEGRALS CANNOT BE EXPRESSED IN TERMS OF ELEMENTARY FUNCTIONS

In Sec. 10.1 we pointed out (without proof) that any function $f(x)$ continuous on an interval (a, b) has an antiderivative on that interval; in other words, there exists a function $F(x)$ such that $F'(x) = f(x)$. However, **not every antiderivative**, even when it exists, **is expressible, in closed form, in terms of elementary functions.**

Such are the antiderivatives expressed by the integrals $\int e^{-x^2} dx$, $\int \frac{\sin x}{x} dx$, $\int \frac{\cos x}{x} dx$, $\int \sqrt{1-k^2 \sin^2 x} \, dx$, $\int \frac{dx}{\ln x}$ and many others.

In all such cases, the antiderivative is obviously some new function which does not reduce to a combination of a finite number of elementary functions.

For example, that one of the antiderivatives

$$\frac{2}{\sqrt{\pi}} \int e^{-x^2} dx + C$$

which vanishes for $x = 0$ is called the *Laplace function* and is denoted by $\Phi(x)$. Thus,

$$\Phi(x) = \frac{2}{\sqrt{\pi}} \int e^{-x^2} dx + C_1 \text{ if } \Phi(0) = 0$$

This function has been studied in detail. Tables of its values for various values of x have been compiled. We shall see how this is done in Sec. 16.21 (Vol. II). Figs. 208 and 209 show the graph of the integrand $y = e^{-x^2}$ and the graph of the Laplace function $y = \Phi(x)$. That one of the antiderivatives

$$\int \sqrt{1-k^2 \sin^2 x} \, dx + C \quad (k < 1)$$

---

* $\sqrt{1-\sin^2 z} = |\cos z|$. For the sake of definiteness, we only examine the case $|\cos z| = \cos z$.

which vanishes for $x = 0$ is called an *elliptic integral* and is denoted by $E(x)$,

$$E(x) = \int \sqrt{1 - k^2 \sin^2 x}\, dx + C_2 \text{ if } E(0) = 0$$

Tables of the values of this function have also been compiled for various values of x.

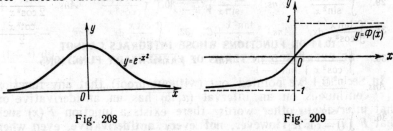

Fig. 208   Fig. 209

Exercises on Chapter 10

I. Compute the integrals: 1. $\int x^5\, dx$. *Ans.* $\dfrac{x^6}{6} + C$. 2. $\int (x + \sqrt{x})\, dx$.

Ans. $\dfrac{x^2}{2} + \dfrac{2x\sqrt{x}}{3} + C$. 3. $\int \left(\dfrac{3}{\sqrt{x}} - \dfrac{x\sqrt{x}}{4} \right) dx$. *Ans.* $6\sqrt{x} - \dfrac{1}{10}x^2\sqrt{x} + C$.

4. $\int \dfrac{x^2\, dx}{\sqrt{x}}$. *Ans.* $\dfrac{2}{5} x^2 \sqrt{x} + C$. 5. $\int \left(\dfrac{1}{x^2} + \dfrac{4}{x\sqrt{x}} + 2 \right) dx$:

Ans. $-\dfrac{1}{x} - \dfrac{8}{\sqrt{x}} + 2x + C$. 6. $\int \dfrac{dx}{\sqrt[4]{x}}$. *Ans.* $\dfrac{4}{3} \sqrt[4]{x^3} + C$.

7. $\int \left(x^2 + \dfrac{1}{\sqrt[3]{x}} \right)^2 dx$. *Ans.* $\dfrac{x^5}{5} + \dfrac{3}{4} x^2 \sqrt[3]{x^2} + 3\sqrt[3]{x} + C$.

Integration by substitution: 8. $\int e^{5x}\, dx$. *Ans.* $\dfrac{1}{5} e^{5x} + C$. 9. $\int \cos 5x\, dx$.

Ans. $\dfrac{\sin 5x}{5} + C$. 10. $\int \sin ax\, dx$. *Ans.* $-\dfrac{\cos ax}{a} + C$. 11. $\int \dfrac{\ln x}{x}\, dx$.

Ans. $\dfrac{1}{2} \ln^2 x + C$. 12. $\int \dfrac{dx}{\sin^2 3x}$. *Ans.* $-\dfrac{\cot 3x}{3} + C$. 13. $\int \dfrac{dx}{\cos^2 7x}$.

Ans. $\dfrac{\tan 7x}{7} + C$. 14. $\int \dfrac{dx}{3x - 7}$. *Ans.* $\dfrac{1}{3} \ln |3x - 7| + C$. 15. $\int \dfrac{dx}{1 - x}$.

Ans. $-\ln |1 - x| + C$. 16. $\int \dfrac{dx}{5 - 2x}$. *Ans.* $-\dfrac{1}{2} \ln |5 - 2x| + C$. 17. $\int \tan 2x\, dx$.

Ans. $-\dfrac{1}{2} \ln |\cos 2x| + C$. 18. $\int \cot (5x - 7)\, dx$. *Ans.* $\dfrac{1}{5} \ln |\sin (5x - 7)| + C$.

19. $\int \dfrac{dy}{\cot 3y}$. *Ans.* $-\dfrac{1}{3} \ln |\cos 3y| + C$. 20. $\int \cot \dfrac{x}{3}\, dx$. *Ans.* $3 \ln \left| \sin \dfrac{x}{3} \right| + C$.

21. $\int \tan \varphi \cdot \sec^2 \varphi\, d\varphi$. *Ans.* $\dfrac{1}{2} \tan^2 \varphi + C$. 22. $\int (\cot e^x) e^x\, dx$. *Ans.* $\ln |\sin e^x| + C$.

23. $\int \left(\tan 4S - \cot \dfrac{S}{4} \right) dS$. *Ans.* $-\dfrac{1}{4} \ln |\cos 4S| - 4 \ln \left| \sin \dfrac{S}{4} \right| + C$.

24. $\int \sin^2 x \cos x\, dx.$ *Ans.* $\dfrac{\sin^3 x}{3} + C.$ **25.** $\int \cos^3 x \sin x\, dx.$ *Ans.* $-\dfrac{\cos^4 x}{4} + C.$

26. $\int \sqrt{x^2+1}\, x\, dx.$ *Ans* $\dfrac{1}{3}\sqrt{(x^2+1)^3} + C.$ **27.** $\int \dfrac{x\, dx}{\sqrt{2x^2+3}}.$

Ans. $\dfrac{1}{2}\sqrt{2x^2+3} + C.$ **28.** $\int \dfrac{x^2\, dx}{\sqrt{x^3+1}}.$ *Ans.* $\dfrac{2}{3}\sqrt{x^3+1} + C.$

29. $\int \dfrac{\cos x\, dx}{\sin^2 x}.$ *Ans.* $-\dfrac{1}{\sin x} + C.$ **30.** $\int \dfrac{\sin x\, dx}{\cos^3 x}.$ *Ans.* $\dfrac{1}{2\cos^2 x} + C.$

31. $\int \dfrac{\tan x}{\cos^2 x}\, dx.$ *Ans.* $\dfrac{\tan^2 x}{2} + C.$ **32.** $\int \dfrac{\cot x}{\sin^2 x}\, dx.$ *Ans.* $-\dfrac{\cot^2 x}{2} + C.$

33. $\int \dfrac{dx}{\cos^2 x \sqrt{\tan x - 1}}.$ *Ans.* $2\sqrt{\tan x - 1} + C.$ **34.** $\int \dfrac{\ln(x+1)}{x+1}\, dx.$

Ans. $\dfrac{\ln^2(x+1)}{2} + C.$ **35.** $\int \dfrac{\cos x\, dx}{\sqrt{2\sin x + 1}}.$ *Ans.* $\sqrt{2\sin x + 1} + C.$

36. $\int \dfrac{\sin 2x\, dx}{(1+\cos 2x)^2}.$ *Ans.* $\dfrac{1}{2(1+\cos 2x)} + C.$ **37.** $\int \dfrac{\sin 2x\, dx}{\sqrt{1+\sin^2 x}}.$

Ans. $2\sqrt{1+\sin^2 x} + C.$ **38.** $\int \dfrac{\sqrt{\tan x + 1}}{\cos^2 x}\, dx.$ *Ans.* $\dfrac{2}{3}\sqrt{(\tan x+1)^3} + C.$

39. $\int \dfrac{\cos 2x\, dx}{(2+3\sin 2x)^3}.$ *Ans.* $-\dfrac{1}{12}\dfrac{1}{(2+3\sin 2x)^2} + C.$ **40.** $\int \dfrac{\sin 3x\, dx}{\sqrt[3]{\cos^4 3x}}.$

Ans. $\dfrac{1}{\sqrt[3]{\cos 3x}} + C.$ **41.** $\int \dfrac{\ln^2 x\, dx}{x}.$ *Ans.* $\dfrac{\ln^3 x}{3} + C.$ **42.** $\int \dfrac{\arcsin x\, dx}{\sqrt{1-x^2}}.$

Ans. $\dfrac{\arcsin^2 x}{2} + C.$ **43.** $\int \dfrac{\arctan x\, dx}{1+x^2}.$ *Ans.* $\dfrac{\arctan^2 x}{2} + C.$

44. $\int \dfrac{\arccos^2 x}{\sqrt{1-x^2}}\, dx.$ *Ans.* $-\dfrac{\arccos^3 x}{3} + C.$ **45.** $\int \dfrac{\operatorname{arccot} x}{1+x^2}\, dx.$ *Ans.* $-\dfrac{\operatorname{arccot}^2 x}{2} + C.$

46. $\int \dfrac{x\, dx}{x^2+1}.$ *Ans.* $\dfrac{1}{2}\ln(x^2+1) + C.$ **47.** $\int \dfrac{x+1}{x^2+2x+3}\, dx.$ *Ans.* $\dfrac{1}{2}\ln(x^2+2x+3) + C.$

48. $\int \dfrac{\cos x\, dx}{2\sin x + 3}.$ *Ans.* $\dfrac{1}{2}\ln(2\sin x + 3) + C.$ **49.** $\int \dfrac{dx}{x\ln x}.$ *Ans.* $\ln|\ln x| + C.$

50. $\int 2x\,(x^2+1)^4\, dx.$ *Ans.* $\dfrac{(x^2+1)^5}{5} + C.$ **51.** $\int \tan^4 x\, dx.$ *Ans.* $\dfrac{\tan^3 x}{3} - \tan x + x + C.$

52. $\int \dfrac{dx}{(1+x^2)\arctan x}.$ *Ans.* $\ln|\arctan x| + C.$ **53.** $\int \dfrac{dx}{\cos^2 x\,(3\tan x + 1)}.$

Ans. $\dfrac{1}{3}\ln|3\tan x + 1| + C.$ **54.** $\int \dfrac{\tan^3 x}{\cos^2 x}\, dx.$ *Ans.* $\dfrac{\tan^4 x}{4} + C.$ **55.** $\int \dfrac{dx}{\sqrt{1-x^2}\arcsin x}.$

Ans. $\ln|\arcsin x| + C.$ **56.** $\int \dfrac{\cos 2x}{2+3\sin 2x}\, dx.$ *Ans.* $\dfrac{1}{6}\ln|2+3\sin 2x| + C.$

57. $\int \cos(\ln x)\dfrac{dx}{x}.$ *Ans.* $\sin(\ln x) + C.$ **58.** $\int \cos(a+bx)\, dx.$ *Ans.* $\dfrac{1}{b}\sin(a+bx) + C.$

59. $\int e^{2x}\, dx.$ *Ans.* $\dfrac{1}{2}e^{2x} + C.$ **60.** $\int e^{\frac{x}{3}}\, dx.$ *Ans.* $3e^{\frac{x}{3}} + C.$ **61.** $\int e^{\sin x}\cos x\, dx.$

Ans. $e^{\sin x} + C.$ **62.** $\int a^{x^2} x\, dx.$ *Ans.* $\dfrac{a^{x^2}}{2\ln a} + C.$ **63** $\int e^{\frac{x}{a}}\, dx.$ *Ans.* $ae^{\frac{x}{a}} + C.$

64. $\int (e^{2x})^2 \, dx$. *Ans.* $\frac{1}{4} e^{4x} + C$. **65.** $\int 3^x e^x \, dx$. *Ans.* $\frac{3^x e^x}{\ln 3 + 1} + C$. **66.** $\int e^{-3x} \, dx$.

Ans. $-\frac{1}{3} e^{-3x} + C$. **67.** $\int (e^{5x} + a^{5x}) \, dx$. *Ans.* $\frac{1}{5} \left(e^{5x} + \frac{a^{5x}}{\ln a} + C \right)$.

68. $\int e^{x^2 + 4x + 3} (x + 2) \, dx$. *Ans.* $\frac{1}{2} e^{x^2 + 4x + 3} + C$. **69.** $\int \frac{(a^x - b^x)^2}{a^x b^x} \, dx$.

Ans. $\dfrac{\left(\dfrac{a}{b}\right)^x - \left(\dfrac{b}{a}\right)^x}{\ln a - \ln b} - 2x + C$. **70.** $\int \frac{e^x \, dx}{3 + 4e^x}$. *Ans.* $\frac{1}{4} \ln (3 + 4e^x) + C$.

71. $\int \frac{e^{2x} \, dx}{2 + e^{2x}}$. *Ans.* $\frac{1}{2} \ln (2 + e^{2x}) + C$. **72.** $\int \frac{dx}{1 + 2x^2}$. *Ans.* $\frac{1}{\sqrt{2}} \arctan (\sqrt{2}x) + C$.

73. $\int \frac{dx}{\sqrt{1 - 3x^2}}$. *Ans.* $\frac{1}{\sqrt{3}} \arcsin (\sqrt{3}x) + C$. **74.** $\int \frac{dx}{\sqrt{16 - 9x^2}}$.

Ans. $\frac{1}{3} \arcsin \frac{3x}{4} + C$. **75.** $\int \frac{dx}{\sqrt{9 - x^2}}$. *Ans.* $\arcsin \frac{x}{3} + C$. **76.** $\int \frac{dx}{4 + x^2}$.

Ans. $\frac{1}{2} \arctan \frac{x}{2} + C$. **77.** $\int \frac{dx}{9x^2 + 4}$. *Ans.* $\frac{1}{6} \arctan \frac{3x}{2} + C$. **78.** $\int \frac{dx}{4 - 9x^2}$.

Ans. $\frac{1}{12} \ln \left| \frac{2 + 3x}{2 - 3x} \right| + C$. **79.** $\int \frac{dx}{\sqrt{x^2 + 9}}$. *Ans.* $\ln |x + \sqrt{x^2 + 9}| + C$.

80. $\int \frac{dx}{\sqrt{b^2 x^2 - a^2}}$. *Ans.* $\frac{1}{b} \ln |bx + \sqrt{b^2 x^2 - a^2}| + C$. **81.** $\int \frac{dx}{\sqrt{b^2 + a^2 x^2}}$.

Ans. $\frac{1}{a} \ln |ax + \sqrt{b^2 + a^2 x^2}| + C$. **82.** $\int \frac{dx}{a^2 x^2 - c^2}$. *Ans.* $\frac{1}{2ac} \ln \left| \frac{ax - c}{ax + c} \right| + C$.

83. $\int \frac{x^2 \, dx}{5 - x^6}$. *Ans.* $\frac{1}{6\sqrt{5}} \ln \left| \frac{x^3 + \sqrt{5}}{x^3 - \sqrt{5}} \right| + C$. **84.** $\int \frac{x \, dx}{\sqrt{1 - x^4}}$. *Ans.* $\frac{1}{2} \arcsin x^2 + C$.

85. $\int \frac{x \, dx}{x^4 + a^4}$. *Ans.* $\frac{1}{2a^2} \arctan \frac{x^2}{a^2} + C$. **86.** $\int \frac{e^x \, dx}{\sqrt{1 - e^{2x}}}$. *Ans.* $\arcsin e^x + C$.

87. $\int \frac{dx}{\sqrt{3 - 5x^2}}$. *Ans.* $\frac{1}{\sqrt{5}} \arcsin \sqrt{\frac{5}{3}} x + C$. **88.** $\int \frac{\cos x \, dx}{a^2 + \sin^2 x}$.

Ans. $\frac{1}{a} \arctan \left(\frac{\sin x}{a} \right) + C$. **89.** $\int \frac{dx}{x \sqrt{1 - \ln^2 x}}$. *Ans.* $\arcsin (\ln x) + C$.

90. $\int \frac{\arccos x - x}{\sqrt{1 - x^2}} \, dx$. *Ans.* $-\frac{1}{2} (\arccos x)^2 + \sqrt{1 - x^2} + C$.

91. $\int \frac{x - \arctan x}{1 + x^2} \, dx$. *Ans.* $\frac{1}{2} \ln (1 + x^2) - \frac{1}{2} (\arctan x)^2 + C$. **92.** $\int \frac{\sqrt{1 + \ln x}}{x} \, dx$.

Ans. $\frac{2}{3} \sqrt{(1 + \ln x)^3} + C$. **93.** $\int \frac{\sqrt{1 + \sqrt{x}}}{\sqrt{x}} \, dx$. *Ans.* $\frac{4}{3} \sqrt{(1 + \sqrt{x})^3} + C$.

94. $\int \frac{dx}{\sqrt{x} \sqrt{1 + \sqrt{x}}}$. *Ans.* $4 \sqrt{1 + \sqrt{x}} + C$. **95.** $\int \frac{e^x \, dx}{1 + e^{2x}}$. *Ans.* $\arctan e^x + C$.

96. $\int \frac{\cos x \, dx}{\sqrt[3]{\sin^2 x}}$. *Ans.* $3 \sqrt[3]{\sin x} + C$. **97.** $\int \sqrt{1 + 3 \cos^2 x} \sin 2x \, dx$.

Ans. $-\frac{2}{9} \sqrt{(1 + 3 \cos^2 x)^3} + C$. **98.** $\int \frac{\sin 2x \, dx}{\sqrt{1 + \cos^2 x}}$. *Ans.* $-2 \sqrt{1 + \cos^2 x} + C$.

99. $\int \dfrac{\cos^3 x}{\sin^4 x}\,dx.$ Ans. $\dfrac{1}{\sin x}-\dfrac{1}{3\sin^3 x}+C.$ **100.** $\int \dfrac{\sqrt[3]{\tan^2 x}}{\cos^2 x}\,dx.$ Ans. $\dfrac{3}{5}\sqrt[3]{\tan^5 x}+C.$

101. $\int \dfrac{dx}{2\sin^2 x+3\cos^2 x}.$ Ans. $\dfrac{1}{\sqrt{6}}\arctan\left(\sqrt{\dfrac{2}{3}}\,\tan x\right)+C.$

Integrals of the form $\int \dfrac{Ax+B}{ax^2+bx+c}\,dx$: **102.** $\int \dfrac{dx}{x^2+2x+5}.$ Ans. $\dfrac{1}{2}\arctan\dfrac{x+1}{2}+C.$

103. $\int \dfrac{dx}{3x^2-2x+4}.$ Ans. $\dfrac{1}{\sqrt{11}}\arctan\dfrac{3x-1}{\sqrt{11}}+C.$ **104.** $\int \dfrac{dx}{x^2+3x+1}.$

Ans. $\dfrac{1}{\sqrt{5}}\ln\left|\dfrac{2x+3-\sqrt{5}}{2x+3+\sqrt{5}}\right|+C.$ **105.** $\int \dfrac{dx}{x^2-6x+5}.$ Ans. $\dfrac{1}{4}\ln\left|\dfrac{x-5}{x-1}\right|+C.$

106. $\int \dfrac{dz}{2z^2-2z+1}.$ Ans. $\arctan(2z-1)+C.$ **107.** $\int \dfrac{dx}{3x^2-2x+2}.$

Ans. $\dfrac{1}{\sqrt{5}}\arctan\dfrac{3x-1}{\sqrt{5}}+C.$ **108.** $\int \dfrac{(6x-7)\,dx}{3x^2-7x+11}.$ Ans. $\ln|3x^2-7x+11|+C.$

109. $\int \dfrac{(3x-2)\,dx}{5x^2-3x+2}.$ Ans. $\dfrac{3}{10}\ln(5x^2-3x+2)-\dfrac{11}{5\sqrt{31}}\arctan\dfrac{10x-3}{\sqrt{31}}+C.$

110. $\int \dfrac{3x-1}{x^2-x+1}\,dx.$ Ans. $\dfrac{3}{2}\ln(x^2-x+1)+\dfrac{1}{\sqrt{3}}\arctan\dfrac{2x-1}{\sqrt{3}}+C.$

111. $\int \dfrac{7x+1}{6x^2+x-1}\,dx.$ Ans. $\dfrac{2}{3}\ln(3x-1)+\dfrac{1}{2}\ln(2x+1)+C.$ **112.** $\int \dfrac{2x-1}{5x^2-x+2}\,dx.$

Ans. $\dfrac{1}{5}\ln(5x^2-x+2)-\dfrac{8}{5\sqrt{39}}\arctan\dfrac{10x-1}{\sqrt{39}}+C.$

113. $\int \dfrac{6x^4-5x^3+4x^2}{2x^2-x+1}\,dx.$ Ans. $x^3-\dfrac{x^2}{2}+\dfrac{1}{4}\ln|2x^2-x+1|+\dfrac{1}{2\sqrt{7}}\arctan\dfrac{4x-1}{\sqrt{7}}+C.$

114. $\int \dfrac{dx}{2\cos^2 x+\sin x\cos x+\sin^2 x}.$ Ans. $\dfrac{2}{\sqrt{7}}\arctan\dfrac{2\tan x+1}{\sqrt{7}}+C.$

Integrals of the form $\int \dfrac{Ax+B}{\sqrt{ax^2+bx+C}}\,dx$: **115.** $\int \dfrac{dx}{\sqrt{2-3x-4x^2}}.$

Ans. $\dfrac{1}{2}\arcsin\dfrac{8x+3}{\sqrt{41}}+C.$ **116.** $\int \dfrac{dx}{\sqrt{1+x+x^2}}.$ Ans. $\ln\left|x+\dfrac{1}{2}+\sqrt{x^2+x+1}\right|+C.$

117. $\int \dfrac{dS}{\sqrt{2aS+S^2}}.$ Ans. $\ln|S+a+\sqrt{2aS+S^2}|+C.$

118. $\int \dfrac{dx}{\sqrt{5-7x-3x^2}}.$ Ans. $\dfrac{1}{\sqrt{3}}\arcsin\dfrac{6x+7}{\sqrt{109}}+C.$ **119.** $\int \dfrac{dx}{\sqrt{x(3x+5)}}.$

Ans. $\dfrac{1}{\sqrt{3}}\ln|6x+5+\sqrt{12x(3x+5)}|+C.$ **120.** $\int \dfrac{dx}{\sqrt{2-3x-x^2}}.$

Ans. $\arcsin\dfrac{2x+3}{\sqrt{17}}+C.$ **121.** $\int \dfrac{dx}{\sqrt{5x^2-x-1}}.$

Ans. $\dfrac{1}{\sqrt{5}}\ln|10x-1+\sqrt{20(5x^2-x-1)}|+C.$ **122.** $\int \dfrac{2ax+b}{\sqrt{ax^2+bx+C}}\,dx.$

Ans. $2\sqrt{ax^2+bx+c}+C.$

123. $\int\dfrac{(x+3)\,dx}{\sqrt{4x^2+4x+3}}.$

Ans. $\dfrac{1}{4}\sqrt{4x^2+4x+3}+\dfrac{5}{4}\ln|2x+1+\sqrt{4x^2+4x+3}|+C.$

124. $\int\dfrac{(x-3)\,dx}{\sqrt{3+66x-11x^2}}.$

Ans. $-\dfrac{1}{11}\sqrt{3+66x-11x^2}+C.$

125. $\int\dfrac{(x+3)\,dx}{\sqrt{3+4x-4x^2}}.$ *Ans.* $-\dfrac{1}{4}\sqrt{3+4x-4x^2}+\dfrac{7}{4}\arcsin\dfrac{2x-1}{2}+C.$

126. $\int\dfrac{3x+5}{\sqrt{x(2x-1)}}\,dx.$ *Ans.* $\dfrac{3}{2}\sqrt{2x^2-x}+\dfrac{23}{4\sqrt{2}}\ln(4x-1+\sqrt{8(2x^2-x)})+C.$

II. Integration by parts:

127. $\int xe^x\,dx.$ *Ans.* $e^x(x-1)+C.$ **128.** $\int x\ln x\,dx.$ *Ans.* $\dfrac{1}{2}x^2\left(\ln x-\dfrac{1}{2}\right)+C.$

129. $\int x\sin x\,dx.$ *Ans.* $\sin x-x\cos x+C.$ **130.** $\int\ln x\,dx.$ *Ans.* $x(\ln x-1)+C.$

131. $\int\arcsin x\,dx.$ *Ans.* $x\arcsin x+\sqrt{1-x^2}+C.$ **132.** $\int\ln(1-x)\,dx.$

Ans. $-x-(1-x)\ln(1-x)+C.$ **133.** $\int x^n\ln x\,dx.$ *Ans.* $\dfrac{x^{n+1}}{n+1}\left(\ln x-\dfrac{1}{n+1}\right)+C.$

134. $\int x\arctan x\,dx.$ *Ans.* $\dfrac{1}{2}[(x^2+1)\arctan x-x]+C.$ **135.** $\int x\arcsin x\,dx.$

Ans. $\dfrac{1}{4}[(2x^2-1)\arcsin x+x\sqrt{1-x^2}]+C.$ **136.** $\int\ln(x^2+1)\,dx.$

Ans. $x\ln(x^2+1)-2x+2\arctan x+C.$ **137.** $\int\arctan\sqrt{x}\,dx.$

Ans. $(x+1)\arctan\sqrt{x}-\sqrt{x}+C.$ **138.** $\int\dfrac{\arcsin\sqrt{x}}{\sqrt{x}}\,dx.$

Ans. $2\sqrt{x}\arcsin\sqrt{x}+2\sqrt{1-x}+C.$ **139.** $\int\arcsin\sqrt{\dfrac{x}{x+1}}\,dx.$

Ans. $x\arcsin\sqrt{\dfrac{x}{x+1}}-\sqrt{x}+\arctan\sqrt{x}+C.$ **140.** $\int x\cos^2 x\,dx.$

Ans. $\dfrac{x^2}{4}+\dfrac{1}{4}x\sin 2x+\dfrac{1}{8}\cos 2x+C.$ **141.** $\int\dfrac{x\arcsin x}{\sqrt{1-x^2}}\,dx.$

Ans. $x-\sqrt{1-x^2}\arcsin x+C.$ **142.** $\int\dfrac{x\arctan x}{(x^2+1)^2}\,dx.$

Ans. $\dfrac{x}{4(1+x^2)}+\dfrac{1}{4}\arctan x-\dfrac{1}{2}\dfrac{\arctan x}{1+x^2}+C.$ **143.** $\int x\arctan\sqrt{x^2-1}\,dx.$

Ans. $\dfrac{1}{2}x^2\arctan\sqrt{x^2-1}-\dfrac{1}{2}\sqrt{x^2-1}+C.$ **144.** $\int\dfrac{\arcsin x}{x^2}\,dx.$

Ans. $\ln\left|\dfrac{1-\sqrt{1-x^2}}{x}\right|-\dfrac{1}{x}\arcsin x+C.$ **145.** $\int\ln(x+\sqrt{1+x^2})\,dx.$

Ans. $x\ln|x+\sqrt{1+x^2}|-\sqrt{1+x^2}+C.$ **146.** $\int\arcsin x\,\dfrac{x\,dx}{\sqrt{(1-x^2)^3}}.$

Ans. $\dfrac{\arcsin x}{\sqrt{1-x^2}}+\dfrac{1}{2}\ln\left|\dfrac{1-x}{1+x}\right|+C.$

Use trigonometric substitutions in the following examples:

147. $\int \dfrac{\sqrt{a^2-x^2}}{x^2}\,dx.$ *Ans.* $-\dfrac{\sqrt{a^2-x^2}}{x}-\arcsin\dfrac{x}{a}+C.$ **148.** $\int x^2\sqrt{4-x^2}\,dx.$

Ans. $2\arcsin\dfrac{x}{2}-\dfrac{1}{2}x\sqrt{4-x^2}+\dfrac{1}{4}x^3\sqrt{4-x^2}+C.$ **149.** $\int\dfrac{dx}{x^2\sqrt{1+x^2}}.$

Ans. $-\dfrac{\sqrt{1+x^2}}{x}+C.$ **150.** $\int\dfrac{\sqrt{x^2-a^2}}{x}\,dx.$ *Ans.* $\sqrt{x^2-a^2}-a\,\text{arccos}\,\dfrac{a}{x}+C.$

151. $\int\dfrac{dx}{\sqrt{(a^2+x^2)^3}}.$ *Ans.* $\dfrac{x}{a^2}\dfrac{1}{\sqrt{a^2+x^2}}+C.$

Integration of rational fractions:

152. $\int\dfrac{2x-1}{(x-1)(x-2)}\,dx.$ *Ans.* $\ln\left|\dfrac{(x-2)^3}{x-1}\right|+C.$ **153.** $\int\dfrac{x\,dx}{(x+1)(x+3)(x+5)}.$

Ans. $\dfrac{1}{8}\ln\dfrac{(x+3)^6}{|x+5|^5|x+1|}+C.$ **154.** $\int\dfrac{x^5+x^4-8}{x^3-4x}\,dx.$

Ans. $\dfrac{x^3}{3}+\dfrac{x^2}{2}+4x+\ln\left|\dfrac{x^2(x-2)^5}{(x+2)^3}\right|+C.$ **155.** $\int\dfrac{x^4\,dx}{(x^2-1)(x+2)}.$

Ans. $\dfrac{x^2}{2}-2x+\dfrac{1}{6}\ln\dfrac{|x-1|}{|x+1|^3}+\dfrac{16}{3}\ln|x+2|+C.$ **156.** $\int\dfrac{dx}{(x-1)^2(x-2)}.$

Ans. $\dfrac{1}{x-1}+\ln\left|\dfrac{x-2}{x--1}\right|+C.$ **157.** $\int\dfrac{x-8}{x^3-4x^2+4x}\,dx.$ *Ans.* $\dfrac{3}{x-2}+\ln\dfrac{(x-2)^2}{x^2}+C.$

158. $\int\dfrac{3x+2}{x(x+1)^3}\,dx.$ *Ans.* $\dfrac{4x+3}{2(x+1)^2}+\ln\dfrac{x^2}{(x+1)^2}+C.$ **159.** $\int\dfrac{x^2\,dx}{(x+2)^2(x+4)^2}.$

Ans. $-\dfrac{5x+12}{x^2+6x+8}+\ln\left(\dfrac{x+4}{x+2}\right)^2+C.$ **160.** $\int\dfrac{dx}{x(x^2+1)}.$ *Ans.* $\ln\dfrac{|x|}{\sqrt{x^2+1}}+C.$

161. $\int\dfrac{2x^2-3x-3}{(x-1)(x^2-2x+5)}\,dx.$ *Ans.* $\ln\dfrac{(x^2-2x+5)^{\frac{3}{2}}}{|x-1|}+\dfrac{1}{2}\arctan\dfrac{x-1}{2}+C.$

162. $\int\dfrac{x^3-6}{x^4+6x^2+8}\,dx.$ *Ans.* $\ln\dfrac{x^2+4}{\sqrt{x^2+2}}+\dfrac{3}{2}\arctan\dfrac{x}{2}-\dfrac{3}{\sqrt{2}}\arctan\dfrac{x}{\sqrt{2}}+C.$

163. $\int\dfrac{dx}{x^3+1}.$ *Ans.* $\dfrac{1}{6}\ln\dfrac{(x+1)^2}{x^2-x+1}+\dfrac{1}{\sqrt{3}}\arctan\dfrac{2x-1}{\sqrt{3}}+C.$

164. $\int\dfrac{3x-7}{x^3+x^2+4x+4}.$ *Ans.* $\ln\dfrac{x^2+4}{(x+1)^2}+\dfrac{1}{2}\arctan\dfrac{x}{2}+C.$ **165.** $\int\dfrac{4\,dx}{x^4+1}.$

Ans. $\dfrac{1}{\sqrt{2}}\ln\dfrac{x^2+x\sqrt{2}+1}{x^2-x\sqrt{2}+1}+\sqrt{2}\arctan\dfrac{x\sqrt{2}}{1-x^2}+C.$ **166.** $\int\dfrac{x^5}{x^3-1}\,dx.$

Ans. $\dfrac{1}{3}[x^3+\ln(x^3-1)]+C.$ **167.** $\int\dfrac{x^3+x-1}{(x^2+2)^2}\,dx.$

Ans. $\dfrac{2-x}{4(x^2+2)}+\ln(x^2+2)^{\frac{1}{2}}-\dfrac{1}{4\sqrt{2}}\arctan\dfrac{x}{\sqrt{2}}+C.$ **168.** $\int\dfrac{(4x^2-8x)\,dx}{(x-1)^2(x^2+1)^2}.$

Ans. $\dfrac{3x^2-x}{(x-1)(x^2+1)}+\ln\dfrac{(x-1)^2}{x^2+1}+\arctan x+C.$ **169.** $\int\dfrac{dx}{(x^2-x)(x^2-x+1)^2}.$

Ans. $\ln\left|\dfrac{x-1}{x}\right|-\dfrac{10}{3\sqrt{3}}\arctan\dfrac{2x-1}{\sqrt{3}}-\dfrac{2x-1}{3(x^2-x+1)}+C.$

Integration of irrational functions:

170. $\displaystyle\int \frac{\sqrt{x}}{\sqrt[4]{x^3+1}}\,dx.$ Ans. $\dfrac{4}{3}\left[\sqrt[4]{x^3}-\ln\left(\sqrt[4]{x^3}+1\right)\right]+C.$

171. $\displaystyle\int \frac{\sqrt{x^3}-\sqrt[3]{x}}{6\sqrt[4]{x}}\,dx.$ Ans. $\dfrac{2}{27}\sqrt[4]{x^9}-\dfrac{2}{13}\sqrt[12]{x^{13}}+C.$ **172.** $\displaystyle\int \frac{\sqrt[6]{x}+1}{\sqrt[6]{x^7}+\sqrt[4]{x^5}}\,dx.$

Ans. $-\dfrac{6}{\sqrt[6]{x}}+\dfrac{12}{\sqrt[12]{x}}+2\ln x-24\ln\left(\sqrt[12]{x}+1\right)+C.$

173. $\displaystyle\int \frac{2+\sqrt[3]{x}}{\sqrt[5]{x}+\sqrt[3]{x}+\sqrt{x}+1}\,dx.$

Ans. $\dfrac{6}{5}\sqrt[6]{x^5}-\dfrac{3}{2}\sqrt[3]{x^2}+4\sqrt{x}-6\sqrt[3]{x}+6\sqrt[6]{x}-9\ln\left(\sqrt[6]{x}+1\right)+$

$+\dfrac{3}{2}\ln\left(\sqrt[3]{x}+1\right)+3\arctan\sqrt[6]{x}+C.$ **174.** $\displaystyle\int \sqrt{\frac{1-x}{1+x}}\frac{dx}{x^2}.$

Ans. $\ln\left|\dfrac{\sqrt{1-x}+\sqrt{1+x}}{\sqrt{1-x}-\sqrt{1+x}}\right|-\dfrac{\sqrt{1-x^2}}{x}+C.$ **175.** $\displaystyle\int \sqrt{\frac{1-x}{1+x}}\frac{dx}{x}.$

Ans. $2\arctan\sqrt{\dfrac{1-x}{1+x}}+\ln\left|\dfrac{\sqrt{1+x}-\sqrt{1-x}}{\sqrt{1+x}+\sqrt{1-x}}\right|+C.$ **176.** $\displaystyle\int \frac{\sqrt[7]{x}+\sqrt{x}}{\sqrt[7]{x^8}+\sqrt[14]{x^{15}}}\,dx.$

Ans. $14\left[\sqrt[14]{x}-\dfrac{1}{2}\sqrt[7]{x}+\dfrac{1}{3}\sqrt[14]{x^3}-\dfrac{1}{4}\sqrt[7]{x^2}+\dfrac{1}{5}\sqrt[14]{x^5}\right]+C.$

177. $\displaystyle\int \sqrt{\frac{2+3x}{x-3}}\,dx.$ Ans. $\sqrt{3x^2-7x-6}+\dfrac{11}{2\sqrt{3}}\times$

$\times\ln\left(x-\dfrac{7}{6}+\sqrt{x^2-\dfrac{7}{3}x-2}\right)+C.$

Integrals of the form $\displaystyle\int R\left(x,\ \sqrt{ax^2+bx+c}\right)dx$:

178. $\displaystyle\int \frac{dx}{x\sqrt{x^2-x+3}}.$ Ans. $\dfrac{1}{\sqrt{3}}\ln\left|\dfrac{\sqrt{x^2-x+3}-\sqrt{3}}{3}+\dfrac{1}{2\sqrt{3}}\right|+C.$

179. $\displaystyle\int \frac{dx}{x\sqrt{2+x-x^2}}.$ Ans. $-\dfrac{1}{\sqrt{2}}\ln\left|\dfrac{\sqrt{2+x-x^2}+\sqrt{2}}{x}+\dfrac{1}{2\sqrt{2}}\right|+C.$

180. $\displaystyle\int \frac{dx}{x\sqrt{x^2+4x-4}}.$ Ans. $\dfrac{1}{2}\arcsin\dfrac{x-2}{x\sqrt{2}}+C.$ **181.** $\displaystyle\int \frac{\sqrt{x^2+2x}}{x}\,dx.$

Ans. $\sqrt{x^2+2x}+\ln\left|x+1+\sqrt{x^2+2x}\right|+C.$ **182.** $\displaystyle\int \frac{dx}{\sqrt{(2x-x^2)^3}}.$

Ans. $\dfrac{x-1}{\sqrt{2x-x^2}}+C.$ **183.** $\displaystyle\int \sqrt{2x-x^2}\,dx.$

Ans. $\dfrac{1}{2}\left[(x-1)\sqrt{2x-x^2}+\arcsin(x-1)\right]+C.$ **184.** $\displaystyle\int \frac{dx}{x-\sqrt{x^2-1}}.$

Ans $\dfrac{x^2}{2}+\dfrac{x}{2}\sqrt{x^2-1}-\dfrac{1}{2}\ln\left|x+\sqrt{x^2-1}\right|+C.$ **185.** $\displaystyle\int \frac{dx}{(1+x)\sqrt{1+x+x^2}}.$

Ans.　$\ln\left|\dfrac{x+\sqrt{1+x+x^2}}{2+x+\sqrt{1+x+x^2}}\right|+C.$　186.　$\displaystyle\int\frac{(x+1)}{(2x+x^2)\sqrt{2x+x^2}}\,dx.$

Ans.　$-\dfrac{1}{\sqrt{2x+x^2}}+C.$　187.　$\displaystyle\int\frac{1-\sqrt{1+x+x^2}}{x\sqrt{1+x+x^2}}\,dx.$

Ans.　$\ln\left|\dfrac{2+x-2\sqrt{1+x+x^2}}{x^2}\right|+C.$　188.　$\displaystyle\int\frac{\sqrt{x^2+4x}}{x^2}\,dx.$

Ans.　$-\dfrac{8}{x+\sqrt{x^2+4x}}+\ln\left|x+2+\sqrt{x^2+4x}\right|+C.$

Integration of trigonometric functions:

189.　$\displaystyle\int\sin^3 x\,dx.$　*Ans.*　$\dfrac{1}{3}\cos^3 x-\cos x+C.$　190.　$\displaystyle\int\sin^5 x\,dx.$

Ans.　$-\cos x+\dfrac{2}{3}\cos^3 x-\dfrac{\cos^5 x}{5}+C.$　191.　$\displaystyle\int\cos^4 x\sin^3 x\,dx.$

Ans.　$-\dfrac{1}{5}\cos^5 x+\dfrac{1}{7}\cos^7 x+C.$　192.　$\displaystyle\int\frac{\cos^3 x}{\sin^4 x}\,dx.$ *Ans.* $\csc x-\dfrac{1}{3}\csc^3 x+C.$

193.　$\displaystyle\int\cos^2 x\,dx.$　*Ans.*　$\dfrac{x}{2}+\dfrac{1}{4}\sin 2x+C.$　194.　$\displaystyle\int\sin^4 x\,dx.$

Ans.　$\dfrac{3}{8}x-\dfrac{\sin 2x}{4}+\dfrac{\sin 4x}{32}+C.$　195.　$\displaystyle\int\cos^6 x\,dx.$

Ans.　$\dfrac{1}{16}\left(5x+4\sin 2x-\dfrac{\sin^3 2x}{3}+\dfrac{3}{4}\sin 4x\right)+C.$　196.　$\displaystyle\int\sin^4 x\cos^4 x\,dx.$

Ans. $\dfrac{1}{128}\left(3x-\sin 4x+\dfrac{\sin 8x}{8}\right)+C.$ 197. $\displaystyle\int\tan^3 x\,dx.$ *Ans.* $\dfrac{\tan^2 x}{2}+\ln|\cos x|+C.$

198.　$\displaystyle\int\cot^5 x\,dx.$　*Ans.*　$-\dfrac{1}{4}\cot^4 x+\dfrac{1}{2}\cot^2 x+\ln|\sin x|+C.$ 199. $\displaystyle\int\cot^3 x\,dx.$

Ans.　$-\dfrac{\cot^2 x}{2}-\ln|\sin x|+C.$　200.　$\displaystyle\int\sec^8 x\,dx.$

Ans.　$\dfrac{\tan^7 x}{7}+\dfrac{3\tan^5 x}{5}+\tan^3 x+\tan x+C.$　201.　$\displaystyle\int\tan^4 x\sec^4 x\,dx.$

Ans.　$\dfrac{\tan^7 x}{7}+\dfrac{\tan^5 x}{5}+C.$　202.　$\displaystyle\int\frac{dx}{\cos^4 x}.$　*Ans.* $\tan x+\dfrac{1}{3}\tan^3 x+C.$

203.　$\displaystyle\int\frac{\cos x}{\sin^2 x}\,dx.$　*Ans.*　$C-\csc x.$　204.　$\displaystyle\int\frac{\sin^3 x\,dx}{\sqrt[3]{\cos^4 x}}$

Ans. $\dfrac{3}{5}\cos^{\frac{5}{3}}x+3\cos^{-\frac{1}{3}}x+C.$ 205. $\displaystyle\int\sin x\sin 3x\,dx.$ *Ans.* $-\dfrac{\sin 4x}{8}+\dfrac{\sin 2x}{4}+C.$

206.　$\displaystyle\int\cos 4x\cos 7x\,dx.$　*Ans.*　$\dfrac{\sin 11x}{22}+\dfrac{\sin 3x}{6}+C.$　207.　$\displaystyle\int\cos 2x\sin 4x\,dx.$

Ans.　$-\dfrac{\cos 6x}{12}-\dfrac{\cos 2x}{4}+C.$ 208. $\displaystyle\int\sin\frac{1}{4}x\cos\frac{3}{4}x\,dx.$ *Ans.* $-\dfrac{\cos x}{2}+\cos\dfrac{1}{2}x+C.$

209.　$\displaystyle\int\frac{dx}{4-5\sin x}.$　*Ans.*　$\dfrac{1}{3}\ln\left|\dfrac{\tan\frac{x}{2}-2}{2\tan\frac{x}{2}-1}\right|+C.$　210.　$\displaystyle\int\frac{dx}{5-3\cos x}.$

Ans. $\dfrac{1}{2}\arctan\left|2\tan\dfrac{x}{2}\right|+C.$ **211.** $\displaystyle\int\dfrac{\sin x\,dx}{1+\sin x}.$ **Ans.** $\dfrac{2}{1+\tan\dfrac{x}{2}}+x+C.$

212. $\displaystyle\int\dfrac{\cos x\,dx}{1+\cos x}.$ **Ans.** $x-\tan\dfrac{x}{2}+C.$ **213.** $\displaystyle\int\dfrac{\sin 2x}{\cos^4 x+\sin^4 x}\,dx.$

Ans. $\arctan(2\sin^2 x-1)+C.$ **214.** $\displaystyle\int\dfrac{dx}{(1+\cos x)^2}$ **Ans.** $\dfrac{1}{2}\tan\dfrac{x}{2}+\dfrac{1}{6}\tan^3\dfrac{x}{2}+C.$

215. $\displaystyle\int\dfrac{dx}{\sin^2 x+\tan^2 x}.$ **Ans.** $-\dfrac{1}{2}\left[\cot x+\dfrac{1}{\sqrt 2}\arctan\left(\dfrac{\tan x}{\sqrt 2}\right)\right]+C.$

216. $\displaystyle\int\dfrac{\sin^2 x}{1+\cos^2 x}\,dx.$ **Ans.** $\sqrt 2\arctan\left(\dfrac{\tan x}{\sqrt 2}\right)-x+C.$

CHAPTER 11

THE DEFINITE INTEGRAL

11.1 STATEMENT OF THE PROBLEM.
LOWER AND UPPER SUMS

The **definite integral** is one of the basic concepts of mathematical analysis and is a powerful research tool in mathematics, physics, mechanics, and other disciplines. Calculation of areas bounded by curves, of arc lengths, volumes, work, velocity, path length, moments of inertia, and so forth reduce to the evaluation of a definite integral.

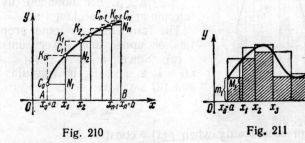

Fig. 210 Fig. 211

Let a **continuous** function $y = f(x)$ be given on an interval $[a, b]$ (Figs. 210 and 211). Denote by m and M its smallest and largest values on this interval. Divide the interval $[a, b]$ into n subintervals:

$$a = x_0, \ x_1, \ x_2, \ \ldots, \ x_{n-1}, \ x_n = b$$

so that

$$x_0 < x_1 < x_2 < \ldots < x_n$$

and put

$$x_1 - x_0 = \Delta x_1, \ x_2 - x_1 = \Delta x_2, \ \ldots, \ x_n - x_{n-1} = \Delta x_n$$

Then denote the smallest and greatest values of the function $f(x)$

on the subinterval $[x_0, x_1]$ by m_1 and M_1
on the subinterval $[x_1, x_2]$ by m_2 and M_2
. . . .
on the subinterval $[x_{n-1}, x_n]$ by m_n and M_n

Form the sums

$$s_n = m_1 \Delta x_1 + m_2 \Delta x_2 + \ldots + m_n \Delta x_n = \sum_{i=1}^{n} m_i \Delta x_i \qquad (1)$$

$$\bar{s}_n = M_1 \Delta x_1 + M_2 \Delta x_2 + \ldots + M_n \Delta x_n = \sum_{i=1}^{n} M_i \Delta x_i \qquad (2)$$

The sum s_n is called the *lower (integral) sum*, and the sum $\bar{s}_n$ is called the *upper (integral) sum*.

If $f(x) \geqslant 0$, then the lower sum is numerically equal to the area of an "inscribed step-like figure" $AC_0N_1C_1N_2\ldots C_{n-1}N_nBA$ bounded

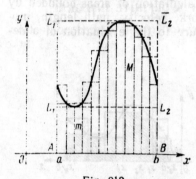

Fig. 212

by an "inscribed" broken line, the upper sum is equal numerically to the area of a "circumscribed step-like figure" $AK_0C_1K_1\ldots$ $\ldots C_{n-1}K_{n-1}C_nBA$ bounded by a "circumscribed" broken line.

The following are some properties of upper and lower sums.

(a) Since $m_i \leqslant M_i$ for any $i\,(i = 1, 2, \ldots, n)$, by formulas (1) and (2) we have

$$s_n \leqslant \bar{s}_n \qquad (3)$$

(The equal sign occurs only when $f(x) = \text{const.}$)

(b) Since

$$m_1 \geqslant m, \ m_2 \geqslant m, \ \ldots, \ m_n \geqslant m,$$

where m is the smallest value of $f(x)$ on $[a, b]$, we have

$$s_n = m_1 \Delta x_1 + m_2 \Delta x_2 + \ldots + m_n \Delta x_n \geqslant m \Delta x_1 + m \Delta x_2 + \ldots + m \Delta x_n$$
$$= m (\Delta x_1 + \Delta x_2 + \ldots + \Delta x_n) = m (b-a)$$

Thus,

$$s_n \geqslant m (b-a) \qquad (4)$$

(c) Since

$$M_1 \leqslant M, \ M_2 \leqslant M, \ \ldots, \ M_n \leqslant M$$

where M is the greatest value of $f(x)$ on $[a, b]$, we have

$$\bar{s}_n = M_1 \Delta x_1 + M_2 \Delta x_2 + \ldots + M_n \Delta x_n \leqslant M \Delta x_1 + M \Delta x_2 + \ldots + M \Delta x_n$$
$$= M (\Delta x_1 + \Delta x_2 + \ldots + \Delta x_n) = M (b-a)$$

Thus,

$$\bar{s}_n \leqslant M (b-a) \qquad (5)$$

Combining the inequalities obtained, we get

$$m(b-a) \leqslant \underline{s_n} \leqslant \overline{s_n} \leqslant M(b-a)$$

If $f(x) \geqslant 0$, then the last inequality has a simple geometric meaning (Fig. 212), because the products $m(b-a)$ and $M(b-a)$ are, respectively, numerically equal to the areas of the "inscribed" rectangle AL_1L_2B and the "circumscribed" rectangle $A\overline{L}_1\overline{L}_2B$.

11.2 THE DEFINITE INTEGRAL.
PROOF OF THE EXISTENCE OF A DEFINITE INTEGRAL

We continue examining the question of the preceding section. In each of the subintervals $[x_0, x_1]$, $[x_1, x_2]$, ..., $[x_{n-1}, x_n]$ take

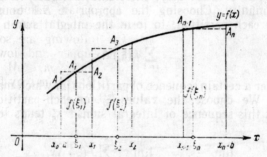

Fig. 213

a point and denote the points by ξ_1, ξ_2, ..., ξ_n (Fig. 213):

$$x_0 < \xi_1 < x_1, \ x_1 < \xi_2 < x_2, \ \ldots, \ x_{n-1} < \xi_n < x_n$$

At each of these points find the value of the function $f(\xi_1)$, $f(\xi_2)$, ..., $f(\xi_n)$. Form the sum

$$s_n = f(\xi_1)\Delta x_1 + f(\xi_2)\Delta x_2 + \ldots + f(\xi_n)\Delta x_n = \sum_{i=1}^{n} f(\xi_i)\Delta x_i \quad (1)$$

This sum is called the *integral sum* of the function $f(x)$ on the interval $[a, b]$. Since for an arbitrary ξ_i belonging to the interval $[x_{i-1}, x_i]$ we will have

$$m_i \leqslant f(\xi_i) \leqslant M_i$$

and all $\Delta x_i > 0$, it follows that

$$m_i \Delta x_i \leqslant f(\xi_i)\Delta x_i \leqslant M_i \Delta x_i$$

and consequently

$$\sum_{i=1}^{n} m_i \Delta x_i \leqslant \sum_{i=1}^{n} f(\xi_i)\Delta x_i \leqslant \sum_{i=1}^{n} M_i \Delta x_i$$

or

$$s_n \leqslant s_n \leqslant \bar{s}_n \tag{2}$$

The geometric meaning of the latter inequality for $f(x) \geqslant 0$ consists in the fact that the figure whose area is equal to s_n is bounded by a broken line lying between the "inscribed" broken line and the "circumscribed" broken line.

The sum s_n depends upon the way in which the interval $[a, b]$ is divided into the subintervals $[x_{i-1}, x_i]$ and also upon the choice of points ξ_i inside the resulting subintervals.

Let us now denote by max $[x_{i-1}, x_i]$ the largest of the subintervals $[x_0, x_1]$, $[x_1, x_2]$, ... $[x_{n-1}, x_n]$. Let us consider different partitions of the interval $[a, b]$ into subintervals $[x_{i-1}, x_i]$ such that max $[x_{i-1}, x_i] \to 0$. Obviously, the number of subintervals n then approaches infinity. Choosing the appropriate values of ξ_i, it is possible, for each partition, to form the integral sum

$$s_n = \sum_{i=1}^{n} f(\xi_i)\, \Delta x_i \tag{3}$$

We consider a certain sequence of partitions for which max $\Delta x_i \to 0$ as $n \to \infty$. We choose the values ξ_i for each partition. Let us suppose that this sequence of integral sums * s_n^* tends to a certain limit

$$\lim_{\max \Delta x_i \to 0} s_n^* = \lim_{\max \Delta x_i \to 0} \sum_{i=1}^{n} f(\xi_i)\, \Delta x_i = s \tag{4}$$

We are now able to state the following.

Definition 1. If for arbitrary partitions of the interval $[a, b]$ such that max $\Delta x_i \to 0$ and for any choice of the points ξ_i on the subintervals $[x_{i-1}, x_i]$ the integral sum

$$s_n = \sum_{i=1}^{n} f(\xi_i)\, \Delta x_i \tag{5}$$

tends to one and the same limit s, then this limit is termed the *definite integral* of the function $f(x)$ on the interval $[a, b]$ and is denoted by

$$\int_a^b f(x)\, dx$$

Thus, by definition,

$$\lim_{\max \Delta x_i \to 0} \sum_{i=1}^{n} f(\xi_i)\, \Delta x_i = \int_a^b f(x)\, dx \tag{6}$$

---

* In this case the sum is an ordered variable quantity.

The number a is termed the *lower limit* of the integral, b, the *upper limit* of the integral. The interval $[a, b]$ is called the *interval of integration* and x is the *variable of integration*.

Definition 2. If for a function $f(x)$ the limit (6) exists, then we say the function *is integrable on the interval* $[a, b]$.

Note that the lower sum s_n and the upper sum $\overline{s}_n$ are particular cases of the sum (5) and so if $f(x)$ is integrable, then the lower and upper sums tend to the same limit s and therefore, by (6), we can write

$$\lim_{\max \Delta x_i \to 0} \sum_{i=1}^{n} m_i \, \Delta x_i = \int_a^b f(x)\,dx \qquad (7)$$

$$\lim_{\max \Delta x_i \to 0} \sum_{i=1}^{n} M_i \, \Delta x_i = \int_a^b f(x)\,dx \qquad (7')$$

If we construct the graph of the integrand $y = f(x)$, then in the case of $f(x) \geqslant 0$ the integral

$$\int_a^b f(x)\,dx$$

will be numerically equal to the **area** of a so-called *curvilinear trapezoid* bounded by the given curve, the straight lines $x = a$ and $x = b$, and the x-axis (Fig. 214).

For this reason, if it is required to compute the area of a curvilinear trapezoid bounded by the curve $y = f(x)$, the straight lines $x = a$ and $x = b$, and the x-axis, this area Q is computed by means of the integral

$$Q = \int_a^b f(x)\,dx \qquad (8)$$

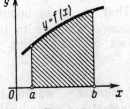

Fig. 214

We will prove the following theorem.

Theorem 1. *If a function $f(x)$ is continuous on an interval $[a, b]$, then it is integrable on that interval.*

Proof. Again partition the interval $[a, b]$ ($a < b$) into subintervals $[x_0, x_1], [x_1, x_2], \ldots, [x_{i-1}, x_i], \ldots, [x_{n-1}, x_n]$. Form the lower and upper sums:

$$\underline{s}_n = \sum_{i=1}^{n} m_i \, \Delta x_i \qquad (9)$$

$$\overline{s}_n = \sum_{i=1}^{n} M_i \, \Delta x_i \qquad (10)$$

For what follows we will need certain properties of upper and lower sums.

Property 1. *If the number of subintervals into which $[a, b]$ is partitioned by adding points of division is increased, the lower sum can only increase and the upper sum can only decrease.*

Proof. Let the interval $[a, b]$ be partitioned into n' subintervals by adding new points of division ($n' > n$). If some subinterval $[x_{k-1}, x_k]$ is split up into several parts, say p_k parts, then in the new lower sum $s_{n'}$ the subinterval $[x_{k-1}, x_k]$ will be associated with p_k summands, which we denote by $\underline{s}^*_{p_k}$. In the sum $\underline{s}_n$, this subinterval will correspond to one term $m_k(x_k - x_{k-1})$. But then an inequality, similar to the inequality (4) of Sec. 11.1, holds true for the sum $\underline{s}^*_{p_k}$ and the quantity $m_k(x_k - x_{k-1})$. We can write

$$\underline{s}^*_{p_k} \geqslant m_\kappa(x_k - x_{k-1})$$

Writing down the appropriate inequalities for each subinterval and summing the left and right members, we get

$$\underline{s}_{n'} \geqslant \underline{s}_n \quad (n' > n) \tag{11}$$

This completes the proof of Property 1.

Property 2. *In the case of an unlimited increase in the number of subintervals accomplished by adding new division points, the lower sum (9) and the upper sum (10) tend to certain limits $\underline{s}$ and $\bar{s}$.*

Proof. By inequality (6) of Sec. 11.1 we can write

$$\underline{s}_n \leqslant M(b-a)$$

That is, $\underline{s}_n$ is bounded for all n. By Property 1, $\underline{s}_n$ increases monotonically with increasing n. Hence, by Theorem 7 on limits (see Sec. 2.5), this variable has a limit, which we denote by $\underline{s}$:

$$\lim_{n \to \infty} \underline{s}_n = \underline{s} \tag{12}$$

Similarly, we find that $\bar{s}_n$ is bounded below and decreases monotonically. Consequently, $\bar{s}_n$ has a limit, which we denote by $\bar{s}$:

$$\lim_{n \to \infty} \bar{s}_n = \bar{s}$$

Property 3. *If a function $f(x)$ is continuous on a closed interval $[a, b]$, then the limits $\underline{s}$ and $\bar{s}$, defined by Property 2 on the condition that* $\max \Delta x_i \to 0$, *are equal.*

We denote this common limit by s:

$$\underline{s} = \bar{s} = s \tag{13}$$

Proof. Let us consider the difference between the upper and lower sums:

$$\bar{s}_n - \underline{s}_n = (M_1 - m_1)\,\Delta x_1 + (M_2 - m_2)\,\Delta x_2 + \ldots$$

$$+ (M_i - m_i)\,\Delta x_i + \ldots + (M_n - m_n)\,\Delta x_n = \sum_{i=1}^{n}(M_i - m_i)\,\Delta x_i \quad (14)$$

Denote by ε_n the maximum difference $(M_i - m_i)$ for a given partition:

$$\varepsilon_n = \max\,(M_i - m_i)$$

It may be proved (though we will not do so) that if a function $f(x)$ is continuous on a closed interval, then for any mode of partition of the interval $[a, b]$, $\varepsilon_n \to 0$ provided max $\Delta x_i \to 0$:

$$\lim_{\max \Delta x_i \to 0} \varepsilon_n = 0 \quad (15)$$

The property of a continuous function on a closed interval as expressed by equation (15) is called *uniform continuity* of the function.

We will thus make use of the theorem that *a function continuous on a closed interval is uniformly continuous on that interval.*

Reverting to (14), we replace each difference $(M_i - m_i)$ on the right by ε_n, which is at least equal to the difference. This yields the inequality

$$\bar{s}_n - \underline{s}_n \leqslant \varepsilon_n\,\Delta x_1 + \varepsilon_n\,\Delta x_2 + \ldots + \varepsilon_n\,\Delta x_n =$$

$$= \varepsilon_n\,(\Delta x_1 + \Delta x_2 + \ldots + \Delta x_n) = \varepsilon_n\,(b - a)$$

Passing to the limit as max $\Delta x_i \to 0$ $(n \to \infty)$, we get

$$\lim_{\max \Delta x_i \to 0} (\bar{s}_n - \underline{s}_n) \leqslant \lim_{\max \Delta x_i \to 0} \varepsilon_n\,(b - a) = (b - a)\lim_{\max \Delta x_i \to 0} \varepsilon_n = 0 \quad (16)$$

That is,

$$\lim \bar{s}_n = \lim \underline{s}_n = s \quad (17)$$

or $s = \bar{s} = s$, which completes the proof.

Property 4. *Let $\underline{s}_{n_1}$ and $\bar{s}_{n_2}$ be the lower and upper sums corresponding to partitions of the interval $[a, b]$ into n_1 and n_2 subintervals, respectively. We then have the inequality*

$$\underline{s}_{n_1} \leqslant \bar{s}_{n_2} \quad (18)$$

for arbitrary n_1 and n_2.

Proof. Consider a partition of $[a, b]$ into $n_3 = n_1 + n_2$ subintervals, where the division points are those of the first and second partitions.

By inequality (3) of Sec. 11.1, we have

$$\underline{s}_{n_3} \leqslant \bar{s}_{n_3} \tag{19}$$

On the basis of Property 1, we have

$$\underline{s}_{n_1} \leqslant \underline{s}_{n_3} \tag{20}$$

$$\bar{s}_{n_3} \leqslant \bar{s}_{n_2} \tag{21}$$

Using relations (20) and (21), we can extend inequality (19)

$$\underline{s}_{n_1} \leqslant \underline{s}_{n_3} \leqslant \bar{s}_{n_3} \leqslant \bar{s}_n$$

or

$$\underline{s}_{n_1} \leqslant \bar{s}_{n_2}$$

which completes the proof.

Property 5. *If a function $f(x)$ is continuous on an interval $[a, b]$, then for any sequence of partitions of $[a, b]$ into subintervals $[x_{i-1}, x_i]$, not necessarily by means of adjoining new points of division, provided $\max \Delta x_i \to 0$, the lower (integral) sum $\underline{s}_m^*$ and the upper (integral) sum $\bar{s}_m^*$ tend to the limit s defined by Property 3.*

Proof. Let us consider a sequence of partitions of the sequence of upper sums $\bar{s}_n$ defined by Property 2. For arbitrary values of n and m [by inequality (18)], we can write

$$\underline{s}_m^* \leqslant \bar{s}_n$$

Passing to the limit as $n \to \infty$ we can write, by (15),

$$\underline{s}_m^* \leqslant s$$

Similarly we can prove that $s \leqslant \bar{s}_m^*$.

Thus,

$$\underline{s}_m^* \leqslant s \leqslant \bar{s}_m^*$$

or

$$s - \underline{s}_m^* \geqslant 0, \quad \bar{s}_m^* - s \geqslant 0 \tag{22}$$

Consider the limit of the difference:

$$\lim_{\max \Delta x_i \to 0} (\bar{s}_m^* - \underline{s}_m^*)$$

Since the function $f(x)$ is continuous on the closed interval $[a, b]$ we will prove [in the same way as for Property 3, see equation (16)] that

$$\lim_{\max \Delta x_i \to 0} (\bar{s}_m^* - \underline{s}_m^*) = 0$$

We rewrite this relation as

$$\lim_{\max \Delta x_i \to 0} [(\bar{s}_m^* - s) + (s - \underline{s}_m^*)] = 0$$

By (22), each of the differences in the square brackets is nonnegative. Hence,

$$\lim_{\max \Delta x_i \to 0} (\bar{s}_m^* - s) = 0, \qquad \lim_{\max \Delta x_i \to 0} (s - \underline{s}_m^*) = 0$$

and we finally get

$$\lim_{\max \Delta x_i \to 0} \underline{s}_m^* = s, \qquad \lim_{\max \Delta x_i \to 0} \bar{s}_m^* = s \qquad (23)$$

This completes the proof.

Now we can prove the foregoing theorem. Let a function $f(x)$ be continuous on an interval $[a, b]$. We consider an arbitrary sequence of (integral) sums

$$s_n = \sum_{i=1}^{n} f(\xi_i) \Delta x_i$$

such that $\max \Delta x_i \to 0$ and ξ_i is an arbitrary point in the subinterval $[x_{i-1}, x_i]$.

We consider the appropriate sequences of upper and lower sums s_n and $\bar{s}_n$ for the given sequence of partitions. The relations (2) hold true for each partition:

$$\underline{s}_n < s_n < \bar{s}_n$$

Passing to the limit as $\max \Delta x_i \to 0$ and using equations (23) and Theorem 4, Sec. 2.5, we get

$$\lim_{\max \Delta x_i \to 0} s_n = s$$

where s is the limit defined by Property 3.

As already stated, this limit is termed the definite integral $\int_a^b f(x)\,dx$. Thus, if $f(x)$ is continuous on the interval $[a, b]$, then

$$\lim_{\max \Delta x_i \to 0} \sum f(\xi_i) \Delta x_i = \int_a^b f(x)\,dx \qquad (24)$$

It may be noted that there are both integrable and nonintegrable functions in the class of discontinuous functions.

Note 1. It will be noted that the definite integral depends only on the form of the function $f(x)$ and the limits of integration, and not on the variable of integration, which may be denoted by any letter. Thus, without changing the magnitude of a definite integral it is possible to replace the letter x by any other letter:

$$\int_a^b f(x)\,dx = \int_a^b f(t)\,dt = \ldots = \int_a^b f(z)\,dz$$

Note 2. When introducing the concept of the definite integral $\int_a^b f(x)\,dx$ we assumed that $a < b$. In the case where $b < a$ we will, **by definition,** have

$$\int_a^b f(x)\,dx = -\int_b^a f(x)\,dx \qquad (25)$$

Thus, for instance,

$$\int_5^0 x^2\,dx = -\int_0^5 x^2\,dx$$

Note 3. In the case of $a = b$ we assume, **by definition,** that for any function $f(x)$ we have

$$\int_a^a f(x)\,dx = 0 \qquad (26)$$

This is natural also from the geometric standpoint. Indeed, the base of a curvilinear trapezoid has length equal to zero; consequently, its area is zero too.

Example 1. Compute the integral $\int_a^b kx\,dx\,(b > a)$.

Solution. Geometrically, the problem is equivalent to computing the area Q of a trapezoid bounded by the lines $y = kx$, $x = a$, $x = b$, $y = 0$ (Fig. 215).

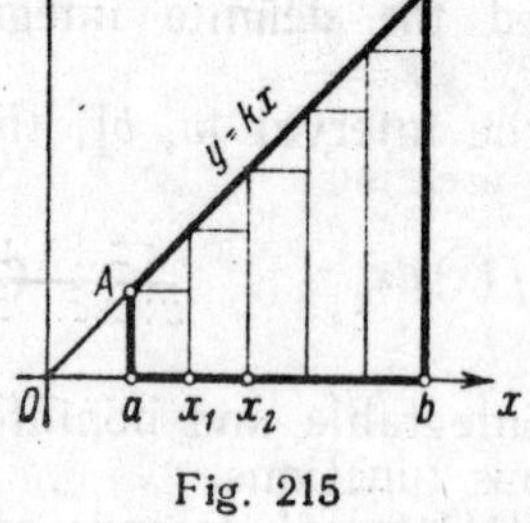

Fig. 215

The function $y = kx$ under the integral sign is continuous. Therefore, in order to compute the definite integral we have the right, as was stated above, to divide the interval $[a, b]$ in any way and choose arbitrary intermediate points ξ_k. The result of computing a definite integral is independent of the way in which the integral sum is formed, provided that the subinterval approaches zero.

Divide the interval $[a, b]$ into n equal subintervals.

The length Δx of each subinterval is $\Delta x = \dfrac{b-a}{n}$; this number is the partition unit.

The division points have coordinates:

$$x_0 = a,\ x_1 = a + \Delta x,$$
$$x_2 = a + 2\Delta x,\ \ldots,\ x_n = a + n\Delta x$$

For the points ξ_k take the left end points of each subinterval:

$$\xi_1 = a, \quad \xi_2 = a + \Delta x, \quad \xi_3 = a + 2\Delta x, \quad \ldots, \quad \xi_n = a + (n-1)\Delta x$$

Form the integral sum (1). Since $f(\xi_i) = k\xi_i$, we have

$$
\begin{aligned}
s_n &= k\xi_1 \Delta x + k\xi_2 \Delta x + \ldots + k\xi_n \Delta x \\
&= ka \Delta x + [k(a + \Delta x)] \Delta x + \ldots + \{k[a + (n-1)\Delta x]\} \Delta x \\
&= k\{a + (a + \Delta x) + (a + 2\Delta x) + \ldots + [a + (n-1)\Delta x]\} \Delta x \\
&= k\{na + [\Delta x + 2\Delta x + \ldots + (n-1)\Delta x]\} \Delta x \\
&= k\{na + [1 + 2 + \ldots + (n-1)]\Delta x\} \Delta x
\end{aligned}
$$

where $\Delta x = \dfrac{b-a}{n}$. Taking into account that

$$1 + 2 + \ldots + (n-1) = \frac{n(n-1)}{2}$$

(as the sum of an arithmetic progression), we get

$$s_n = k\left[na + \frac{n(n-1)}{2}\frac{b-a}{n}\right]\frac{b-a}{n} = k\left[a + \frac{n-1}{n}\frac{b-a}{2}\right](b-a)$$

Since $\lim\limits_{n \to \infty} \dfrac{n-1}{n} = 1$, it follows that

$$\lim_{n \to \infty} s_n = Q = k\left[a + \frac{b-a}{2}\right](b-a) = k\frac{b^2 - a^2}{2}$$

Thus,

$$\int_a^b kx\,dx = k\frac{b^2 - a^2}{2}$$

The area of *ABba* (Fig. 215) is readily computed by the methods of elementary geometry. The result will be the same.

Example 2. Evaluate $\int_0^b x^2\,dx$.

Fig. 216

Solution. The given integral is equal to the area Q of a curvilinear trapezoid bounded by a parabola $y = x^2$, the ordinate $x = b$, and the straight line $y = 0$ (Fig. 216).

Divide the interval $[a, b]$ into n equal parts by the points

$$x_0 = 0, \quad x_1 = \Delta x, \quad x_2 = 2\Delta x, \quad \ldots, \quad x_n = b = n\Delta x, \quad \Delta x = \frac{b}{n}$$

For the ξ_i points take the right extremities of each subinterval. Form the integral sum

$$
\begin{aligned}
s_n &= x_1^2 \Delta x + x_2^2 \Delta x + \ldots + x_n^2 \Delta x \\
&= [(\Delta x)^2 \Delta x + (2\Delta x)^2 \Delta x + \ldots + (n\Delta x)^2 \Delta x] = (\Delta x)^3 [1^2 + 2^2 + \ldots + n^2]
\end{aligned}
$$

As we know,

$$1^2 + 2^2 + 3^2 + \ldots + n^2 = \frac{n(n+1)(2n+1)}{6}$$

therefore

$$s_n = \frac{b^3}{n^3} \frac{n(n+1)(2n+1)}{6} = \frac{b^3}{6}\left(1+\frac{1}{n}\right)\left(2+\frac{1}{n}\right)$$

$$\lim_{n \to \infty} s_n = Q = \int_0^b x^2\, dx = \frac{b^3}{3}$$

Example 3. Evaluate $\int_a^b m\, dx$ ($m = \text{const}$).

Solution.

$$\int_a^b m\, dx = \lim_{\max \Delta x_i \to 0} \sum_{i=1}^n m\, \Delta x_i = \lim_{\max \Delta x_i \to 0} m \sum_{i=1}^n \Delta x_i$$

$$= m \lim_{\max \Delta x_i \to 0} \sum_{i=1}^n \Delta x_i = m\,(b-a)$$

Here, $\sum_{i=1}^n \Delta x_i$ is the sum of the lengths of the subintervals into which the interval $[a, b]$ was divided. No matter what the method of partition, the sum is equal to the length of the segment $b-a$.

Example 4. Evaluate $\int_a^b e^x\, dx$.

Solution. Again divide the interval $[a, b]$ into n equal parts:

$$x_0 = a,\ x_1 = a + \Delta x,\ \ldots,\ x_n = a + n\Delta x,\ \ \Delta x = \frac{b-a}{n}$$

Take the left extremities as the points ξ_i. Then form the sum

$$s_n = e^a\, \Delta x + e^{a+\Delta x}\, \Delta x + \ldots + e^{a+(n-1)\Delta x}\, \Delta x$$
$$= e^a\,(1 + e^{\Delta x} + e^{2\Delta x} + \ldots + e^{(n-1)\,\Delta x})\, \Delta x$$

The expression in the brackets is a geometric progression with common ratio $e^{\Delta x}$ and first term 1; therefore

$$s_n = e^a\, \frac{e^{n\Delta x}-1}{e^{\Delta x}-1}\, \Delta x = e^a\,(e^{n\Delta x}-1)\, \frac{\Delta x}{e^{\Delta x}-1}$$

Then we have

$$n\Delta x = b-a,\ \lim_{\Delta x \to 0} \frac{\Delta x}{e^{\Delta x}-1} = 1$$

$\left(\text{By l'Hospital's rule } \lim_{z \to 0} \frac{z}{e^z-1} = \lim_{z \to 0} \frac{1}{e^z} = 1.\right)$ Thus,

$$\lim_{n \to \infty} s_n = Q = e^a\,(e^{b-a}-1)\cdot 1 = e^b - e^a$$

that is,

$$\int_a^b e^x\, dx = e^b - e^a$$

Note 4. The foregoing examples show that the direct evaluation of definite integrals as the limits of integral sums involves great difficulties. Even when the integrands are very simple (kx, x^2, e^x), this method involves cumbersome computations. The finding of definite integrals of more complicated functions leads to still greater difficulties. The natural problem that arises is to find some practically convenient way of evaluating definite integrals. This method, which was discovered by Newton and Leibniz, utilizes the profound relationship that exists between integration and differentiation. The following sections of this chapter are devoted to the exposition and substantiation of this method.

11.3 BASIC PROPERTIES OF THE DEFINITE INTEGRAL

Property 1. *A constant factor may be taken outside the sign of the definite integral: if $A = $ const, then*

$$\int_a^b Af(x)\,dx = A \int_a^b f(x)\,dx \tag{1}$$

Proof.

$$\int_a^b Af(x)\,dx = \lim_{\max \Delta x_i \to 0} \sum_{i=1}^n Af(\xi_i)\,\Delta x_i$$

$$= A \lim_{\max \Delta x_i \to 0} \sum_{i=1}^n f(\xi_i)\,\Delta x_i = A \int_a^b f(x)\,dx$$

Property 2. *The definite integral of an algebraic sum of several functions is equal to the algebraic sum of the integrals of the summands.* Thus, in the case of two terms

$$\int_a^b [f_1(x) + f_2(x)]\,dx = \int_a^b f_1(x)\,dx + \int_a^b f_2(x)\,dx \tag{2}$$

Proof.

$$\int_a^b [f_1(x) + f_2(x)]\,dx = \lim_{\max \Delta x_i \to 0} \sum_{i=1}^n [f_1(\xi_i) + f_2(\xi_i)]\,\Delta x_i$$

$$= \lim_{\max \Delta x_i \to 0} \left[\sum_{i=1}^n f_1(\xi_i)\,\Delta x_i + \sum_{i=1}^n f_2(\xi_i)\,\Delta x_i \right]$$

$$= \lim_{\max \Delta x_i \to 0} \sum_{i=1}^n f_1(\xi_i)\,\Delta x_i + \lim_{\max \Delta x_i \to 0} \sum_{i=1}^n f_2(\xi_i)\,\Delta x_i$$

$$= \int_a^b f_1(x)\,dx + \int_a^b f_2(x)\,dx$$

The proof is similar for any number of terms.

Properties 1 and 2, though proved only for the case $a < b$, hold also for $a \geqslant b$.

However, the following property holds only for $a < b$:

Property 3. *If on an interval* $[a, b]$ $(a < b)$, *the functions* $f(x)$ *and* $\varphi(x)$ *satisfy the condition* $f(x) \leqslant \varphi(x)$, *then*

$$\int_a^b f(x)\, dx \leqslant \int_a^b \varphi(x)\, dx \qquad (3)$$

Proof. Let us consider the difference

$$\int_a^b \varphi(x)\, dx - \int_a^b f(x)\, dx = \int_a^b [\varphi(x) - f(x)]\, dx$$

$$= \lim_{\max \Delta x_i \to 0} \sum_{i=1}^{n} [\varphi(\xi_i) - f(\xi_i)]\, \Delta x_i.$$

Here, each difference $\varphi(\xi_i) - f(\xi_i) \geqslant 0$, $\Delta x_i \geqslant 0$. Thus, each term of the sum is nonnegative, the entire sum is nonnegative, and its limit is nonnegative; that is,

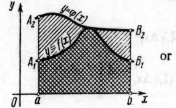

Fig. 217

$$\int_a^b [\varphi(x) - f(x)]\, dx \geqslant 0$$

or

$$\int_b^b \varphi(x)\, dx - \int_a^b f(x)\, dx \geqslant 0$$

whence follows inequality (3).

If $f(x) > 0$ and $\varphi(x) > 0$, then this property is nicely illustrated geometrically (Fig. 217). Since $\varphi(x) \geqslant f(x)$, the area of the curvilinear trapezoid aA_1B_1b does not exceed the area of the curvilinear trapezoid aA_2B_2b.

Property 4. *If m and M are the smallest and greatest values of a function* $f(x)$ *on an interval* $[a, b]$ *and* $a \leqslant b$, *then*

$$m(b-a) \leqslant \int_a^b f(x)\, dx \leqslant M(b-a) \qquad (4)$$

Proof. It is given that

$$m \leqslant f(x) \leqslant M$$

On the basis of Property (3) we have

$$\int_a^b m\, dx \leqslant \int_a^b f(x)\, dx \leqslant \int_a^b M\, dx \qquad (4')$$

But

$$\int\limits_a^b m\,dx = m\,(b-a), \qquad \int\limits_a^b M\,dx = M\,(b-a)$$

(see Example 3, Sec. 11.2). Putting these expressions into inequality (4'), we get inequality (4).

If $f(x) \geqslant 0$, this property can easily be illustrated geometrically (Fig 218). The area of the curvilinear trapezoid $aABb$ lies between the areas of the rectangles aA_1B_1b and aA_2B_2b.

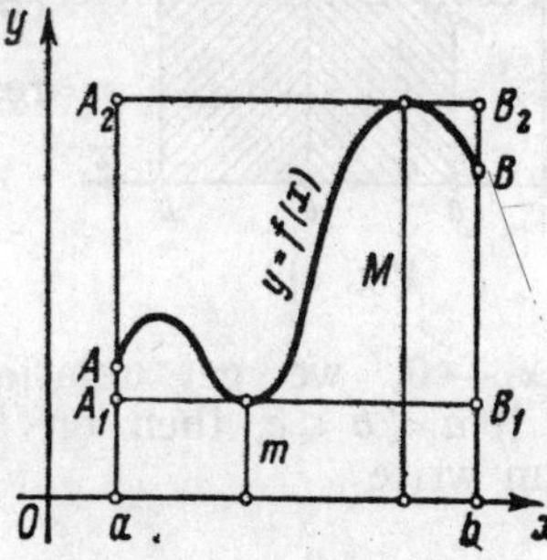

Property 5 (Mean-value theorem). *If a function $f(x)$ is continuous on an interval $[a, b]$, then there is a point ξ on this interval such that the following equation holds:*

$$\int\limits_a^b f(x)\,dx = (b-a)\,f(\xi) \qquad (5)$$

Fig. 218

Proof. For definiteness let $a < b$. If m and M are, respectively, the smallest and greatest values of $f(x)$ on $[a, b]$, then by virtue of (4)

$$m \leqslant \frac{1}{b-a}\int\limits_a^b f(x)\,dx \leqslant M$$

whence

$$\frac{1}{b-a}\int\limits_a^b f(x)\,dx = \mu, \quad \text{where} \quad m \leqslant \mu \leqslant M$$

Since $f(x)$ is continuous on $[a, b]$, it takes on all intermediate values between m and M. Therefore, for some value $\xi\,(a \leqslant \xi \leqslant b)$ we will have $\mu = f(\xi)$, or

$$\int\limits_a^b f(x)\,dx = f(\xi)\,(b-a)$$

Property 6. *For any three numbers a, b, c the equation*

$$\int\limits_a^b f(x)\,dx = \int\limits_a^c f(x)\,dx + \int\limits_c^b f(x)\,dx \qquad (6)$$

is true, provided all these three integrals exist.

Proof. First suppose that $a < c < b$, and form the integral sum of the function $f(x)$ on the interval $[a, b]$.

26—2081

Since the limit of the integral sum is independent of the way in which the interval $[a, b]$ is divided into subintervals, we divide $[a, b]$ into subintervals such that the point c is the division point. Then we partition the sum $\sum\limits_{a}^{b}$, which corresponds to the interval $[a, b]$, into two sums: $\sum\limits_{a}^{c}$, which corresponds to $[a, c]$, and $\sum\limits_{c}^{b}$, which corresponds to $[c, b]$. Then

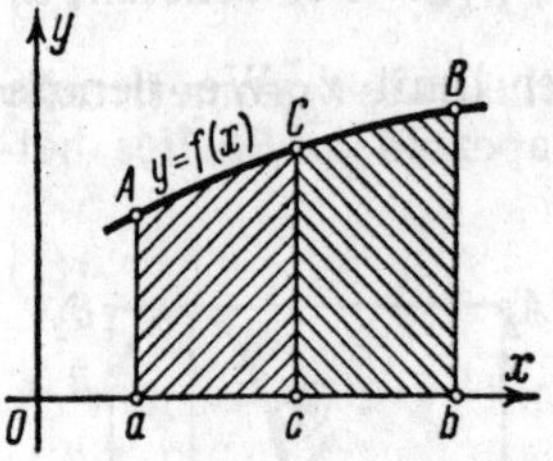

$$\sum_{a}^{b} f(\xi_i)\,\Delta x_i = \sum_{a}^{c} f(\xi_i)\,\Delta x_i + \sum_{c}^{b} f(\xi_i)\,\Delta x_i$$

Fig. 219

Now, passing to the limit as max $\Delta x_i \to 0$, we get relation (6).

If $a < b < c$, then on the basis of what has been proved we can write

$$\int_a^c f(x)\,dx = \int_a^b f(x)\,dx + \int_b^c f(x)\,dx \quad \text{or} \quad \int_a^b f(x)\,dx = \int_a^c f(x)\,dx - \int_b^c f(x)\,dx$$

but by formula (4), Sec. 11.2, we have

$$\int_b^c f(x)\,dx = -\int_c^b f(x)\,dx$$

Therefore,

$$\int_a^b f(x)\,dx = \int_a^c f(x)\,dx + \int_c^b f(x)\,dx$$

This property is similarly proved for any other arrangement of points a, b, and c.

Fig. 219 illustrates Property 6, geometrically, or the case where $f(x) > 0$ and $a < c < b$: the area of the trapezoid $aABb$ is equal to the sum of the areas of the trapezoids $aACc$ and $cCBb$.

11.4 EVALUATING A DEFINITE INTEGRAL.
THE NEWTON-LEIBNIZ FORMULA

In a definite integral

$$\int_a^b f(x)\,dx$$

let the lower limit a be fixed and let the upper limit b vary. Then the value of the integral will vary as well: that is, the integral is a **function of the upper limit.**

So as to retain customary notations, we shall denote the upper limit by x, and to avoid confusion we shall denote the variable of integration by t. (This change in notation does not change the value of the integral.) We get the integral $\int\limits_a^x f(t)\,dt$. For constant a, this integral will be a function of the upper limit x. We denote this function by $\Phi(x)$:

$$\Phi(x) = \int\limits_a^x f(t)\,dt \tag{1}$$

If $f(t)$ is a nonnegative function, the quantity $\Phi(x)$ is numerically equal to the area of the curvilinear trapezoid $aAXx$ (Fig. 220). It is obvious that this area varies with x.

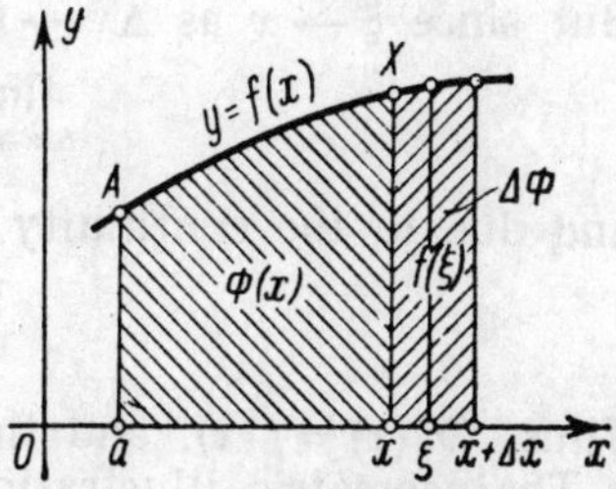

Let us find the derivative of $\Phi(x)$ with respect to x, i. e., the derivative of the definite integral (1) with respect to the upper limit.

Theorem 1. *If $f(x)$ is a continuous function and $\Phi(x) = \int\limits_a^x f(t)\,dt$, then we have the equation*

Fig. 220

$$\Phi'(x) = f(x)$$

In other words, *the derivative of a definite integral with respect to the upper limit is equal to the integrand in which the value of the upper limit replaces the variable of integration* (provided that the integrand is continuous).

Proof. Let us give the argument x a positive or negative increment Δx; then (taking into account Property 6 of a definite integral) we get

$$\Phi(x+\Delta x) = \int\limits_a^{x+\Delta x} f(t)\,dt = \int\limits_a^x f(t)\,dt + \int\limits_x^{x+\Delta x} f(t)\,dt$$

The increment of the function $\Phi(x)$ is equal to

$$\Delta\Phi = \Phi(x+\Delta x) - \Phi(x) = \int\limits_a^x f(t)\,dt + \int\limits_x^{x+\Delta x} f(t)\,dt - \int\limits_a^x f(t)\,dt$$

that is,

$$\Delta\Phi = \int\limits_x^{x+\Delta x} f(t)\,dt$$

26*

Apply to the latter integral the mean-value theorem (Property 5 of a definite integral):

$$\Delta\Phi = f(\xi)(x + \Delta x - x) = f(\xi)\,\Delta x$$

where ξ lies between x and $x + \Delta x$.

Find the ratio of the increment of the function to the increment of the argument:

$$\frac{\Delta\Phi}{\Delta x} = \frac{f(\xi)\,\Delta x}{\Delta x} = f(\xi)$$

Hence,

$$\Phi'(x) = \lim_{\Delta x \to 0} \frac{\Delta\Phi}{\Delta x} = \lim_{\Delta x \to 0} f(\xi)$$

But since $\xi \to x$ as $\Delta x \to 0$, we have

$$\lim_{\Delta x \to 0} f(\xi) = \lim_{\xi \to x} f(\xi)$$

and due to the continuity of the function $f(x)$,

$$\lim_{\xi \to x} f(\xi) = f(x)$$

Thus, $\Phi'(x) = f(x)$, and the theorem is proved.

The geometric illustration of this theorem (Fig. 220) is simple; the increment $\Delta\Phi = f(\xi)\,\Delta x$ is equal to the area of a curvilinear trapezoid with base Δx, and the derivative $\Phi'(x) = f(x)$ is equal to the length of the segment xX.

Note. One consequence of the theorem that has been proved is that *every continuous function has an antiderivative*. Indeed, if the function $f(t)$ is continuous on the interval $[a, x]$, then, as was pointed out in Sec. 11.2, in this case the definite integral $\int_a^x f(t)\,dt$ exists, which is to say that the following function exists:

$$\Phi(x) = \int_a^x f(t)\,dt$$

But from what has already been proved, it is the **antiderivative** of $f(x)$.

Theorem 2. *If $F(x)$ is some antiderivative of a continuous function $f(x)$, then the formula*

$$\int_a^b f(x)\,dx = F(b) - F(a) \qquad (2)$$

holds.

This formula is known as the *Newton-Leibniz formula.**
Proof. Let $F(x)$ be some antiderivative of the function $f(x)$. By
Theorem 1, the function $\int_a^x f(t)\,dt$ is also an antiderivative of $f(x)$.
But any two antiderivatives of a given function differ by a constant C^*. And so we can write

$$\int_a^x f(t)\,dt = F(x) + C^* \tag{3}$$

For an appropriate choice of C^*, this equation holds for all values of x, that is, it is an identity. To determine the constant C^* put $x = a$ in the identity; then

$$\int_a^a f(t)\,dt = F(a) + C^*$$

or

$$0 = F(a) + C^*$$

whence

$$C^* = -F(a)$$

Hence,

$$\int_a^x f(t)\,dt = F(x) - F(a)$$

Putting $x = b$, we obtain the Newton-Leibniz formula:

$$\int_a^b f(t)\,dt = F(b) - F(a)$$

or, replacing the notation of the variable of integration by x,

$$\int_a^b f(x)\,dx = F(b) - F(a)$$

It will be noted that the difference $F(b) - F(a)$ is independent of the choice of antiderivative F, since all antiderivatives differ by a constant quantity, which disappears upon subtraction anyway.

---

* It is necessary to point out that the name of formula (2) is not exact, since neither Newton nor Leibniz had any such formula in the exact meaning of the word. The important thing, however, is that namely Leibniz and Newton were the first to establish a relationship between integration and differentiaton, thus making possible the rule for evaluating definite integrals.

If we introduce the notation *

$$F(b) - F(a) = F(x)\big|_a^b$$

then formula (2) may be rewritten as follows:

$$\int_a^b f(x)\, dx = F(x)\big|_a^b = F(b) - F(a)$$

The Newton-Leibniz formula yields a practical and convenient method for computing definite integrals in cases where the antiderivative of the integrand is known. Only when this formula was established did the definite integral acquire its present significance in mathematics. Although the ancients (Archimedes) were familiar with a process similar to the computation of a definite integral as the limit of an integral sum, the applications of this method were confined to the very simple cases where the limit of the sum could be computed directly. The Newton-Leibniz formula greatly expanded the field of application of the definite integral, because mathematics obtained a **general method** for solving various problems of a particular type and so could considerably extend the range of applications of the definite integral to technology, mechanics, astronomy, and so on.

Example 1.

$$\int_a^b x\, dx = \frac{x^2}{2}\bigg|_a^b = \frac{b^2 - a^2}{2}$$

Example 2.

$$\int_a^b x^2\, dx = \frac{x^3}{3}\bigg|_a^b = \frac{b^3 - a^3}{3}$$

Example 3.

$$\int_a^b x^n\, dx = \frac{x^{n+1}}{n+1}\bigg|_a^b = \frac{b^{n+1} - a^{n+1}}{n+1} \quad (n \neq -1)$$

Example 4.

$$\int_a^b e^x\, dx = e^x\big|_a^b = e^b - e^a$$

---

* The expression $\big|_a^b$ is called the sign of double substitution. In the literature we find two notations:

$$F(b) - F(a) = [F(x)]_a^b$$

or

$$F(b) - F(a) = F(x)\big|_a^b$$

We shall use both notations.

Example 5.

$$\int_0^{2\pi} \sin x \, dx = -\cos x \Big|_0^{2\pi} = -(\cos 2\pi - \cos 0) = 0$$

Example 6.

$$\int_0^1 \frac{x \, dx}{\sqrt{1+x^2}} = \sqrt{1+x^2}\Big|_0^1 = \sqrt{2} - 1$$

11.5 CHANGE OF VARIABLE IN THE DEFINITE INTEGRAL

Theorem. *Given an integral*

$$\int_a^b f(x) \, dx$$

where the function $f(x)$ is continuous on the interval $[a, b]$. Introduce a new variable t using the formula

$$x = \varphi(t)$$

If
(1) $\varphi(\alpha) = a$, $\varphi(\beta) = b$,
(2) $\varphi(t)$ and $\varphi'(t)$ are continuous on $[\alpha, \beta]$,
(3) $f[\varphi(t)]$ is defined and is continuous on $[\alpha, \beta]$, then

$$\int_a^b f(x) \, dx = \int_\alpha^\beta f[\varphi(t)] \, \varphi'(t) \, dt \qquad (1)$$

Proof. If $F(x)$ is an antiderivative of the function $f(x)$, we can write the following equations:

$$\int f(x) \, dx = F(x) + C \qquad (2)$$

$$\int f[\varphi(t)] \, \varphi'(t) \, dt = F[\varphi(t)] + C \qquad (3)$$

The truth of the latter equation is checked by differentiation of both sides with respect to t. [It likewise follows from formula (2), Sec. 10.4]. From (2) we have

$$\int_a^b f(x) \, dx = F(x) \Big|_a^b = F(b) - F(a)$$

From (3) we have

$$\int_\alpha^\beta f[\varphi(t)] \, \varphi'(t) \, dt = F[\varphi(t)] \Big|_\alpha^\beta$$
$$= F[\varphi(\beta)] - F[\varphi(\alpha)]$$
$$= F(b) - F(a)$$

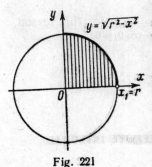

Fig. 221

The right sides of these expressions are equal, and so the left sides are equal as well, thus proving the theorem.

Note. It will be noted that when computing the definite integral from formula (1) we do not return to the old variable. If we compute the second of the definite integrals of (1), we get a certain number; the first integral is also equal to this number.

Example. Compute the integral

$$\int_0^r \sqrt{r^2-x^2}\, dx$$

Solution. Make a change of variable:

$$x=r\sin t, \quad dx=r\cos t\, dt$$

Determine the new limits:

$$x=0 \quad \text{for} \quad t=0$$
$$x=r \quad \text{for} \quad t=\frac{\pi}{2}$$

Consequently,

$$\int_0^r \sqrt{r^2-x^2}\, dx=\int_0^{\frac{\pi}{2}} \sqrt{r^2-r^2\sin^2 t}\; r\cos t\, dt=r^2\int_0^{\frac{\pi}{2}} \sqrt{1-\sin^2 t}\cos t\, dt$$

$$=r^2\int_0^{\frac{\pi}{2}} \cos^2 t\, dt=r^2\int_0^{\frac{\pi}{2}} \left(\frac{1}{2}+\frac{1}{2}\cos 2t\right) dt=r^2\left[\frac{t}{2}+\frac{\sin 2t}{4}\right]_0^{\frac{\pi}{2}}=\frac{\pi r^2}{4}$$

Geometrically, the computed integral is $\frac{1}{4}$ the area of the circle bounded by the circumference $x^2+y^2=r^2$ (Fig. 221).

11.6 INTEGRATION BY PARTS

Let u and v be differentiable functions of x. Then

$$(uv)' =u'v+uv'$$

Integrating both sides of the identity from a to b, we have

$$\int_a^b (uv)'\, dx=\int_a^b u'v\, dx+\int_a^b uv'\, dx \tag{1}$$

Since $\int (uv)' \, dx = uv + C$, we have $\int\limits_a^b (uv)' \, dx = uv \, |_a^b$; for this reason, the equation can be written in the form

$$uv \, |_a^b = \int\limits_a^b v \, du + \int\limits_a^b u \, dv$$

or, finally,

$$\int\limits_a^b u \, dv = uv \, |_a^b - \int\limits_a^b v \, du$$

Example. Evaluate the integral $I_n = \int\limits_0^{\frac{\pi}{2}} \sin^n x \, dx$.

$$I_n = \int\limits_0^{\frac{\pi}{2}} \sin^n x \, dx = \int\limits_0^{\frac{\pi}{2}} \sin^{n-1} x \sin x \, dx = - \int\limits_0^{\frac{\pi}{2}} \underbrace{\sin^{n-1} x}_{u} \underbrace{d \cos x}_{dv}$$

$$= -\sin^{n-1} x \cos x \, \Big|_0^{\frac{\pi}{2}} + (n-1) \int\limits_0^{\frac{\pi}{2}} \sin^{n-2} x \cos x \cos x \, dx$$

$$= (n-1) \int\limits_0^{\frac{\pi}{2}} \sin^{n-2} x \cos^2 x \, dx$$

$$= (n-1) \int\limits_0^{\frac{\pi}{2}} \sin^{n-2} x \, (1 - \sin^2 x) \, dx$$

$$= (n-1) \int\limits_0^{\frac{\pi}{2}} \sin^{n-2} x \, dx - (n-1) \int\limits_0^{\frac{\pi}{2}} \sin^n x \, dx$$

In the notation chosen we can write the latter equation as

$$I_n = (n-1) I_{n-2} - (n-1) I_n$$

whence we find

$$I_n = \frac{n-1}{n} I_{n-2} \qquad\qquad (2)$$

Using the same technique, we find

$$I_{n-2} = \frac{n-3}{n-2} I_{n-4}$$

and so

$$I_n = \frac{n-1}{n} \frac{n-3}{n-2} I_{n-4}$$

Continuing in the same way, we arrive at I_0 or I_1 depending on whether the number n is even or odd.

Let us consider two cases:

(1) n is even, $n = 2m$:

$$I_{2m} = \frac{2m-1}{2m} \cdot \frac{2m-3}{2m-2} \cdots \frac{3}{4} \cdot \frac{1}{2} I_0$$

(2) n is odd, $n = 2m+1$:

$$I_{2m+1} = \frac{2m}{2m+1} \cdot \frac{2m-2}{2m-1} \cdots \frac{4}{5} \cdot \frac{2}{3} I_1$$

but since

$$I_0 = \int_0^{\frac{\pi}{2}} \sin^0 x \, dx = \int_0^{\frac{\pi}{2}} dx = \frac{\pi}{2}, \qquad I_1 = \int_0^{\frac{\pi}{2}} \sin x \, dx = 1$$

we have

$$I_{2m} = \int_0^{\frac{\pi}{2}} \sin^{2m} x \, dx = \frac{2m-1}{2m} \cdot \frac{2m-3}{2m-2} \cdots \frac{5}{6} \cdot \frac{3}{4} \cdot \frac{1}{2} \cdot \frac{\pi}{2}$$

$$I_{2m+1} = \int_0^{\frac{\pi}{2}} \sin^{2m+1} x \, dx = \frac{2m}{2m+1} \cdot \frac{2m-2}{2m-1} \cdots \frac{6}{7} \cdot \frac{4}{5} \cdot \frac{2}{3}$$

From these formulas there follows the *Wallis formula*, which expresses the number $\frac{\pi}{2}$ in the form of an infinite product.

Indeed from the latter two equations we find, by means of termwise division,

$$\frac{\pi}{2} = \left(\frac{2 \cdot 4 \cdot 6 \ldots 2m}{3 \cdot 5 \ldots (2m-1)} \right)^2 \frac{1}{2m+1} \frac{I_{2m}}{I_{2m+1}} \tag{3}$$

We shall now prove that

$$\lim_{m \to \infty} \frac{I_{2m}}{I_{2m+1}} = 1$$

For all x of the interval $\left(0, \frac{\pi}{2} \right)$ the inequalities

$$\sin^{2m-1} x > \sin^{2m} x > \sin^{2m+1} x$$

hold.

Integrating from 0 to $\frac{\pi}{2}$, we get

$$I_{2m-1} \geqslant I_{2m} \geqslant I_{2m+1}$$

whence

$$\frac{I_{2m-1}}{I_{2m+1}} \geqslant \frac{I_{2m}}{I_{2m+1}} \geqslant 1 \tag{4}$$

From (2) it follows that

$$\frac{I_{2m-1}}{I_{2m+1}} = \frac{2m+1}{2m}$$

Hence

$$\lim_{m \to \infty} \frac{I_{2m-1}}{I_{2m+1}} = \lim_{m \to \infty} \frac{2m+1}{2m} = 1$$

From inequality (4) we have

$$\lim_{m \to \infty} \frac{I_{2m}}{I_{2m+1}} = 1$$

Passing to the limit in formula (3), we get *Wallis' formula (Wallis' product)* for

$$\frac{\pi}{2} = \lim_{m \to \infty} \left[\left(\frac{2 \cdot 4 \cdot 6 \ \ldots \ 2m}{3 \cdot 5 \ \ldots \ (2m-1)} \right)^2 \frac{1}{2m+1} \right]$$

This formula may be written in the form

$$\frac{\pi}{2} = \lim_{m \to \infty} \left(\frac{2}{1} \cdot \frac{2}{3} \cdot \frac{4}{3} \cdot \frac{4}{5} \cdot \frac{6}{5} \cdots \frac{2m-2}{2m-1} \cdot \frac{2m}{2m-1} \cdot \frac{2m}{2m+1} \right)$$

11.7 IMPROPER INTEGRALS

1. Integrals with infinite limits. Let a function $f(x)$ be defined and continuous for all values of x such that $a \leqslant x < +\infty$. Consider the integral

$$I(b) = \int_a^b f(x)\, dx$$

This integral is meaningful for any $b > a$. The integral varies with b and is a continuous function of b (see Sec. 11.4). Let us consider the behaviour of this integral when $b \to +\infty$ (Fig. 222).

Definition. If there exists a finite limit

$$\lim_{b \to +\infty} \int_a^b f(x)\, dx$$

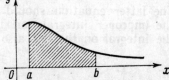

Fig. 222

then this limit is called the *improper integral* of the function $f(x)$ on the interval $[a, +\infty)$ and is denoted by the symbol

$$\int_a^{+\infty} f(x)\, dx$$

Thus, by definition, we have

$$\int_a^{+\infty} f(x)\, dx = \lim_{b \to +\infty} \int_a^b f(x)\, dx$$

In this case it is said that the improper integral $\int\limits_{a}^{+\infty} f(x)\,dx$ exists

or *converges*. If $\int\limits_{a}^{b} f(x)\,dx$ as $b \longrightarrow +\infty$ does not have a finite limit,

one says that $\int\limits_{a}^{+\infty} f(x)\,dx$ does *not exist* or *diverges*.

It is easy to see the geometric meaning of an improper integral

for the case where $f(x) \geqslant 0$: if the integral $\int\limits_{a}^{b} f(x)\,dx$ expresses the

area of a region bounded by the curve $y = f(x)$, the x-axis and
the ordinates $x = a$, $x = b$, it is natural to consider that the im-

proper integral $\int\limits_{a}^{+\infty} f(x)\,dx$ expresses the area of an unbounded (in-

finite) region lying between the lines $y = f(x)$, $x = a$, and the axis
of abscissas.

We similarly define the improper integrals of other infinite intervals:

$$\int\limits_{-\infty}^{a} f(x)\,dx = \lim_{\alpha \to -\infty} \int\limits_{\alpha}^{a} f(x)\,dx$$

$$\int\limits_{-\infty}^{+\infty} f(x)\,dx = \int\limits_{-\infty}^{c} f(x)\,dx + \int\limits_{c}^{+\infty} f(x)\,dx$$

The latter equation should be understood as follows: if each of
the improper integrals on the right exists, then, by definition,
the integral on the left also exists (converges).

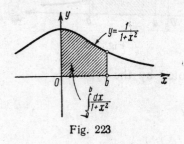

Fig. 223

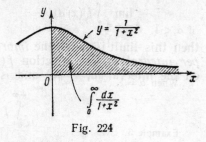

Fig. 224

Example 1. Evaluate the integral $\int\limits_{0}^{+\infty} \dfrac{dx}{1+x^2}$ (see Figs. 223 and 224).

Solution. By the definition of an improper integral we find

$$\int_{0}^{+\infty} \frac{dx}{1+x^2} = \lim_{b \to +\infty} \int_{0}^{b} \frac{dx}{1+x^2} = \lim_{b \to +\infty} \arctan x \Big|_{0}^{b} = \lim_{b \to +\infty} \arctan b = \frac{\pi}{2}$$

This integral expresses the area of an infinite curvilinear trapezoid cross-hatched in Fig. 224.

Example 2. Find out at which values of α (Fig. 225) the integral

$$\int_{1}^{+\infty} \frac{dx}{x^{\alpha}}$$

converges and at which it diverges.

Solution. Since (when $\alpha \neq 1$)

$$\int_{1}^{b} \frac{dx}{x^{\alpha}} = \frac{1}{1-\alpha} x^{1-\alpha} \Big|_{1}^{b} = \frac{1}{1-\alpha} (b^{1-\alpha} - 1)$$

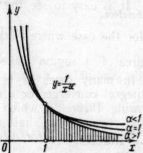

Fig. 225

we have

$$\int_{1}^{+\infty} \frac{dx}{x^{\alpha}} = \lim_{b \to +\infty} \frac{1}{1-\alpha} (b^{1-\alpha} - 1)$$

Consequently, with respect to this integral we conclude that

if $\alpha > 1$, then $\int_{1}^{+\infty} \frac{dx}{x^2} = \frac{1}{\alpha - 1}$, and the integral converges;

if $\alpha < 1$, then $\int_{1}^{+\infty} \frac{dx}{x^2} = \infty$, and the integral diverges

When $\alpha = 1$, $\int_{1}^{+\infty} \frac{dx}{x} = \ln x \Big|_{1}^{+\infty} = \infty$, and the integral diverges.

Example 3. Evaluate $\int_{-\infty}^{+\infty} \frac{dx}{1+x^2}$.

Solution.

$$\int_{-\infty}^{+\infty} \frac{dx}{1+x^2} = \int_{-\infty}^{0} \frac{dx}{1+x^2} + \int_{0}^{+\infty} \frac{dx}{1+x^2}$$

The second integral is equal to $\dfrac{\pi}{2}$ (see Example 1). Compute the first integral:

$$\int_{-\infty}^{0} \frac{dx}{1+x^2} = \lim_{\alpha \to -\infty} \int_{\alpha}^{0} \frac{dx}{1+x^2} = \lim_{\alpha \to -\infty} \arctan x \Big|_{\alpha}^{0}$$

$$= \lim_{\alpha \to -\infty} (\arctan 0 - \arctan \alpha) = \frac{\pi}{2}$$

Therefore,

$$\int_{-\infty}^{+\infty} \frac{dx}{1+x^2} = \frac{\pi}{2} + \frac{\pi}{2} = \pi$$

In many cases it is sufficient to determine whether the given integral converges or diverges, and to estimate its value. The following theorems, which we give without proof, may be useful in this respect. We shall illustrate their application in a few cases.

Theorem 1. *If for all* $x\,(x \geqslant a)$ *the inequality*

$$0 \leqslant f(x) \leqslant \varphi(x)$$

is fulfilled and if $\displaystyle\int_{a}^{+\infty} \varphi(x)\,dx$ *converges, then* $\displaystyle\int_{a}^{+\infty} f(x)\,dx$ *also converges, and*

$$\int_{a}^{+\infty} f(x)\,dx \leqslant \int_{a}^{+\infty} \varphi(x)\,dx$$

Example 4. Investigate the integral

$$\int_{1}^{+\infty} \frac{dx}{x^2(1+e^x)}$$

for convergence.

Solution. It will be noted that when $1 \leqslant x$,

$$\frac{1}{x^2(1+e^x)} < \frac{1}{x^2}$$

And

$$\int_{1}^{+\infty} \frac{1}{x^2}\,dx = -\frac{1}{x}\Big|_{1}^{+\infty} = 1$$

Consequently,

$$\int_{1}^{+\infty} \frac{dx}{x^2(1+e^x)}$$

converges, and its value is less than 1.

Theorem 2. *If for all* $x\,(x \geqslant a)$ *the inequality* $0 \leqslant \varphi(x) \leqslant f(x)$ *holds true and* $\int\limits_{a}^{+\infty} \varphi(x)\,dx$ *diverges, then the integral* $\int\limits_{a}^{+\infty} f(x)\,dx$ *also diverges.*

Example 5. Find out whether the following integral converges or diverges:

$$\int\limits_{1}^{+\infty} \frac{x+1}{\sqrt{x^3}}\,dx$$

We notice that

$$\frac{x+1}{\sqrt{x^3}} > \frac{x}{\sqrt{x^3}} = \frac{1}{\sqrt{x}}$$

But

$$\int\limits_{1}^{+\infty} \frac{dx}{\sqrt{x}} = \lim_{b \to +\infty} 2\sqrt{x}\,\Big|_{1}^{b} = +\infty$$

Consequently, the given integral also diverges.

In the last two theorems we considered improper integrals of nonnegative functions. For the case of a function $f(x)$ which changes its sign over an infinite interval we have the following theorem.

Theorem 3. *If the integral* $\int\limits_{a}^{+\infty} |f(x)|\,dx$ *converges, then the integral* $\int\limits_{a}^{+\infty} f(x)\,dx$ *also converges.*

In this case, the latter integral is called an *absolutely convergent integral.*

Example 6. Investigate the convergence of the integral

$$\int\limits_{1}^{+\infty} \frac{\sin x}{x^3}\,dx$$

Solution. Here, the integrand is an alternating function. We note that

$$\left|\frac{\sin x}{x^3}\right| \leqslant \left|\frac{1}{x^3}\right|. \quad \text{But} \quad \int\limits_{1}^{+\infty} \frac{dx}{x^3} = -\frac{1}{2x^2}\,\Big|_{1}^{+\infty} = \frac{1}{2}$$

Therefore, the integral $\int\limits_{1}^{+\infty} \left|\frac{\sin x}{x^3}\right|\,dx$ converges. Whence it follows that the given integral also converges.

2. The integral of a discontinuous function. A function $f(x)$ is defined and continuous when $a \leqslant x < c$, and either not defined or discontinuous when $x = c$. In this case, one cannot speak of the integral $\int\limits_a^c f(x)\,dx$ as the limit of integral sums, because $f(x)$ is not continuous on the interval $[a, c]$, and for this reason the limit may not exist.

The integral $\int\limits_a^c f(x)\,dx$ of the function $f(x)$ **discontinuous at the point** c is defined as follows:

$$\int\limits_a^c f(x)\,dx = \lim_{b \to c-0} \int\limits_a^b f(x)\,dx$$

If the limit on the right exists, the integral is called an improper *convergent* integral, otherwise it is *divergent*.

If the function $f(x)$ is discontinuous at the left extremity of the interval $[a, c]$ (that is, for $x = a$), then **by definition**

$$\int\limits_a^c f(x)\,dx = \lim_{b \to a+0} \int\limits_b^c f(x)\,dx$$

If the function $f(x)$ is discontinuous at some point $x = x_0$ **inside** the interval $[a, c]$, we put

$$\int\limits_a^c f(x)\,dx = \int\limits_a^{x_0} f(x)\,dx + \int\limits_{x_0}^c f(x)\,dx$$

if both improper integrals on the right side of the equation exist.

Example 7. Evaluate

$$\int\limits_0^1 \frac{dx}{\sqrt{1-x}}$$

Solution.

$$\int\limits_0^1 \frac{dx}{\sqrt{1-x}} = \lim_{b \to 1-0} \int\limits_0^b \frac{dx}{\sqrt{1-x}} = - \lim_{b \to 1-0} 2\sqrt{1-x}\,\Big|_0^b$$

$$= - \lim_{b \to 1-0} 2\,(\sqrt{1-b}-1) = 2$$

Example 8. Evaluate the integral $\int\limits_{-1}^1 \frac{dx}{x^2}$.

Solution. Since inside the interval of integration there exists a point $x = 0$ where the integrand is discontinuous, the integral must be represented as the sum of two terms:

$$\int_{-1}^{1} \frac{dx}{x^2} = \lim_{\varepsilon_1 \to -0} \int_{-1}^{\varepsilon_1} \frac{dx}{x^2} + \lim_{\varepsilon_2 \to +0} \int_{\varepsilon_2}^{1} \frac{dx}{x^2}$$

Calculate each limit separately:

$$\lim_{\varepsilon_1 \to -0} \int_{-1}^{\varepsilon_1} \frac{dx}{x^2} = -\lim_{\varepsilon_1 \to -0} \frac{1}{x}\Big|_{-1}^{\varepsilon_1} = -\lim_{\varepsilon_1 \to -0} \left(\frac{1}{\varepsilon_1} - \frac{1}{-1}\right) = \infty$$

Thus, the integral diverges on the interval $|-1, 0|$:

$$\lim_{\varepsilon_2 \to +0} \int_{\varepsilon_2}^{1} \frac{dx}{x^2} = -\lim_{\varepsilon_2 \to +0} \left(1 - \frac{1}{\varepsilon_2}\right) = \infty$$

And this means that the integral also diverges on the interval $[0, 1]$.

Hence, the given integral diverges on the entire interval $|-1, 1|$.

It should be noted that if we had begun to evaluate the given integral without paying attention to the discontinuity of the integrand at the point $x = 0$, the result would have been wrong. Indeed,

$$\int_{-1}^{1} \frac{dx}{x^2} = -\frac{1}{x}\Big|_{-1}^{1} = -\left(\frac{1}{1} - \frac{1}{-1}\right) = -2$$

which is impossible (Fig. 226).

Note. If the function $f(x)$, defined on the interval $[a, b]$, has, within this interval, a finite number of points of discontinuity a_1, a_2 ..., a_n, then the integral of the function $f(x)$ on the interval $[a, b]$ is defined as follows:

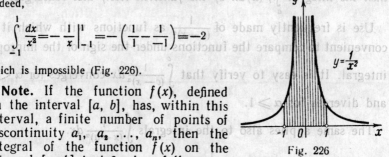

Fig. 226

$$\int_{a}^{b} f(x)\,dx = \int_{a}^{a_1} f(x)\,dx + \int_{a_1}^{a_2} f(x)\,dx + \ldots + \int_{a_n}^{b} f(x)\,dx$$

if each of the improper integrals on the right side of the equation converges. But if even one of these integrals diverges, then $\int_{a}^{b} f(x)\,dx$ too is called divergent.

For determining the convergence of improper integrals of discontinuous functions and for estimating their values, one can frequently make use of theorems similar to those used to estimate integrals with infinite limits.

Theorem 1′. *If on the interval $[a, c]$ the functions $f(x)$ and $\varphi(x)$ are discontinuous at the point c, and at all points of this interval* the inequalities $\varphi(x) \geqslant f(x) \geqslant 0$ *hold and* $\int\limits_a^c \varphi(x)\,dx$ *converges, then*

$\int\limits_a^c f(x)\,dx$ *also converges.*

Theorem 2'. *If on the interval* $[a, c]$ *the functions* $f(x)$ *and* $\varphi(x)$ *are discontinuous at the point* c, *and at all points of this interval the inequalities* $f(x) \geqslant \varphi(x) \geqslant 0$ *hold and* $\int\limits_a^c \varphi(x)\,dx$ *diverges, then*

$\int\limits_a^c f(x)\,dx$ *also diverges.*

Theorem 3'. *If* $f(x)$ *is an alternating function on the interval* $[a, c]$ *and discontinuous only at the point* c, *and the improper integral* $\int\limits_a^c |f(x)|\,dx$ *of the absolute value of this function converges, then the integral* $\int\limits_a^c f(x)\,dx$ *of the function itself also converges.*

Use is frequently made of $\dfrac{1}{(c-x)^\alpha}$ as functions with which it is convenient to compare the functions under the sign of the improper integral. It is easy to verify that $\int\limits_a^c \dfrac{1}{(c-x)^\alpha}\,dx$ converges for $\alpha < 1$, and diverges for $\alpha \geqslant 1$.

The same applies also to the integrals $\int\limits_a^c \dfrac{1}{(x-a)^\alpha}\,dx$.

Example 9. Does the integral $\int\limits_0^1 \dfrac{1}{\sqrt{x}+4x^3}\,dx$ converge?

Solution. The integrand is discontinuous at the left extremity of the interval $[0, 1]$. Comparing it with the function $\dfrac{1}{\sqrt{x}}$, we have

$$\frac{1}{\sqrt{x}+4x^3} < \frac{1}{\sqrt{x}}$$

The improper integral $\int\limits_0^1 \dfrac{dx}{x^{1/2}}$ exists. Consequently, the improper integral of a lesser function, that is $\int\limits_0^1 \dfrac{1}{\sqrt{x}+4x^3}\,dx$, also exists.

11.8 APPROXIMATING DEFINITE INTEGRALS

At the end of Chapter 10 it was pointed out that not for every continuous function is its antiderivative expressible in terms of elementary functions. In these cases, computation of definite integrals by the Newton-Leibniz formula is involved, and various methods of **approximation** are used to evaluate the definite integrals. The following are several methods of approximate integration based on the concept of a definite integral as the limit of a sum.

I. Rectangular formula. Let a continuous function $y = f(x)$ be given on an interval $[a, b]$. It is required to evaluate the definite integral

$$\int_a^b f(x)\,dx$$

Divide the interval $[a, b]$ by the points $a = x_0,\ x_1,\ x_2,\ \ldots,\ x_n = b$ into n equal parts of length Δx:

$$\Delta x = \frac{b-a}{n}$$

Then denote by $y_0,\ y_1,\ y_2,\ \ldots,\ y_{n-1},\ y_n$ the values of the function $f(x)$ at the points $x_0,\ x_1,\ x_2,\ \ldots,\ x_n$; that is,

$$y_0 = f(x_0),\ \ y_1 = f(x_1),\ \ \ldots,\ \ y_n = f(x_n)$$

Form the sums:

$$y_0\Delta x + y_1\Delta x + \ldots + y_{n-1}\Delta x$$
$$y_1\Delta x + y_2\Delta x + \ldots + y_n\Delta x$$

Each of these sums is an integral sum of $f(x)$ on the interval $[a, b]$ and for this reason approximately expresses the integral

$$\int_a^b f(x)\,dx \approx \frac{b-a}{n}(y_0 + y_1 + y_2 + \ldots + y_{n-1}) \tag{1}$$

$$\int_a^b f(x)\,dx \approx \frac{b-a}{n}(y_1 + y_2 + \ldots + y_n). \tag{1'}$$

This is the *rectangular formula*. From Fig. 227 it is evident that if $f(x)$ is a positive and increasing function, then formula (1) expresses the area of the step-like figure composed of "inside" rectangles, while formula (1') yields the area of the step-like figure composed of "outside" rectangles.

The error made when calculating integrals by the rectangular formula diminishes with increasing n $\Big($that is, the smaller the divisions $\Delta x = \frac{b-a}{n}\Big)$.

27*

11. The trapezoidal rule. It is natural to expect that we will obtain a more exact value of the definite integral if we replace the curve $y = f(x)$ not by a step-like line, as in the rectangular formula, but by an **inscribed** broken line (Fig. 228). Then the area of the curvilinear trapezoid $aABb$ will be replaced by the sum of the areas of the rectilinear trapezoids bounded from above

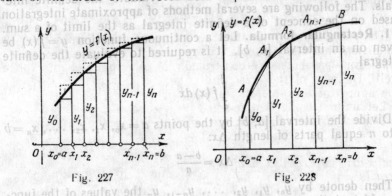

Fig. 227   Fig. 228

by the chords AA_1, A_1A_2, ..., $A_{n-1}B$. Since the area of the first of these trapezoids is $\frac{y_0 + y_1}{2} \Delta x$, the area of the second is $\frac{y_1 + y_2}{2} \Delta x$, and so forth, so

$$\int_a^b f(x)\,dx \approx \left(\frac{y_0 + y_1}{2} \Delta x + \frac{y_1 + y_2}{2} \Delta x + \cdots + \frac{y_{n-1} + y_n}{2} \Delta x \right)$$

or

$$\int_a^b f(x)\,dx \approx \frac{b-a}{n} \left(\frac{y_0 + y_n}{2} + y_1 + y_2 + \cdots + y_{n-1} \right) \qquad (2)$$

This is the *trapezoidal formula (trapezoidal rule)*. Note that the number on the right of (2) is the arithmetic mean of the numbers in the right members of (1) and (1').

The choice of n is arbitrary. The greater this number, the smaller will be the division (subinterval) $\Delta x = \frac{b-a}{n}$ and the greater will be the accuracy with which the sum, written on the right side of the approximate equation (2), yields the value of the integral.

III. Parabolic formula (Simpson's rule). Divide the interval $[a, b]$ into an **even** number of parts $n = 2m$. Replace the area of the curvilinear trapezoid, corresponding to the first two subintervals $[x_0, x_1]$ and $[x_1, x_2]$ and bounded by the given curve $y = f(x)$, by the area of a curvilinear trapezoid such that is bounded by a

quadratic parabola passing through three points:

$$M(x_0,\ y_0),\quad M_1(x_1,\ y_1),\quad M_2(x_2,\ y_2)$$

and with an axis parallel to the y-axis (Fig. 229). We shall call this kind of curvilinear trapezoid a *parabolic* trapezoid.

The equation of a parabola with axis parallel to the y-axis is of the form

$$y = Ax^2 + Bx + C$$

The coefficients A, B and C are uniquely determined from the condition that the parabola passes through three specified points. Analogous parabolas are constructed for other pairs of intervals as well. The sum of the areas of the parabolic trapezoids will yield the approximate value of the integral.

Let us first compute the area of one parabolic trapezoid.

Lemma. *If a curvilinear trapezoid is bounded by the parabola*

$$y = Ax^2 + Bx + C$$

the x-axis and two ordinates separated by a distance 2h, then its area is

$$S = \frac{h}{3}(y_0 + 4y_1 + y_2) \tag{3}$$

where y_0 and y_2 are the extreme ordinates and y_1 is the ordinate of the curve at the midpoint of the interval.

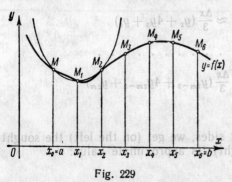

Fig. 229

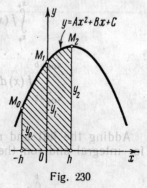

Fig. 230

Proof. Arrange an auxiliary coordinate system as shown in Fig. 230.

The coefficients in the equation of the parabola $y = Ax^2 + Bx + C$ are determined from the following equations:

$$\left.\begin{array}{lll} \text{if } x_0 = -h, & \text{then } y_0 = Ah^2 - Bh + C \\ \text{if } x_1 = 0, & \text{then } y_1 = \qquad\quad C \\ \text{if } x_2 = h, & \text{then } y_2 = Ah^2 + Bh + C \end{array}\right\} \tag{4}$$

Considering the coefficients A, B, C known, we determine the area of the parabolic trapezoid with the aid of a definite integral:

$$S = \int_{-h}^{h} (Ax^2 + Bx + C)\, dx = \left[\frac{Ax^3}{3} + \frac{Bx^2}{2} + Cx \right]_{-h}^{h} = \frac{h}{3} (2Ah^2 + 6C)$$

But from equalities (4) it follows that

$$y_0 + 4y_1 + y_2 = 2Ah^2 + 6C$$

Hence,

$$S = \frac{h}{3} (y_0 + 4y_1 + y_2)$$

which is what had to be proved.

Let us come back to our basic problem (see Fig. 229). Using formula (3) we can write the following approximate equations ($h = \Delta x$):

$$\int_{a=x_0}^{x_2} f(x)\, dx \approx \frac{\Delta x}{3} (y_0 + 4y_1 + y_2)$$

$$\int_{x_2}^{x_4} f(x)\, dx \approx \frac{\Delta x}{3} (y_2 + 4y_3 + y_4)$$

$$\cdots \cdots \cdots \cdots \cdots \cdots \cdots$$

$$\int_{x_{2m-2}}^{x_{2m}=b} f(x)\, dx \approx \frac{\Delta x}{3} (y_{2m-2} + 4y_{2m-1} + y_{2m})$$

Adding the left and right sides, we get (on the left) the sought-for integral and (on the right) its approximate value:

$$\int_{a}^{b} f(x)\, dx \approx \frac{\Delta x}{3} (y_0 + 4y_1 + 2y_2 + 4y_3$$

$$+ \ldots + 2y_{2m-2} + 4y_{2m-1} + y_{2m}) \tag{5}$$

or

$$\int_{a}^{b} f(x)\, dx \approx \frac{b-a}{6m} [y_0 + y_{2m} + 2(y_2 + y_4 + \ldots + y_{2m-2})$$

$$+ 4(y_1 + y_3 + \ldots + y_{2m-1})]$$

This is *Simpson's formula (rule).* Here, the number of division points $2m$ is arbitrary; but the more of them there are, the more accurately the sum on the right side of (5) yields the value of the integral.*

Example. Evaluate approximately

$$\ln 2 = \int_{1}^{2} \frac{dx}{x}$$

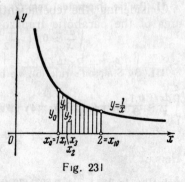

Fig. 231

Solution. Divide the interval [1, 2] into 10 equal parts (Fig. 231). Assuming

$$\Delta x = \frac{2-1}{10} = 0.1$$

we make a table of the values of the integrand:

x	$y = \frac{1}{x}$	x	$y = \frac{1}{x}$
$x_0 = 1.0$	$y_0 = 1.00000$	$x_6 = 1.6$	$y_6 = 0.62500$
$x_1 = 1.1$	$y_1 = 0.90909$	$x_7 = 1.7$	$y_7 = 0.58824$
$x_2 = 1.2$	$y_2 = 0.83333$	$x_8 = 1.8$	$y_8 = 0.55556$
$x_3 = 1.3$	$y_3 = 0.76923$	$x_9 = 1.9$	$y_9 = 0.52632$
$x_4 = 1.4$	$y_4 = 0.71429$	$x_{10} = 2.0$	$y_{10} = 0.50000$
$x_5 = 1.5$	$y_5 = 0.66667$		

I. By the first rectangular formula (1) we get

$$\int_{1}^{2} \frac{dx}{x} \approx 0.1 \, (y_0 + y_1 + \ldots + y_9) = 0.1 \cdot 7.18773 = 0.71877$$

By the second rectangular formula (1') we get

$$\int_{1}^{2} \frac{dx}{x} \approx 0.1 \, (y_1 + y_2 + \ldots + y_{10}) = 0.1 \cdot 6.68773 = 0.66877$$

It follows directly from Fig. 231 that in this case the first formula yields the value of the integral with an **excess**, the second, with a **defect**.

---

* To find out how many division points are needed to compute an integral to the desired number of decimal places, one can make use of formulas for estimating the error resulting from approximating the integral. We do not give these estimates here. The reader will find them in more advanced courses of analysis; see, for example, Fikhtengolts, *Course of Differential and Integral Calculus*, 1962, Vol. II, Ch. IX, Sec. 5. (in Russian).

II. By the trapezoidal rule (2), we have

$$\int_1^2 \frac{dx}{x} \approx 0.1\left(\frac{1+0.5}{2} + 6.18773\right) = 0.69377$$

III. By Simpson's rule (5), we have

$$\int_1^2 \frac{dx}{x} \approx \frac{0.1}{3}\,[y_0+y_{10}+2(y_2+y_4+y_6+y_8)+4(y_1+y_3+y_5+y_7+y_9)]$$

$$= \frac{0.1}{3}\,(1+0.5+2\cdot2.72818+4\cdot3.45955) = 0.69315$$

Actually, ln $2 = \int_1^2 \frac{dx}{x} = 0.6931472$ (to seven decimal places).

Thus, when dividing the interval [0, 1] into 10 parts by Simpson's rule, we get five significant decimals; by the trapezoidal rule, only three; and by the rectangular formula, we are sure only of the first decimal.

11.9 CHEBYSHEV'S FORMULA

In engineering computations, use is frequently made of Chebyshev's formula of approximate integration.

Once again, let it be required to compute $\int_a^b f(x)\,dx$.

Replace the integrand by the Lagrange interpolation polynomial $P(x)$ (Sec. 7.9) and take certain n values of the function on the interval $[a, b]$: $f(x_1), f(x_2), \ldots, f(x_n)$, where $x_1, x_2, \ldots, x_n$ are any points of the interval $[a, b]$:

$$P(x) = \frac{(x-x_2)(x-x_3)\ldots(x-x_n)}{(x_1-x_2)(x_1-x_3)\ldots(x_1-x_n)}\,f(x_1)$$
$$+ \frac{(x-x_1)(x-x_3)\ldots(x-x_n)}{(x_2-x_1)(x_2-x_3)\ldots(x_2-x_n)}\,f(x_2)$$
$$\cdots$$
$$+ \frac{(x-x_1)(x-x_2)\ldots(x-x_{n-1})}{(x_n-x_1)(x_n-x_2)\ldots(x_n-x_{n-1})}\,f(x_n) \tag{1}$$

We get the following approximate formula of integration:

$$\int_a^b f(x)\,dx \approx \int_a^b P(x)\,dx \tag{2}$$

After some computation it takes the form

$$\int_a^b f(x)\,dx \approx C_1 f(x_1) + C_2 f(x_2) + \ldots + C_n f(x_n) \tag{3}$$

where the coefficients C_i are calculated by the formulas

$$C_i = \int_a^b \frac{(x-x_1)\ldots(x-x_{i-1})(x-x_{i+1})\ldots(x-x_n)}{(x_i-x_1)\ldots(x_i-x_{i-1})(x_i-x_{i+1})\ldots(x_i-x_n)}\,dx \tag{4}$$

Formula (3) is cumbersome and inconvenient for computation because the coefficients C_i are expressed by complex fractions.

Chebyshev posed the inverse problem: specify not the abscissas $x_1, x_2, \ldots, x_n$ but the coefficients $C_1, C_2, \ldots, C_n$ and determine the abscissas $x_1, x_2, \ldots, x_n$.

The coefficients C_i are specified so that formula (3) should be as simple as possible for computation. This will obviously occur when all the coefficients C_i are equal:

$$C_1 = C_2 = \ldots = C_n$$

If we denote the total value of the coefficients $C_1, C_2, \ldots, C_n$ by C_n, formula (3) will take the form

$$\int_a^b f(x)\,dx \approx C_n\,[f(x_1)+f(x_2)+\ldots+f(x_n)] \tag{5}$$

Formula (5) is, generally speaking, an **approximate** equation, but if $f(x)$ is a polynomial of degree not higher than $n-1$, then the equation will be **exact**. This circumstance is what permits determining the quantities $C_n, x_1, x_2, \ldots, x_n$.

To obtain a formula that is convenient for any interval of integration, let us transform the interval of integration $[a, b]$ into the interval $[-1, 1]$. To do this, put

$$x = \frac{a+b}{2} + \frac{b-a}{2}\,t$$

then for $t=-1$ we will have $x=a$, for $t=1$, $x=b$.

Hence,

$$\int_a^b f(x)\,dx = \frac{b-a}{2}\int_{-1}^1 f\left(\frac{a+b}{2}+\frac{b-a}{2}\,t\right)dt = \frac{b-a}{2}\int_{-1}^1 \varphi(t)\,dt$$

where $\varphi(t)$ denotes the function of t under the integral sign. Thus, the problem of integrating the given function $f(x)$ on the interval $[a, b]$ can always be reduced to integrating some other function $\varphi(x)$ on the interval $[-1, 1]$.

To summarize, then, the problem has reduced to choosing in the formula

$$\int_{-1}^1 f(x)\,dx = C_n\,[f(x_1)+f(x_2)+\ldots+f(x_n)] \tag{6}$$

the numbers C_n, x_1, x_2, ..., x_n so that this formula will be exact for any function $f(x)$ of the form

$$f(x) = a_0 + a_1 x + a_2 x^2 + \ldots + a_{n-1} x^{n-1} \tag{7}$$

It will be noted that

$$\int_{-1}^{1} f(x)\,dx = \int_{-1}^{1} (a_0 + a_1 x + a_2 x^2 + \ldots + a_{n-1} x^{n-1})\,dx$$

$$= \begin{cases} 2\left(a_0 + \dfrac{a_2}{3} + \dfrac{a_4}{5} + \dfrac{a_6}{7} + \ldots + \dfrac{a_{n-1}}{n}\right) & \text{if } n \text{ is odd} \\[2mm] 2\left(a_0 + \dfrac{a_2}{3} + \ldots + \dfrac{a_{n-2}}{n-1}\right) & \text{if } n \text{ is even} \end{cases} \tag{8}$$

On the other hand, the sum on the right side of (6) will, on the basis of (7), be equal to

$$C_n [na_0 + a_1 (x_1 + x_2 + \ldots + x_n) + a_2 (x_1^2 + x_2^2 + \ldots + x_n^2)$$
$$+ \ldots + a_{n-1} (x_1^{n-1} + x_2^{n-1} + \ldots + x_n^{n-1})] \tag{9}$$

Equating expressions (8) and (9), we get an equation that should hold for any a_0, a_1, a_2, ..., a_{n-1}:

$$2\left(a_0 + \frac{a_2}{3} + \frac{a_4}{5} + \frac{a_6}{7} + \ldots\right) = C_n [na_0 + a_1 (x_1 + x_2 + \ldots + x_n)$$
$$+ a_2 (x_1^2 + x_2^2 + \ldots + x_n^2) + \ldots + a_{n-1} (x_1^{n-1} + x_2^{n-1} + \ldots + x_n^{n-1})]$$

Equate the coefficients of a_0, a_1, a_2, a_3, ..., a_{n-1} on the left and right sides of the equation:

$$\left. \begin{aligned} 2 &= C_n n \quad \text{or} \quad C_n = \frac{2}{n} \\ x_1 + x_2 + \ldots + x_n &= 0 \\ x_1^2 + x_2^2 + \ldots + x_n^2 &= \frac{2}{3C_n} = \frac{n}{3} \\ x_1^3 + x_2^3 + \ldots + x_n^3 &= 0 \\ x_1^4 + x_2^4 + \ldots + x_n^4 &= \frac{2}{5C_n} = \frac{n}{5} \\ \cdots \cdots \cdots \cdots & \end{aligned} \right\} \tag{10}$$

From these $n-1$ equations we find the abscissas x_1, x_2, ..., x_n. These solutions were found by Chebyshev for various values of n. The following solutions are those that he found for cases when the number of intermediate points n is equal to 3, 4, 5, 6, 7, 9:

Number of ordinates n	Coefficient C_n	Values of abscissas $x_1, x_2, \ldots, x_n$
3	$\dfrac{2}{3}$	$x_1 = -x_3 = 0.707107$ $x_2 = 0$
4	$\dfrac{1}{2}$	$x_1 = -x_4 = 0.794654$ $x_2 = -x_3 = 0.187592$
5	$\dfrac{2}{5}$	$x_1 = -x_5 = 0.832498$ $x_2 = -x_4 = 0.374541$ $x_3 = 0$
6	$\dfrac{1}{3}$	$x_1 = -x_6 = 0.866247$ $x_2 = -x_5 = 0.422519$ $x_3 = -x_4 = 0.266635$
7	$\dfrac{2}{7}$	$x_1 = -x_7 = 0.883862$ $x_2 = -x_6 = 0.529657$ $x_3 = -x_5 = 0.323912$ $x_4 = 0$
9	$\dfrac{2}{9}$	$x_1 = -x_9 = 0.911589$ $x_2 = -x_8 = 0.601019$ $x_3 = -x_7 = 0.528762$ $x_4 = -x_6 = 0.167906$ $x_5 = 0$

Thus, on the interval $[-1, 1]$, an integral can be approximated by the following *Chebyshev formula*:

$$\int_{-1}^{1} f(x)\, dx = \frac{2}{n}\left[f(x_1) + f(x_2) + \ldots + f(x_n) \right]$$

where n is one of the numbers 3, 4, 5, 6, 7 or 9, and $x_1, \ldots, x_n$ are the numbers given in the table. Here, n cannot be 8 or any number exceeding 9, for then the system of equations (10) yields imaginary roots.

When the given integral has limits of integration a and b, the Chebyshev formula takes on the form

$$\int_a^b f(x)\,dx = \frac{b-a}{n}\,[f(X_1)+f(X_2)+\cdots+f(X_n)]$$

where $X_i = \frac{b+a}{2} + \frac{b-a}{2}\,x_i$ $(i=1, 2, \ldots, n)$ and x_i have the values given in the table.

The following example illustrates the use of Chebyshev's approximation formula for calculating an integral.

Example. Evaluate $\int_1^2 \frac{dx}{x}$ $(= \ln 2)$.

Solution. First, by a change of variable, transform this integral into a new one with limits of integration -1 and 1:

$$x = \frac{1+2}{2} + \frac{2-1}{2}\,t = \frac{3}{2} + \frac{t}{2} = \frac{3+t}{2}$$

$$dx = \frac{dt}{2}$$

Then

$$\int_1^2 \frac{dx}{x} = \int_{-1}^1 \frac{dt}{3+t}$$

Compute the latter integral by Chebyshev's formula. taking $n=3$:

$$\int_{-1}^1 f(t)\,dt = \frac{2}{3}\,[f(0.707107)+f(0)+f(-0.707107)]$$

Since

$$f(0.707107) = \frac{1}{3+0.707107} = \frac{1}{3.707107} = 0.269752$$

$$f(0) = \frac{1}{3+0} = 0.333333$$

$$f(-0.707107) = \frac{1}{3-0.707107} = \frac{1}{2.292893} = 0.436130$$

we have

$$\int_{-1}^1 \frac{dt}{3+t} = \frac{2}{3}\,(0.269752+0.333333+0.436130)$$

$$= \frac{2}{3} \cdot 1.039215 = 0.692810 \approx 0.693$$

Comparing this result with the results of computation using the rectangular formulas, the trapezoidal rule, and Simpson's rule (see the example in the preceding section), we note that the result given by Chebyshev's formula (with three intermediate points) is in better agreement with the true value of the integral than the result obtained by the trapezoidal rule (with nine intermediate points).

The theory of approximation of integrals was further developed in the works of Academician A. N. Krylov (1863-1945).

11.10 INTEGRALS DEPENDENT ON A PARAMETER.
THE GAMMA FUNCTION

Differentiating integrals dependent on a parameter. Suppose we have an integral

$$I(\alpha) = \int_a^b f(x, \alpha)\, dx \tag{1}$$

in which the integrand is dependent upon some parameter α. If the parameter α varies, then the value of the definite integral will also vary. Thus the definite integral is a **function** of α; we can therefore denote it by $I(\alpha)$.

1. Suppose that $f(x, \alpha)$ and $f'_\alpha(x, \alpha)$ are continuous functions when

$$c \leqslant \alpha \leqslant d \quad \text{and} \quad a \leqslant x \leqslant b \tag{2}$$

Find the derivative of the integral with respect to the parameter α:

$$\lim_{\Delta\alpha \to 0} \frac{I(\alpha + \Delta\alpha) - I(\alpha)}{\Delta\alpha} = I'_\alpha(\alpha)$$

In finding this derivative we note that

$$\frac{I(\alpha + \Delta\alpha) - I(\alpha)}{\Delta\alpha} = \frac{1}{\Delta\alpha}\left[\int_a^b f(x, \alpha + \Delta\alpha)\, dx - \int_a^b f(x, \alpha)\, dx\right]$$

$$= \int_a^b \frac{f(x, \alpha + \Delta\alpha) - f(x, \alpha)}{\Delta\alpha}\, dx$$

Applying the Lagrange theorem to the integrand we have

$$\frac{f(x, \alpha + \Delta\alpha) - f(x, \alpha)}{\Delta\alpha} = f'_\alpha(x, \alpha + \theta\,\Delta\alpha)$$

where $0 < \theta < 1$. Since $f'_\alpha(x, \alpha)$ is continuous in the closed domain (2), we have

$$f'_\alpha(x, \alpha + \theta\,\Delta\alpha) = f'_\alpha(x, \alpha) + \varepsilon$$

where the quantity ε, which depends on x, α, $\Delta\alpha$, approaches zero as $\Delta\alpha \to 0$.

Thus,

$$\frac{I(\alpha+\Delta\alpha)-I(\alpha)}{\Delta\alpha} = \int_a^b [f_\alpha'(x,\alpha)+\varepsilon]\,dx = \int_a^b f_\alpha'(x,\alpha)\,dx + \int_a^b \varepsilon\,dx$$

Passing to the limit as $\Delta\alpha \to 0$, we have *

$$\lim_{\Delta\alpha \to 0} \frac{I(\alpha+\Delta\alpha)-I(\alpha)}{\Delta\alpha} = I_\alpha'(\alpha) = \int_a^b f_\alpha'(x,\alpha)\,dx$$

or

$$\left[\int_a^b f(x,\alpha)\,dx \right]_\alpha' = \int_a^b f_\alpha'(x,\alpha)\,dx$$

This formula is called the *Leibniz formula*.

2. Now suppose that in the integral (1) the *limits of integration a and b are functions of* α:

$$I(\alpha) = \Phi[\alpha, a(\alpha), b(\alpha)] = \int_{a(\alpha)}^{b(\alpha)} f(x,\alpha)\,dx \qquad (1')$$

$\Phi[\alpha, a(\alpha), b(\alpha)]$ is a composite function of α, and a and b are intermediate arguments. To find the derivative of $I(\alpha)$, apply the rule for differentiating a composite function of several variables (see Sec. 8.10):

$$I'(\alpha) = \frac{\partial\Phi}{\partial\alpha} + \frac{\partial\Phi}{\partial a}\frac{da}{d\alpha} + \frac{d\Phi}{\partial b}\frac{db}{d\alpha} \qquad (3)$$

By the theorem on the differentiation of a definite integral with respect to a variable upper limit (see Sec. 11.4) we get

$$\frac{\partial\Phi}{\partial b} = \frac{\partial}{\partial b}\int_a^b f(x,\alpha)\,dx = f[b(\alpha),\alpha]$$

$$\frac{\partial\Phi}{\partial a} = \frac{\partial}{\partial a}\int_a^b f(x,\alpha)\,dx = -\frac{\partial}{\partial a}\int_b^a f(x,\alpha)\,dx = -f[a(\alpha),\alpha]$$

---

* The integrand in the integral $I = \int_a^b \varepsilon\,d\alpha$ approaches zero as $\Delta\alpha \to 0$. From the fact that the integrand approaches zero at each point it does not always follow that the integral also approaches zero. However, in the given case, I approaches zero as $\Delta\alpha \to 0$. We accept this fact without proof.

Finally, to evaluate $\frac{\partial \Phi}{\partial \alpha}$ use the above-derived Leibniz formula:

$$\frac{\partial \Phi}{\partial \alpha} = \int\limits_a^b f_\alpha'(x, \alpha)\, dx$$

Substituting into (3) the expressions obtained for the derivatives, we have

$$I_\alpha'(\alpha) = \int\limits_{a(\alpha)}^{b(\alpha)} f_\alpha'(x, \alpha)\, dx + f\,[b(\alpha),\ \alpha]\,\frac{db}{d\alpha} - f\,[a(\alpha),\ \alpha]\,\frac{da}{d\alpha} \qquad (4)$$

Using the Leibniz formula it is possible to compute certain definite integrals.

Example. Evaluate the integral

$$I(\alpha) = \int\limits_0^\infty e^{-x}\,\frac{\sin \alpha x}{x}\, dx$$

Solution. First note that it is impossible to compute the integral directly, because the antiderivative of the function $e^{-x}\,\frac{\sin \alpha x}{x}$ is not expressible in terms of elementary functions. To compute this integral we shall consider it as a function of the parameter α. Then its derivative with respect to α is found from the above-derived Leibniz formula *:

$$I'(\alpha) = \int\limits_0^\infty \left[e^{-x}\,\frac{\sin \alpha x}{x} \right]_\alpha'\, dx = \int\limits_0^\infty e^{-x} \cos \alpha x\, dx$$

But the latter integral is readily evaluated by means of elementary functions; it is equal to $\frac{1}{1+\alpha^2}$. Therefore,

$$I'(\alpha) = \frac{1}{1+\alpha^2}$$

Integrating the identity obtained, we find $I(\alpha)$:

$$I(\alpha) = \arctan \alpha + C$$

We have C to determine now. To do this, we note that

$$I(0) = \int\limits_0^\infty e^{-x}\,\frac{\sin 0 \cdot x}{x}\, dx = \int\limits_0^\infty 0\, dx = 0$$

---

* Leibniz' formula was derived on the assumption that the limits of integration a and b are finite. However, in this case Leibniz' formula also holds, even though one of the limits of integration is equal to infinity. For the conditions under which differentiation of improper integrals with respect to a parameter is permissible. See G. M. Fikhtengolts, *Course of Differential and Integral Calculus*, Fizmatgiz, 1962, Vol. II, Ch. XIV, Sec. 3 (in Russian).

Besides, arctan $0 = 0$. Substituting into (5) $\alpha = 0$, we get

$$I(0) = \arctan 0 + C$$

whence $C = 0$. Hence, for any value of α we have $I(\alpha) = \arctan \alpha$, that is,

$$\int_0^\infty e^{-x} \frac{\sin \alpha x}{x} \, dx = \arctan \alpha$$

Example 2. The gamma function.

We consider an integral dependent on a parameter α,

$$\int_0^\infty x^{\alpha-1} e^{-x} \, dx \qquad (6)$$

and we will show that this improper integral exists (converges) for $\alpha > 0$. We represent it in the form of a sum

$$\int_0^\infty x^{\alpha-1} e^{-x} \, dx = \int_0^1 x^{\alpha-1} e^{-x} \, dx + \int_1^\infty x^{\alpha-1} e^{-x} \, dx$$

The first integral on the right converges, since

$$0 < \int_0^1 x^{\alpha-1} e^{-x} \, dx < \int_0^1 x^{\alpha-1} \, dx = \frac{1}{\alpha}$$

The second integral likewise converges. Indeed, let n be an integer such that $n > \alpha - 1$. Then clearly

$$0 < \int_1^\infty x^{\alpha-1} e^{-x} \, dx < \int_1^\infty x^n e^{-x} \, dx < \infty$$

Integrate the latter integral by parts noting that

$$\lim_{x \to +\infty} \frac{x^k}{e^x} = 0 \qquad (7)$$

for an arbitrary positive integer k. Thus, integral (6) defines a certain function α. This function is denoted by $\Gamma(\alpha)$ and is called the *gamma function*:

$$\Gamma(\alpha) = \int_0^\infty x^{\alpha-1} e^{-x} \, dx \qquad (8)$$

It is widely used in applied mathematics. Let us find the values of $\Gamma(\alpha)$ for integral α. For $\alpha = 1$ we have

$$\Gamma(1) = \int_0^\infty e^{-x} \, dx = 1 \qquad (9)$$

Let the integer $\alpha > 1$. We integrate by parts:

$$\Gamma(\alpha) = \int_0^\infty x^{\alpha-1} e^{-x} \, dx = -x^{\alpha-1} e^{-x} \Big|_0^\infty + (\alpha-1) \int_0^\infty x^{\alpha-2} e^{-x} \, dx$$

or, taking into account (7),

$$\Gamma(\alpha) = (\alpha - 1)\,\Gamma(\alpha - 1) \tag{10}$$

By (10) and (9), we find that for $\alpha = n$

$$\Gamma(n) = (n-1)! \tag{11}$$

11.11 INTEGRATION OF A COMPLEX FUNCTION OF A REAL VARIABLE

In Sec. 7.4 we defined a complex function $\tilde{f}(x) = u(x) + iv(x)$ of a real variable x and also its derivative $\tilde{f}'(x) = u'(x) + iv'(x)$.

Definition. A function $\tilde{F}(x) = U(x) + iV(x)$ is called an *antiderivative of a complex function of a real variable* $\tilde{f}(x)$ if

$$\tilde{F}'(x) = \tilde{f}(x) \tag{1}$$

that is, if

$$U'(x) + iV'(x) = u(x) + iv(x) \tag{2}$$

From (2) it follows that $U'(x) = u(x)$, $V'(x) = v(x)$, that is, $U(x)$ is an antiderivative of $u(x)$ and $V(x)$ is an antiderivative of $v(x)$.

It follows, from this definition and from the remark, that if $\tilde{F}(x) = U(x) + iV(x)$ is an antiderivative of the function $\tilde{f}(x)$, then any antiderivative of $\tilde{f}(x)$ is of the form $\tilde{F}(x) + C$, where C is an arbitrary complex constant. We will call the expression $\tilde{F}(x) + C$ the *indefinite integral of a complex function of a real variable* and we will write

$$\int \tilde{f}(x)\,dx = \int u(x)\,dx + i\int v(x)\,dx = \tilde{F}(x) + C \tag{3}$$

The *definite integral* of a complex function of a real variable, $f(x) = u(x) + iv(x)$, is defined as follows:

$$\int_a^b \tilde{f}(x)\,dx = \int_a^b u(x)\,dx + i\int_a^b v(x)\,dx \tag{4}$$

This definition does not contradict and is in full agreement with the definition of the definite integral as the limit of a sum.

Exercises on Chapter 11

1. Form the integral sum s_n and pass to the limit to compute the following definite integrals $\int_a^b x^2\,dx$. **Hint.** Divide the interval $[a, b]$ into n parts by the points $x_i = aq^i$ $(i = 0, 1, 2, \ldots, n)$, where $q = \sqrt[n]{\dfrac{b}{a}}$. **Ans.** $\dfrac{b^3 - a^3}{3}$.

28—2081

2. $\displaystyle\int_a^b \frac{dx}{x}$, where $0 < a < b$. *Ans.* $\ln \dfrac{b}{a}$. **Hint.** Divide the interval $[a, b]$ in the same way as in the preceding exercise.

3. $\displaystyle\int_a^b \sqrt{x}\ dx$. *Ans.* $\dfrac{2}{3}(b^{3/2} - a^{3/2})$. **Hint.** See Exercise 2.

4. $\displaystyle\int_a^b \sin x\ dx$. *Ans.* $\cos a - \cos b$.

Hint. First establish the following identity:

$$\sin a + \sin (a+h) + \sin (a+2h) + \ldots + \sin [a+(n-1)h]$$
$$= \frac{\cos (a-h) - \cos (a+nh)}{2 \sin h}$$

To do this, multiply and divide all the terms of the left side by $\sin h$ and replace the product of sines by the difference of cosines.

5. $\displaystyle\int_a^b \cos x\ dx$. *Ans.* $\sin b - \sin a$.

Using the Newton-Leibniz formula, compute the following definite integrals:

6. $\displaystyle\int_0^1 x^4\ dx$. *Ans.* $\dfrac{1}{5}$. **7.** $\displaystyle\int_0^1 e^x\ dx$. *Ans.* $e-1$. **8.** $\displaystyle\int_0^{\frac{\pi}{2}} \sin x\ dx$. *Ans.* 1.

9. $\displaystyle\int_0^1 \frac{dx}{1+x^2}$. *Ans.* $\dfrac{\pi}{4}$. **10.** $\displaystyle\int_0^{\frac{\sqrt{2}}{2}} \frac{dx}{\sqrt{1-x^2}}$. *Ans.* $\dfrac{\pi}{4}$. **11.** $\displaystyle\int_0^{\frac{\pi}{3}} \tan x\ dx$. *Ans.* $\ln 2$.

12. $\displaystyle\int_1^e \frac{dx}{x}$. *Ans.* 1. **13.** $\displaystyle\int_1^x \frac{dx}{x}$. *Ans.* $\ln |x|$. **14.** $\displaystyle\int_0^x \sin x\ dx$. *Ans.* $2 \sin^2 \dfrac{x}{2}$.

15. $\displaystyle\int_{\sqrt[3]{a}}^x x^2\ dx$. *Ans.* $\dfrac{x^3 - a}{3}$. **16.** $\displaystyle\int_1^2 \frac{dx}{2x-1}$. *Ans.* $\ln (2z - 1)$. **17.** $\displaystyle\int_0^{\frac{\pi}{2}} \cos^2 x\ dx$.

Ans. $\dfrac{\pi}{4}$. **18.** $\displaystyle\int_0^{\frac{\pi}{2}} \sin^2 x\ dx$. *Ans.* $\dfrac{\pi}{4}$.

Evaluate the following integrals applying the indicated substitutions:

19. $\displaystyle\int_0^{\frac{\pi}{2}} \sin x \cos^2 x\ dx$, $\cos x = t$. *Ans.* $\dfrac{1}{3}$. **20.** $\displaystyle\int_0^{\pi} \frac{dx}{3+2\cos x}$, $\tan \dfrac{x}{2} = t$.

Ans. $\dfrac{\pi}{\sqrt{5}}$. **21.** $\displaystyle\int_1^4 \dfrac{x\,dx}{\sqrt{2+4x}}$, $2+4x=t^2$. Ans. $\dfrac{3\sqrt{2}}{2}$. **22.** $\displaystyle\int_{-1}^1 \dfrac{dx}{(1+x^2)^2}$,

$x=\tan t$. Ans. $\dfrac{\pi}{4}+\dfrac{1}{2}$. **23.** $\displaystyle\int_1^5 \dfrac{\sqrt{x-1}}{x}\,dx$, $x-1=t^2$. Ans. $2\,(2-\arctan 2)$.

24. $\displaystyle\int_{\frac{3}{4}}^{\frac{4}{3}} \dfrac{dz}{z\,\sqrt{z^2+1}}$, $z=\dfrac{1}{x}$. Ans. $\ln\dfrac{3}{2}$. **25.** $\displaystyle\int_0^{\frac{\pi}{2}} \dfrac{\cos\varphi\,d\varphi}{6-5\sin\varphi+\sin^2\varphi}$, $\sin\varphi=t$.

Ans. $\ln\dfrac{4}{3}$.

Prove that **26.** $\displaystyle\int_0^1 x^m\,(1-x)^n\,dx=\int_0^1 x^n\,(1-x)^m\,dx$ $(m>0,\ \ n>0)$.

27. $\displaystyle\int_a^b f\,(x)\,dx=\int_a^b f\,(a+b-x)\,dx$. **28.** $\displaystyle\int_0^a f\,(x^2)\,dx=\dfrac{1}{2}\int_{-a}^a f\,(x^2)\,dx$.

Evaluate the following improper integrals:

29. $\displaystyle\int_0^1 \dfrac{x\,dx}{\sqrt{1-x^2}}$. Ans. 1. **30.** $\displaystyle\int_0^\infty e^{-x}\,dx$. Ans. 1. **31.** $\displaystyle\int_0^\infty \dfrac{dx}{a^2+x^2}$. Ans. $\dfrac{\pi}{2a}$ $(a>0)$.

32. $\displaystyle\int_0^1 \dfrac{dx}{\sqrt{1-x^2}}$. Ans. $\dfrac{\pi}{2}$. **33.** $\displaystyle\int_1^\infty \dfrac{dx}{x^5}$. Ans. $\dfrac{1}{4}$. **34.** $\displaystyle\int_0^1 \ln x\,dx$. Ans. -1.

35. $\displaystyle\int_0^\infty x\sin x\,dx$. Ans. The integral diverges. **36.** $\displaystyle\int_1^\infty \dfrac{dx}{\sqrt{x}}$. Ans. The integral

diverges. **37.** $\displaystyle\int_{-\infty}^{+\infty} \dfrac{dx}{x^2+2x+2}$. Ans. π. **38.** $\displaystyle\int_0^1 \dfrac{dx}{\sqrt[3]{x}}$. Ans. $\dfrac{3}{2}$. **39.** $\displaystyle\int_0^2 \dfrac{dx}{x^3}$. Ans. The

integral diverges. **40.** $\displaystyle\int_1^\infty \dfrac{dx}{x\,\sqrt{x^2-1}}$. Ans. $\dfrac{\pi}{2}$. **41.** $\displaystyle\int_{-1}^1 \dfrac{dx}{x^4}$. Ans. The integral di-

verges. **42.** $\displaystyle\int_0^\infty e^{-ax}\sin bx\,dx$ $(a>0)$. Ans. $\dfrac{b}{a^2+b^2}$. **43.** $\displaystyle\int_0^\infty e^{-ax}\cos bx\,dx$ $(a>0)$.

Ans. $\dfrac{a}{a^2+b^2}$.

Evaluate the following integrals approximately:

44 $\ln 5=\displaystyle\int_1^5 \dfrac{dx}{x}$ by the trapezoidal rule and by Simpson's rule $(n=12)$.

Ans. 1.6182 (by the trapezoidal rule); 1.6098 (by Simpson's rule).

45. $\int\limits_{1}^{11} x^3 \, dx$ by the trapezoidal rule and by Simpson's rule $(n = 10)$.

Ans. 3690, 3660. **46.** $\int\limits_{0}^{1} \sqrt{1 - x^3} \, dx$ by the trapezoidal rule $(n = 6)$. *Ans.* 0.8109.

47. $\int\limits_{1}^{3} \frac{dx}{2x - 1}$ by Simpson's rule $(n = 4)$. *Ans.* 0.8111. **48.** $\int\limits_{4}^{10} \log_{10} x \, dx$ by the trapezoidal rule and by Simpson's rule $(n = 10)$. *Ans.* 6.0656, 6.0896. **49.** Evaluate π from the relation $\frac{\pi}{4} = \int\limits_{0}^{1} \frac{dx}{1 + x^2}$ applying Simpson's rule $(n = 10)$.

Ans. 3.14159. **50.** $\int\limits_{0}^{\frac{\pi}{2}} \frac{\sin x}{x} \, dx$ by Simpson's rule $(n = 10)$. *Ans.* 1.371. **51.** Evaluate $\int\limits_{0}^{\infty} e^{-x} x^n \, dx$ for integral $n > 0$ by proceeding from the equation

$\int\limits_{0}^{\infty} e^{-\alpha x} \, dx = \frac{1}{\alpha}$ where $\alpha > 0$. *Ans.* $n!$ **52.** Proceeding from equation

$\int\limits_{0}^{\infty} \frac{dx}{x^2 + a} = \frac{\pi}{2 \sqrt{a}}$, evaluate the integral $\int\limits_{0}^{\infty} \frac{dx}{(x^2 + 1)^{n+1}}$. *Ans.* $\frac{\pi}{2} \frac{1 \cdot 3 \cdot 5 \ldots (2n - 1)}{2^n n!}$.

53. Evaluate the integral $\int\limits_{0}^{\infty} \frac{1 - e^{-\alpha x}}{x e^x} \, dx$. *Ans.* $\ln(1 + \alpha) \, (\alpha > -1)$. **54.** Utilizing the equation $\int\limits_{0}^{1} x^{n-1} \, dx = \frac{1}{n}$, compute the integral $\int\limits_{0}^{1} x^{n-1} (\ln x)^k \, dx$.

Ans. $(-1)^k \frac{k!}{n^{k+1}}$

CHAPTER 12

GEOMETRIC AND MECHANICAL APPLICATIONS
OF THE DEFINITE INTEGRAL

12.1 COMPUTING AREAS IN RECTANGULAR COORDINATES

If on the interval $[a, b]$ the function $f(x) \geqslant 0$, then, as we know from Sec. 11.2, the *area of a curvilinear trapezoid* bounded by the curve $y = f(x)$, the x-axis, and the straight lines $x = a$ and $x = b$ (Fig. 214) is

$$Q = \int_a^b f(x)\, dx \qquad (1)$$

If $f(x) \leqslant 0$ $[a, b]$, then the definite integral $\int_a^b f(x)\, dx$ is also $\leqslant 0$. It is equal, in absolute value, to the area Q corresponding to the curvilinear trapezoid:

$$-Q = \int_a^b f(x)\, dx$$

If $f(x)$ changes sign on the interval $[a, b]$ a finite number of times, then we break up the integral throughout $[a, b]$ into the sum of integrals over the subintervals. The integral will be positive on those subintervals where $f(x) \geqslant 0$, and negative where $f(x) \leqslant 0$. The integral over the entire interval will yield the difference of the areas above and below the x-axis (Fig. 232). To find the sum of the areas in the ordinary sense, one has to find the sum of the absolute values

Fig. 232

of the integrals over the above-indicated subintervals or compute the integral

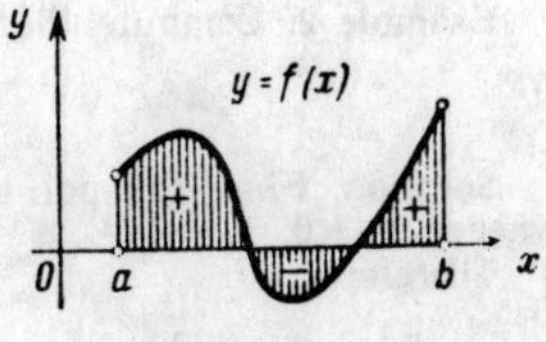

$$Q = \int_a^b |f(x)|\, dx$$

Example 1. Compute the area Q bounded by the **sine curve** $y = \sin x$ and the x-axis, for $0 \leqslant x \leqslant 2\pi$ (Fig. 233).

Solution. Since $\sin x \geqslant 0$ when $0 \leqslant x \leqslant \pi$ and $\sin x \leqslant 0$ when $\pi < x \leqslant 2\pi$, we have

$$Q = \int_0^\pi \sin x \, dx + \left| \int_\pi^{2\pi} \sin x \, dx \right| = \int_0^{2\pi} |\sin x| \, dx$$

$$\int_0^\pi \sin x \, dx = -\cos x \Big|_0^\pi = -(\cos \pi - \cos 0) = -(-1-1) = 2$$

$$\int_\pi^{2\pi} \sin x \, dx = -\cos x \Big|_\pi^{2\pi} = -(\cos 2\pi - \cos \pi) = -2$$

Consequently, $Q = 2 + |-2| = 4$.

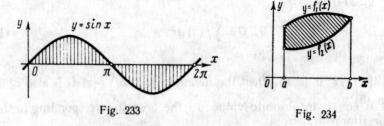

Fig. 233   Fig. 234

If one needs to compute the area bounded by the curves $y = f_1(x)$, $y = f_2(x)$ and the ordinates $x = a$, $x = b$, then provided $f_1(x) \geqslant f_2(x)$ we will obviously have (Fig. 234)

$$Q = \int_a^b f_1(x) \, dx - \int_a^b f_2(x) \, dx = \int_a^b [f_1(x) - f_2(x)] \, dx \qquad (2)$$

Example 2. Compute the area bounded by the curves (Fig. 235)

$$y = \sqrt{x} \quad \text{and} \quad y = x^2$$

Solution. Find the points of intersection of the curves: $\sqrt{x} = x^2$, $x = x^4$, whence $x_1 = 0$, $x_2 = 1$.
Therefore,

$$Q = \int_0^1 \sqrt{x} \, dx - \int_0^1 x^2 \, dx = \int_0^1 (\sqrt{x} - x^2) \, dx = \frac{2}{3} x^{3/2} \Big|_0^1 - \frac{x^3}{3} \Big|_0^1 = \frac{2}{3} - \frac{1}{3} = \frac{1}{3}$$

Now let us compute the area of the curvilinear trapezoid bounded by a curve represented by parametric equations (Fig. 236):

$$x = \varphi(t), \quad y = \psi(t) \qquad (3)$$

where $\alpha \leqslant t \leqslant \beta$ and $\varphi(\alpha) = a$, $\varphi(\beta) = b$. Let equations (3) define some function $y = f(x)$ on the interval $[a, b]$ and, consequently, the area of the curvilinear trapezoid may be computed from the formula

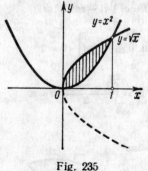

$$Q = \int_a^b f(x)\,dx = \int_a^b y\,dx$$

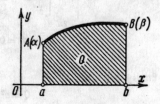

Fig. 235   Fig. 236

Change the variable in this integral:

$$x = \varphi(t), \quad dx = \varphi'(t)\,dt$$

From (3) we have

$$y = f(x) = f[\varphi(t)] = \psi(t)$$

Consequently,

$$Q = \int_\alpha^\beta \psi(t)\,\varphi'(t)\,dt \qquad (4)$$

This is the formula for computing the area of a curvilinear trapezoid bounded by a curve represented parametrically.

Example 3. Compute the area of a region bounded by the ellipse

$$x = a \cos t, \quad y = b \sin t$$

Solution. Compute the area of the upper half of the ellipse and double it. Here, x varies from $-a$ to $+a$, and so t varies between π and 0,

$$Q = 2 \int_\pi^0 (b \sin t)(-a \sin t\,dt) = -2ab \int_\pi^0 \sin^2 t\,dt = 2ab \int_0^\pi \sin^2 t\,dt$$

$$= 2ab \int_0^\pi \frac{1-\cos 2t}{2}\,dt = 2ab \left[\frac{t}{2} - \frac{\sin 2t}{4} \right]_0^\pi = \pi ab$$

Example 4. Compute the area bounded by the x-axis and an arch of the cycloid

$$x = a(t - \sin t), \quad y = a(1 - \cos t)$$

Solution. The variation of x from 0 to $2\pi a$ corresponds to the variation of t from 0 to 2π.

From (4) we have

$$Q = \int_0^{2\pi} a\,(1-\cos t)\,a\,(1-\cos t)\,dt = a^2 \int_0^{2\pi} (1-\cos t)^2\,dt$$

$$= a^2 \left[\int_0^{2\pi} dt - 2 \int_0^{2\pi} \cos t\,dt + \int_0^{2\pi} \cos^2 t\,dt \right]$$

$$\int_0^{2\pi} dt = 2\pi, \quad \int_0^{2\pi} \cos t\,dt = 0, \quad \int_0^{2\pi} \cos^2 t\,dt = \int_0^{2\pi} \frac{1+\cos 2t}{2}\,dt = \pi$$

We finally get

$$Q = a^2\,(2\pi + \pi) = 3\pi a^2$$

12.2 THE AREA OF A CURVILINEAR SECTOR IN POLAR COORDINATES

Suppose in a polar coordinate system we have a curve given by the equation

$$\rho = f(\theta)$$

where $f(\theta)$ is a continuous function for $\alpha \leqslant \theta \leqslant \beta$.

Let us determine the area of the sector OAB bounded by the curve $\rho = f(\theta)$ and by the radius vectors $\theta = \alpha$ and $\theta = \beta$.

Divide the given area by radius vectors $\theta_0 = \alpha$, $\theta = \theta_1$, ..., $\theta_n = \beta$ into n parts. Denote by $\Delta\theta_1$, $\Delta\theta_2$, ..., $\Delta\theta_n$ the angles between the radius vectors that we have drawn (Fig. 237).

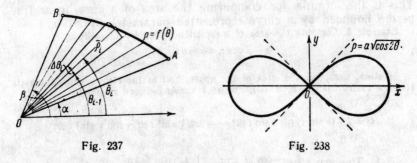

Fig. 237   Fig. 238

Denote by $\bar{\rho}_i$ the length of a radius vector corresponding to some angle $\bar{\theta}_i$ between θ_{i-1} and θ_i.

Let us consider the circular sector with radius $\bar{\rho}_i$ and central angle $\Delta\theta_i$. Its area will be

$$\Delta Q_i = \frac{1}{2}\bar{\rho}_i^2 \Delta\theta_i$$

The sum

$$Q_n = \frac{1}{2} \sum_{i=1}^{n} \overline{\rho_i^2} \, \Delta\theta_i = \frac{1}{2} \sum_{i=1}^{n} [f(\overline{\theta}_i)]^2 \, \Delta\theta_i$$

will yield the area of the "step-like" sector.

Since this sum is an integral sum of the function $\rho^2 = [f(\theta)]^2$ on the interval $\alpha \leqslant \theta \leqslant \beta$, its limit, as $\max \Delta\theta_i \to 0$, is the definite integral

$$\frac{1}{2} \int_{\alpha}^{\beta} \rho^2 \, d\theta$$

It is not dependent on which radius vector $\overline{\rho}_i$ we take inside the angle $\Delta\theta_i$. It is natural to consider this limit the sought-for area of the figure *.

Thus, the area of the sector OAB is

$$Q = \frac{1}{2} \int_{\alpha}^{\beta} \rho^2 \, d\theta \tag{1}$$

or

$$Q = \frac{1}{2} \int_{\alpha}^{\beta} [f(\theta)]^2 \, d\theta \tag{1'}$$

Example. Compute the area bounded by the lemniscate $\rho = a\sqrt{\cos 2\theta}$ (Fig. 238).

Solution. The radius vector will describe one fourth of the sought-for area if θ varies between 0 and $\frac{\pi}{4}$:

$$\frac{1}{4} Q = \frac{1}{2} \int_{0}^{\frac{\pi}{4}} \rho^2 \, d\theta = \frac{1}{2} a^2 \int_{0}^{\frac{\pi}{4}} \cos 2\theta \, d\theta = \frac{a^2}{2} \frac{\sin 2\theta}{2} \Big|_{0}^{\frac{\pi}{4}} = \frac{a^2}{4}$$

Hence

$$Q = a^2$$

12.3 THE ARC LENGTH OF A CURVE

1. The arc length of a curve in rectangular coordinates. Let a curve be given by the equation $y = f(x)$ in rectangular coordinates in a plane.

Let us find the length of the arc AB of this curve between the vertical straight lines $x = a$ and $x = b$ (Fig. 239).

---

* We could show that this determination of the area does not contradict that given earlier. In other words, if one computes the area of a curvilinear sector by means of curvilinear trapezoids, the result will be the same.

The definition of arc length was given in Sec. 6.1. Let us recall that definition. On an arc AB take points A, M_1, M_2, $\ldots$, M_i, $\ldots$, B with abscissas $x_0 = a$, x_1, x_2, $\ldots$, x_i, $\ldots$, $x_n = b$ and

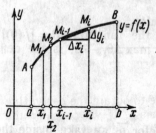

draw chords AM_1, M_1M_2, $\ldots$, $M_{n-1}B$ whose lengths we shall denote by Δs_1, Δs_2, $\ldots$, Δs_n, respectively. This gives the broken line $AM_1M_2\ldots M_{n-1}B$ inscribed in the arc $\widehat{AB}$. The length of the broken line is

$$s_n = \sum_{i=1}^{n} \Delta s_i$$

Fig. 239

The *length s of the arc AB* is the limit which the length of the inscribed broken line approaches when the length of its greatest segment approaches zero:

$$s = \lim_{\max \Delta s_i \to 0} \sum_{i=1}^{n} \Delta s_i \tag{1}$$

We shall now prove that if on the interval $a \leqslant x \leqslant b$ the function $f(x)$ and its derivative $f'(x)$ are continuous, then this limit exists. At the same time we shall specify a technique for computing the arc length.

We introduce the notation

$$\Delta y_i = f(x_i) - f(x_{i-1})$$

Then

$$\Delta s_i = \sqrt{(\Delta x_i)^2 + (\Delta y_i)^2} = \sqrt{1 + \left(\frac{\Delta y_i}{\Delta x_i}\right)^2}\,\Delta x_i$$

By Lagrange's theorem we have

$$\frac{\Delta y_i}{\Delta x_i} = \frac{f(x_i) - f(x_{i-1})}{x_i - x_{i-1}} = f'(\xi_i)$$

where

$$x_{i-1} < \xi_i < x_i$$

Hence,

$$\Delta s_i = \sqrt{1 + [f'(\xi_i)]^2}\,\Delta x_i$$

Thus, the length of an inscribed broken line is

$$s_n = \sum_{i=1}^{n} \sqrt{1 + [f'(\xi_i)]^2}\,\Delta x_i$$

It is given that $f'(x)$ is continuous; hence, the function $\sqrt{1 + [f'(x)]^2}$ is also continuous. Therefore, this integral sum has a limit that is equal to a definite integral:

$$s = \lim_{\max \Delta x_i \to 0} \sum_{i=1}^{n} \sqrt{1 + [f'(\xi_i)]^2}\, \Delta x_i = \int_a^b \sqrt{1 + [f'(x)]^2}\, dx$$

We thus have a formula for computing the arc length:

$$s = \int_a^b \sqrt{1 + [f'(x)]^2}\, dx = \int_a^b \sqrt{1 + \left(\frac{dy}{dx}\right)^2}\, dx \qquad (2)$$

Note 1. Using this formula, it is possible to obtain the derivative of the arc length with respect to the abscissa. If we consider the upper limit of integration as variable and denote it by x (we shall not change the variable of integration), then the arc length s will be a function of x:

$$s(x) = \int_a^x \sqrt{1 + \left(\frac{dy}{dx}\right)^2}\, dx$$

Differentiating this integral with respect to the upper limit, we obtain

$$\frac{ds}{dx} = \sqrt{1 + \left(\frac{dy}{dx}\right)^2} \qquad (3)$$

This formula was derived in Sec. 6.1 on certain other assumptions.

Example 1. Determine the circumference of the circle

$$x^2 + y^2 = r^2$$

Solution. First compute the length of a fourth part of the circumference lying in the first quadrant. Then the equation of the arc AB will be

$$y = \sqrt{r^2 - x^2}$$

whence

$$\frac{dy}{dx} = -\frac{x}{\sqrt{r^2 - x^2}}$$

Consequently,

$$\frac{1}{4}\, s = \int_0^r \sqrt{1 + \frac{x^2}{r^2 - x^2}}\, dx = \int_0^r \frac{r}{\sqrt{r^2 - x^2}}\, dx = r \arcsin \frac{x}{r}\Big|_0^r = r\, \frac{\pi}{2}$$

The length of the circumference is $s = 2\pi r$.

Let us now find the arc length of a curve when the equation of the curve is represented in parametric form:

$$x = \varphi(t), \quad y = \psi(t) \quad (\alpha \leqslant t \leqslant \beta) \qquad (4)$$

where $\varphi(t)$ and $\psi(t)$ are continuous functions with continuous derivatives, and $\varphi'(t)$ does not vanish in the given interval. In this case, equations (4) define a function $y = f(x)$ which is continuous and has a continuous derivative:

$$\frac{dy}{dx} = \frac{\psi'(t)}{\varphi'(t)}$$

Let $a = \varphi(\alpha)$, $b = \varphi(\beta)$. Then substituting in the integral (2)

$$x = \varphi(t)$$
$$dx = \varphi'(t)\,dt$$

we have

$$s = \int_{\alpha}^{\beta} \sqrt{1 + \left[\frac{\psi'(t)}{\varphi'(t)}\right]^2}\,\varphi'(t)\,dt, \text{ or } s = \int_{\alpha}^{\beta} \sqrt{[\varphi'(t)]^2 + [\psi'(t)]^2}\,dt \quad (5)$$

Note 2. It may be proved that formula (5) holds also for curves that are crossed by vertical lines in more than one point (in particular, for closed curves), provided that both derivatives $\varphi'(t)$ and $\psi'(t)$ are continuous at all points of the curve.

Example 2. Compute the length of the astroid:

$$x = a\cos^3 t, \quad y = a\sin^3 t$$

Solution. Since the curve is symmetric about both coordinate axes, we shall first compute the length of a fourth part of it located in the first quadrant. We find

$$\frac{dx}{dt} = -3a\cos^2 t \sin t$$

$$\frac{dy}{dt} = 3a\sin^2 t \cos t$$

The parameter t will vary from 0 to $\frac{\pi}{2}$. Hence

$$\frac{1}{4}\,s = \int_0^{\frac{\pi}{2}} \sqrt{9a^2\cos^4 t \sin^2 t + 9a^2\sin^4 t \cos^2 t}\,dt = 3a \int_0^{\frac{\pi}{2}} \sqrt{\cos^2 t \sin^2 t}\,dt$$

$$= 3a \int_0^{\frac{\pi}{2}} \sin t \cos t\,dt = 3a\,\frac{\sin^2 t}{2}\bigg|_0^{\frac{\pi}{2}} = \frac{3a}{2}, \quad s = 6a$$

Note 3. If a **space** curve is represented by the parametric equations

$$x = \varphi(t), \quad y = \psi(t), \quad z = \chi(t) \quad (6)$$

where $\alpha \leqslant t \leqslant \beta$ (see Sec. 9.1), then the length of its arc is defined (in the same way as for a plane arc) as the limit which the length of an inscribed broken line approaches when the length of the greatest segment approaches zero. If the functions $\varphi(t)$, $\psi(t)$, and $\chi(t)$ are continuous and have continuous derivatives on an interval $[\alpha, \beta]$, then the curve has a definite length (that is, it has the above-mentioned limit) which is computed from the formula

$$s = \int_\alpha^\beta \sqrt{[\varphi'(t)]^2 + [\psi'(t)]^2 + [\chi'(t)]^2}\, dt \qquad (7)$$

This result we accept without proof.

Example 3. Compute the arc length of the helix

$$x = a \cos t, \quad y = a \sin t, \quad z = amt$$

as t varies from 0 to 2π.

Solution. From the given equations we have

$$dx = -a \sin t\, dt, \quad dy = a \cos t\, dt, \quad dz = am\, dt$$

Substituting into formula (7), we have

$$s = \int_0^{2\pi} \sqrt{a^2 \sin^2 t + a^2 \cos^2 t + a^2 m^2}\, dt = a \int_0^{2\pi} \sqrt{1+m^2}\, dt = 2\pi a \sqrt{1+m^2}$$

2. The arc length of a curve in polar coordinates. Given (in polar coordinates) the equation of the curve

$$\rho = f(\theta) \qquad (8)$$

where ρ is the radius vector and θ is the vectorial (polar) angle.

Let us write the formulas for passing from polar coordinates to Cartesian coordinates:

$$x = \rho \cos \theta, \quad y = \rho \sin \theta$$

If in place of ρ we put its expression (8) in terms of θ, we get the equations

$$x = f(\theta) \cos \theta, \quad y = f(\theta) \sin \theta$$

These equations may be regarded as the parametric equations of the curve and we can apply formula (5) for computing the arc length. To do this, find the derivatives of x and y with respect to the parameter θ:

$$\frac{dx}{d\theta} = f'(\theta) \cos \theta - f(\theta) \sin \theta$$

$$\frac{dy}{d\theta} = f'(\theta) \sin \theta + f(\theta) \cos \theta$$

Then

$$\left(\frac{dx}{d\theta}\right)^2 + \left(\frac{dy}{d\theta}\right)^2 = [f'(\theta)]^2 + [f(\theta)]^2 = \rho'^2 + \rho^2$$

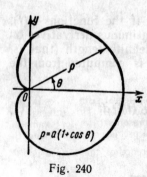

$\rho = a(1 + \cos \theta)$

Fig. 240

Hence,

$$s = \int_{\theta_0}^{\theta} \sqrt{\rho'^2 + \rho^2}\, d\theta$$

Example 4. Find the length of the cardioid

$$\rho = a(1 + \cos \theta)$$

(Fig. 240).

Varying the vectorial angle θ from 0 to π, we get half the sought-for length. Here, $\rho' = -a \sin \theta$. Hence,

$$s = 2 \int_0^{\pi} \sqrt{a^2 (1 + \cos \theta)^2 + a^2 \sin^2 \theta}\, d\theta$$

$$= 2a \int_0^{\pi} \sqrt{2 + 2 \cos \theta}\, d\theta$$

$$= 4a \int_0^{\pi} \cos \frac{\theta}{2}\, d\theta = 8a \sin \frac{\theta}{2} \Big|_0^{\pi} = 8a$$

Example 5. Compute the length of the ellipse

$$\left. \begin{array}{l} x = a \cos t \\ y = b \sin t \end{array} \right\} \quad 0 \leqslant t \leqslant 2\pi$$

assuming that $a > b$.

Solution. We take advantage of formula (5), first computing $\frac{1}{4}$ the arc length; that is, the length of the arc that corresponds to a variation of the parameter from $t = 0$ to $t = \frac{\pi}{2}$:

$$\frac{s}{4} = \int_0^{\frac{\pi}{2}} \sqrt{a^2 \sin^2 t + b^2 \cos^2 t}\, dt$$

$$= \int_0^{\frac{\pi}{2}} \sqrt{a^2 (1 - \cos^2 t) + b^2 \cos^2 t}\, dt = \int_0^{\frac{\pi}{2}} \sqrt{a^2 - (a^2 - b^2) \cos^2 t}\, dt$$

$$= a \int_0^{\frac{\pi}{2}} \sqrt{1 - \frac{a^2 - b^2}{a^2} \cos^2 t}\, dt = a \int_0^{\frac{\pi}{2}} \sqrt{1 - k^2 \cos^2 t}\, dt$$

where $k = \dfrac{\sqrt{a^2 - b^2}}{a} < 1$. Hence,

$$s = 4a \int_0^{\frac{\pi}{2}} \sqrt{1 - k^2 \cos^2 t}\; dt$$

The only thing that remains is to compute the last integral. But we know that it is not expressible in elementary functions (see Sec. 10.14). This integral can be computed only by approximate methods (by Simpson's rule, for example).

For instance, if the semi-major axis of an ellipse is equal to 5 and the semi-minor axis is 4, then $k = \dfrac{3}{5}$, and the circumference of the ellipse is

$$s = 4 \cdot 5 \int_0^{\frac{\pi}{2}} \sqrt{1 - \left(\frac{3}{5}\right)^2 \cos^2 t}\; dt$$

Computing this integral by Simpson's rule $\left(\text{by dividing the interval}\; \left[0, \dfrac{\pi}{2}\right]\right.$ into four parts$\Big)$ we get an approximate value of the integral:

$$\int_0^{\frac{\pi}{2}} \sqrt{1 - \frac{3}{5} \cos^2 t}\; dt \approx 1.298$$

and so the length of the arc of the entire ellipse is approximately equal to $s \approx 25.96$ units of length.

12.4 COMPUTING THE VOLUME OF A SOLID FROM THE AREAS OF PARALLEL SECTIONS (VOLUMES BY SLICING)

Suppose we have some solid T. Let us assume that we know the area of any section of this solid made by a plane perpendicular to the x-axis (Fig. 241). This area will depend on the position of the cutting plane; that is, it will be a **function of** x:

$$Q = Q(x)$$

We assume that $Q(x)$ is a continuous function of x and calculate the volume of the body.

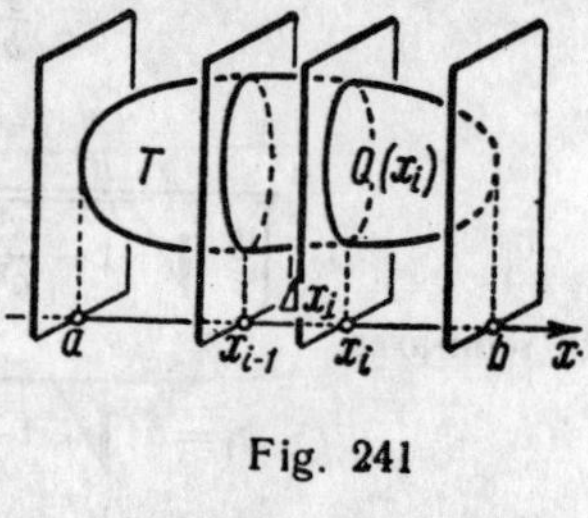

Draw the planes $x = x_0 = a$, $x = x_1$, $x = x_2$, ..., $x = x_n = b$.

Fig. 241

These planes will cut the solid up into layers (slices).

In each subinterval $x_{i-1} \leqslant x \leqslant x_i$ we choose an arbitrary point ξ_i and for each value $i = 1, 2, ..., n$ we construct a cylindrical body, the generatrix of which is parallel to the x-axis, while the directrix is the boundary of the slice of the solid T made by the plane $x = \xi_i$.

The volume of such an elementary cylinder, the area of the base of which is

$$Q(\xi_i) \; (x_{i-1} \leqslant \xi_i \leqslant x_i)$$

and the altitude Δx_i, is

$$Q(\xi_i)\,\Delta x_i$$

The volume of all the cylinders will be

$$v_n = \sum_{i=1}^{n} Q(\xi_i)\,\Delta x_i$$

The limit of this sum as $\max \Delta x_i \to 0$ (if it exists) is the volume of the given solid:

$$v = \lim_{\max \Delta x_i \to 0} \sum_{i=1}^{n} Q(\xi_i)\,\Delta x_i$$

Since v_n is obviously the integral sum of the continuous function $Q(x)$ on the interval $a \leqslant x \leqslant b$, the indicated limit exists and is expressed by the definite integral

$$v = \int_a^b Q(x)\,dx \qquad\qquad (1)$$

Example. Compute the volume of the triaxial ellipsoid (Fig. 242).

$$\frac{x^2}{a^2} + \frac{y^2}{b^2} + \frac{z^2}{c^2} = 1$$

Solution. In a section of the ellipsoid made by a plane parallel to the yz-plane and at a distance x from it, we have the ellipse

$$\frac{y^2}{b^2} + \frac{z^2}{c^2} = 1 - \frac{x^2}{a^2}$$

or

$$\frac{y^2}{\left[b\sqrt{1 - \dfrac{x^2}{a^2}} \right]^2} + \frac{z^2}{\left[c\sqrt{1 - \dfrac{x^2}{a^2}} \right]^2} = 1$$

with semi-axes

$$b_1 = b\sqrt{1 - \frac{x^2}{a^2}}, \qquad c_1 = c\sqrt{1 - \frac{x^2}{a^2}}$$

But the area of such an ellipse is $\pi b_1 c_1$. (See example 3, Sec. 12.1).

Therefore,

$$Q(x) = \pi bc \left(1 - \frac{x^2}{a^2} \right)$$

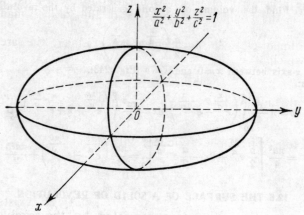

Fig. 242

The volume of the ellipsoid will be

$$v = \pi bc \int\limits_{-a}^{a} \left(1 - \frac{x^2}{a^2}\right) dx = \pi bc \left(x - \frac{x^3}{3a^2}\right)\Big|_{-a}^{a} = \frac{4}{3}\,\pi abc$$

In the particular case, $a = b = c$, the ellipsoid turns into a sphere, and we have

$$v = \frac{4}{3}\,\pi a^3$$

12.5 THE VOLUME OF A SOLID OF REVOLUTION

Let us consider a solid generated by the revolution, about the x-axis, of a curvilinear trapezoid $aABb$ bounded by the curve $y = f(x)$, the x-axis, and the lines $x = a$, $x = b$.

In this case, an arbitrary section of the solid made by a plane perpendicular to the x-axis is a circle of area

$$Q = \pi y^2 = \pi\,[f(x)]^2$$

Applying the general formula for computing a volume [(1), Sec. 12.4], we get a formula for calculating the volume of a **solid of revolution:**

$$v = \pi \int\limits_{a}^{b} y^2\,dx = \pi \int\limits_{a}^{b} [f(x)]^2\,dx$$

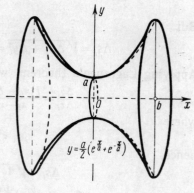

$$y = \frac{a}{2}\left(e^{\frac{x}{a}} + e^{-\frac{x}{a}}\right)$$

Fig. 243

Example. Find the volume of a solid generated by the revolution of the catenary

$$y = \frac{a}{2}\left(e^{\frac{x}{a}} + e^{-\frac{x}{a}}\right)$$

about the x-axis between $x = 0$ and $x = b$ (Fig. 243).
Solution.

$$v = \pi \frac{a^2}{4} \int_0^b \left(e^{\frac{x}{a}} + e^{-\frac{x}{a}}\right)^2 dx = \frac{\pi a^2}{4} \int_0^b \left(e^{\frac{2x}{a}} + 2 + e^{-\frac{2x}{a}}\right) dx$$

$$= \frac{\pi a^2}{4} \left[\frac{a}{2} e^{\frac{2x}{a}} + 2x - \frac{a}{2} e^{-\frac{2x}{a}}\right]_0^b = \frac{\pi a^3}{8}\left(e^{\frac{2b}{a}} - e^{-\frac{2b}{a}}\right) + \frac{\pi a^2 b}{2}$$

12.6 THE SURFACE OF A SOLID OF REVOLUTION

Suppose we have a surface generated by the revolution of a curve $y = f(x)$ about the x-axis. Let us determine the area of this

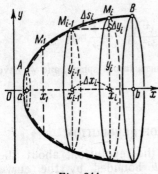

surface on the interval $a \leqslant x \leqslant b$. We take the function $f(x)$ to be continuous and to have a continuous derivative at all points of the interval $[a, b]$.

As in Sec. 12.3, draw the chords AM_1, M_1M_2, ..., $M_{n-1}B$, whose lengths are denoted by Δs_1, Δs_2, ..., Δs_n (Fig. 244).

Each chord of length Δs_i ($i = 1, 2, \ldots, n$) describes (in the process of revolution) a truncated cone whose surface ΔP_i is

Fig. 244

$$\Delta P_i = 2\pi \frac{y_{i-1} + y_i}{2} \Delta s_i$$

But

$$\Delta s_i = \sqrt{\overline{\Delta x_i^2 + \Delta y_i^2}} = \sqrt{1 + \left(\frac{\Delta y_i}{\Delta x_i}\right)^2} \, \Delta x_i$$

Applying Lagrange's theorem, we get

$$\frac{\Delta y_i}{\Delta x_i} = \frac{f(x_i) - f(x_{i-1})}{x_i - x_{i-1}} \equiv f'(\xi_i)$$

where

$$x_{i-1} < \xi_i < x_i$$

hence,

$$\Delta s_i = \sqrt{1 + f'^2(\xi_i)} \, \Delta x_i$$

$$\Delta P_i = 2\pi \frac{y_{i-1} + y_i}{2} \sqrt{1 + f'^2(\xi_i)} \, \Delta x_i$$

The surface described by the broken line will be equal to the sum

$$P_n = 2\pi \sum_{i=1}^{n} \frac{y_{i-1}+y_i}{2} \sqrt{1+f'^2(\xi_i)}\, \Delta x_i$$

or the sum

$$P_n = \pi \sum_{i=1}^{n} [f(x_{i-1})+f(x_i)] \sqrt{1+f'^2(\xi_i)}\, \Delta x_i \qquad (1)$$

extended over all segments of the broken line. The limit of this sum, when the largest segment Δs_i approaches zero, is called the *area of the surface of revolution* under consideration. The sum (1) is not the integral sum of the function

$$2\pi f(x) \sqrt{1+f'(x)^2} \qquad (2)$$

because the term corresponding to the interval $[x_{i-1}, x_i]$ involves several points of this interval x_{i-1}, x_i, ξ_i. But it is possible to prove that the limit of the sum (1) is equal to the limit of the integral sum of function (2); that is,

$$P = \lim_{\max \Delta x_i \to 0} \pi \sum_{i=1}^{n} [f(x_{i-1})+f(x_i)] \sqrt{1+[f'(\xi_i)]^2}\, \Delta x_i$$

$$= \lim_{\max \Delta x_i \to 0} \pi \sum_{i=1}^{n} 2f(\xi_1) \sqrt{1+[f'(\xi_i)]^2}\, \Delta x_i$$

or

$$P = 2\pi \int_{a}^{b} f(x) \sqrt{1+f'^2(x)}\, dx \qquad (3)$$

Example. Determine the surface of a paraboloid generated by revolution about the x-axis of an arc of the parabola $y^2 = 2px$, which corresponds to the variation of x from $x=0$ to $x=a$:

Solution.

$$y = \sqrt{2px}, \quad y' = \frac{\sqrt{2p}}{2\sqrt{x}}, \quad \sqrt{1+y'^2} = \sqrt{1+\frac{2p}{4x}} = \sqrt{\frac{2x+p}{2x}}$$

By (3) we have

$$P = 2\pi \int_{0}^{a} \sqrt{2px}\, \sqrt{\frac{2x+p}{2x}}\, dx = 2\pi \sqrt{p} \int_{0}^{a} \sqrt{2x+p}\, dx$$

$$= 2\pi \sqrt{p}\, \frac{2}{3}(2x+p)^{3/2}\, \frac{1}{2}\Big|_{0}^{a} = \frac{2\pi \sqrt{p}}{3}\,[(2a+p)^{3/2}-p^{3/2}]$$

12.7 COMPUTING WORK BY THE DEFINITE INTEGRAL

Suppose a material point M is moving in a straight line Os under a force F, and the direction of the force coincides with the direction of motion. It is required to find the work performed by the force F as the point M is moved from $s=a$ to $s=b$.

(1) If the force F is constant, then the work A is expressed by the product of the force F by the path length:

$$A = F(b-a)$$

(2) Let us assume that the force F is constantly varying, depending on the position of the material point; that is to say, it is a function $F(s)$ continuous on the interval $a \leqslant s \leqslant b$.

Divide the interval $[a, b]$ into n arbitrary parts of length

$$\Delta s_1, \ \Delta s_2, \ \ldots, \ \Delta s_n$$

Then in each subinterval $[s_{i-1}, s_i]$ choose an arbitrary point ξ_i and replace the work of the force $F(s)$ along the path Δs_i $(i = 1, 2, \ldots, n)$ by the product

$$F(\xi_i) \Delta s_i$$

This means that within the limits of each subinterval we take the force F to be constant: we assume $F = F(\xi_i)$. Here, the expression $F(\xi_i) \Delta s_i$ will yield an approximate value of the work done by the force F over the path Δs_i (for a sufficiently small Δs_i), and the sum

$$A_n = \sum_{i=1}^{n} F(\xi_i) \Delta s_i$$

will be an approximate expression of the work of the force F over the interval $[a, b]$.

Obviously, A_n is an integral sum of the function $F = F(s)$ on the interval $[a, b]$. The limit of this sum as $\max(\Delta s_i) \to 0$ exists and expresses the work of the force $F(s)$ over the path from $s=a$ to $s=b$:

$$A = \int_a^b F(s)\,ds \tag{1}$$

Example 1. The compression S of a helical spring is proportional to the applied force F. Compute the work of the force F when the spring is compressed 5 cm, if a force of one kilogram is required to compress it 1 cm (Fig. 245).

Solution. It is given that the force F and the distance covered S are connected by the relation $F = kS$, where k is a constant.

Let us express S in metres and F in kilograms. When $S = 0.01$, $F = 1$, that is, $1 = k \cdot 0.01$, whence $k = 100$, $F = 100S$.

By (1) we have

$$A = \int\limits_0^{0.05} 100S\,dS = 100\,\frac{S^2}{2}\Big|_0^{0.05} = 0.125 \text{ kilogram-metre}$$

Example 2. The force F with which an electric charge e_1 repulses another charge e_2 (of the same sign) at a distance of r is expressed by the formula

$$F = k\,\frac{e_1 e_2}{r^2}$$

where k is a constant.

Determine the work done by a force F in moving the charge e_2 from the point A_1 (at a distance of r_1 from e_1) to A_2 (at a distance of r_2 from e_1) assuming that e_1 is located at the point A_0 as the origin.

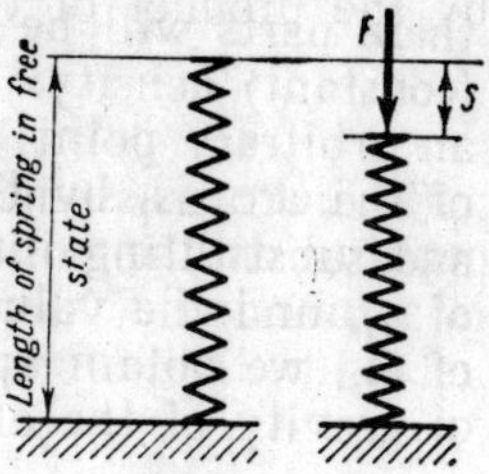

Solution. From formula (1) we have

$$A = \int\limits_{r_1}^{r_2} k\,\frac{e_1 e_2}{r^2}\,dr = -k e_1 e_2\,\frac{1}{r}\,\Big|_{r_1}^{r_2} = k e_1 e_2 \left(\frac{1}{r_1} - \frac{1}{r_2}\right)$$

Fig. 245

When $r_2 = \infty$, we have

$$A = \int\limits_{r_1}^{\infty} \frac{k e_1 e_2}{r^2}\,dr = \frac{k e_1 e_2}{r_1}$$

When $e_2 = 1$, $A = k\,\dfrac{e_1}{r}$. This quantity is called the *potential of the field* generated by the charge e_1.

12.8 COORDINATES OF THE CENTRE OF GRAVITY

Suppose on an xy-plane we have a system of material points

$$P_1(x_1,\ y_1),\ P_2(x_2,\ y_2),\ \ldots,\ P_n(x_n,\ y_n)$$

with masses $m_1,\ m_2,\ \ldots,\ m_n$.

The products $x_i m_i$ and $y_i m_i$ are called the *static moments* of the mass m_i relative to the y- and x-axes.

We denote by x_c and y_c the coordinates of the centre of gravity of the given system. Then, as we know from mechanics, the coordinates of the centre of gravity of this material system will be defined by the formulas

$$x_c = \frac{x_1 m_1 + x_2 m_2 + \ldots + x_n m_n}{m_1 + m_2 + \ldots + m_n} = \frac{\sum\limits_{i=1}^{n} x_i m_i}{\sum\limits_{i=1}^{n} m_i} \tag{1}$$

$$y_c = \frac{y_1 m_1 + y_2 m_2 + \ldots + y_n m_n}{m_1 + m_2 + \ldots + m_n} = \frac{\sum\limits_{i=1}^{n} y_i m_i}{\sum\limits_{i=1}^{n} m_i} \tag{2}$$

We shall use these formulas in finding the centres of gravity of various figures and solids.

1. The centre of gravity of a plane line. Let there be a curve AB given by the equation $y = f(x)$, $a \leqslant x \leqslant b$, and let this curve be a **material** line.

Let the linear density* of such a material curve be γ. Divide the line into n parts of length Δs_1, Δs_2, ..., Δs_n. The masses of these parts will be equal to the product of their lengths by the (constant) density: $\Delta m_i = \gamma \Delta s_i$. On each part of the arc Δs_i take an arbitrary point with abscissa ξ_i. Now representing each part of the arc Δs_i by the material point $P_i [\xi_i, f(\xi_i)]$ with mass $\gamma \Delta s_i$ and substituting into (1) and (2) ξ_i in place of x_i, $f(\xi_i)$ in place of y_i, and the value of $\gamma \Delta s_i$ (the masses of the parts Δs_i) in place of m_i, we obtain approximate formulas for determining the centre of gravity of the arc:

$$x_c \approx \frac{\sum \xi_i \gamma \Delta s_i}{\sum \gamma \Delta s_i}, \qquad y_c \approx \frac{\sum f(\xi_i) \gamma \Delta s_i}{\sum \gamma \Delta s_i}$$

If the function $y = f(x)$ is continuous and has a continuous derivative, the sums in the numerator and denominator of each fraction have, as max $\Delta s_i \rightarrow 0$, limits equal to the limits of the corresponding integral sums. Thus, the coordinates of the centre of gravity of the arc are expressed by definite integrals:

$$x_c = \frac{\int\limits_a^b x \, ds}{\int\limits_a^b ds} = \frac{\int\limits_a^b x \sqrt{1 + f'^2(x)} \, dx}{\int\limits_a^b \sqrt{1 + f'^2(x)} \, dx} \qquad (1')$$

$$y_c = \frac{\int\limits_a^b f(x) \, ds}{\int\limits_a^b ds} = \frac{\int\limits_a^b f(x) \cdot \sqrt{1 + f'^2(x)} \, dx}{\int\limits_a^b \sqrt{1 + f'^2(x)} \, dx} \qquad (2')$$

Example 1. Find the coordinates of the centre of gravity of the semi-circle $x^2 + y^2 = a^2$ situated above the x-axis.

---

* **Linear** density is the mass of unit length of a given line. We assume that the linear density is the same in all portions of the curve.

Solution. Determine the ordinate of the centre of gravity:

$$y = \sqrt{a^2 - x^2}, \quad \frac{dy}{dx} = -\frac{x}{\sqrt{a^2 - x^2}}, \quad ds = \sqrt{1 + \left(\frac{dy}{dx}\right)^2}\, dx, \quad ds = \frac{a}{\sqrt{a^2 - x^2}}\, dx$$

$$y_c = \frac{\displaystyle\int_{-a}^{a} \sqrt{a^2 - x^2}\, \frac{a}{\sqrt{a^2 - x^2}}\, dx}{\pi a} = \frac{a \displaystyle\int_{-a}^{a} dx}{\pi a} = \frac{2a^2}{\pi a} = \frac{2a}{\pi}$$

$x_c = 0$ (since the semi-circle is symmetric about the y-axis).

2. The centre of gravity of a plane figure. Given a figure bounded by the lines $y = f_1(x)$, $y = f_2(x)$, $x = a$, $x = b$, which is a **material** plane figure. We consider constant the surface density, which is the mass of unit area of the surface. It is equal to δ for all parts of the figure.

Divide the given figure by straight lines $x = a$, $x = x_1$, ..., $x = x_n = b$ into strips of width Δx_1, Δx_2, ..., Δx_n. The mass of each strip will be equal to the product of its area by the density δ. If each strip is replaced by a rectangle (Fig. 246) with base Δx_i and altitude

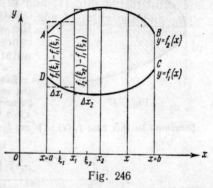

Fig. 246

$f_2(\xi_i) - f_1(\xi_i)$, where $\xi_i = \dfrac{x_{i-1} + x_i}{2}$, then the mass of a strip will be approximately equal to

$$\Delta m_i = \delta\, [f_2(\xi_i) - f_1(\xi_i)]\, \Delta x_i \quad (i = 1, 2, \ldots, n)$$

The centre of gravity of this strip will be situated approximately in the centre of the appropriate rectangle:

$$(x_i)_c = \xi_i, \quad (y_i)_c = \frac{f_2(\xi_i) + f_1(\xi_i)}{2}$$

Now replacing each strip by a material point, whose mass is equal to the mass of the corresponding strip and is concentrated at the centre of gravity of this strip, we find the approximate value of the coordinates of the centre of gravity of the entire figure [by formulas (1) and (2)]:

$$x_c \approx \frac{\sum \xi_i \delta\, [f_2(\xi_i) - f_1(\xi_i)]\, \Delta x_i}{\sum \delta\, [f_2(\xi_i) - f_1(\xi_i)]\, \Delta x_i}$$

$$y_c \approx \frac{\dfrac{1}{2} \sum [f_2(\xi_i) + f_1(\xi_i)]\, \delta\, [f_2(\xi_i) - f_1(\xi_i)]\, \Delta x_i}{\sum \delta\, [f_2(\xi_i) - f_1(\xi_i)]\, \Delta x_i}$$

Passing to the limit as $\Delta x_i \to 0$, we obtain

$$x_c = \frac{\int_a^b x\,[f_2(x) - f_1(x)]\,dx}{\int_a^b [f_2(x) - f_1(x)]\,dx}, \qquad y_c = \frac{\frac{1}{2}\int_a^b [f_2(x) + f_1(x)]\,[f_2(x) - f_1(x)]\,dx}{\int_a^b [f_2(x) - f_1(x)]\,dx}$$

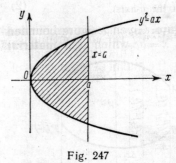

Fig. 247

These formulas hold for any homogeneous (that is, having constant density at all points) plane figure. We see that the coordinates of the centre of gravity are independent of the density δ of the figure (δ was cancelled out in the process of computation).

Example 2. Determine the coordinates of the centre of gravity of a segment of the parabola $y^2 = ax$ cut off by the straight line $x = a$ (Fig. 247).

Solution. In this case $f_2(x) = \sqrt{ax}$, $f_1(x) = -\sqrt{ax}$, therefore

$$x_c = \frac{2\int_0^a x\sqrt{ax}\,dx}{2\int_0^a \sqrt{ax}\,dx} = \frac{\frac{2}{5}\,2\sqrt{ax}^{5/2}\Big|_0^a}{2\sqrt{a}\,\frac{2}{3}\,x^{3/2}\Big|_0^a} = \frac{\frac{4}{5}\,a^3}{\frac{4}{3}\,a^2} = \frac{3}{5}\,a$$

$y_c = 0$ (since the segment is symmetric about the x-axis).

12.9 COMPUTING THE MOMENT OF INERTIA OF A LINE, A CIRCLE, AND A CYLINDER BY MEANS OF A DEFINITE INTEGRAL

Suppose, in an xy-plane, we have a system of material points $P_1(x_1, y_1)$, $P_2(x_2, y_2)$, ..., $P_n(x_n, y_n)$ with masses $m_1, m_2, \ldots, m_n$. Then, as we know from mechanics, the *moment of inertia* of the system of points with respect to the point O is defined as

$$I_O = \sum_{i=1}^{n} (x_i^2 + y_i^2)\,m_i \qquad \text{or} \qquad I_O = \sum_{i=1}^{n} r_i^2 m_i \qquad (1)$$

where $r_i = \sqrt{x_i^2 + y_i^2}$.

As in Sec. 12.8, let the curve AB be given by an equation $y = f(x)$, $a \leqslant x \leqslant b$, where $f(x)$ is a continuous function. Let this curve be a *material line*. Let the linear density of the line be γ. Again, partition the line into n parts of length $\Delta s_1, \Delta s_2, \ldots, \Delta s_n$, where $\Delta s_i = \sqrt{\Delta x_i^2 + \Delta y_i^2}$ and the masses of these parts, $\Delta m_1 = \gamma \Delta s_1$, $\Delta m_2 = \gamma \Delta s_2$, ..., $\Delta m_n = \gamma \Delta s_n$. Take an arbitrary point with abscissa ξ_i on each part of the arc (on each subarc). The ordinate of this point will be $\eta_i = f(\xi_i)$. The moment of inertia of the arc about the point O will, in accord with (1), be approximately equal to

$$I_O \approx \sum_{i=1}^{n} (\xi_i^2 + \eta_i^2)\, \gamma \Delta s_i \tag{2}$$

If the function $y = f(x)$ and its derivative $f'(x)$ are continuous, then the sum (2) has a limit as $\Delta s_i \to 0$. This limit, which is expressed by a definite integral, defines the moment of inertia of the material line:

$$I_O = \gamma \int_a^b [x^2 + f^2(x)]\, \sqrt{1 + [f'(x)]^2}\, dx \tag{3}$$

1. The moment of inertia of a thin homogeneous rod of length l about its end point. Make the rod coincide with part of the x-axis:

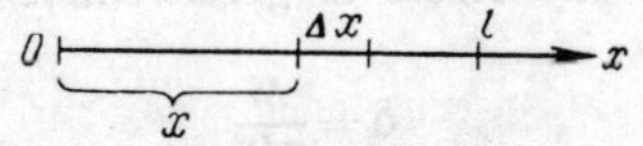

Fig. 248

$0 \leqslant x \leqslant l$ (Fig. 248). In this case, $\Delta s_i = \Delta x_i$, $\Delta m_i = \gamma \Delta x_i$, $r_i^2 = x_i^2$ and formula (3) takes the form

$$I_{O_c} = \gamma \int_0^l x^2 dx = \gamma \frac{l^3}{3} \tag{4}$$

If the mass M of the rod is given, then $\gamma = M/l$ and (4) assumes the form

$$I_{O_c} = \frac{1}{3} M l^2 \tag{5}$$

2. The moment of inertia of a circle of radius r about the centre. Since all points of the circumference are distant r from the centre, and the mass $m = 2\pi r \cdot \gamma$, the moment of inertia of the circle is

$$I_O = mr^2 = \gamma 2\pi r \cdot r^2 = \gamma 2\pi r^3 \tag{6}$$

3. The moment of inertia of a homogeneous circle of radius R about the centre. Let δ be the mass of unit area of the circle. Partition the circle into n annuli.

We consider one annulus (Fig. 249) with inner radius r_i and outer radius $r_i + \Delta r_i$. The mass Δm_i of this annulus, to within higher-order infinitesimals with respect to Δr_i, is $\Delta m_i = \delta 2\pi r_i \Delta r_i$.

By formula (6), the moment of inertia of this mass about the centre is roughly

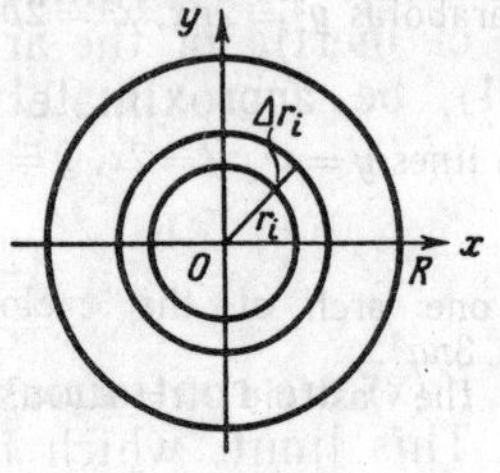

$$(\Delta I_O)_i \approx \delta 2\pi r_i \Delta r_i \cdot r_i^2 = \delta 2\pi r_i^3 \cdot \Delta r_i$$

The moment of inertia of the entire circle, as a system of annuli, will be given by the approximate formula

Fig. 249

$$I_O \approx \sum_{i=1}^{n} \delta 2\pi r_i^3 \Delta r_i \tag{7}$$

Passing to the limit as max $\Delta r_i \to 0$, we get the moment of inertia of the area of the circle with respect to the centre:

$$I_O = \delta 2\pi \int_0^R r^3 \, dr = \pi \delta \frac{R^4}{2} \tag{8}$$

If the mass M of the circle is given, then the surface density δ is defined as

$$\delta = \frac{M}{\pi R^2}$$

Substituting this value, we finally get

$$I_O = MR^2/2 \tag{9}$$

4. It is obvious that if we have a circular cylinder with base radius R and mass M, its moment of inertia about the axis will be given by formula (9).

Exercises on Chapter 12

Computing Areas

1. Find the area of a figure bounded by the lines $y^2 = 9x$, $y = 3x$. Ans. $\dfrac{1}{2}$.

2. Find the area of a figure bounded by the equilateral hyperbola $xy = a^2$, the x-axis, and the lines $x = a$, $x = 2a$. Ans. $a^2 \ln 2$.

3. Find the area of a figure lying between the curve $y = 4 - x^2$ and the x-axis. Ans. $10\dfrac{2}{3}$.

4. Find the area of a figure bounded by the astroid $x^{\frac{2}{3}} + y^{\frac{2}{3}} = a^{\frac{2}{3}}$. Ans. $\dfrac{3}{8} \pi a^2$.

5. Find the area of a figure bounded by the catenary $y = a \cosh \dfrac{x}{a}$, the x-axis, the y-axis, and the straight line $x = a$. Ans. $a^2 \sinh e$.

6. Find the area of a figure bounded by the curve $y = x^3$, the line $y = 8$, and the y-axis. *Ans.* 12.

7. Find the area of a region bounded by one arch of a sine wave and the x-axis. *Ans.* 2.

8. Find the area of a region lying between the parabolas $y^2 = 2px$, $x^2 = 2py$. *Ans.* $\dfrac{4}{3} p^2$.

9. Find the total area of a figure bounded by the lines $y = x^3$, $y = 2x$, $y = x$. *Ans.* $\dfrac{3}{2}$.

10. Find the area of a region bounded by one arch of the cycloid $x = a(t - \sin t)$, $y = a(1 - \cos t)$ and the x-axis. *Ans.* $3\pi a^2$.

11. Find the area of a figure bounded by the astroid $x = a \cos^3 t$, $y = a \sin^3 t$. *Ans.* $\dfrac{3}{8} \pi a^2$.

12. Find the area of the entire region bounded by the lemniscate $\rho^2 = a^2 \cos 2\varphi$. *Ans.* a^2.

13. Compute the area of a region bounded by one loop of the curve $\rho = a \sin 2\varphi$. *Ans.* $\dfrac{1}{8} \pi a^2$.

14. Compute the total area of a region bounded by the cardioid $\rho = a(1 - \cos \varphi)$. *Ans.* $\dfrac{3}{2} \pi a^2$.

15. Find the area of the region bounded by the curve $\rho = a \cos \varphi$. *Ans.* $\dfrac{\pi a^2}{4}$.

16. Find the area of the region bounded by the curve $\rho = a \cos 2\varphi$. *Ans.* $\dfrac{\pi a^2}{4}$.

17. Find the area of the region bounded by the curve $\rho = \cos 3\varphi$. *Ans.* $\dfrac{\pi}{4}$.

18. Find the area of the region bounded by the curve $\rho = a \cos 4\varphi$. *Ans.* $\dfrac{\pi a^2}{4}$.

Computing Volumes

19. The ellipse $\dfrac{x^2}{a^2} + \dfrac{y^2}{b^2} = 1$ revolves about the x-axis. Find the volume of the solid of revolution. *Ans.* $\dfrac{4}{3} \pi a b^2$.

20. The segment of a line connecting the origin with the point (a, b) revolves about the y-axis. Find the volume of the resulting cone. *Ans.* $\dfrac{1}{3} \pi a^2 b$.

21. Find the volume of a torus generated by revolution of the circle $x^2 + (y - b)^2 = a^2$ about the x-axis (it is assumed that $b \geqslant a$). *Ans.* $2\pi^2 a^2 b$.

22. The area bounded by the lines $y^2 = 2px$ and $x = a$ revolves about the x-axis. Find the volume of the solid of revolution. *Ans.* $\pi p a^2$.

23. A figure bounded by the astroid $x^{\frac{2}{3}} + y^{\frac{2}{3}} = a^{\frac{2}{3}}$ is revolved about the x-axis. Find the volume of the solid of revolution. *Ans.* $\dfrac{32\pi a^3}{105}$.

24. A figure bounded by one arch of the sine wave $y = \sin x$ and the x-axis is revolved about the x-axis. Find the volume of the solid of revolution. *Ans.* $\dfrac{\pi^2}{2}$.

25. A figure bounded by the parabola $y^2 = 4x$ and the straight line $x = 4$ is revolved about the x-axis. Find the volume of the solid of revolution. *Ans.* 32π.

26. A figure bounded by the curve $y = xe^x$ and the straight lines $y = 0$, $x = 1$ is revolved about the x-axis. Find the volume of the solid of revolution. *Ans.* $\dfrac{\pi}{4}(e^2 - 1)$.

27. A figure bounded by one arch of a cycloid $x = a(t - \sin t)$, $y = a(1 - \cos t)$ and the x-axis is revolved about the x-axis. Find the volume of the solid of revolution. *Ans.* $5\pi^2 a^3$.

28. The same figure as in Problem 27 is revolved about the y-axis. Find the volume of the solid of revolution. *Ans.* $6\pi^2 a^3$.

29. The same figure as in Problem 27 is revolved about a straight line that is parallel to the y-axis and passes through the vertex of a cycloid. Find the volume of the solid of revolution. *Ans.* $\dfrac{\pi a^3}{6}(9\pi^2 - 16)$.

30. The same figure as in Problem 27 is revolved about a straight line parallel to the x-axis and passing through the vertex of a cycloid. Find the volume of the solid of revolution. *Ans.* $7\pi^2 a^3$.

31. A cylinder of radius R is cut by a plane that passes through the diameter of the base at an angle α to the plane of the base. Find the volume of the cut-off part. *Ans.* $\dfrac{2}{3} R^3 \tan \alpha$.

32. Find a volume that is common to the two cylinders: $x^2 + y^2 = R^2$, $y^2 + z^2 = R^2$. *Ans.* $\dfrac{16}{3} R^3$.

33. The point of intersection of the diagonals of a square is in motion along the diameter of a circle of radius a; the plane in which the square lies remains perpendicular to the plane of the circle, while the two opposite vertices of the square move along the circle (as a result of this motion, the size of the square obviously varies). Find the volume of the solid generated by this moving square. *Ans.* $\dfrac{8}{3} a^3$.

34. Compute the volume of a segment cut off from the elliptical paraboloid $\dfrac{y^2}{2p} + \dfrac{z^2}{2q} = x$ by the plane $x = a$. *Ans.* $\pi a^2 \sqrt{pq}$.

35. Compute the volume of a solid bounded by the planes $z = 0$, $y = 0$, the cylindrical surfaces $x^2 = 2py$ and $z^2 = 2px$ and the plane $x = a$. *Ans.* $\dfrac{a^3 \sqrt{2a}}{7 \sqrt{p}}$ (in first octant).

36. A straight line is in motion parallel to the yz-plane, and cuts two ellipses $\dfrac{x^2}{a^2} + \dfrac{y^2}{b^2} = 1$, $\dfrac{x^2}{a^2} + \dfrac{z^2}{c^2} = 1$ lying in the xy- and xz-planes. Compute the volume of the solid thus obtained. *Ans.* $\dfrac{8}{3} abc$.

Computing Arc Lengths

37. Find the entire length of the hypocycloid $x^{\frac{2}{3}} + y^{\frac{2}{3}} = a^{\frac{2}{3}}$. *Ans.* $6a$.

38. Compute the arc length of the semicubical parabola $ay^2 = x^3$ between the origin and a point with abscissa $x = 5a$. *Ans.* $\dfrac{335}{27} a$.

39. Find the arc length of the catenary $y = a \cosh \dfrac{x}{a}$ from the origin to the point (x, y). *Ans.* $a \sinh \dfrac{x}{a} = \sqrt{y^2 - a^2}$.

40. Find the length of one arch of the cycloid $x = a(t - \sin t)$, $y = a(1 - \cos t)$. *Ans.* $8a$.

41. Find the length of an arc of the curve $y = \ln x$ between $x = \sqrt{3}$ and $x = \sqrt{8}$. *Ans.* $1 + \dfrac{1}{2} \ln \dfrac{3}{2}$.

42. Find the arc length of the curve $y = 1 - \ln \cos x$ between $x = 0$ and $x = \dfrac{\pi}{4}$. *Ans.* $\ln \tan \dfrac{3\pi}{8}$.

43. Find the length of the spiral of Archimedes $\rho = a\varphi$ from the pole to the end of the first loop. *Ans.* $\pi a \sqrt{1 + 4\pi^2} + \dfrac{a}{2} \ln(2\pi + \sqrt{1 + 4\pi^2})$.

44. Find the length of the spiral $\rho = e^{\alpha\varphi}$ from the pole to the point (ρ, φ). *Ans.* $\dfrac{\sqrt{1 + \alpha^2}}{\alpha} e^{\alpha\varphi} = \dfrac{\rho}{\alpha} \sqrt{1 + \alpha^2}$.

45. Find the entire length of the curve $\rho = a \sin^3 \dfrac{\varphi}{3}$. *Ans.* $\dfrac{3}{2} \pi a$.

46. Find the length of the evolute of the ellipse $x = \dfrac{c^2}{a} \cos^3 t$, $y = \dfrac{c^2}{b} \sin^3 t$. *Ans.* $\dfrac{4(a^3 - b^3)}{ab}$.

47. Find the length of the cardioid $\rho = a(1 + \cos \varphi)$. *Ans.* $8a$.

48. Find the arc length of the involute of the circle $x = a(\cos \varphi + \varphi \sin \varphi)$, $y = a(\sin \varphi - \varphi \cos \varphi)$ between $\varphi = 0$ and $\varphi = \varphi_1$. *Ans.* $\dfrac{1}{2} a\varphi_1^2$.

Computing Surface Areas of Solids of Revolution

49. Find the area of a surface obtained by revolving the parabola $y^2 = 4ax$ about the x-axis, from the origin O to a point with abscissa $x = 3a$. *Ans.* $\dfrac{56}{3} \pi a^2$.

50. Find the area of the surface of a cone generated by the revolution of a line segment $y = 2x$ from $x = 0$ to $x = 2$: (a) About the x-axis. *Ans.* $8\pi \sqrt{5}$. (b) About the y-axis. *Ans.* $4\pi \sqrt{5}$.

51. Find the area of the surface of a torus obtained by revolving the circle $x^2 + (y - b)^2 = a^2$ about the x-axis. $(b > a)$. *Ans.* $4\pi^2 ab$.

52. Find the surface area of a solid generated by revolving a cardioid about the x-axis. The cardioid is represented by the parametric equations $x = a(2 \cos \varphi - \cos 2\varphi)$, $y = a(2 \sin \varphi - \sin 2\varphi)$. *Ans.* $\dfrac{128}{5} \pi a^2$.

53. Find the area of the surface of a solid obtained by revolving one arch of a cycloid $x = a(t - \sin t)$, $y = a(1 - \cos t)$ about the x-axis. *Ans.* $\dfrac{64\pi a^2}{3}$.

54. The arch of a cycloid (see Problem 53) is revolved about the y-axis. Find the surface area of the solid of revolution. *Ans.* $16\pi^2 a^2 + \dfrac{64}{3} \pi a^2$.

55. The arch of a cycloid (see Problem 53) is revolved about a tangent line parallel to the x-axis and passing through the vertex. Find the surface area of the solid of revolution. *Ans.* $\dfrac{32\pi a^2}{3}$.

56. The astroid $x = a \sin^3 t$, $y = a \cos^3 t$ is revolved about the x-axis. Find the surface of the solid of revolution. *Ans.* $\dfrac{12\pi a^2}{5}$.

57. An arch of the sine wave $y = \sin x$ from $x = 0$ to $x = 2\pi$ is revolved about the x-axis. Find the surface of the solid of revolution. *Ans.* $4\pi [\sqrt{2} + + \ln(\sqrt{2}+1)]$.

58. The ellipse $\dfrac{x^2}{a^2} + \dfrac{y^2}{b^2} = 1$ $(a > b)$ revolves about the x-axis. Find the surface of the solid of revolution. *Ans.* $2\pi b^2 + 2\pi ab \dfrac{\arcsin e}{c}$, where $e = \dfrac{\sqrt{a^2 - b^2}}{a}$.

Various Applications of the Definite Integral

59. Find the centre of gravity of the area of one-fourth of the ellipse $\dfrac{x^2}{a^2} + \dfrac{y^2}{b^2} = 1$ $(x \geqslant 0,\ y \geqslant 0)$. *Ans.* $\dfrac{4a}{3\pi}$, $\dfrac{4b}{3\pi}$.

60. Find the centre of gravity of the area of a figure bounded by the parabola $x^2 + 4y - 16 = 0$ and the x-axis. *Ans.* $\left(0,\ \dfrac{8}{5}\right)$.

61. Find the centre of gravity of the volume of a hemisphere. *Ans.* On the axis of symmetry at a distance $\dfrac{3}{8} R$ from the base.

62. Find the centre of gravity of the surface of a hemisphere. *Ans.* On the axis of symmetry at a distance $\dfrac{R}{2}$ from the base.

63. Find the centre of gravity of the surface of a right circular cone, the radius of the base of which is R and the altitude h. *Ans.* On the axis of symmetry at a distance $\dfrac{h}{3}$ from the base.

64. The figure is bounded by the lines $y = \sin x$ $(0 \leqslant x \leqslant \pi)$, $y = 0$. Find the centre of gravity of the area of this figure. *Ans.* $\left(\dfrac{\pi}{2},\ \dfrac{\pi}{8}\right)$.

65. Find the centre of gravity of the area of a figure bounded by the parabolas $y^2 = 20x$, $x^2 = 20y$. *Ans.* (9, 9).

66. Find the centre of gravity of the area of a circular sector with central angle 2α and radius R. *Ans.* On the axis of symmetry at a distance $\dfrac{2}{3} R \dfrac{\sin \alpha}{\alpha}$ from the vertex of the sector.

67. Find the pressure of water on a rectangle vertically submerged in water at a depth of 5 metres if it is known that the base is 8 metres, the altitude, 12 metres, and the upper base is parallel to the free surface of the water. *Ans.* 1056 metres.

68. The upper edge of a canal lock has the shape of a square with a side of 8 m lying on the surface of the water. Determine the pressure on each part of the lock formed by dividing the square by one of its diagonals. *Ans.* 85,333.33 kg, 170,666.67 kg.

69. Compute the work needed to pump the water out of a hemispherical vessel of diameter 20 metres. *Ans.* $2.5 \times 10^6 \pi$ kg-m.

70. A body is in rectilinear motion according to the law $x = ct^3$, where x is the path length traversed in time t, $c = $ const. The resistance of the medium is proportional to the square of the velocity, and k is the constant of proportionality. Find the work done by the resistance when the body moves from the point $x = 0$ to the point $x = a$. *Ans.* $\dfrac{27}{7} k \sqrt[3]{c^2 a^7}$.

71. Compute the work that has to be done in order to pump a liquid of density γ from a reservoir having the shape of a cone with vertex pointing down, altitude H and radius of base R. *Ans.* $\dfrac{\pi\gamma R^2 H^2}{12}$.

72. A wooden float of cylindrical shape whose basal area $S = 4,000$ cm² and altitude $H = 50$ cm is floating on the surface of the water. What work must be done to pull the float up to the surface? (Specific weight of the wood, 0.8). *Ans.* $\dfrac{\gamma^2 H^2 S}{2} = 32$ kg-m.

73. Compute the force with which the water presses on a dam in the form of an equilateral trapezoid (upper base $a = 6.4$ m, lower base $b = 4.2$ m, altitude $H = 3$ m). *Ans.* 22.2 m.

74. Find the axial component P kg of total pressure of steam on the spherical bottom of a boiler. The diameter of the cylindrical part of the boiler is D mm, the pressure of the steam in the boiler is p kg/cm². *Ans.* $P = \dfrac{\pi p D^2}{400}$.

75. The end of a vertical shaft of radius r is supported by a flat thrust bearing. The weight of the shaft P is distributed equally over the entire surface of the support. Compute the total work of friction, in one rotation of the shaft Coefficient of friction is μ. *Ans.* $\dfrac{4}{3}\pi\mu Pr$.

76. A vertical shaft ends in a thrust pin having the shape of a truncated cone. The specific pressure of the pin on the thrust bearing is constant and equal to P. The upper diameter of the pin is D, the lower d, and the angle at the vertex of the cone is 2α. Coefficient of friction, μ. Find the work of friction for one rotation of the shaft. *Ans.* $\dfrac{\pi^2 P\mu}{6\sin\alpha}(D^3 - d^3)$.

77. A prismatic rod of length l is slowly extended by a force increasing from 0 to P so that at each moment the tensile force is balanced by the forces of elasticity of the rod. Compute the work A expended by the force on tension, assuming that the tension occurred within the limits of elasticity. F is the cross-sectional area of the rod, and E is the modulus of elasticity of the material.
Hint. If x is the elongation of the rod and f is the corresponding force, then $f = \dfrac{FE}{l}x$. The elongation due to the force P is equal to $\Delta l = \dfrac{Pl}{EF}$. *Ans.* $A = \dfrac{P\Delta l}{2} = \dfrac{P^2 l}{2EF}$.

78. A prismatic beam is suspended vertically and a tensile force P is applied to its lower end. Compute the elongation of the beam due to its weight and to the force P if it is given that the original length of the beam is l, the cross-sectional area F, the weight Q and the modulus of elasticity of the material E. *Ans.* $\Delta l = \dfrac{(Q + 2P)l}{2EF}$.

79. Determine the time during which a liquid will flow out of a prismatic vessel filled to a height H. The cross-sectional area of the vessel is F, the area of the opening f, the exit velocity is computed from the formula $v = \mu\sqrt{2gh}$, where μ is the coefficient of viscosity, g is the acceleration of gravity, and h is the distance from the opening to the level of the liquid. *Ans.* $T = \dfrac{2FH}{\mu f\sqrt{2gH}} = \dfrac{F}{\mu f}\sqrt{\dfrac{2H}{g}}$.

80. Determine the discharge Q (the quantity of water flowing in unit time) over a spillway of rectangular cross section. Height of spillway, h, width, b. Ans. $Q = \frac{2}{3} \mu b h \sqrt{2gh}$.

81. Determine the discharge of water Q flowing from a side rectangular opening of height a and width b, if the height of the open surface of the water above the lower side of the opening is H. Ans. $Q = \frac{2b\mu \sqrt{2g}}{3} \left[H^{3/2} - (H-a)^{3/2} \right]$.

TO THE READER

Mir Publishers welcome your comments on the content, translation and design of this book.

We would also be pleased to receive any suggestions you care to make about our future publications.

Our address is:

Mir Publishers
2 Pervy Rizhsky Pereulok,
I-110, GSP, Moscow, 129820
USSR

Printed in the Union of Soviet Socialist Republics